MATTER AND ENERGY

Human footprints on the moon, 1969 07 21.
Astronaut Edwin Aldrin has a suited mass of 160 kg
and is carrying a 40 kg equipment package in each
hand. What force must he exert to support
each package? (See page 54.)

MATTER AND ENERGY
THE FOUNDATIONS OF MODERN PHYSICS

JAMES H. MacLACHLAN

KENNETH G. McNEILL

JOHN M. BELL

PETER T. SPENCER

Revised Edition

IRWIN PUBLISHING, TORONTO, CANADA

Copyright © Irwin Publishing Inc., 1977

Formerly a Clarke, Irwin & Company Limited Book

ISBN 0-7720-1160-5

Canadian Cataloguing in Publication Data

Main entry under title:

Matter and energy

For use in secondary schools.

Includes index.
ISBN 0-7720-1160-5

1. Physics.   I. MacLachlan, James H., 1928-

QC23.M38 1977   530   C77-001684-7

6 7 8 9 BP 87 86 85 84

Printed in Canada

Contents

Preface

Following the enthusiastic acceptance by students and teachers of the first edition, *Matter and Energy* now appears in a new dress. The text has been revised in the light of the experience of many people, which has led us to add to the *Exercises* and to include a new section of *Laboratory Investigations*. A number of the Investigations have been marked to indicate our recommendation that they be undertaken *before* the related text material is studied. Such a procedure will properly stress the importance for students to realize that physics is firmly rooted in phenomena.

The first unit has been almost entirely rewritten. Other units have been revised and rearranged. Solid-state electronics based on atomic theory has been added to replace the vacuum tubes of the first edition. SI units are used exclusively throughout the book. Illustrations have been only minimally captioned so that classes can discuss what is being shown, unencumbered by explicit statements from us about what they are supposed to see.

This whole course could be completed in one year's study if you arranged to spend one week each on most chapters, allowing no more than about six to run to a full two weeks. If you feel that more than six chapters require more than a week, some others must be selected for omission, or for a very quick treatment.

For most chapters, the majority of the students should be able to complete most questions and problems of the **A** part of the *Exercises*. The **B** parts are provided for those chapters which your class will study more intensively. The **C** parts are intended only for the minority of students who seek mind-expansion through physics. Most answers to numerical problems have been given using the appropriate SI prefixes. Although the calculations are more readily performed in power-of-ten notation, using prefixes in the answers provides many chances for students to become familiar with their use. An additional feature is the quiz on SI units, Table 2 in Appendix I.

Acknowledgments

The authors and publisher would like to thank the following individuals and organizations who have made available the photographs on the pages listed. Photographs not otherwise credited were taken by J. Lyons and J. MacLachlan.

Aptec Engineering Limited, Downsview, Ontario / 308 (24-4)

Atlas of Optical Phenomena, Cagnet, Francon and Thrierr. Prentice-Hall Inc. and Springer-Verlag OHC, Berlin / 185 (14-2)

Atomic Energy of Canada Limited / 298, 300 (23-7), 302 (both), 309, 312 (24-9)

Bausch & Lomb Incorporated, Rochester, New York / 220 (16-17), 223 (16-22)

BBC Publications / 288

Brookhaven National Laboratory / 304

Canadian General Electric Company Limited / 123 (10-7)

Canadian Kodak Company, Limited / 213 (16-2), 214 (16-4)

Dame Kathleen Lonsdale, University College, London / 77 (6-4 b, c)

Dr. A. F. Gregory, Department of Mines and Technical Surveys / 310

Education Development Center, Inc., Newton, Massachusetts / 48

Ford Motor Company, Canada / 157 (all)

Miller Services Limited, Toronto / xi, xiv, 2, 20, 39, 56 (bottom), 61 (photo by Neil Newton), 74, 84 (both), 85, 110, 120 (top), 154 (both), 155, 156, 161, 171, 182 (both), 189, 226 (both), 227, 228, 268, 291

Mount Wilson and Palomar Observatory / 191 (14-25), 193

National Aeronautics and Space Administration (NASA) / ii, 44, 56, 83, 97 (8-2)

Northrop Corporation, Public Relations, Beverley Hills, California / 41

Ohio State University and Franklin Miller, Jr., Department of Physics, Kenyon College, Gamber, Ohio, from the film *Tacoma Narrows Bridge Collapse,* produced under a grant from the National Science Foundation (U.S.) / 160

Ontario Hydro, 146 (11-6 b, c, d, e, f, g, i), 300 (23-8)

Pergamon Press, Inc. / 242, 307

Professor Erwin W. Mueller, The Pennsylvania State University / 76
PSSC PHYSICS, D. C. Heath and Company, Lexington, Massachusetts, 1965, courtesy Education Development Center, Inc., Newton, Massachusetts / 1, 159 (12-8), 163 (12-9), 164 (12-21, 12-22), 165, 166 (12-26), 167 (12-25), 174 (13-5), 185 (14-1), 187 (14-8), 196
Square D Company, Canada, Limited / 149 (11-19)
The Ontario Cancer Institute / 311
The Ontario Cancer Institute and The Princess Margaret Hospital / 313 (24-11)
United States Defense Mapping Agency Depot / 111, 112 (9-4)
U.S. Energy Research and Development Administration, SLAC Facility / 313 (24-12)
Waterfall, Engraving by M. C. Escher, in *The Graphic Works of M. C. Escher,* Meredith Press / 69

Every effort has been made to acknowledge correctly the sources of the illustrations reproduced in this book. The publisher welcomes any information that will enable him to rectify, in subsequent editions, any errors or omissions which may have been made in crediting the photographs.

Canada Canada
metric métrique

The stylized M and Maple Leaf show that Metric Commission Canada has granted use of the National Symbol for Metric Conversion. The symbol confirms that the units used in *Matter and Energy* adhere to The International System of Units, the simplest, most advanced and universal metric measurement system.

Foreword

Stonehenge is located on Salisbury Plain in southern England.

On fait la science avec des faits comme une maison avec des pierres, mais une accumulation des faits n'est pas plus une science qu'un tas de pierres n'est une maison.
—Henri Poincaré, 1854-1912
La science et l'hypothèse (1902)

Science is built with facts just as a house is built with bricks, but a collection of facts is no more a science than a pile of bricks is a house.

In the daytime sky the sun appears to be an orange ball moving along an arc from east to west. For thousands of years the sun has fascinated human minds. By 1900 BC or earlier, Britons had constructed Stonehenge to keep a record of solar positions. In Greek mythology the sun was explained as the god Helios driving his fiery chariot across the sky. Although you might consider the attitudes of earlier humans to be crudely unscientific, they mark out for us a range of human behaviours that are involved in present-day scientific investigations. Scientists observe and measure, and they speculate in order to fit their observations into an understandable scheme.

Today the sun is still as far away from the earth as it has ever been. Yet the advances of science, particularly in physics, have yielded to human understanding a vastly more detailed and reliable view of the sun than could even have been imagined in earlier times. In the scientific enterprise, careful observation and measurement are combined with controlled speculation. Our knowledge of the sun comes from a close examination of the radiations emitted by the sun — light and heat and radio waves. An analysis of the spectrum of sunlight led in 1868 to the discovery of a new element, helium, more than twenty years before the element was found on the earth. Theoretical astrophysics accounts for the helium in the sun as a product of the nuclear fusion reaction that produces the sun's heat. This is a speculation, but it is securely founded on experiment and logic. On earth, the nuclear fusion reaction powers hydrogen bombs, and is being actively investigated as a way to produce energy for human needs, fuelled by hydrogen extracted from the waters of the earth.

Such facts and theories of physics provide the foundation on which many modern industries depend. Televisions and cameras, automobiles and the nuclear generation of electricity all result from applications of knowledge produced by physicists. The early seeds from which this knowledge has grown were sown almost 400 years ago. In Italy Galileo Galilei (1564-1642) began a new era in the study of the motion of falling objects by investigating them with mathematics and experiments. The work of Galileo and others was extended by Isaac Newton (1642-1727) in England. In imagining gravity to extend throughout space, Newton coupled speculation with mathematical and experimental analyses. He created a systematic picture of the planets moving about the sun in orbits controlled by the force of gravity. Much of the work of physicists in succeeding generations has been devoted to refining and extending the ideas introduced by Newton.

Your study of physics will in some ways imitate the steps by which more accurate knowledge of the world has been gradually won. Instead of plunging into the interior of a television set or an automobile engine, you will begin with simpler situations. As in the historical development, an analysis of the motions of things is a good place to start. By reading and experimenting you will learn how to make the measurements and calculations that are needed for an adequate description of the motions of runners and autos and rockets and electrons. Gradually your knowledge will be extended to arrive at the ability to use the concept of energy to analyze a wide range of activities—running upstairs, shooting arrows, getting rockets into space.

By the end of Unit I you will have developed a much more refined way of discussing these matters than can be done at this stage. Yet, right now you should know that in unsophisticated language *matter* is the stuff of which things are made, and *energy* is what makes things go. Your study of physics will make it possible for you to gain a clearer understanding of the current views that physicists have of the structure and behaviour of things—of matter and energy.

After you have progressed from motion to energy in Unit I, you will be able to build on that foundation in the study of electrical energy. Benjamin Franklin (1706-1790) in America was able to show that lightning was essentially a gigantic electric spark. Charles Coulomb (1738-1806) in France developed apparatus for measuring quantities of electricity. Then Alessandro Volta (1745-1827) in Italy invented a way to make electricity continuously, and André Ampère (1775-1836) in France developed laws of motion for electricity. Electricity and magnetism were linked by Hans Oersted (1777-1851) in Denmark, with Michael Faraday (1791-1867) in England greatly extending those links. The work of these physicists is the basis for the modern electrical devices that provide so many of the comforts of modern life and power the factories and workplaces of our highly technological society.

In Unit II you will make electrical measurements in laboratory investigations, and learn how to use them to calculate electrical energy. You will also be able to investigate the basis of the operation of electric motors and generators. Then, in Unit III you will go on to study some of the properties of the sound and light that come from such electrical devices as stereos and searchlights. Toward the end of Unit III you will have the opportunity to construct optical instruments such as telescopes and microscopes.

The transmission of energy in sound and light is accomplished by wave motions. You will investigate some of the basic properties of waves in ripple tanks. Waves were first studied seriously by Robert Hooke (1635-1703) and Newton in England, and by Christian Huygens (1629-1695) in Holland and France. These men agreed that sound was a wave phenomenon, but disagreed bitterly about the nature of light. The wave nature of light was firmly established by experiment and theory in the nineteenth century as a result of the work of Thomas Young (1773-1829) in England and Augustin Fresnel (1788-1827) in France.

Toward the end of the nineteenth century, 300 years of mathematics and experimenting and speculating had provided physicists with quite a full understanding of many aspects of motion and electricity, and of sound, light, and heat. Some physicists in England boldly calculated the age of the earth from its rate of cooling and used the result to oppose Darwin's theory of evolution. For, they said, the hundred million years we calculate provides too short a time for all the species changes that Darwin's theory requires. But they theorized without a knowledge of a source of heat within the earth's crust—from such radioactive elements as uranium and radium. The discovery of radioactivity in 1895 heralded the start of a new era in physics. As for the age of the earth, recent calculations indicate at least four billion years—ample time for evolution.

About the year 1900 physicists were actively investigating a wholly unforeseen panorama of new radiations—x-rays and cathode rays, as well as those from radioactive substances. You will be introduced to these investigations in Unit IV. They will lead you to a deeper understanding of the structure of matter—to electrons and atoms and nuclei—as well as to new sources of energy. In this unit you will have an opportunity to study the principles that are the basis of the operation of television tubes, transistors, and the nuclear reactors that are producing an increasing share of our electrical energy.

Physics is an ongoing international enterprise with a long history. Humanity is indebted for its present knowledge of matter and energy to many people from many countries. However, it is important for you to realize that this knowledge is changeable— it is constantly being tested and occasionally revised. For that reason we present it to you, not as absolute truth engraved on stone, but often as arguments based on experience and reasoning. We want you to take every opportunity to participate in the scientific activities that contribute to making human knowledge as reliable and useful as possible.

A rocket stands tall on the launching pad, sunlight glinting off its smooth shell. The motor is ignited and hot gases are expelled downward through nozzles. Supporting beams fall away and the rocket begins to rise slowly. Gradually the rocket gathers speed; soon it is a tiny speck in the sky, carrying its payload out into an orbit about the earth.

To be able to describe the details of the rocket's operation you have to use measurements expressed in their appropriate units. If you were to be involved in the design of such a rocket you would have to know the *relations* among various measured quantities; for example, to know how much fuel is needed for the size of the payload, and how to achieve sufficient speed to get the rocket into orbit.

In this unit you will make the measurements and learn the relations that exist among such quantities as speed, acceleration, force, and energy. With these quantities you will be able to make a variety of calculations that can be used to describe and explain the motions of arrows that strike targets and electrons that strike the face of a TV picture tube.

I

Motion and Energy

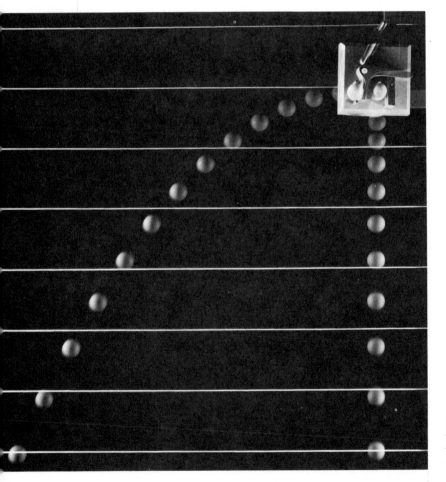

Released at the same moment the projected ball and the falling ball have the same *vertical* motion.

CHAPTER 1

Mathematics
in
Physics

GETTING STARTED

Most of the basic mathematical ideas needed for your study of physics this year are contained here in Chapter 1. Some classes will want to begin the year with about a week on this chapter. Others may choose to begin more concretely by plunging directly into the study of motion in Chapter 2. If so, the material of Chapter 1 can be introduced gradually as it becomes appropriate. In either case, students should expect to refer back to this chapter frequently to review the essential mathematical notions contained here.

The tonne is a mass unit, equal to one thousand kilograms.

Have you ever watched the hydraulic lift in a service station raise up a car so that a mechanic can work on the underside of it? The lift is operated by air that is compressed to about ten times the pressure of the earth's atmosphere. The design of a lift that can handle cars of two tonnes or more depends on a knowledge of certain basic physical relations. One of the most important relations is that between the measured quantities of pressure, area, and force.

To be able to understand such relations, you will have to know how to make measurements of various quantities, and to find how changes in one quantity are affected by changes in another quantity. The purpose of this chapter is to introduce you to the basic ingredients of measurements, and the mathematics necessary to be able to find relations among measurements.

MEASUREMENT OF QUANTITIES

I often say that when you can measure what you are speaking about, and express it in numbers, you know something about it; but when you cannot express it in numbers, your knowledge is of a meagre and unsatisfactory kind; it may be the beginning of knowledge, but you have scarcely, in your thoughts, advanced to the stage of *Science*, whatever the matter may be.
—Lord Kelvin, 1898

A quantity is a property of an object that can be measured. To be able to measure the quantity requires that you have a defined unit and some device for counting units. Your height is one of your measurable properties, and is expressed in the unit the metre by some number in the range from 1.4 to 2.0. The metre-stick or tape measure is the device you use for counting the number of units and fractions of units that extend from top to toe.

Measurement consists of counting units. You can measure the length of a football field by moving a metre stick end to end from one goal line to the other. Ordinarily, of course, you will use a tape that is many metres long. However, the tape is simply a convenient way to have much of the counting done for you. When you find the length of the field, you express it by a number and a unit—101 metres. The same length in the unit used in football—110 yards—has a larger number because the unit yard is smaller in length than the unit metre. In either case, however, the size of the field, its *magnitude*, is the same.

As your physics course unfolds, you will learn the relations that make it possible to define and measure new quantities. After you have studied force in Chapter 4, and energy in Chapter 6, you will be able to describe some of the important quantities involved in rocket shots and space travel. Our job now is to build up gradually to the definitions and units needed for such quantities as force, pressure, and energy.

SI UNITS

Many physical quantities are related quite directly to other quantities. For example, the density of an object depends on its volume and its mass. Although any arbitrary unit of density could be defined, simplicity is maintained if the unit of density is related to the units of volume and mass. And a unit of volume can be based on the unit for length. Thus a *system* of units can be established by paying attention to the relations among quantities. The system will be founded on a small set of units that are defined more or less independently of others. Then, all other units will be defined by their relations with the original set.

In 1960, a world conference on weights and measures adopted the International System of Units. This system is abbreviated SI, for the French title of *Système internationale d'unités*. In SI, the set of fundamental units is kept to only seven **base units**. These seven, including units for length, mass, time, temperature, and electric current, comprise a minimum set of quantities. The relations that exist among physical quantities are used to define all other units in terms of these seven. The base units are shown in Table 1-1. Since the definitions of the base units depend on a knowledge of a lot of physics, they are collected for you in the Appendix.

All other units, which are defined by using the base units, are called **derived units**. A few derived units which you can understand without knowing a lot of physics are given in Table 1-2, along with their definitions in terms of the base units.

A basic rule for writing units in SI is that whenever a numerical measurement is given, the number should be followed by the *symbol* (or abbreviation) for the unit; the unit should not be spelled out. From Table 1-2 you can see that the name for the unit of frequency is the hertz, meaning a cycle per second. The frequency of the electric supply to your home is 60 Hz, for which you say "sixty hertz"—

Table 1-1

SI BASE UNITS

Quantity	Name of unit	Symbol for unit
length	metre	m
mass	kilogram	kg
time	second	s
electric current	ampere	A
thermodynamic temperature	kelvin	K
amount of substance	mole	mol
luminous intensity	candela	cd

Table 1-2

SOME SI DERIVED UNITS

Quantity	Name of unit	Symbol for unit
frequency	hertz = cycle per second	$Hz = s^{-1}$
speed	metre per second	m/s
area	square metre	m^2
volume	cubic metre	m^3
density	kilogram per cubic metre	kg/m^3

Table 1-3

SOME UNITS PERMITTED FOR USE WITH SI

Quantity	Name	Symbol	Definition
time	minute	min	1 min = 60 s
	hour	h	1 h = 3600 s
	day	d	1 d = 86 400 s
	year	a	1 a = 365.24 d (approx.)
volume	litre	L	1 L = 1 dm^3
temperature	degree Celsius	°C	0°C = 273.15 K
	(However, for intervals, 1°C = 1 K.)		
mass	tonne	t	1 t = 1 000 kg

Table 1-4

SI PREFIXES

Multiplying factor	Name of prefix	Symbol for prefix	Pronunciation
10^{18}	exa	E	ex'-ah
10^{15}	peta	P	pet'-ah
10^{12}	tera	T	tare'-ah
10^{9}	giga	G	gee'-gah
10^{6}	mega	M	meg'-ah
10^{3}	kilo	k	kill'-oh
10^{2}	hecto	h	heck'-toe
10^{1}	deca	da	deck'-ah
10^{-1}	deci	d	dess'-ee
10^{-2}	centi	c	cent'-ee
10^{-3}	milli	m	mill'-ee
10^{-6}	micro	μ	mike'-roe
10^{-9}	nano	n	nan'-oe
10^{-12}	pico	p	pea'-coe
10^{-15}	femto	f	fem'-toe
10^{-18}	atto	a	at'-toe

in this case the plural is the same as the singular. The time required for the electricity to complete 15 cycles is 0.25 s—do not write out "second."

There are also a few common units that are permitted for use with SI, although they are not part of SI. They are listed in Table 1-3.

In many practical cases the basic SI units are of an inconvenient size. For example, the thickness of commercial gold leaf is about 0.000 000 1 m, and the distance from the sun to Pluto is about 6 000 000 000 000 m. All those zeros are hard to keep track of. Instead of defining entirely new units, the SI system attaches multiplying prefixes to the standard units. The prefixes are symbols that represent particular powers of 10. Between 0.001 and 1000 the prefixes take steps of ten as shown in Table 1-4. However, the prefixes hecto, deca, and deci are not widely used. Outside of that range, the prefixes take steps of 1000 = 10^3. The usual way to use the prefixes is to choose one that makes the numerical part of a measurement fall in the range from 0.1 to 1000. Thus the distance from the sun to Pluto is about 6 Tm (terametres). The thickness of commercial gold leaf can be written either 0.1μm (micrometre, where μ is the Greek letter "mu"), or 100 nm (nanometres).

When you write the symbols for units and prefixes, you must be sure to stick to the capital letters and lower case letters that are shown. The following combinations show places where difficulties could arise if you do not keep the symbols straight.

1mm (millimetre) = 10^{-3} m   1 Mm (megametre) = 10^6 m

1 am = one attometre = 10^{-18} m   1 mA = one milliampere

The meaning of negative indices (exponents), and the rules for calculating with indices are given in Table 1-5.

STANDARD FORM

The average distance from the earth to the sun has been found by astronomers to be 149 600 000 000 m. To get an idea of how big the number is, you will count the digits. It would be useful to have a way to keep that count. The SI prefixes provide one method, since taking the digits in groups of three is like talking through the prefixes: "kilo, mega, giga." 1 Gm = 10^9 m, so you move the decimal nine places to the left and express the earth-sun distance as 149.6 Gm.

If you are going to perform calculations with the number, you will prefer to keep it in entirely numerical form. For many purposes the most convenient and widely used way to keep the count of the digits in the measurement is to express it as   × 10^{11} m. This is called **standard form.** For it, you move the decimal point along until a single digit (not zero) precedes the decimal. Then you multiply by the power of ten needed to compensate for the shift in the position of the decimal.

Table 1-5

INDEX RULES

(1) Multiplication

$$(x^a)(x^b) = x^{a+b}$$

e.g.,
$$(x^2)(x^3) = x^{2+3} = x^5,$$
since
$$(xx)(xxx) = xxxxx$$

(2) Division

$$\frac{x^a}{x^b} = x^{a-b}$$

e.g.,
$$\frac{x^6}{x^2} = x^{6-2} = x^4$$

since
$$\frac{xxxxxx}{xx} = xxxx$$

(3) Negative index

To divide x^2 by x^5:
$$\frac{x^2}{x^5} = x^{2-5} = x^{-3};$$

or, .
$$\frac{xx}{xxxxx} = \frac{1}{xxx} = \frac{1}{x^3}.$$

So,
$$x^{-3} = \frac{1}{x^3}, \text{ and } x^{-a} = \frac{1}{x^a}, \text{ and } x^a = \frac{1}{x^{-a}}$$

(4) Operations with negative index

$$(x^3)(x^{-7}) = x^{-4}$$

$$\frac{x^3}{x^{-7}} = x^{10}$$

(5) Zero index

$$\frac{x^a}{x^a} = x^{a-a} = x^0.$$

But
$$\frac{x^a}{x^a} = 1.$$

Therefore,
$$x^0 = 1.$$

Example: The diameter of a human hair is measured to be 0.076 mm. Express the diameter in standard form (a) in millimetres, (b) in metres. Then, (c) give the diameter using the most appropriate SI prefix.

(a) To get standard form in millimetres, move the decimal along to between the "7" and the "6." A move of two places to the right means to multiply by 10^2. To avoid changing the magnitude of the quantity, that has to be compensated by multiplying by 10^{-2}. Thus,

$$\text{diameter} = 0.076 \text{ mm} = 7.6 \times 10^{-2} \text{ mm}.$$

(b) Since 1 mm $= 10^{-3}$ m, we can write

$$\text{diameter} = (7.6 \times 10^{-2})(10^{-3}) \text{ m} = 7.6 \times 10^{-5} \text{ m}.$$

(c) The nearest appropriate SI prefix is 1 μm $= 10^{-6}$ m. Since the "−6" index for "micro" is one smaller than the "−5" index in the diameter, we move the decimal one to the right to compensate:

$$7.6 \times 10^{-5} \text{ m} = 76 \times 10^{-6} \text{ m} = 76 \ \mu\text{m}.$$

ACCURACY OF MEASUREMENTS

No measurement can be made with perfect exactness. The best you can do is to note which of the divisions on a measuring scale is closest to the point marking the size of the quantity. For example, you might find the length of your eraser to be 37 mm, to the nearest millimetre. However, in any measured number there is a range of uncertainty amounting to 0.5 of the value of the last measured digit. Thus, to say that the length of the eraser is nearer to 37 mm than to either 36 mm or 38 mm means that the length is somewhere in the range from 36.5 mm to 37.5 mm (Fig. 1-1), since the uncertainty in the measurement 37 mm is 0.5 mm. The extent of the uncertainty is 0.5 in 37, or a little more than 1%.

The **accuracy** of a measured number is an indication of the size of the uncertainty relative to the size of the measurement. To avoid having always to calculate percentages, it is often sufficient to note the number of measured digits in the quantity. The length of 37 mm is a measurement of two-digit accuracy. To see the relation between the number of digits and the percentage uncertainty in a measurement, consider the width of a football field measured to the nearest 0.1 m to be 59.4 m. The uncertainty is 0.05 m. The percentage uncertainty is

$$\frac{0.05}{59.4} \times 100\% = 0.1\% \text{ (approximately)}.$$

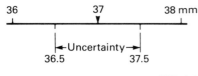

FIG. 1-1

$$\frac{0.5}{37} \times 100\% = 1.4\%.$$

Three-digit accuracy involves an uncertainty of about one-tenth of one percent. If the measurement had been made only to the nearest metre, 59 m, the two-digit accuracy would have given

$$\text{percentage uncertainty} = \frac{0.5}{59} \times 100\% = 1\% \text{ (approximately)}.$$

A two-digit measurement to the nearest metre has roughly the same percentage uncertainty as a two-digit measurement to the nearest millimetre. Indeed, all two-digit measurements can be said to have roughly the same degree of accuracy. Three-digit measurements are more accurate, and one-digit measurements are less accurate.

Measurements of the distances of discus throws at the Olympic Games are made to the nearest centimetre. In 1976 Evelin Schlaak set an Olympic record with a throw of 6900 cm. When the distance is expressed that way, you cannot be sure whether the zeros are measured digits or simply place-holding zeros. Because these are in fact measured digits, it is better to express the distance as 6.900×10^3 cm, or 69.00 m. When zeros appear after the decimal, they must be measured digits, because they have no other use. If they are not measured digits they should not appear. The use of zeros for place-holding purposes before the decimal is eliminated by using standard form, where the power of ten does all the place-holding work. Expressing numbers in standard form shows the number of digits in the accuracy immediately. Thus, the use of standard form tells you at once that 6.900×10^3 cm has a four-digit accuracy.

CALCULATIONS WITH MEASURED NUMBERS

A certain automotive piston has a measured diameter (d) of 8.75 cm. With its three-digit accuracy, this measurement has an uncertainty of about 0.1%. Whenever a measurement is used in calculations, it necessarily carries its uncertainty with it. Thus, the value of the calculated circumference (C) of the piston must be limited to three-digit accuracy. The value of π can be found to any desired accuracy, so it will not contribute any significant uncertainty to the result. In this case, we choose the value of π that has four-digit accuracy. Then the circumference of the piston will be

$$C = \pi d = (3.142)(8.75 \text{ cm})$$

$$= 27.4925 \text{ cm} = 27.5 \text{ cm } (rounded \text{ } value).$$

$\pi = 3.14159265\ldots$

In general, for **multiplication and division**, the number of digits in a result using measured numbers must be limited to the number of digits in the least accurate measurement used in the calculation. If you use a calculator, you can carry as many digits as you wish through intermediate calculations, but you must round off the final answer to conform to the rule for accuracy.

Accuracy out cannot exceed accuracy in.

Example: The distance from the sun to Pluto is 5.9×10^{12} m. How many times is that greater than the earth-sun distance?

Divide the Pluto-sun distance by the earth-sun distance (1.496×10^{11} m). The result is the ratio of the two distances.

$$\text{Ratio} = \frac{5.9 \times 10^{12} \text{ m}}{1.496 \times 10^{11} \text{ m}} = 3.94 \ldots \times 10^1 = 39 \; (\textit{rounded value}).$$

Pluto is 39 times farther from the sun than the earth is. Notice that in standard form, you divide the powers of ten and the numerical factors separately, and then combine them in the result. The result is limited to two digits, because there were only two digits in the measurement of the Pluto-sun distance.

Table 1-6

ROUND OFF TO
ONE DECIMAL
PLACE

6.348 → 6.3
6.351 → 6.4
6.35 → 6.4
6.45 → 6.4
6.55 → 6.6

In **rounding off** numbers (Table 1-6), if the first dropped digit is 0 to 4, the last retained digit is unchanged. And, with one exception, if the first dropped digit is 5 to 9, the last retained digit is increased by one. This method ensures that the result is correct to the *nearest* division on the relevant scale of measurement. The exception noted above refers to numbers where the digit to be dropped is a single 5, which makes "nearest" ambiguous. If one is always added to the last retained digit, sums of measurements rounded that way will be made larger than they ought to be. Thus, when dropping a single 5 we add one when the last retained digit is odd, and not when the last retained digit is even. Thus, the rounded result will always have its final digit even.

In adding and subtracting measured numbers, you have to pay attention to the number of decimal places rather than to the number of measured digits. That is because measurements to be added or subtracted have to be in the same units. When the moon is on the side of the earth away from the sun, how far is it from the moon to the sun? The earth-moon distance is 3.84×10^8 m, and the earth-sun distance is 1.496×10^{11} m. Choose gigametres as the unit to express them in:

Distance moon to earth = 0.384 Gm.

Distance earth to sun = 149.6?? Gm.

The "?" indicates that in the second measurement the hundredths and thousandths of gigametres are not known. Thus, you are not entitled to express the result to the nearest thousandth of a gigametre. The sum must be rounded to the nearest tenth of a gigametre:

Distance moon to sun = 149.9(84) Gm = 150.0 Gm (*rounded value*).

The result of the **addition and subtraction** of measured numbers must be rounded to the same number of decimal places as there are in the measurement with the least number of decimal places. Of course, if there are no decimals in a measurement, a shift of unit can be made so that there are. That is not necessary as long as you know which digits are measured digits.

Example: The earth has a polar radius of 6357 km, and an equatorial radius of 6378 km. What is the difference between the two?

The measurements are in the same unit, and have the same degree of accuracy, so they can be subtracted directly.

$$\text{Difference} = 6378 \text{ km} - 6357 \text{ km} = 21 \text{ km}.$$

The absence of decimals in these numbers should not prevent you from applying the rule for subtracting measured numbers. However, there is one interesting feature to notice: the original measurements have four-digit accuracy, but their difference has only two-digit accuracy. Subtraction is a process by which accuracy can be lost.

Think of an example in which accuracy could be gained by addition. (See I at the end of Chapter 1 Exercises.)

RELATIONS AMONG QUANTITIES

Many of the important statements that you will study in physics describe relations among two or more quantities. Frequently it will be important to find how changes in one quantity affect the values of another quantity. The regularity of such relations in nature provides the foundation for the whole structure of physics. Most of the relations are fairly simple, the most frequent ones being direct variation and inverse variation.

DIRECT VARIATION

The density of steel is about 8 t/m³. This statement means that the relation between the masses of steel castings (in tonnes) and their volumes (in cubic metres) is that shown in Table 1-7. This relation between volume (V) and mass (m) is called direct variation. The properties of direct variation relations can be described in a series of three steps. First, you can see that as V increases (from 1 m³ to 6 m³), m increases (from 8 t to 48 t). However, simply to have both quantities increase is not sufficient for direct variation. The second feature to note is that when V is doubled (e.g., from 3 m³ to 6 m³), m is doubled (from 24 t to 48 t). More generally, multiplying any value of V by a number will lead to a value for m that is multiplied by the same number. For example, with 1 m³ for V corresponding to 8 t for m, multiplying both by 5 gives the pair of values of 5 m³ for V and 40 t for m.

The third feature of direct variation is the most general. It is that the *ratio* of each corresponding pair of quantities has the same ratio.

Or, the ratio $\dfrac{m}{V} = \text{constant.}$

Table 1-7

FOR STEEL CASTINGS

Volume (m³)	1	2	3	4	5	6
Mass (t)	8	16	24	32	40	48

In our example, the constant ratio is 8 t/m³. This is the quantity density (*D*), which is constant for steel castings, whether their volume is small or large. The relation can be expressed in an equation or formula, either

$$\frac{m}{V} = D, \quad \text{or} \quad m = DV.$$

The relation can be expressed in words in two ways: we can say either that *m* varies directly as *V*, or that *m* is directly proportional to *V*.

Any set of values for two quantities that have the features described here are related by direct variation.

INVERSE VARIATION

In the process of making gold leaf, a small flat piece of gold is beaten thinner and thinner in a series of stages. As the process reduces the thickness of the gold, it increases its area. Starting with about 11 g of gold, when the thickness (*d*) has been reduced to 0.60 μm, the area (*A*) is 1.0 m². Continued beating increases the area and decreases the thickness as shown in Table 1-8.

This relation between area and thickness is called inverse variation. The properties of inverse variation relations can be described in a series of three steps. First you can see that as *A* increases (from 1.0 m² to 6.0 m²) *d* decreases (from 0.60 μm to 0.10 μm). However, simply to have one quantity decrease as the other increases is not sufficient for inverse variation. The second feature to note is that when *A* is doubled (e.g., from 3.0 m² to 6.0 m²), *d* is halved (from 0.20 μm to 0.10 μm). More generally, multiplying any value of *A* by a number will lead to a value for *d* that is divided by the same number. For example, with 1.0 m² for *A* corresponding to 0.60 μm for *d*, multiplying *A* by 5 and dividing *d* by 5 gives the pair of values of 5.0 m² for *A* and 0.12 μm for *d*.

The third feature of inverse variation is the most general. It is that the *product* of each corresponding pair of quantities has the same value:

$$(2.0 \text{ m}^2)(0.30 \ \mu\text{m}) = (2.0 \text{ m}^2)(0.30 \times 10^{-6} \text{ m}) = 0.60 \times 10^{-6} \text{ m}^3.$$

In general $\qquad Ad = \text{constant.}$

The constant product, 0.60 x 10⁻⁶ m³, is the volume of 11 g of gold. The relation can be expressed in an equation or formula, either

$$Ad = V, \quad \text{or} \quad d = \frac{V}{A}.$$

The relation can be expressed in words in two ways: we can say ei-

Table 1-8

MAKING 11 g OF GOLD INTO GOLD LEAF

Area	Thickness
1.0 m²	0.60 μm
2.0	0.30
3.0	0.20
4.0	0.15
5.0	0.12
6.0	0.10

Since 1 cm³ = (1 × 10⁻² m)³ = 1 × 10⁻⁶ m³, the volume of this 11 g of gold is 0.60 cm³.

ther that d varies inversely as A, or that d is inversely proportional to A.

Any set of values for two quantities that have the features described here are related by inverse variation.

GRAPHS OF RELATIONS

The relations of direct and inverse variation can be shown visually on graphs. Points for each corresponding pair of values are plotted on rectangular axes. Since the relations will hold for intermediate values, the points can be joined with a smooth line.

For direct variation, we plot the mass-volume relation for the steel castings (Fig. 1-2). The line joining the points is a straight line passing through the origin (0,0). Whenever the plot of the results of experimental measurements is such a line, the relation between the quantities is direct variation.

The graph of the thickness-area relation for gold foil is plotted in Fig. 1-3. The shape of this graph, with the line approaching one axis upward, and the other to the right, is called a rectangular hyperbola. Whenever the graph of experimental measurements has this shape the relation between the quantities is inverse variation.

Graphs can also be used to display relations more complicated than direct and inverse variation. For example, measurements can be made to determine the relation between gasoline consumption and speed of travel for an automobile. The amount of gasoline consumed is measured for a fixed distance for each of several constant speeds. The gasoline consumptions are then calculated in the standard unit of litres per 100 km. The results of one such experiment are shown in Table 1-9, and plotted on the graph of Fig. 1-4.

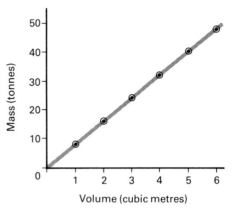

FIG. 1-2

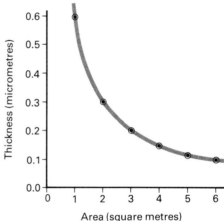

FIG. 1-3

Table 1-9

AUTO GASOLINE
CONSUMPTION DEPENDS
ON SPEED

Constant Speed	Gas Consumption
20.0 km/h	15.5 L/100 km
40.0	13.4
60.0	12.8
80.0	13.5
100.0	15.8
120.0	19.6

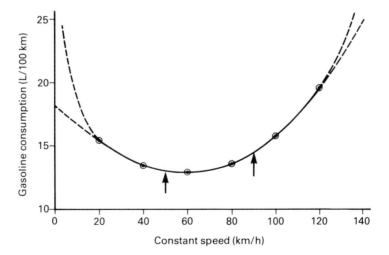

FIG. 1-4

Since the points on the graph are distributed in a regular way, we can join them with a smooth curve. Then the graph can be used to read off the gasoline consumption at speeds not used in the tests. According to the graph, we should expect a gasoline consumption of

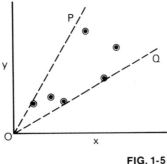

FIG. 1-5

13.0 L/100 km at a speed of 50 km/h. At 90 km/h, the consumption should be 14.5 L/100 km. This process of determining values for intermediate points on a graph is called **interpolation**. If a smooth curve can reasonably be drawn through points obtained by measurement, then interpolation is likely to be quite reliable. If the measured points are scattered on the graph (Fig. 1-5), interpolation is less likely to give a reliable result. If you want to find y for another value of x, about the best you might do would be to give y the range of values that lie between the two lines OP and OQ. No regular relation is evident, so interpolation is unreliable in this case.

The graph of Fig. 1-4 has been extended beyond the experimental points with several dashed lines. Using a graph to infer points outside the experimental range is called **extrapolation**. Beyond the speed of 120 km/h two possible extrapolations have been drawn. Without further experimenting there is no way of telling which is correct. One continuation of the graph below 20 km/h suggests that if you had zero speed, your gas consumption would be 18 L/100 km. But if the engine runs without moving the car, you'll never travel 100 km. The other downward extrapolation is probably more correct. What you should realize is that extrapolation is very often a risky matter.

ANALYSIS OF EXPERIMENTAL MEASUREMENTS

After measurements have been collected from an experimental arrangement, you have to see if the quantities measured are related in a regular way. Since the relation among experimental numbers is unlikely to be exact, you should also get some idea of the degree to which the measurements conform to an exact relation. Both of these procedures will be illustrated using experimental data published by Robert Boyle in England in 1662. Boyle made measurements of the volume of a certain amount of air as the pressure on it was varied. Since he did not make his measurements in SI units, we shall give his numbers without units. His pressures were measured to the nearest eighth of a unit, which we have converted to the nearest tenth.

Boyle's data for corresponding volumes (V) and pressures (p) are shown in Table 1-10 and plotted on the graph of Fig. 1-6. The graph is very close to being a rectangular hyperbola, so that we can say that the relation between pressure and volume is very nearly inverse variation—that is that the applied pressure is inversely proportional to the volume for a fixed mass of gas.

The next thing to do is to express the numerical relation that exists between pressure and volume. There are two ways to do that. The first is graphical, based on the idea that we can get a visual impression of how closely the data fit an exact relation if they can be plotted in a way that should be a straight line. The following algebraic relations show how to proceed. We start with the inverse relation,

$$pV = k \text{ (a constant)}.$$

Table 1-10

THE RESULTS OF
BOYLE'S EXPERIMENT

Volume (V)	Pressure (p)
1.00	29.8
2.00	14.4
3.00	9.1
4.00	7.1
5.00	5.6
6.00	4.9
7.00	4.2
8.00	3.8
9.00	3.4
10.00	3.0

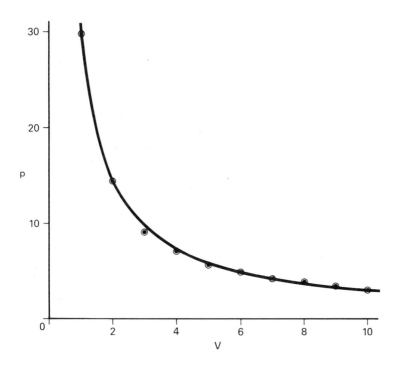

FIG. 1-6

Alternatively, we can write

$$p = k(1/V) \qquad \text{or} \qquad \frac{p}{(1/V)} = k.$$

This last relation shows that the *ratio* of p and $1/V$ is constant. That means that there is a relation of direct variation between p and $1/V$. If we plot p against $1/V$, the graph should be a straight line through the origin. The data to do this for Boyle's results are shown in Table 1-11 and they are plotted on the graph of Fig. 1-7. Since a straight line fits the points very closely, we know that the experimental data do come very close to a constant value for k.

The value of that constant can be found directly from the graph. It is the slope of the line. In Fig. 1-8, choose any two points P and Q on the line, with Q to the right of P. Complete the right-angle triangle PQR, by drawing PR horizontally to the right from P, and RQ vertically up to Q. The **slope** of the line is defined by the ratio

$$\text{slope} = \frac{\text{rise}}{\text{run}} = \frac{RQ}{PR}.$$

Table 1-11

1/V	p
1.000	29.8
0.500	14.4
0.333	9.1
0.250	7.1
0.200	5.6
0.167	4.9
0.143	4.2
0.125	3.8
0.111	3.4
0.100	3.0

FIG. 1-7 appears on page 14.

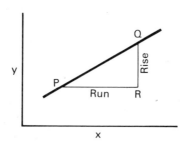

FIG. 1-8

FIG. 1-7

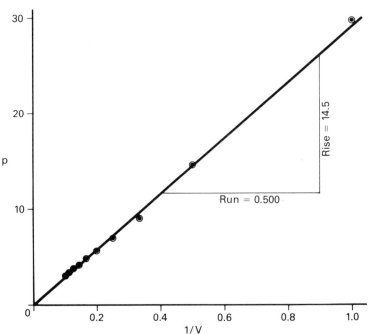

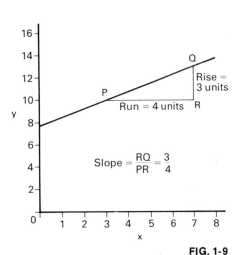

Slope = $\frac{RQ}{PR} = \frac{3}{4}$

FIG. 1-9

Slope = $\frac{RQ}{PR} = -\frac{9}{5}$

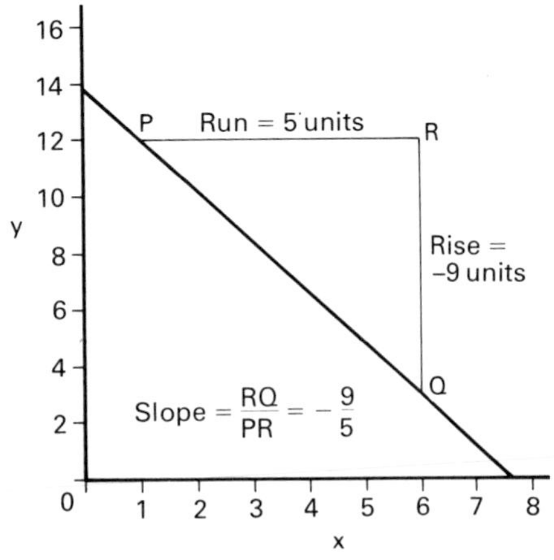

FIG. 1-10

Even though honesty demands that you accept the results of experimental measurements, you are not cheating if you repeat a measurement that produced a result that deviates wildly from the trend of other results.

The slopes of the lines in Figs. 1-9 and 1-10 are calculated on the graphs. As long as the axes are positive in the directions upward and to the right, lines that point up to the right have positive slopes and lines that point downward to the right have negative slopes.

The slope of the graph of p versus $1/V$ can now be found. The usual procedure is to choose round numbers to terminate the run-line. Here they are 0.400 and 0.900. Careful measurement gives a value of 14.5 for the corresponding rise. Then the slope of the line is

$$\frac{p}{1/V} = \frac{14.5}{0.500} = 29.0.$$

Or, we can write

$$pV = 29.0.$$

Drawing the best straight line through the points is a way of getting the average value for the constant k. Thus, the result of Boyle's experiment is that the product of pressure and volume has an average value of 29.0.

Often this graphical method of analysis is the simplest and most instructive. Even when it is not, the advantage of drawing a quick graph is that you can readily see if some points deviate widely from the trend of the majority. When that happens you can repeat certain measurements to improve your results.

There is also a purely numerical method of analysis, which has the advantage of allowing you to determine the extent to which measured results deviate from a regular relation. The major step in numerical analysis is to determine which arithmetical operation with the data should lead to a constant number for every pair of measurements. For direct variation you seek a constant *ratio* of the pairs of values. For inverse variation you seek a constant *product* of the pairs of values. However, because of the inexactness of measurements, you will never expect to find a perfectly constant result. The final steps in the numerical analysis will determine the deviation.

In Robert Boyle's experiment, we have determined that the relation is very nearly inverse variation, so that the product $pV = 29.0$, approximately. Table 1-12 shows the steps in the numerical analysis. The pairs of values for volume and pressure in the first two columns are multiplied together to give the products in the third column. The numbers in the third column are approximately constant, ranging from 27.3 to 30.6. To find their average, add them and divide by 10. The average is 29.2. The 29.0 that we got from the graph was the closest that could be obtained by measurement on the graph.

In the fourth column of Table 1-12, the average of 29.2 is subtracted from each of the values in column 3. These give the deviations of each product from the average. The fifth column gives the percentage deviation (neglecting the signs), calculated from the rule:

$$\text{percentage deviation of result} = \frac{\text{result} - \text{average}}{\text{average}} \times 100\%.$$

The average of the percentage deviations is about 3%. Thus, from the numerical analysis of Boyle's experiment, we conclude that

$$pV = 29.2 \text{ (within about 3\%)}.$$

In many of your experiments you will have to be satisfied with average percentage deviations of up to 10%. Expensive precision measuring instruments are often needed to reduce deviations to less than 1%.

You should not suppose that every straight-line graph will pass through the origin. Consider the following example. The height of a plant was measured once every five days for three weeks. The results are shown in Table 1-13 and on the graph of Fig. 1-11. The slope of the best straight line through the points is shown to be 0.50 cm/d. On the average, through the course of the time-period the plant gained 0.50 cm in height each day. For a complete expression of the relation between height and time you will also have to take account of the initial height of 4.0 cm.

The equation that shows the relation of the height (h) to the time (t) can be written as

Table 1-12

NUMERICAL ANALYSIS OF BOYLE'S EXPERIMENT

V	p	pV	Deviation	Percentage deviation
1.00	29.8	29.8	+ 0.6	2.1
2.00	14.4	28.8	− 0.4	1.4
3.00	9.1	27.3	− 1.9	6.5
4.00	7.1	28.4	− 0.8	2.7
5.00	5.6	28.0	− 1.2	4.1
6.00	4.9	29.4	+ 0.2	0.7
7.00	4.2	29.4	+ 0.2	0.7
8.00	3.8	30.4	+ 1.2	4.1
9.00	3.4	30.6	+ 1.4	4.8
10.00	3.0	30.9	+ 0.8	2.7
	Sums	292.1		29.8%

Table 1-13

HEIGHT OF PLANT
MEASURED FOR
THREE WEEKS

Time	Height
0.0 d	4.0 cm
5.0	6.4
10.0	9.2
15.0	12.0
20.0	13.4

This 3% uncertainty is greater even than the uncertainty implied by a two-digit number (i.e., 29). Thus, to give the product pV as 29.2 without qualification would imply a much greater accuracy than the experimental measurements warrant.

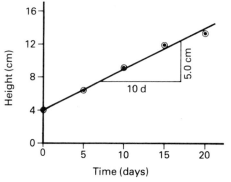

FIG. 1-11

$$h = 4.0 \text{ cm} + (0.50 \text{ cm/d}) \, t.$$

For a numerical analysis to find the percentage deviation of the rate of growth from 0.50 cm/d, you will have to subtract 4.0 cm from each of the other heights. That will give the distance grown at each time. Then you can calculate the extent of the deviation of each ratio of distance grown to time from the average value of the ratio. The percentage deviation works out to an average of 5%.

Since the equation above is that of a straight line, we can say that the relation between height and time is a **linear relation**, even though the graph does not pass through the origin.

THE ALGEBRA OF UNITS

The quantities you deal with in physics are expressed by a number *and* a unit. When you perform calculations with quantities, you should include the units and treat them in the same way that you would treat algebraic expressions. The main reason for doing so is that the result of any calculation requires a correct unit just as much as a correct numerical value.

For example, use the equation above for the height of the plant, considering that it will still be true after four weeks. How tall will the plant be after four weeks? Although "week" is not an SI unit, suppose for this example that its abbreviation is "wk". Then you might want to substitute 4 wk for *t* in the equation. And if you did not include the units you might get a numerical answer without bothering to check to see if it made sense. If you include the units, you will see that the last term has "wk" in the numerator and "d" for "days" in the denominator. Since these are inconsistent, you have to make some adjustment. The best way to do it is to compose a fraction with a value of "l" that has "wk" in the denominator and "d" in the numerator. Because l wk = 7 d, that fraction is 7d/1 wk. Since numerator and denominator are equal, you can multiply any quantity by this fraction without changing the value of the quantity. Now write the equation:

A fraction used to convert from one unit to another, such as 7 d/1 wk = 1, is called a **conversion factor**

$$h = 4.0 \text{ cm} + \left(\frac{0.50 \text{ cm}}{\text{d}}\right) (4 \text{ wk}) \left(\frac{7 \text{ d}}{1 \text{ wk}}\right).$$

Now, the units wk and d will divide out, and you will be left with

$$h = 4.0 \text{ cm} + (0.50 \text{ cm})(28) = 4.0 \text{ cm} + 14 \text{ cm} = 18 \text{ cm}.$$

Using the units that way also makes it possible to see that the last numerical addition is legitimate, since both terms are expressed in the same unit, centimetres. The equation would not have been wrong if the growth rate had been expressed as 5.0 mm/d; but you would have had to adjust the length units before performing the final addition. To include units in all calculations with quantities will help you to avoid performing incorrect operations. And if you perform the algebra of units carefully, you will have a check on the rightness of your answer, because the unit you get by calculation has to be an appropriate unit for the quantity whose value you are calculating.

If you want to know how to put mass and density together to calculate volume, it can help to know that the answer has to be in volume units. The density of air is about 1.3 g/L. To find the volume of 29 g of air, we need a number with "litres" in the numerator, and with "grams" missing. To do that, we first invert (or divide by) the density. That puts "litres" into the numerator and "grams" into the denominator. To eliminate "grams" requires putting the mass, 29 g, into the numerator. Thus, the volume is

$$V = \frac{29 \text{ g}}{1.3 \text{ g/L}} = 22 \text{ g} \times \frac{\text{L}}{\text{g}} = 22 \text{ L}.$$

To divide by a fraction, invert and multiply:
$1 \div \text{g/L} = 1 \times \text{L/g}.$

Although you knew directly how to do that with the formula ($V = m/D$), you may find this technique useful in other cases where you may on occasion remember the units but forget the formula. But don't forget, *quantities have units attached.*

Exercises

A

1. Draw up a table that lists the power of 10 that corresponds to each multiple of 10 in the range from 10 000 to 0.000 01.

2. Write the following numbers as powers of 10:
   (a) one million
   (b) one thousand million
   (c) one million million
   (d) one million million million
   (e) one millionth
   (f) one thousandth of a millionth
   (g) one millionth of a millionth.

3. Calculate
   (a) $10^5 \times 10^7$
   (b) $10^{-4} \times 10^{-3}$
   (c) $10^7 \times 10^{-5}$
   (d) $10^{-11} \times 10^6$
   (e) $\dfrac{10^9}{10^6}$
   (f) $\dfrac{10^3}{10^7}$
   (g) $\dfrac{10^{-4}}{10^{-1}}$
   (h) $\dfrac{10^{-3}}{10^{-5}}$
   (i) $\dfrac{10^4}{10^{-19}}$
   (j) $\dfrac{10^8}{10^{-9}}$
   (k) $\dfrac{10^{-5}}{10^3}$

4. The earth's diameter is of the order of magnitude of 10^7 m. The sun's diameter is of the order of magnitude of 10^9 m. The radius of the earth's orbit about the sun is of the order of 10^{11} m. Calculate

   (a) the approximate number of earth diameters in the diameter of the sun;
   (b) the approximate number of earth diameters in the radius of the earth's orbit.

5. Atoms have diameters of the order of 10^{-10} m. Red blood cells have diameters of about 10^{-5} m. How many atoms could lie side by side across a red blood cell?

6. Convert the powers of ten in the following to convenient prefixes of the units, so that the multiplying number is greater than 1 but less than 1000:
   (a) 3×10^4 m   (e) 3.1×10^{16} m
   (b) 7×10^{-5} s   (f) 6.2×10^{-10} s
   (c) 4.6×10^{-3} g   (g) 8.9×10^3 kg/m³
   (d) 3.0×10^8 m/s   (h) 4.0×10^{-7} m

7. Write the following numbers in standard form:
   (a) 17 500   (f) 84×10^{-3}
   (b) 0.000 35   (g) 257×10^3
   (c) 437 000   (h) 0.043×10^{-7}
   (d) 0.000 089 45   (i) 0.603×10^{24}
   (e) 0.69×10^{-5} (j) 160.2×10^{-21}

8. Replace the following metric prefixes by the power of ten that converts the quantity to standard form in the fundamental unit:

(a) 5 km
(b) 16 mm
(c) 350 MHz
(d) 0.73 μs
(e) 583 nm
(f) 149.6 Gm
(g) 1.8 as
(h) 513 THz

9. The diameter of a red blood cell is measured to be 7.5×10^{-6} m. The range of uncertainty of the diameter is therefore from 7.45×10^{-6} m to 7.55×10^{-6} m. State the range of uncertainty for the following quantities:
   (a) The average density of the earth is 5.5×10^3 kg/m³;
   (b) The radius of the moon is 1.74×10^6 m;
   (c) The distance to the star Sirius is 8.8 light years;
   (d) The density of air at 0°C and at standard atmospheric pressure is 1.293 kg/m³;
   (e) The speed of light is 2.99793×10^8 m/s.

10. Write the difference between the end values in the range of uncertainty for the speed of light in standard form (see 9(e) above).

11. For each of the following, perform the required calculations with the given measured numbers, and give your answer to the precision or accuracy permitted:
    (a) The sides of a triangular plot are 15 m, 13.5 m, and 9.25 m. Calculate the perimeter of the field.
    (b) The time for a car to coast a distance of 1.0 km was measured six times (starting each time from the same initial speed). The measured times were 44 s, 46.5 s, 44.8 s, 46 s, 45.5 s, 46.2 s. Calculate the average time.
    (c) Find the area of a rectangle having sides 7.2 cm and 4.3 cm.
    (d) Find the average density of a steel casting of volume 3.5 m³ and a mass of 2.72×10^4 kg.
    (e) Find the volume of a cylinder of base area 6.2 cm² and height 23.4 cm.

12. Following are eleven statements. For each, tell whether it refers to direct variation or inverse variation.
    (a) When x increases, y decreases.
    (b) When the ratios of corresponding pairs of x and y are calculated, they are found to be equal.
    (c) When x is multiplied by some number, y is multiplied by the same number.
    (d) When x is divided by some number, y is divided by the same number.
    (e) A graph of y versus x is a hyperbola.
    (f) A graph of y versus x is a straight line through the origin.
    (g) A graph of y versus $1/x$ is a straight line through the origin.
    (h) When x increases, y increases.
    (i) When x is multiplied by some number, y is divided by the same number.
    (j) When x is divided by some number, y is multiplied by the same number.
    (k) When the products of corresponding pairs of x and y are calculated, they are found to be equal.

13. Redraw the following graph on squared paper and

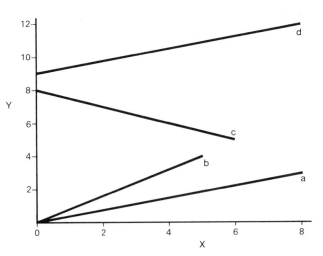

determine the slope of each of the four lines on the graph.

14. Determine the relation between p and F that the following graph illustrates. What value of p corres-

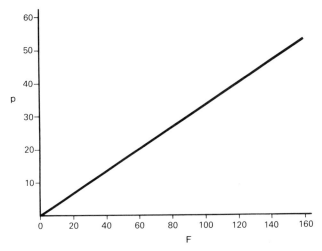

ponds to $F = 100$? What value of F corresponds to $p = 45$?

15. Determine the relation between p and V illustrated on the following graph. What value of V corresponds to $p = 20$? What value of p corresponds to $V = 33$?

16. Plot a graph of the data in the following table and determine the equation that describes the relation between x and y.

x	3	6	9	12	15
y	6	12	18	24	30

17. Plot a graph of the data in the following table and determine the equation that describes the relation between p and A.

p	1	2	3	4	6	9	12	18	36
A	36	18	12	9	6	4	3	2	1

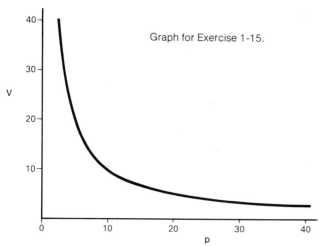

Graph for Exercise 1-15.

18. Construct a table of five or six pairs of values that satisfy the relation $V = 15\ I$, and use them to plot a graph of V vertically against I horizontally.

19. Construct a table of six to eight pairs of values that satisfy the relation $DV = 60$, and use them to plot a graph of D vertically against V horizontally.

20. State whether the variation is direct or inverse for each of the questions 14 to 19.

21. Simplify the units in the following expressions:

(a) $\dfrac{km}{h} \times h$ (c) $\dfrac{L}{L/100\ km}$ (e) $\sqrt{\dfrac{m}{m/s^2}}$

(b) $\dfrac{kg/m^3}{kg}$ (d) $\dfrac{kg}{kg/m^3}$ (f) $\dfrac{m^3}{kg \cdot s^2} \times \dfrac{kg^2}{m^2}$

B

22. The following graph shows the variation since 1900 in the percentage of heat energy that fuel-burning plants can convert to electricity. The percentage that the energy produced in electrical form represents of the total heat energy supplied is called *efficiency*.

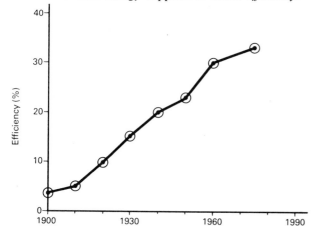

(a) What was the efficiency in 1950?
(b) In what year was the efficiency 20%?
(c) In what year was the efficiency 30%?
(d) What will the efficiency be in the year 2000?

23. After every trip a salesman has his gas tank refilled to the same level. He then records the gasoline consumption and the length of the trip. The following table shows a selection of such records:

Distance (km)	160	210	250	320	370	420
Gas consumed (L)	14	19	22	29	32	37

(a) Plot a graph of the data.
(b) Find the slope of the best straight line through the points.
(c) Find the gas consumption in L/100 km for each trip and compare with the slope of the line.
(d) Call the consumption of gas C and the distance travelled d. Write the equation that expresses the relation between the two.

24. A tank of water can be emptied through any one of five pipes located near its bottom. Each pipe has a different cross-sectional area. The following table shows the times it takes for the water to empty out through the pipes, one at a time:

Area of opening (m²)	0.020	0.050	0.070	0.100	0.130
Time to empty (min)	7.4	3.0	1.9	1.4	1.1

(a) Draw a graph of these data.
(b) Find the relation between the two quantities and express it as an equation.

25. Find the approximate number of kilometres in the distance light can travel in one year. Do it by rounding off the numbers involved to 1 digit and a power of ten. That is, take 3×10^8 m/s for the speed of light, 4000 s in an hour, 20 h in a day, and 400 d in a year. Round off your answer to 1 digit times a power of ten.

26. A newspaper has reported that particle pollution in an industrial city amounts to 400 t/a on each square kilometre (1 t = 1 Mg). Estimate the mass in kilograms that fall on each square metre.

27. The volume of water trapped in glaciers and the polar icecaps is about 1.6×10^7 km³. The area of the world's oceans is about 3.6×10^8 km². By how much would the ocean depth increase if all the ice melted? Give your answer in a reasonable unit.

C

28. On the average, 1 kg of matter consists of about 10^{26} atoms. The mass of an average star is about 10^{30} kg. There are about 10^{11} stars in a galaxy, and about 10^{11} galaxies in the observed universe. What is the approximate number of atoms in the universe?

Answer to text question

I. The sum of two 2-digit numbers may be a 3-digit number; e.g., $5.6 + 8.3 = 13.9$.

CHAPTER **2**

Motion on Road and Track

Andrea Lynch of Great Britain at the start of a 100 m Olympic trial race in 1976.

Sprinting along a 100 m track in Sacramento, California, in 1968, Jim Hines was the first man to beat the ten-second barrier— running the 100 m in 9.9 s. Eight years later in Montreal Jim Montgomery set a world record in 100 m freestyle swimming, covering the distance in 49.5 s. A comparison of the two times shows that the swimmer took five times longer than the sprinter to go the same distance. Other motions could be compared with these if we knew the time needed to complete 100 m. The normal method of comparison, however, is to say that Hines had five times the speed of Montgomery.

SPEED

Thus, rather than looking for the lengths of time taken to cover a standard distance, we reduce motions to the same time by calculating speeds. Any motion involves a distance travelled and a time elapsed; **speed** gives the rate of the motion (it does not include direction). The average speed of a motion is the total distance travelled (d) divided by the elapsed time (t),

distance
time
velocity (speed)

$$v = \frac{d}{t}.$$

The symbol for speed is v (from "velocity," which will be discussed in Chapter 3). Hines' average speed was

$$v = \frac{100 \text{ m}}{9.9 \text{ s}} = 1.0 \times 10^1 \text{ m/s}.$$

Montgomery's average speed was

$$v = \frac{100 \text{ m}}{49.5 \text{ s}} = 2.02 \text{ m/s}.$$

In a quick spurt a runner can average about 10 m/s. What speed can he average on a sustained run? At the Montreal Olympics in 1976, Waldemar Cierpinski ran the marathon distance of 42 195 m in 2 h 9 min 55 s (7795 s), making his average speed

$$v = \frac{42\ 195\ \text{m}}{7795\ \text{s}} = 5.413\ \text{m/s}.$$

Thus a trained runner can maintain a speed of just over half his maximum for a couple of hours.

Comparing the rates of different motions is not the only use to which speed calculations can be put.

On a highway trip an average (legal) speed of about 80 km/h can be maintained. Since you can go 80 km in each hour, how far could you go in 6.0 h? Let's see how that works in the formula.

Since $$v = \frac{d}{t}, \quad \text{then} \quad d = vt.$$

Notice that the symbols stand for *quantities*, the number combined with the unit. In the calculation the units can be handled in much the same way that algebraic numbers are.

$$\text{km} = \frac{\text{km}}{\text{h}} \times \text{h}.$$

Thus $$d = (80\ \text{km/h})(6.0\ \text{h}) = 4.8 \times 10^2\ \text{km}.$$

The distance from Guelph to Ottawa is 480 km.

Example: The highway distance from Windsor to Hamilton is 304 km. Averaging 80 km/h how long will it take you to drive this distance?

Since $$d = vt,$$

then $$t = \frac{d}{v} = \frac{304\ \text{km}}{80\ \text{km/h}} = 3.8\ \text{km} \times \frac{\text{h}}{\text{km}} = 3.8\ \text{h}.$$

The trip will take about 3 h 50 min.

ACCELERATION

Average speeds are fine when talking about races and trips, but speeds themselves change. Just before the start of a race or a trip your speed is zero. Then, you push off, gradually increasing your speed, until you reach some steady value that you will maintain for a while. The rate at which speed changes is called **acceleration.**

The more general definition of acceleration is rate of change of velocity—see Chapter 3.

When you are driving at a steady speed of 20 m/s, and in 5.0 s you increase your speed to 30 m/s, the acceleration can be readily calculated. The change in speed is 30 m/s – 20 m/s = 10 m/s. On the average, the speed increased at the rate of

The unit of acceleration is
(m/s)/s = m/s².

$$\frac{10 \text{ m/s}}{5.0 \text{ s}} = 2.0 \text{ m/s}^2.$$

This is read as two metres per second squared.

You should not think that we have introduced a quantity of "square seconds," but that two divisions by time have been performed. The first division of distance by time gave speed. The second division by time gives acceleration.

In physical formulas, the idea of a difference or an interval is expressed by the Greek capital letter delta, Δ. So, a formula for acceleration can be derived from the idea that

$$\text{acceleration} = \frac{\text{change in speed}}{\text{time interval}}$$

$$a = \frac{\Delta v}{\Delta t}.$$

If we call the initial speed v_1 and the final speed v_2, we can write

$$a = \frac{v_2 - v_1}{\Delta t}.$$

To find the speed achieved after an acceleration, we can multiply both sides of the equation by Δt to get

$$a\Delta t = v_2 - v_1$$

and then re-arrange the equation to get

$$v_2 = v_1 + a\Delta t.$$

In words: if you are travelling at an initial speed of v_1, and undergo an acceleration of a for a time interval Δt, the final speed v_2 is the sum of the initial speed and the product of the acceleration and the time.

A moped driver is caught in traffic and travels at 6.0 m/s. Then a clear path appears ahead and the driver accelerates at 1.6 m/s² for 5.0 s. What speed has the driver achieved?

The given quantities are

$$v_1 = 6.0 \frac{\text{m}}{\text{s}} \qquad a = 1.6 \frac{\text{m}}{\text{s}^2} \qquad \Delta t = 5.0 \text{ s}.$$

Substitute in the formula

$$v_2 = v_1 + a\Delta t$$

$$= 6.0\,\frac{m}{s} + (1.6\,\frac{m}{s^2})(5.0\ s)$$

$$= 6.0\,\frac{m}{s} + 8.0\,\frac{m}{s} = 14.0\,\frac{m}{s}.$$

The moped's speed increased to 14.0 m/s after 5.0 s.

You might want to know how far along the road the moped driver travelled during the accelerated motion just described. In general, this distance is not easy to calculate. However, if the acceleration was *constant*—with the speed increasing uniformly—the distance travelled can be found quite readily. If the driver had not accelerated, the moped would have travelled at 6.0 m/s for 5.0 s, travelling a distance of 30 m. On the other hand, if the driver had spent the 5.0 s at the higher speed of 14.0 m/s, the distance travelled would have been 70 m. In fact, the 5.0 s was spent in a *uniform* increase from 6.0 m/s to 14.0 m/s. The actual distance travelled must be more than 30 m and less than 70 m. The most reasonable value to settle on is the middle value, 50 m, the average of the two distances. This argument is made graphically on pages 26-7.

> The average of two numbers is half their sum.

See now how the calculation works:

$$d = \tfrac{1}{2}(6.0\,\frac{m}{s} \times 5.0\ s + 14.0\,\frac{m}{s} \times 5.0\ s)$$

$$= \tfrac{1}{2}(6.0\,\frac{m}{s} + 14.0\,\frac{m}{s}) \times 5.0\ s$$

$$= 10\,\frac{m}{s} \times 5.0\ s = 50\ m.$$

This calculation shows that the same result would be obtained by multiplying the time by the average of the two speeds. When acceleration is constant (*and only then*) the average speed is the average of the initial and final speeds.

$$d = \tfrac{1}{2}(v_1 + v_2)\,\Delta t \quad \text{[for constant } a\text{]}.$$

Example: Suppose to pass a car on the highway you increase your speed from 20 m/s to 30 m/s in 6.0 s. Since you shouldn't pass if an approaching car is too close, you need to know how far you will travel while passing.

$$v_1 = 20\,\frac{m}{s} \qquad v_2 = 30\,\frac{m}{s} \qquad \Delta t = 6.0\ s.$$

$$d = \tfrac{1}{2}(v_1 + v_2)\,\Delta t \quad \text{[if } a \text{ is constant]}$$

$$= \tfrac{1}{2}(20\,\frac{m}{s} + 30\,\frac{m}{s})(6.0\ s) = (25\,\frac{m}{s})(6.0\ s) = 150\ m.$$

Table 2-1

t	d
0 s	0 m
15	400
30	800
45	1200
60	1600

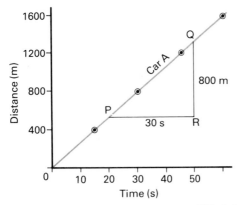

FIG. 2-1

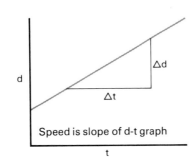

Speed is slope of d-t graph

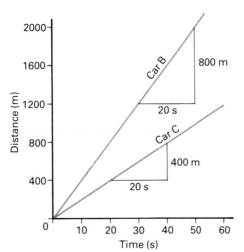

FIG. 2-2

If the approaching car is coming toward you at 50 m/s, it will travel 180 m during that same 6.0 s interval. Let us hope that it is 350 m or more away from you before you pull out to pass.

GRAPHS OF MOTION

The relations developed so far apply only to constant speed or acceleration, or provide only average values. To analyze changing motions in more detail, graphs are a useful tool. Suppose that a police helicopter is timing the passage of cars along a highway with markers every 400 m. The policeman starts his stopwatch when a car passes the marker in front of the stone church on Highway 13. For several kilometres of travel car A takes 15 s to traverse each 400 m interval. Table 2-1 shows the distances travelled during one minute. Plotting corresponding values of time and distance on a graph gives the result shown on the graph in Fig. 2-1; a straight line through the origin.

SPEEDS

The speed of car A is shown on the graph by the slope of the line. The slope is found by choosing two points on the line, as P and Q. Draw a line horizontally from P and one vertically from Q so they meet at R. PR is called the *run* of the line segment PQ, and RQ is called the *rise*. The slope of the line is given by the expression rise/run. Here, that works out as follows:

$$\text{speed} = \text{slope} = \frac{\text{rise}}{\text{run}} = \frac{\text{RQ}}{\text{PR}} = \frac{800 \text{ m}}{30 \text{ s}} = 27 \text{ m/s}.$$

For a straight line, the slope is constant all along the line. Thus, on a *distance-time graph* a line with constant slope represents a motion with constant speed:

$$v = \frac{\Delta d}{\Delta t}.$$

The graph in Fig. 2-2 shows car B breaking the speed limit, with a constant speed of 40 m/s. Car C is dawdling along at 20 m/s. These lines show that greater slope represents greater speed, and lesser slope represents lesser speed.

Now, draw a graph of motion (Fig. 2-3) that corresponds to the times and distances in Table 2-2. The points should be joined by a smooth curve. Where the graph-line is curved, the slope is changing. And therefore the motion it represents is one of changing speed. However, it is reasonable to say that at each point, the line *has* a particular slope for that point. The way to find the slope at any given point on the graph is to draw a straight line at the point so that the

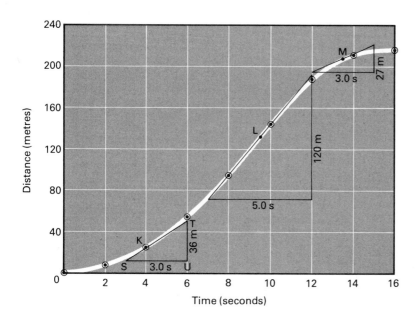

Table 2-2

t	d
0 s	0 m
2	6
4	24
6	54
8	96
10	144
12	189
14	213
16	216

FIG. 2-3

straight line has the same direction as the graph-line there. Such a straight line is called a *tangent*. On the graph in Fig. 2-3, mark the point K on the graph-line at the 4.0 s point. Draw the line ST touching the curved line at K, directed so that the graph curves away from ST at the same rate on either side of K. Complete the right-angle triangle STU.

Since the triangle STU will be used to determine the slope of the graph-line at K, S and T are chosen at points on the tangent at integer values of time—S at the 3.0 s mark and T at the 6.0 s mark. The speed at K (4.0 s) can then be determined from the slope of the tangent:

$$v_K = \frac{\Delta d}{\Delta t} = \frac{36 \text{ m}}{3.0 \text{ s}} = 12 \frac{\text{m}}{\text{s}}.$$

The speeds at point L (9.5 s) and M (13.5 s) can be determined similarly, using the slope triangles of the tangents at those points.

Then, $\qquad v_L = 24 \text{ m/s}, \qquad$ and $\qquad v_M = 10 \text{ m/s}$

Before leaving the graph in Fig. 2-3, notice that its slope at 0.0 s and at 15.0 s is zero—the line is horizontal. The motion that the graph describes began and ended with zero speed, or rest. Notice also that the graph is very close to a straight line between 8 s and 11 s—the speed was constant during that interval. In sum, the graph represents a motion that started from rest, accelerated in about 8 s to 24 m/s, held that constant for about 3 s , and then braked to zero speed 4 s later.

You can draw an accurate tangent to a curve at a point on it with a small plane mirror, e.g., a single-edged razor blade. Set the mirror upright on the page so that it extends across the curve at the point. Looking at both the curve and its reflection in the mirror, rotate the mirror until the reflection appears as a smooth continuation of the curve. Then draw a faint line along the length of the mirror. This line is the normal to the curve at the point. Then draw the tangent through the point perpendicular to the normal.

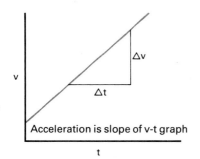

Acceleration is slope of v-t graph

Table 2-3

t	d
0 s	0 m/s
4	12
8	24
9.5	24
11	24
13.5	9
15	0

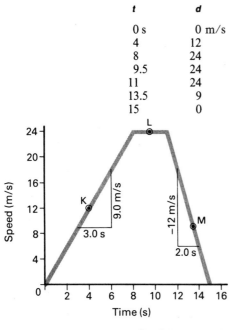

FIG. 2-4. The speeds deduced from Fig. 2-3 are listed in Table 2-3 and plotted here.

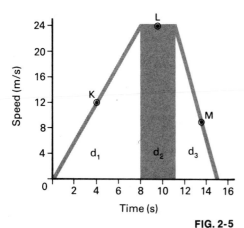

FIG. 2-5

ACCELERATIONS

The speeds obtained from the *distance-time* graph in Fig. 2-3 can be plotted on a *speed-time* graph. If you measured the slopes in Fig. 2-3 at other points you could plot additional speed-time points on the graph in Fig. 2-4. Since we know that

$$a = \frac{\Delta v}{\Delta t},$$

it is clear the slope of the speed-time graph of a motion will give the acceleration of that motion. For the motion we have just been discussing, the speed-time graph is composed of essentially straight lines. This means that the accelerations are constant in each of the three portions of the graph. They can be determined by the slope triangles on the graph, or by a direct application of the formula for acceleration.

Along the line where K is located,

$$a = \frac{9.0 \text{ m/s}}{3.0 \text{ s}} = 3.0 \text{ m/s}^2.$$

The line where L is located is horizontal. Its zero slope means that the acceleration of the motion is zero—the speed is constant from 8.0 to 11.0 s.

$$a = \frac{24 \text{ m/s} - 24 \text{ m/s}}{3.0 \text{ s}} = 0 \text{ m/s}^2.$$

Along the line where M is located,

$$a = \frac{-12 \text{ m/s}}{2.0 \text{ s}} = -6.0 \text{ m/s}^2.$$

The negative acceleration indicates that the speed was decreasing. This is shown on the graph by a line that slopes downward towards the right. That is the reason for the "−12 m/s" label on the "rise" of the slope triangle. The rise should always be read *from* the earlier speed value *to* the later speed value. When acceleration is negative, the rise of the slope is negative (that is, it points downward).

DISTANCES

Speeds are found on distance-time graphs by taking slopes. Accelerations are found on speed-time graphs by taking slopes. Distances can also be found on speed-time graphs. Look at the speed-time graph in Fig. 2-5. From 8.0 s to 11.0 s the speed was constant at 24 m/s. Since the width of the shaded rectangle of the graph is 3.0 s, and the height is 24 m/s, then their product on the graph is the area of the shaded rectangle (d_2). Area on a speed-time graph represents distance. Therefore during the 3.0 s interval, the distance travelled was

$$d_2 = vt = (24 \text{ m/s})(3.0 \text{ s}) = 72 \text{ m}.$$

We can also find the areas of the two triangular portions of the graph in Fig. 2-5 (d_1 and d_3). The area of a triangle is ½ (base) × (height). For triangle d_1, that is

$$d_1 = \frac{1}{2}(8.0 \text{ s})(24 \text{ m/s}) = 96 \text{ m}.$$

And for triangle d_3

$$d_3 = \frac{1}{2}(4.0 \text{ s})(24 \text{ m/s}) = 48 \text{ m}.$$

As a result, we should expect that for the motion in Fig. 2-5, the distance travelled in the first 8.0 s was $d_1 = 96$ m. After 11.0 s, the total distance from the starting-point was $d_1 + d_2 = 96 \text{ m} + 72 \text{ m} = 168$ m. And when the motion ceased, the total distance was ($d_1 + d_2$) $+ d_3 = 168 \text{ m} + 48 \text{ m} = 216$ m. Look back at Table 2-2 and Fig. 2-3 showing distance vs. time for this motion. There you will see that the values we have just calculated fit pretty closely.

Area under a speed-time graph will always give distance travelled, whatever the shape of the graph. However, the simple calculation of the area with the triangle formula only works when the graph-lines are straight—that is, when acceleration is constant.

A general relation can be derived from a speed-time graph for the distance travelled during constant acceleration. On Fig. 2-6 PQ is a straight line, representing a portion of a motion with constant acceleration. The speed increases uniformly from v_1 at time t_1 to v_2 at time t_2. The distance travelled during the time interval $\Delta t = t_2 - t_1$ is given by the area of the figure NPQR.

That area can be calculated by dividing the figure into two triangles. Because the angles at N and R are right angles, the two triangles have the same altitude, a, if you use for the bases of the triangles NP = b_1 and RQ = b_2. The area of the whole figure is the sum of the areas of the two triangles:

$$\text{area} = \frac{1}{2}b_1 a + \frac{1}{2}b_2 a = \frac{1}{2}(b_1 + b_2)a.$$

From the geometric identity of these two diagrams, you should be able to translate the symbols to get

$$d = \frac{1}{2}(v_1 + v_2)\Delta t.$$

Again, remember that this formula works only when acceleration is constant, that is, when speed is changing uniformly for a motion that continues along a straight-line path. Changes of motion that are not along straight-line paths will be discussed in the next chapter.

For curved graph-lines, area can be found by counting the squares on the graph paper beneath the curve.

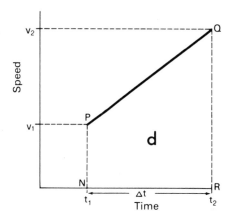

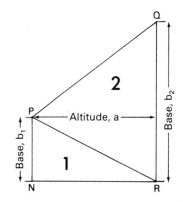

FIG. 2-6

Exercises

A

1. On a trip your car travelled 400 km in 5.0 h. What was your average speed?

2. Calculate the average speed of the sprinter who covered a distance of 200 m in 20.0 s.

3. In 1976, Alberto Jauntoreno set the world record for 800.0 m, running the distance in a time of 103.5 s. What was his average speed?

4. A curling stone takes 18 s to travel the 35 m length of the rink. What is its average speed?

5. If you travel on Highway 17 at the legal maximum speed of 90 km/h for 4.5 h, how far will you go?

6. An arrow shot from a bow travels at an average speed of 35 m/s for 18 s before hitting the target. How far does it travel?

7. The speed of sound in air is about 3.5×10^2 m/s. How far will the sound travel in 4.0×10^{-3} s?

8. The speed of light in a vacuum is about 3.00×10^8 m/s. How far will the light travel in (a) 1.00 s, (b) 1.00 min, (c) 1.00 h, (d) 1.00 d, (e) one year?

9. Bobby Hull's fastest slap-shot from the blue line averages 53 m/s. How long will it take to reach the goal, 20 m away?

10. If you drive at an average speed of 75 km/h, how long will it take you to get from Welland to Windsor, a highway distance of 3.7×10^2 km?

11. On the highway from Barrie to Bracebridge an ambulance averages 120 km/h over the 92 km. How long will it take to reach Bracebridge?

12. The shortest possible distance between Jupiter and the earth is 5.9×10^8 km. How long will it take a radio wave travelling at 3.0×10^8 m/s to traverse the distance? (Note: "km" in distance, and "m/s" in speed.)

13. In an acceleration test of a sports car, from a standing start, the following speeds were recorded: (a) after 5.0 s, the speed was 18 m/s; (b) at 10.0 s, the speed was 29 m/s; (c) at 15.0 s the speed was 35 m/s. For each of the three, calculate the average acceleration from rest.

14. From the data in question 13, calculate the average acceleration of the car from the 10.0 s mark to the 15.0 s mark.

15. If an Olympic cyclist reaches 18 m/s from a standing start in 20 s, what is his average acceleration?

16. When an arrow is shot from a hunting bow, its speed increases from zero to 40 m/s in 0.025 s. What is its average acceleration?

17. A car travelling on the highway at 20 m/s can accelerate at 2.0 m/s². If the car accelerates for 6.0 s, what will be its final speed?

18. A javelin thrower carrying a spear while running at 6.0 m/s thrusts the spear ahead with an acceleration of 250 m/s² for 0.10 s. What is the speed with which the javelin leaves the thrower's hand?

19. In a panic stop, a car's brakes can produce an acceleration of −8.0 m/s². If you are travelling at 35 m/s, what will your speed be after applying the brakes for (a) 2.0 s, (b) 3.0 s?

20. Using the initial data of question 19, calculate the time required to bring the car to a stop from 35 m/s.

21. (a) When you are jogging at 3.0 m/s, how far will you go in 5.0 s?
    (b) If you increase your speed to 7 m/s, how far will you go in 5.0 s at that speed?
    (c) If you increase your speed uniformly from 3.0 m/s to 7.0 m/s in 5.0 s, how far will you travel during that time?

22. How far will a car travel during a 3.0 s interval, during which its speed decreases uniformly from 17.0 m/s to 9.0 m/s?

B

23. A cyclist travelling at a steady speed of 4.0 m/s accelerates at 0.50 m/s² for 14 s. What is the final speed achieved?

24. A spacecraft approaching the moon at 1.12×10^4 m/s has to slow to 1.6×10^3 m/s to achieve lunar orbit. What acceleration will perform the operation in a time of 8.0 min?

25. (a) How long would it take to bring an auto to rest from a speed of 90 km/h with an acceleration of −8.5 m/s²?
    (b) What distance will be traversed by the car in that time?

26. (a) A curling stone is released with a speed of 4.0 m/s and has slowed to 1.0 m/s after travelling 22 m. How long a time did it take? Assume uniform deceleration.
    (b) What was the acceleration of the stone during that time?

27. Describe the motion represented by each of the following distance-time graphs. State what change in speed is represented. What is the significance of where the graph starts on the *d*-axis?

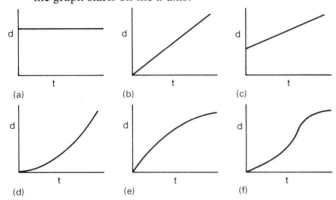

28. Describe the motion represented by each of the following speed-time graphs. State what change in speed and acceleration is represented.

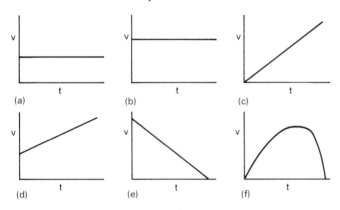

29. For each graph in question 27 state which is the corresponding graph (if any) in question 28. Note that since the scales are not marked on the graphs you may attach any reasonable linear scale to any of the *d*-axes or *v*-axes.

30. For each of the following tables of time-distance data, construct a carefully drawn *d-t* graph. Then use the method of slopes to determine the speed from the graph at two well-spaced points along the graph-line.
    (a) A cyclist on the highway records the times at which a series of hydro poles are passed:

Time (s)	0.0	5.0	10.0	15.0	20.0
Distance (m)	0.0	60.0	120.0	180.0	240.0

    (b) A curling stone is made to slide along the ice beside a 2.0 m stick and is recorded on a movie film. Each fourth frame of the film is measured:

Time (s)	0.00	0.20	0.40	0.60	0.80
Distance (m)	0.00	0.10	0.40	0.90	1.60

    (c) While an auto is braking, the times are recorded as it passes a series of equally spaced markers.

Time (s)	0.00	0.60	1.31	2.23	4.47
Distance (m)	0.00	20.0	40.0	60.0	80.0

31. From the pairs of speeds determined in question 30, calculate the acceleration for each motion.

32. (a) Express the speed of 90.0 km/h in metres per second.
    (b) How many kilometres per hour are equal to a speed of 1.0 m/s?

33. For each of the following tables of speed-time data, draw a careful graph, and determine the acceleration of the motion.
    (a) In a test run from rest, an auto speedometer was read every 2.0 s. Express the acceleration in metres per second squared.

Time (s)	0.0	2.0	4.0	6.0	8.0
Speed (km/h)	0.0	18.0	36.0	54.0	72.0

    (b) During an ascent into orbit, the second stage of a rocket produced the following data:

Time (s)	0	50	100	150
Speed (m/s)	2.0×10^3	4.0×10^3	6.0×10^3	8.0×10^3

    (c) Data from a motion-picture film of a tennis serve produced the following results:

Time (s)	0.0	0.1	0.2	0.3	0.4
Speed (m/s)	68	58	48	38	28

34. For each part of question 33 determine the distance traversed during the portion of the motion recorded in the data.

C

35. Use the following data to determine how fast a runner would have to travel to be "Safe on second!" The pitcher throws the ball a distance of 19.4 m at 40 m/s. The catcher takes 1.0 s to get off his throw at 30 m/s over a distance of 39.7 m to the second baseman. The distance between bases is 27.4 m, but the runner has taken a 1.5 m lead off first. He begins to run at the moment the pitcher releases the ball.

36. A bicycle is travelling along a road at 15 m/s, and is 400 m ahead of a motorcycle travelling at 20 m/s. Draw a distance-time graph to represent the motions and determine how long it will take for the motorcycle to catch up to the bicycle. At what point along the road will that happen?

37. The following graph shows the distance-time relation for the swing of a golf club by an amateur. The first 0.7 s is the motion of the head of the club during the backswing. Determine the maximum speeds achieved in each of the two parts of the swing. Compare them to the speeds illustrated in the graph following question 38.

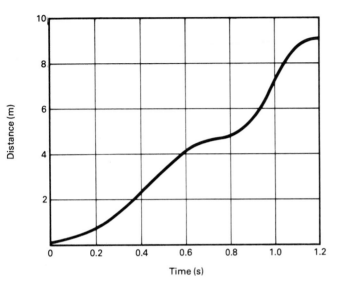

38. The following graph shows the speed-time relation for the swing of a golf club by a professional. Determine about seven values of the acceleration of the head of the club during the swing and plot a graph of the acceleration of the head.

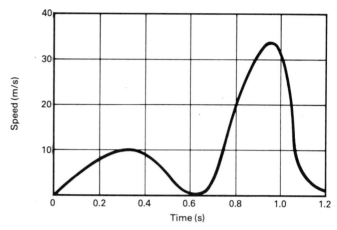

39. A car travelling along the highway passes a particular point travelling at 20 m/s. After 20 s, a police car passes the same point travelling at 30 m/s. How far down the road, and in what time, will the police car reach the first car?

40. Two frames of a motion-picture film taken at 50 frames per second have been analyzed to provide the following data for the collision of a golf club with a ball. Use the data to plot a distance-time graph of the two motions and determine the distance and time during which the club and ball were in contact. In the first frame the club is 0.50 m from the ball at rest on the tee. The club travels at 30 m/s until it hits the ball. From that point on, the speed of the club is 20 m/s. At 0.030 s after the start of the first frame the ball has moved a distance of 0.50 m from its rest position and is travelling at 50 m/s.

CHAPTER 3

Off the Tracks

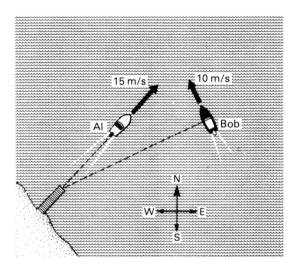

FIG. 3-1

Bob McGoo is running his speedboat on Lake Scugog on a foggy day. He is headed northwest at 10 m/s (Fig. 3-1). Al Fudd has heard Bob's boat on the lake and is rushing out to tell him it's unsafe to operate in foggy weather. Al's boat is headed northeast at 15 m/s. Will Al be able to intercept Bob?

VECTORS

Clearly the answer depends as much on the directions of the boats as on their speeds. To handle problems such as this, we introduce a new kind of quantity–**vectors**–which are specified by number, unit, and direction. Quantities that do not involve direction are called **scalars**. Quantities such as mass, time, temperature, volume, and speed (rate of motion only) are scalars. They need only number and unit to specify them. Also, scalar quantities can be handled with arithmetic alone.

VELOCITY

Since vectors involve direction, they require spatial mathematics, that is, geometry. Thus, vector problems will require the drawing of geometric diagrams. To do that we will have to represent the magnitude of vector quantities by means of a scale. For example, a line of 1.0 cm in length could represent a speed of 5.0 m/s. When we move off the track or road, we have to represent direction as well as magnitude. When direction is included, the rate of motion becomes a vector **velocity**, instead of a scalar speed. To represent direction, we start with the four cardinal directions, North, East, South and West. Directions other than those four are identified by the number of degrees in the angle from either North or South, towards either East or West. Fig. 3-2 illustrates several velocity vectors drawn to a scale of 1 cm representing 5 m/s of speed; e.g., $\vec{v_4}$ = 12 m/s [N60°W]. Notice that an arrow is placed above the symbol for a vector velocity to distinguish it from the symbol for a scalar speed. The direction is enclosed in square brackets.

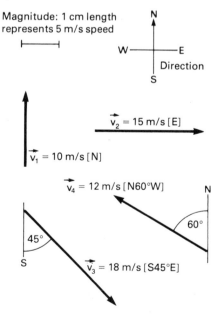

FIG. 3-2

DISPLACEMENT

To solve the problem given at the chapter opening we need to know more than the relevant vector velocities. The initial locations of the two boats are a crucial part of the problem. To indicate location we need a fixed reference point. Let us choose this point to be the dock (D), from which Al's boat started. The locations of the two boats can then be indicated by the length and direction of the lines drawn from the dock to each of them. Directed lines that show locations of points relative to a fixed point are called **displacements** ($\vec{d}$). Using subscripts A for Al and B for Bob, we can identify their initial displacements when we first look in on the problem as

$$\vec{d}_A = \overrightarrow{DA_0} = 200 \text{ m [N45°E]}, \quad \vec{d}_B = \overrightarrow{DB_0} = 400 \text{ m [N60°E]}.$$

These are shown on Fig. 3-3.

Now we are ready to plot the next locations of the two boats. Their velocities were given at the beginning:

FIG. 3-3

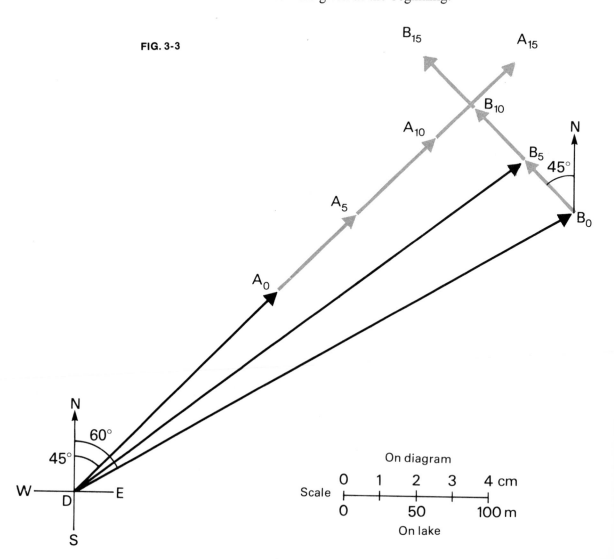

$$\vec{v}_A = 15 \text{ m/s [N45°E]}, \qquad \vec{v}_B = 10 \text{ m/s [N45°W]}.$$

Instead of trying to plunge in to answer the question directly, let's sneak up on the answer. Consider how the locations will change after a time interval of 5.0 s. This is simple for Al's boat because the direction of his velocity is the same as the direction of his displacement from the dock.

Start by finding the change in Al's displacement:

$$\Delta\vec{d} = \vec{v}\Delta t = (15 \text{ m/s [N45°E]})(5.0 \text{ s}) = 75 \text{ m [N45°E]}.$$

In 5.0 s Al will move 75 m farther along the direction in which he is headed. This is shown on the diagram by placing the tail of a 75 m [N45°E] displacement vector $(\overrightarrow{A_0A_5})$ at the head of the original displacement vector $(\overrightarrow{DA_0})$.

Since

$$\vec{d}_2 = \vec{d}_1 + \vec{v}\Delta t,$$

Al's new displacement is

$$\overrightarrow{DA_5} = 275 \text{ m [N45°E]}.$$

This is shown on the diagram by a vector that starts at the tail of the first vector and ends at the head of the second vector.

Bob's change in displacement can be found in the same way:

$$\Delta\vec{d} = \vec{v}\Delta t = (10 \text{ m/s [N45°W]})(5.0 \text{ s}) = 50 \text{ m [N45°W]}.$$

But this time the change in displacement is not in the same direction as the original displacement. Nevertheless, the procedure described above will still work. The tail of the vector $\Delta\vec{d} = \overrightarrow{B_0B_5}$ is put at the head of the original displacement vector $\overrightarrow{DB_0}$. Then the vector sum is obtained by drawing the line from the tail of $\overrightarrow{DB_0}$ at the dock (D) to the head of $\overrightarrow{B_0B_5}$ (at B_5). Bob's new displacement is given by $\overrightarrow{DB_5} = $ 390 m [N53°E], which can be measured by ruler and protractor on the diagram.

From the diagram, you can find that in about another 5.0 s, Bob would have a displacement from the dock of 3.9×10^2 m [N45E°]. That would put him directly in Al's path. But, alas! Al is still 40 m away from that point. It will take him another 2.7 s to get there. By that time Bob will be 27 m to the northwest of Al. Lost in the thickening fog, Fudd and McGoo will never be heard of again.

VECTOR ADDITION

The process described above for adding displacement vectors is the

The product of a vector and a scalar is a vector. Its direction is the same as that of the original vector. Its magnitude is the product of the magnitudes of the scalar and the original vector. The same general principle also applies to the quotient of a vector and a scalar.

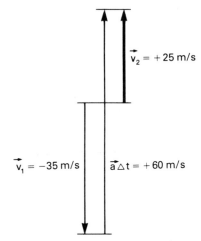

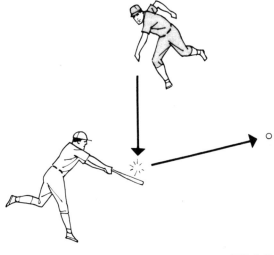

$\vec{v}_2 = +25$ m/s

$\vec{v}_1 = -35$ m/s $\vec{a}\triangle t = +60$ m/s

FIG. 3-4

FIG. 3-5

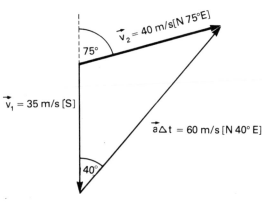

$\vec{v}_2 = 40$ m/s [N 75°E]

75°

$\vec{v}_1 = 35$ m/s [S]

$\vec{a}\triangle t = 60$ m/s [N 40° E]

40°

FIG. 3-6

method to be used whenever vectors are to be added. After the first vector is drawn to scale in the appropriate direction, the next vector is drawn with its tail starting from the head of the first vector. The vector sum is always directed from the tail of the first vector to the head of the last vector. In this way you can add together displacement vectors, or velocity vectors, or acceleration vectors, or force vectors. As in all addition, you can only add together vectors of the same quantity.

ACCELERATION

Acceleration is also a vector quantity because the direction of a change in velocity is meaningful. Thus, we can vectorize one of the basic equations from Chapter 2:

$$\vec{v}_2 = \vec{v}_1 + \vec{a}\Delta t.$$

To see how this works, suppose that a major league baseball pitcher has hurled a ball that arrives at the batter with a velocity of 35 m/s [S]. The batter swings, connects for 0.10 s, giving the ball a constant acceleration of 600 m/s² during that time. Consider two possible directions for the acceleration:

(1) The acceleration is 600 m/s² [N], that is, straight back toward the pitcher. When motions are confined along a single straight line, direction can be shown simply by plus and minus signs. Make one of the directions along the line positive—in this case North. Then

$$\vec{a} = +600 \text{ m/s}^2 \qquad \vec{v}_1 = -35 \text{ m/s} \qquad \Delta t = 0.10 \text{ s}$$

$$\vec{v}_2 = (-35 \text{ m/s}) + (+600 \text{ m/s}^2)(0.10 \text{ s})$$

$$= -35 \text{ m/s} + 60 \text{ m/s} = +25 \text{ m/s}.$$

This is shown in Fig. 3-4. The vector $\vec{a}\Delta t = +60$ m/s is added to the vector $\vec{v}_1 = -35$ m/s, to give $\vec{v}_2 = +25$ m/s. Since we made North the positive direction, the result is that the ball will leave the bat at 25 m/s [N].

(2) The acceleration is 600 m/s² [N40°E]. The batter has "pulled" the ball toward right field (Fig. 3-5). The final velocity can be obtained by using vector addition.

First, find the product of acceleration and time.

$$\vec{a}\Delta t = (600 \text{ m/s}^2 \text{ [N40°E]})(0.10 \text{ s}) = 60 \text{ m/s [N40°E]}.$$

In Fig. 3-6 draw the vector $\vec{v}_1 = 35$ m/s [S], and then from its head draw the $\vec{a}\Delta t = 60$ m/s [N40°E] vector. The sum of the two will be the $\vec{v}_2$ vector, drawn from the tail of the $\vec{v}_1$ vector to the head of the $\vec{a}\Delta t$ vector. From the diagram, measure that $\vec{v}_2 = 40$ m/s [N75°E].

VECTOR SUBTRACTION

A soccer ball is rolling along the ground with a velocity of $\vec{v}_1 = 3$ m/s [N]. You overtake it and give it a kick to increase its velocity to $\vec{v}_2 = 9$ m/s [N]. The change in velocity was $\Delta \vec{v} = 6$ m/s [N]. Starting from the initial velocity, $\vec{v}_1$, we can write a relation to show how to get $\vec{v}_2$.

(1) $$\vec{v}_1 + \Delta \vec{v} = \vec{v}_2$$

Therefore, $$3 \text{ m/s [N]} + 6 \text{ m/s [N]} = 9 \text{ m/s [N]}.$$

The final velocity is the sum of the initial velocity and the change in velocity.

Or we can rewrite the relation to show how to get $\Delta \vec{v}$ by transposing the $\vec{v}_1$ term in (1):

(2) $$\Delta \vec{v} = \vec{v}_2 - \vec{v}_1$$

Therefore, $$6 \text{ m/s [N]} = 9 \text{ m/s [N]} - 3 \text{ m/s [N]}.$$

The change in velocity is equal to the final velocity minus the initial velocity.

Fig. 3-7 illustrates the addition of vectors according to the first equation. The same diagram also shows how to perform **vector subtraction.** Place the two vectors to be subtracted so that their tails are at the same point. Their difference is given by the vector that starts at the head of $\vec{v}_1$ and ends at the head of $\vec{v}_2$. The difference vector starts at the head of the vector being subtracted, and ends at the head of the vector from which it is being subtracted.

Suppose that the soccer ball had been kicked from the side instead. What will $\Delta \vec{v}$ be if $\vec{v}_1 = 3$ m/s [N] and $\vec{v}_2 = 5$ m/s [N53°E]? In Fig. 3-8, place the two velocity vectors with their tails at the same point, always preserving their directions and magnitudes. Then the $\Delta \vec{v}$ vector extends from the head of $\vec{v}_1$ to the head of $\vec{v}_2$. From the diagram you can see that the value of $\Delta \vec{v}$ is 4 m/s [E]. As a check you should see that the addition of 3 m/s [N] to 4 m/s [E] does result in a final velocity of 5 m/s [N53°E].

RELATIVE MOTION

So far in our study of motion we have measured displacements and velocities relative to the earth. That is, we have used the earth to provide fixed reference points. For many motions over the surface of the earth that is quite acceptable. But there are times when we want to know the motion of one object relative to another, rather than relative to the earth.

While sitting in a 747 jet, you throw an orange forward to the cabin attendant. The velocity of the plane is 200 m/s [S] relative to the earth, and the velocity of the orange is 5 m/s [S] relative to the plane (Fig. 3-9). By vector addition, the velocity of the orange rela-

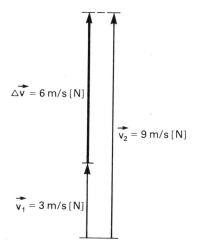

FIG. 3-7

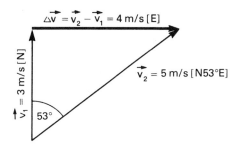

FIG. 3-8

A triangle having sides of length 3, 4, and 5 is right-angled with the 5 side the hypotenuse: $3^2 + 4^2 = 5^2$.

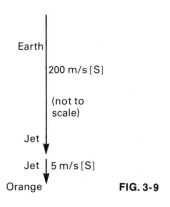

FIG. 3-9

tive to the earth is 205 m/s [S]. However, since the cabin attendant shares in the plane's motion, the attendant will have no trouble catching the orange.

Problems involving relative motion can be solved using vector addition and subtraction. You must be sure to indicate what is relative to what. This is easily done by labelling the vectors, with the object of interest at the head of the arrow, and the reference object at the tail of the arrow. Then, all you have to do is to put vectors together with the same label at the same point. (You should have no trouble in seeing whether addition or subtraction will be the required operation.)

Example: You are on a railroad flatcar, travelling at 15 m/s [E]. You throw one baseball (a) eastward with a speed of 20 m/s, and a second one (b) westward at the same speed. In each case, what will be the velocity of the ball relative to the earth (Fig. 3-10)?

(a) Draw the vectors to scale to represent the velocity of the train relative to the earth, and of the ball relative to the train. Then, with the two "train" labels at the same point you see that the velocity of the ball relative to the earth is 35 m/s [E].

(b) When the same procedure is followed this time, the direction of the ball's velocity relative to the train is opposite to the direction of the train's velocity relative to the earth. Now the velocity of the ball relative to the earth is 5 m/s [W].

Since the vectors were put together tail to head, the process was vector addition.

Example: (a) Robbers are travelling north on a highway at 120 km/h, being pursued by police travelling at 150 km/h. (b) The robbers suddenly make a quick U-turn and resume the same speed in the opposite direction. In each case, what is the velocity of the police relative to the robbers (Fig. 3-11)?

(a) Here, the two "earth" labels are put together. The velocity of the police relative to the robbers is the vector drawn from "robbers" to "police." The police are gaining on the robbers with a relative velocity of 30 km/h [N].

(b) Now the robbers' velocity relative to the earth is 120 km/h [S]. With the "earth" labels placed together, we see that the police are now gaining on the robbers with a relative velocity of 270 km/h [N]. Will they be able to catch them as they zip by?

Here you should notice that when the two velocities are given relative to the same object (the earth), the relative velocity between the two cars is obtained by vector subtraction.

Two vectors joined tail to head are ready for addition. Two vectors joined tail to tail are ready for subtraction.

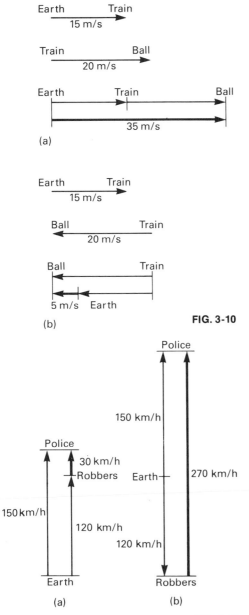

FIG. 3-10

FIG. 3-11

Exercises

When a diagram is required to solve a problem, draw it carefully to scale with a sharp pencil. Specify the scale you are using, and label the magnitudes of the vectors. Make sure that every vector has an arrowhead pointing in the required direction. When your answer is a vector quantity, be sure to specify direction as well as magnitude.

A

1. The dimensions of a hockey rink are close to those that are shown in the figure below. With a scale of 1 cm representing 4 m draw the plan of the rink in your notebook. Face-off points A, B, D, and F are located symmetrically, and GCJ is the midline of the rink. On your diagram draw the following displacement vectors, and measure the magnitude and direction of each one: $\overrightarrow{BA}$, $\overrightarrow{CJ}$, $\overrightarrow{GC}$, $\overrightarrow{DF}$, $\overrightarrow{AG}$, $\overrightarrow{FA}$, $\overrightarrow{JD}$.

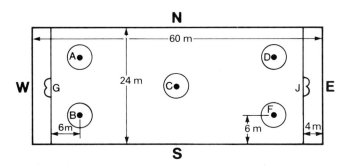

2. Draw a plan of the hockey rink from question 1, then draw velocity vectors using a scale of 1 cm representing 10 m/s. From each of the indicated points draw the indicated vector to represent the velocity of a puck shot from that point: A, 15 m/s [S]; B, 20 m/s [E]; C, 30 m/s [W]; D, 15 m/s [N30°W]; F, 20 m/s [N45°E]; J, 35 m/s [S75°W].

3. The displacement of Oshawa from Ottawa is 310 km [S56°W]. What is the displacement of Ottawa from Oshawa?

4. The displacement of Toronto from Windsor is 3.1×10^2 km [N63°E]. London is midway between Toronto and Windsor. What are the displacements of (a) London from Windsor, (b) London from Toronto, (c) Toronto from London?

5. What is the displacement of your place in the physics classroom from the door by which you entered the room?

6. A race is run counterclockwise on a circular track of diameter 127 m. Abbie Hoffman starts from the most southerly point on the track. What is her dis-

placement from that point when she is
(a) at the most northerly point of the track?
(b) at the most westerly point of the track?
The circumference (C) of a circle is related to diameter (D) by the formula, $C = \pi D$. For this race, calculate the *distance* that Abbie has run when she is
(c) at the most northerly point of the track,
(d) at the most westerly point of the track.

7. A sea trip from St. John's to Halifax can be made by a displacement of 400 km [S] followed by one of 800 km [W]. What is the displacement of Halifax from St. John's?

8. A cyclist rides 8.7×10^2 m [E] and then 1.0×10^3 m [N60°W]. What is his displacement from his initial location?

9. Four aircraft take off from a strip at Otterville, which has a displacement from Malton of 120 km [S45°W]. After they have travelled the displacements indicated, determine their displacements from Malton.
   (a) 130 km [S45°W]   (c) 50 km [N45°W]
   (b) 200 km [N45°E]   (d) 160 km [S45°E]

10. Laura is an avid canoeist. On some northern rivers she encounters currents of various velocities. If she paddles at 4.0 m/s [N] relative to the water, determine her velocity relative to the earth for each river. The stream velocities relative to the earth are

    (a) 3.5 m/s [N]   (d) 3.0 m/s [W]
    (b) 2.5 m/s [S]   (e) 1.5 m/s [N45°E]
    (c) 6.0 m/s [S]   (f) 2.0 m/s [S60°E]

11. The minute hand of a clock is 18 cm long. What is the change in the displacement of the tip of the hand from 11:05 to 11:25?

12. Left fielder Alvis Woods has a displacement of 80.0 m [N] relative to home plate. When a fly ball is hit, he estimates that he can catch it when its displacement from home plate is 90.0 m [N20°E]. He has 4.0 s to get there.
    (a) What must be his change in displacement to be able to catch the ball?
    (b) At what speed will he have to run to make it?

13. An airplane has an air speed of 180 m/s and a heading of S30°W, but is in a wind of velocity 40 m/s [S45°E]. What is the velocity of the plane relative to the ground?

14. An airplane has an air velocity of 95 m/s [N] and a ground velocity of 110 m/s [N30°W]. What is the wind velocity?

15. Tiger Williams' slap-shot travelling at 35 m/s [E] hits the goal post and rebounds at 25 m/s [N30°W]. What is the change in velocity of the puck?

B

16. Otto is in the control tower at Mirabel Airport. Pierre is in a jet trainer, due east of Otto at a distance of 8.0×10^2 m. Pierre is travelling at a constant speed of 150 m/s.
    (a) What is Pierre's initial displacement from Otto?
    (b) After 4.0 s, what is Pierre's displacement for a direction of travel that is (i) eastward, (ii) westward, (iii) northward?

17. Jack is sitting near the edge of the Rideau Canal in winter. Mary's initial displacement from him is 240 m [S30°W]. She then skates with a constant velocity of 7.0 m/s [N] until she is due west of Jack.
    (a) How far did she skate?
    (b) For how long did she skate?
    (c) What is her distance from Jack at that time?

18. Barney's boat is cruising at 12 m/s [E]. What will be its new velocity if it accelerates for 20.0 s (a) at 0.15 m/s² [E], (b) at 0.60 m/s² [W], (c) at 0.30 m/s² [S]?

19. The world record for the javelin throw of over 90 m distance is held by Miklos Nemeth (1976). Running horizontally at 6.0 m/s he hurls the javelin at an angle of 54° from the horizontal, giving it an acceleration of 2.2×10^2 m/s² for 0.12 s. The javelin takes off with the combined velocity of the two motions. What is the velocity of the javelin at the moment it leaves Nemeth's hand?

20. A large passenger jet travelling at 250 m/s must change its course by 60° in 10.0 s. What is the magnitude of the acceleration that is required?

21. In turning a sharp corner, a cyclist changes his velocity from 12 m/s [N] to 12 m/s [E] in 0.40 s. Determine the change in velocity and the acceleration (both magnitude and direction).

22. A tennis ball crossing the net at 35 m/s [S10°W] strikes Billy Jean's racket and the volley returns at 30 m/s [N30°W]. If her racket was in contact with the ball for 5.0×10^{-3} s, determine the acceleration of the ball.

23. From a boat travelling at 20 m/s [W] relative to the land, you shoot arrows at stationary targets in the water with a speed of 30 m/s relative to the boat. What will be the velocity of arrows relative to the targets if the direction you shoot in is (a) westward, (b) eastward, (c) northward, (d) S45°E?

24. Cycling along a straight track at 15 m/s, you see a basket ahead that is 1.5 m distant perpendicularly from your path at point P. Before you get to P you will throw a ball at 10.0 m/s at right angles to your direction of motion.
    (a) At what distance from P should you release the ball so that it will enter the basket?

    (b) What will be the velocity of the ball relative to the ground (specify direction relative to the direction of the track) at the moment you release it?

25. To get to Lake Scugog on that fateful foggy day, Al and Bob had driven their sports cars along two erratic routes. For each of the following pairs of velocities of the cars relative to the earth, determine the velocity of Bob relative to Al.
    (a) Al, 15 m/s [N]; Bob, 25 m/s [N]
    (b) Al, 20 m/s [W]; Bob, 18 m/s [E]
    (c) Al, 17 m/s [S]; Bob, 17 m/s [S]
    (d) Al, 23 m/s [E]; Bob, 14 m/s [E]
    (e) Al, 16 m/s [N45°W]; Bob, 16 m/s [N45°E]
    (f) Al, 30 m/s [N]; Bob, 15 m/s [N60°E].

C

26. Joe can row his boat relative to the water at 2.4 m/s. He wants to cross the Saskatchewan River at a point where it is 1800 m wide, flowing at 1.6 m/s [E].
    (a) How long would it take him to cross if the water was still?
    (b) If Joe heads his boat straight north, how far downstream will he drift in crossing? What will be his velocity relative to the land?
    (c) In order to *travel* straight north, in what direction should Joe head (at 2.4 m/s)? What will be his velocity relative to the land? How long will he take to cross?

27. Robin Hood is travelling by train through Sherwood Forest on his way to Nottingham, with a constant velocity of 20.0 m/s [S]. As he passes a crossroad he spies an evil knight resting beside his trusty Kawasaki at 300 m [E] from the rail line. Taking 5.0 s to load his bow, Robin shoots it from the train with a horizontal speed of 50.0 m/s. (The arrow will have to fly at about 70 m/s at 45° above the horizontal, but overlook that in this instance.) Determine the velocity of the arrow along the path from Robin to the knight, and the direction in which Robin has to aim to take into account the train's motion.

28. A football play begins from a point that is 50.0 m south of the goal line, 20.0 m from the west sideline. From that point, the halfback runs at 7.0 m/s [N30°E]. During the first 3.0 s, the quarterback drops back 10.0 m, then runs at 5.0 m/s [E] for 3.0 s. On the run, the quarterback throws the ball, and 2.5 s later the ball hits the running halfback on the head. Determine the velocity of travel (horizontally) of the ball from quarterback to halfback, and the velocity (horizontally) with which the quarterback throws the ball.

CHAPTER 4

Force
and
Newton's
Laws

As this car travels at constant velocity the *net* force on it (in any direction) is zero.

From a standing start you have to exert an effort to begin to move. And you have a distinct feeling that to move faster you have to exert more effort. Then, you have to continue the effort to continue moving. This is as true of automobiles as it is of running. As a result, it is easy to gain the impression that continued motion requires the continuous exertion of effort, whether of your legs or of the engine of a car.

For a long time the word "force" has been used with the meaning of that which causes motion—in much the same way as we have just used the word "effort." And it was long thought that some force was always needed whenever any object continued in motion. However, if you think of things other than runners and automobiles, you may have trouble locating such a force. When Bobby Hull's slap-shot drives the puck at 50 m/s, you know that it is the force of his stick that gets the puck going. But what force keeps it going? For many centuries people invented all sorts of weird explanations for the force that keeps an object in motion. Finally, in the seventeenth century, they began to consider that the most satisfactory explanation was to say that projectiles just keep going *naturally*.

NEWTON'S FIRST LAW OF MOTION

To say that it is natural for a motion once started to continue may seem to be a "cop-out." It is not, if there is good sense in asking "What else would you expect it to do?" For that is basically what we mean by *natural*. If you set a book down on the table, no one is surprised to see it remain there—what else would you expect it to do? If you push a ball for a moment, you certainly expect it to keep rolling after you stop pushing. You would also expect the ball to continue in the same direction and, unless its motion is impeded, at the same speed. But the ball won't keep rolling forever. Instead of asking what keeps it going, we can ask why it stops. In a small room, the ball may be stopped when it hits the wall. Along the corridor of the school a ball may roll a long way, but it will probably stop before it gets to the end. We say that it has been stopped by friction.

To look at motion this way means to include motion with rest as something natural, something that really needs no explanation. But not every motion should be considered natural. Rather, *constant velocity,* with a constant speed and constant direction, is the only kind of motion that we consider to continue without having to look for a cause.

Any moving object will continue its motion at constant speed without change of direction unless a force acts to change its speed or its direction. This is a principle that is included in Newton's first law of motion (after the English scientist who first stated the principle clearly). Also included in Newton's first law is the idea that objects at rest will continue motionless unless a force is applied.

This law cannot be proved in any simple or direct way, because it is very difficult to find a body that is not being acted on by some force or other. The main value of the law is to provide a starting-point for analyzing motions. Reading the law in a negative way, we can say that whenever we see an object that is not moving with constant speed (including zero) in a constant direction there must be a force acting on it. While this does not provide a satisfactory definition of force, it does suggest that forces are able to change the motion of an object—either its magnitude or its direction, or both.

Consider a hockey puck at rest on an ice surface. Bobby Hull skates rapidly toward the puck, and slaps it toward the goal. The force exerted by his stick changes the speed of the puck in a short period of time from zero to (say) 50 m/s. As the puck moves toward the goal there is only a small amount of friction between the ice and the puck, so that the speed is not decreased very much. The puck collides with the goal post, with the result that the direction of the puck's motion is rapidly changed, though perhaps the speed will not be much affected. Two examples of force may be seen here—the first is Hull's stick, changing the speed of the puck, and the second is the goal post changing the direction of the puck. In both cases, the effect of the force is to produce a change in the velocity of the puck. Since changes in velocity are accelerations, we can say that forces that act on a body produce accelerations.

As you drive along a straight level highway at 80 km/h, the engine in the car is driving the wheels, exerting a force. And that will be true even if the speed remains constant. But if the speed is constant, the force of the engine is not producing an acceleration. Why then is the engine needed? If you take your foot off the gas pedal, you know that the car will gradually reduce speed. Frictional forces in the gearing of the car and of the road and the surrounding air are acting to reduce the speed. They are producing a negative acceleration of the car. When you depress the gas pedal to maintain a constant speed, you are causing the engine of the car to exert exactly enough forward force to compensate for the oppositely directed frictional forces. Here you have forces acting without there being any acceleration. However, the *net* force should be considered to be zero, since it makes sense to say that the forward directed force of the engine (applied at the wheels) is *equal and opposite* to the backward directed forces of friction. The forward force is *balanced* by the backward force. Thus, there is no unbalanced force acting on the car, and its velocity is constant.

Thus Newton's first law may be better expressed:

All objects will continue either at rest or in motion with a velocity that is constant in both magnitude and direction, as long as no unbalanced force acts on them.

◀ **Newton's first law**

Newton's first law is also called the law of inertia. The root meaning of the word "inertia" is "laziness." It was used by Newton to describe the property possessed by objects that makes them behave according to his first law. We can say that it is because objects have the property of inertia that it is necessary to have forces act in order to change the state of motion of an object. In modern physics the word "inertia" is widely used to describe situations in which Newton's first law is taken as the initial starting-point.

For $\vec{F} = 0$, $\vec{v}$ = constant. Therefore $\vec{a} = 0$.

In summary, Newton's first law of motion tells us the following:
1. Inertia is a property of all matter.
2. Stationary objects tend to remain stationary.
3. Moving objects tend to maintain their velocity.
4. If the velocity of an object is constant, no unbalanced force is acting on it.
5. If the velocity of an object changes, the change is caused by an unbalanced force exerted on the object.

NEWTON'S SECOND LAW OF MOTION

Since inertia must be "overcome" in order to change an object's motion, it seems reasonable to suppose that some objects possess more inertia than others. The measure of inertia is given by the *mass* of an object. It takes more force to throw a ten-pin bowling ball with the same speed as a five-pin ball because the larger ball has more mass. If the two balls are made of the same material, and the larger one has 4.5 times the volume, then it will have 4.5 times the mass. Intuitively you would expect that to produce the same change in motion in the larger ball would require 4.5 times the force.

Let us examine that intuition in an imaginary experiment. Suppose that playing a pinball machine, you let the spring plunger accelerate first one ball and then two balls. Both times you pull the plunger back to the same extent, so you should be producing the same force in both cases. The balls start from rest and the force of the spring accelerates them up the track. Suppose that the action in each case lasts for 0.1 s, and with one ball you produce a speed of release of 1.5 m/s. Then, the acceleration is 15 m/s². With two balls started at the same time, the mass to be accelerated is doubled, and you might guess that the same force would produce half the acceleration in the

As the table was whisked away the dishes were left behind as a result of their inertia.

double mass. It would not be too difficult to perform the measurements needed to test that guess.

From these relations it appears that the force which changes the velocity of an object can be calculated from the acceleration and the mass of the object. If either the mass or the acceleration is made larger, a larger force will be required. As a result, it makes sense to *define* force as the product of mass and acceleration:

$$F = ma.$$

Since the unit of mass is the kilogram, and the unit of acceleration is metre per second squared, the unit of force will be kilogram metre per second squared. For convenience, this combination of units is given a special name, the newton.

$$1 \text{ N (newton)} = 1 \text{ kg·m/s}^2.$$

The mass of the ball in a pinball machine is about 0.10 kg. If it is made to accelerate at 15 m/s^2, the force is readily calculated:

$$F = ma = (0.10 \text{ kg})(15 \text{ m/s}^2) = 1.5 \text{ N}.$$

Since acceleration is a vector quantity, the most general idea of this new formula should take direction into account. When a force acts on an object at rest, it produces a motion of the object in the direction in which the force acts. Thus, force is also a vector quantity, and the directions of force and acceleration should be the same. Mass, however, is a scalar quantity. We can write the formula as

$$\vec{F} = m\vec{a}.$$

When this formula is expressed in words, it contains the essential ideas that are known as Newton's second law:

Newton's second law ▶

When an unbalanced force acts on an object it produces an acceleration in the direction of the force, and the magnitude of the force is equal to the product of the acceleration and the mass of the object.

The effect of applying an unbalanced force to an object is to give it an acceleration that varies directly as the net force and inversely as the mass of the object.

This second law of Newton is consistent with the first one. For if the acceleration is zero, then there is not a net force. When no unbalanced force acts, the velocity is constant because there is no acceleration.

NEWTON'S THIRD LAW OF MOTION

A curling stone of mass 18 kg is sliding along the ice with a velocity of 2.0 m/s [E]. If the stone is brought to rest in 0.010 s, the force required can be calculated.

Since $\quad \vec{a} = \dfrac{\vec{\Delta v}}{\Delta t} \quad$ and $\quad \vec{F} = m\vec{a}, \quad$ then $\quad \vec{F} = m\dfrac{\vec{\Delta v}}{\Delta t}.$

$m = 18 \text{ kg} \quad \vec{\Delta v} = 0 - 2.0 \text{ m/s [E]} = 2.0 \text{ m/s [W]} \quad \Delta t = 0.010 \text{ s}$

therefore, $\quad \vec{F} = (18 \text{ kg}) \dfrac{2 \text{ m/s [W]}}{0.010 \text{ s}} = 3.6 \times 10^3 \text{ N [W]}.$

A force of 3600 N directed westward will bring the stone to rest. In curling, that force is often supplied by the collision of the first stone with a second one at rest. After the collision, the second stone will no longer be at rest. The force that set the second stone in motion was applied by the first stone.

If the stones hit head on, the second stone will move off in an eastward direction after the collision. During the 0.010 s interaction, the first stone applied an eastward force on the second one, while the second one applied a westward force on the first one. The two forces act in opposite directions.

Experiments have shown that the velocity with which the second stone leaves the collision is very nearly the same as the velocity with which the first stone entered the collision. From this it is evident that the magnitudes of the two forces were very close to being equal. Further experiments with colliding objects of various masses and velocities have shown this force relation to be generally true (Fig. 4-1).

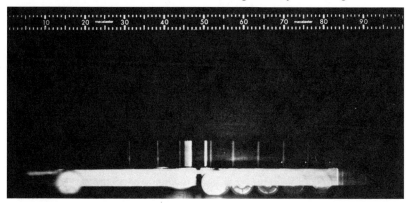

The relation is expressed in Newton's third law:

When objects A and B interact, the force exerted by A on B is equal in magnitude and opposite in direction to the force that B exerts on A.

Newton's third law

FIG. 4-1. The cart on the right was standing at rest when the other cart was pushed toward it from the left. The two carts have the same mass. Compare the velocities before and after the collision. The photograph was taken with a stroboscopic light flashing at 20 Hz.

Perhaps the most direct and obvious application of Newton's third law occurs in the operation of rockets. Initially, the rocket with its fuel tanks is at rest on the launching pad. Then the fuel is ignited and hot gases are expelled rapidly out the rear of the rocket. Think of the gases and the rocket as exerting equal and opposite forces on each other. As a result, the large backward acceleration and small

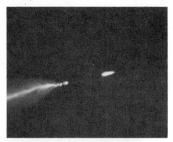

FIG. 4-2. This sequence shows the end of the burn of the *Apollo 11* booster rocket followed by the ignition and burn of the second stage rocket, with the booster being jettisoned along the way. *Apollo 11* was 60 km above the earth and 90 km downrange. The photos were taken from an aircraft flying at an altitude of 11 km.

mass of the gases are matched by a smaller forward acceleration of the larger mass of the rocket.

Example: To see the basic principle of the reaction motor of a rocket, consider a simpler situation. Suppose that a cannon is mounted on a small railway flatcar. Ignore the friction between the wheels and the tracks. The mass of the cannon, ammunition, and platform is 405 kg. A projectile of mass 5.0 kg is fired, leaving the mouth of the cannon with a velocity of +300 m/s. The time of the interaction is the interval during which the projectile travels the length of the barrel, 0.010 s. What will be the velocity of recoil of the cannon and platform?

The strategy of the solution is as follows: (1) Calculate the average acceleration of the projectile. (2) Determine from that the force of the cannon on the projectile. (3) Apply Newton's third law to get the force of the projectile on the cannon. (4) Determine the average acceleration of the cannon and platform. (5) Determine the velocity of the cannon and platform.

(1) Consider the direction of motion of the projectile to be positive. To calculate its average acceleration, we have

$$\Delta \vec{v} = \vec{v}_2 - \vec{v}_1 = (+300 \text{ m/s}) - 0 = +300 \text{ m/s}; \qquad \Delta t = 0.010 \text{ s}.$$

$$\vec{a} = \frac{\Delta \vec{v}}{\Delta t} = \frac{+300 \text{ m/s}}{0.010 \text{ s}} = +3.0 \times 10^4 \text{ m/s}^2.$$

(2) For the average force of the cannon on the projectile,

$$\vec{a} = +3.0 \times 10^4 \text{ m/s}^2, \qquad m = 5.0 \text{ kg}.$$

$$\vec{F} = m\vec{a} = (5.0 \text{ kg})(+3.0 \times 10^4 \text{ m/s}^2) = +1.5 \times 10^5 \text{ N}.$$

(3) By Newton's third law, the force of the projectile on the cannon (and platform) is -1.5×10^5 N.

(4) For the average acceleration of the cannon and platform, (realizing that the mass has been reduced by the loss of the 5.0 kg projectile),

$$\vec{F} = -1.5 \times 10^5 \text{ N}, \qquad m = 4.00 \times 10^2 \text{ kg}.$$

$$\vec{a} = \frac{\vec{F}}{m} = \frac{-1.5 \times 10^5 \text{ kg·m/s}^2}{4.00 \times 10^2 \text{ kg}} = -3.8 \times 10^2 \text{ m/s}^2.$$

(5) For the velocity of the cannon and platform at the end of the interaction,

$$\vec{a} = -3.8 \times 10^2 \text{ m/s}^2, \qquad \vec{v}_1 = 0, \qquad t = 0.010 \text{ s}.$$

$$\vec{v}_2 = \vec{v}_1 + \vec{a}\Delta t$$

$$= 0 + (-3.8 \times 10^2 \text{ m/s}^2)(1.0 \times 10^{-2} \text{ s}) = -3.8 \text{ m/s}.$$

The cannon and platform will recoil (that is, move in the direction opposite to that of the projectile) with a speed of 3.8 m/s.

If you imagine the cannon to be an elementary rocket motor, you can see that it will work more effectively the higher the speed of expulsion of the projectile. In a properly designed rocket, the fuel load is a large fraction of the total mass. To get a rocket into orbit, the fuel is usually contained in several sections, or stages. After all the fuel in a stage has been expelled, the container is dropped to reduce the mass of the remainder of the rocket (Fig. 4-2).

If a number of projectiles are fired one after another to continue to increase the cannon's speed of recoil, the calculation of the speed achieved must take account of two additional factors: (1) the mass of the cannon and platform would decrease by 5.0 kg for each projectile fired; (2) since the velocity of each projectile is known relative to the cannon, account must be taken of the increasing velocity of the cannon relative to the earth.

Exercises

A

1. For each of the following state whether the velocity of the *object* is constant, or not; and if it is not constant, state the source or location of the unbalanced force:
   (a) A *car* is travelling on a straight level road with the speedometer needle steady at 90 km/h.
   (b) Your physics *textbook* is on your desk.
   (c) When the stoplight changes to green you take your foot off the brake and depress the gas pedal of the *car*.
   (d) Your *pencil* falls off the edge of the desk.
   (e) A hockey *puck* is sliding toward the red line after being cleared while the team is killing a penalty.
   (f) A *car* is going round an unbanked curve while the speedometer needle stays steady at 45 km/h.
   (g) Astronauts in a space *capsule* are in a circular orbit about the earth with a constant speed of 2.8×10^4 km/h.

2. The basic SI unit of force is the newton (symbolized by N). For each of the following situations state the net (or unbalanced) force that is acting:
   (a) Alkali Ike is pulling with a force of 500 N [W] and his mule pulls with a force of 500 N [E].
   (b) The force of a car's engine at the wheels is 4.5 kN [S], and the frictional resistance is 3.0 kN [N].
   (c) Each of eight dogs of a sled-team is pulling with a force of 90 N [N60°W], and the friction on the sled is 0.70 kN [S60°E].
   (d) A board is being pulled behind a boat with a force of 110 N [N], while the frictional resistance of the water is 80 N [S].
   (e) Starting with the situation in (d), one edge of the board is tilted so that the water exerts an additional force of 40 N [W].
   (f) A girl is pulling a loaded wagon eastward with a force of 40 N [60° above horizontal]. The frictional resistance is 18 N [W, horizontal].

3. For each of the following situations, (i) name the forces being exerted; (ii) state whether an unbalanced force is acting. If there is any unbalanced force, state (iii) which force in (i) is greater.
   (a) A car is travelling at a constant 80 km/h [S30°W].
   (b) After travelling at 45 km/h [N80°E] a motorboat increases its velocity to 50 km/h [N80°E].
   (c) A car travelling at 65 km/h [W] has its front wheels turned to the right on an icy road and continues at 65 km/h [W].
   (d) A car travelling at 50 km/h [E] goes round a flat curve on a smooth dry road at constant speed, until its velocity is 50 km/h [S].
   (e) A curling stone has been released by the skip. It is travelling eastward and is slowing.

4. Calculate the unbalanced force in each of the following situations:
   (a) A bicycle and rider of combined mass 80 kg accelerate at 0.5 m/s².
   (b) A car of mass 1.5×10^3 kg accelerates at 2.0 m/s².
   (c) A curling stone of mass 18 kg is swung with an acceleration of 3.5 m/s².

5. Calculate the average acceleration experienced by each of the following objects under the action of the unbalanced force:
   (a) A force of 3.0×10^2 N is applied to a discus of mass 2.0 kg.
   (b) An average force of 150 N is applied to an arrow of mass 3.0×10^{-2} kg.
   (c) A car of mass 1.8×10^3 kg is coasting against a frictional resistance of 6.0×10^2 N.

6. A force of 7×10^{-16} N applied to an electron will accelerate it at 8×10^{14} m/s² (for a few nanoseconds). Calculate the electron's mass.

7. A UFO is "parked" at the earth's distance from the sun on the other side of the sun from us. The attraction of the sun causes the UFO, of mass 5×10^5 kg,

to tend to drift toward the sun with an acceleration of 6×10^{-3} m/s². What constant force must the UFO apply to prevent the drift?

8. A team of dolphins can apply a net force of 40 N [W] to a great blue whale of mass 1.2×10^5 kg. What is the acceleration?

9. Identify a pair of action-reaction forces for each of the following situations:
   (a) Car A travelling at 60 km/h [N] collides with car B travelling at 50 km/h [S].
   (b) A rowboat in the middle of a lake points westward. A girl makes a shallow dive off the stern of the boat.
   (c) Blow up a balloon and hold the air in with your thumb and finger on the neck of the balloon. Then, with the neck end facing S45°W, release your hold on the balloon.
   (d) A helicopter lands on the roof of a hospital.
   (e) The planet Venus has an almost circular orbit about the sun.
   (f) You are standing in the middle of a water-bed.

B

10. Explain the following by reference to Newton's first law:
    (a) To get sticky ketchup out of a bottle, grasp the bottle near the bottom in your right hand, invert the bottle and strike the edge that is past the neck against the heel of your left hand. Is that better than hitting the bottom of the bottle?
    (b) You stamp your feet to get the snow off your boots.
    (c) The brakeman has to take care when she releases her hold from the side of the caboose travelling at 5 m/s [E].

11. What is the force of friction on a curling stone (mass = 18 kg) that comes to rest in 15 s from an initial velocity of 3.0 m/s [W]?

12. As a hockey puck (mass = 0.16 kg) is passed across the ice its velocity is increased from zero to 25 m/s [S] in 0.050 s. Calculate the unbalanced force exerted by the stick.

13. A soccer ball of mass 0.44 kg is rolling with a velocity of 3.0 m/s [W], when it is given a kick with a force of 44 N [W]. The duration of contact between foot and ball is 0.10 s. Calculate the acceleration of the ball and the final velocity.

14. A ball of mass 0.15 kg is pitched at 40 m/s [N] and is hit back at 30 m/s [S]. If the ball and bat are in contact for 0.020 s, what is the force exerted by the bat on the ball?

15. A sports car has a mass of 1.2×10^3 kg. While increasing its speed from zero to 20 m/s [W] in 5.0 s, it experiences an average frictional resistance of 5.0×10^2 N [E]. What is the total force that must be exerted on the car during the period of acceleration? Draw a graph of applied force against time for 10 s, if the car maintains a steady speed of 20 m/s after the first five seconds.

16. A curling stone (mass = 18 kg) crosses the hog line with a velocity of 3.0 m/s [W]. It experiences a frictional force of 10.0 N [E] for 2.0 s.
    (a) What velocity will the stone then have?
    (b) How far will it travel during those 2.0 s? (The distance from the hog line to the edge of the outermost circle is 4.57 m.)

17. A spaceship is equipped with sets of rocket motors both fore and aft. Each motor can provide an acceleration of 3.00 m/s². The ship is initially travelling forward in a straight line at 9.10×10^3 m/s.
    (a) One stern rocket motor is operated for 1.00 min. Calculate the new speed of the ship.
    (b) Then five retrorockets are operated to reduce the speed of the ship to zero. How long will that take?

18. A bicycle and rider of mass 90 kg are travelling at 7.8 m/s [N]. Then, in a time interval of 1.0 s, the velocity is changed to 7.8 m/s [E]. Calculate (a) the acceleration and (b) the force involved in making the turn.

19. When a rifle is fired, the 5.0 g bullet reaches a velocity of 3.0×10^2 m/s [W] during the 5.0×10^{-3} s it takes to travel the length of the barrel. Calculate (a) the average force exerted on the bullet, and (b) the recoil force on the rifle and shooter.

20. An armoured vehicle of mass 5.0×10^3 kg is at rest on a frozen lake where the friction is practically zero. It fires a shell of mass 10.0 kg with a muzzle velocity of 8.0×10^2 m/s [N]. Let the time the shell takes to travel the length of the barrel be b s. Calculate
    (a) the acceleration of the shell,
    (b) the force on the shell,
    (c) the force of the shell on the vehicle,
    (d) the acceleration of the vehicle,
    (e) the velocity of the vehicle at the moment the shell leaves the muzzle.

21. (a) A laboratory collision cart (A) of mass 2.0 kg is travelling at 1.5 m/s [E] when it strikes a second cart (B) at rest. Cart A rebounds with a velocity of 0.30 m/s [W]. If the interaction lasts 0.50 s, calculate the average force on cart A.
    (b) What exerts the force on cart A?
    (c) What is the force of cart A on cart B?
    (d) The mass of cart B is 3.0 kg. What velocity will cart B have after the collision?

22. A bowling ball in a ten-pin alley has a mass of 6.0 kg. When travelling at 7.5 m/s [W] the ball strikes a pin of mass 1.5 kg. The pin moves off with a velocity of 12 m/s [W]. Let the time of the collision be d s. Calculate

(a) the acceleration of the pin,
(b) the force of the ball on the pin,
(c) the force of the pin on the ball,
(d) the acceleration of the ball,
(e) the velocity of the ball after striking the pin.

C

23. Suppose you didn't already know Newton's third law. For the following situation calculate the force of A on B and of B on A, and compare them. Block A of mass 5.0 kg rests on a frictionless surface. On the east side of A, block B of mass 3.0 kg is in contact with A. A force of 24 N [E] is applied on the west side of A so that A pushes on B and both blocks move together. Calculate the acceleration of the two blocks considered as a unit. Then calculate the force of each block on the other. Show the forces on a vector diagram. Does your result *prove* the truth of Newton's third law?

24. William Tell is shooting an arrow northward toward the apple on his son's head. Just before the 0.050 kg arrow strikes the apple, it is travelling at 30 m/s. Then, during 0.020 s the apple is impaled on the arrow, and the two continue northward at 10.0 m/s. Calculate the mass of the apple. (Could this problem be solved if the time of the interaction was not known?)

25. Two vehicles on a horizontal air-track have a spring compressed between them. Each vehicle has a mass of 0.55 kg. Then, vehicle A is loaded with a 1.00 kg mass, and B with an unknown mass. Bumpers are located along the track on either side of the vehicles so that when the spring is released both vehicles hit their respective bumpers at the same instant. While A travelled a distance of 1.440 m, B travelled a distance of 0.580 m. Calculate the mass of the load on B. (Could this problem be solved if the masses of the two vehicles were not known?)

26. A certain force gives a mass m_1 an acceleration of 12.0 m/s², and a mass m_2 an acceleration of 36.0 m/s². What acceleration will the same force give the two masses when they are fastened together? (If you find it necessary, assume a value for the applied force; e.g., 72 N. Then show that the result is independent of that particular value.)

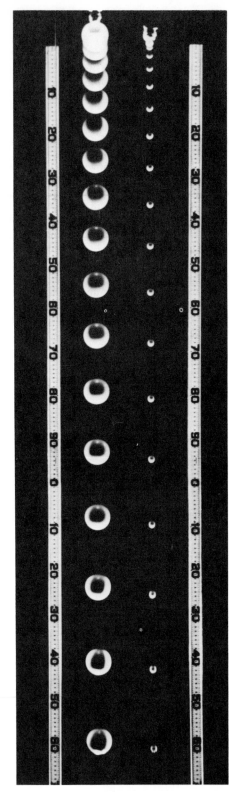

FIG. 5-1. Billiard ball and ball bearing falling side by side. The flash frequency is 30 Hz.

CHAPTER 5

Gravity and Mechanical Forces

THE FORCE OF GRAVITY

Caveman Og stood at the edge of a cliff with a large boulder grasped in his hairy hands. As an unsuspecting antelope ambled by below, Og released the stone, which fell and crushed the skull of his family's next dinner. What can we say about the motion and force associated with that falling stone?

Initially the stone was at rest in Og's hands. When he released his grasp, the stone began to move downward. For the velocity of the stone to change, a force must have acted upon it. What shall we suppose about that force? Will it continue to act? Since we cannot see what is applying the force, we can only infer its action from the motion of the stone. If the stone continues to accelerate, then a force must continue to act. So, armed with Newton's second law, we are able to investigate the force by examining the details of the motion of the stone.

Careful experimental measurements have revealed that reasonably heavy objects fall toward the earth (near its surface) with a constant acceleration of 9.8 m/s² (Fig. 5-1). What is perhaps surprising, this same acceleration applies for the falling motion of a wide variety of masses. Of course, feathers and slips of paper fall less quickly, but we can attribute that to the frictional resistance of the air. So, we might guess that in a vacuum, feathers would fall side by side with hammers.

Of course, everyone knows that it is the force of gravity which causes objects to fall. By giving values to this force we can fit it into our scheme for analyzing forces ($\vec{F} = m\vec{a}$). The force of the earth's gravity on objects is directed toward the centre of the earth. When it is not balanced by any other force, it will produce an acceleration of 9.8 m/s² [downward]. This acceleration is called the **acceleration of gravity** (of the earth), and is expressed by the symbol $\vec{g}$.

Example: If your mass is 60.0 kg, what is the force of gravity acting on you at a place where $\vec{g} = 9.80$ m/s² ?

Since $m = 60.0 \text{ kg}$ and $\vec{a} = \vec{g} = 9.80 \text{ m/s}^2$ [down],

then $\vec{F} = m\vec{g} = (60.0 \text{ kg})(9.80 \text{ m/s}^2 \text{ [down]}) = 5.88 \times 10^2 \text{ N [down]}$.

It might be tempting to suppose that the acceleration of gravity is constant all over the surface of the earth, and that the force of gravity of the earth extends uniformly out into space. But that is not so.

At sea level g varies from 9.78 m/s² at the equator to 9.83 m/s² at the poles; and it is less at elevations above sea level (Fig. 5-2). Careful surveying has shown that the earth is flattened at the poles, so that the poles are closer to the centre of the earth than the equator is. Thus, it appears that the acceleration of gravity is less for points on the surface that are farther from the centre. Then, does the force of the earth's gravity extend out into space, continually diminishing? And if so, can the relation between force and distance be determined?

UNIVERSAL GRAVITATION

Answers to these questions were found in the second half of the seventeenth century by Isaac Newton. He arrived at his conclusions by combining his laws of motion with a formula for the acceleration in circular motion and with data supplied by astronomers. The major astronomical data were the values for the times required for satellites to complete one revolution around their centres, and their distances from the centres. For the moon Newton was able to calculate that the acceleration involved in turning its motion out of straight-line inertial motion was 1/3600 of the acceleration of the earth's gravity (Fig. 5-3). But the moon is 60 times farther from the centre of the earth than the surface of the earth is. Thus, it appeared that if earth's gravity affects the moon, its effect diminishes according to the inverse square of the distance from the centre of the earth. That would mean that if you were 3 earth-radii from the centre of the earth, the force of gravity would be $1/3^2 = 1/9$ of what it is at the earth's surface.

Newton also found that this inverse-square law for the decrease of force with distance applied to the motions of the planets about the sun. At this point he took a great imaginative leap by claiming that the force that acted between the sun and the planets (including the earth) was of the same nature as the force of gravity which had up till then been exclusively earthbound in people's minds. Newton made a gigantic extrapolation from knowledge then current, and insisted that this gravitational force operated throughout the universe.

He applied his theory of gravitation not only to the earth and to the motions of the planets about the sun, but also to the motions of the tides in the earth's oceans (influenced both by moon and sun), and to many of the details of the complex motion of the moon in its orbit about the earth. The results of his work made it clear that these many varied motions could all be accounted for by some force that

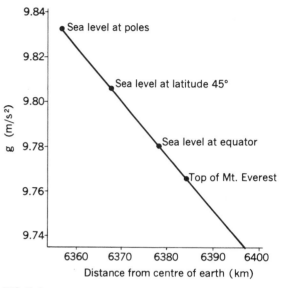

FIG. 5-2

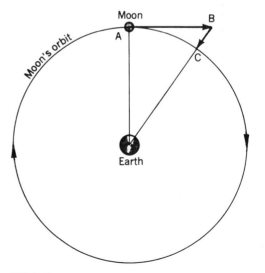

FIG. 5-3

varied inversely as the square of distance, and that it seemed to make sense to identify that force with gravity.

In somewhat modernized form, Newton's principle of **universal gravitation** states that

Between every two particles in the universe there exists a force of gravitational attraction that varies inversely as the square of the distance between them, and directly as the product of their masses (Fig. 5-4).

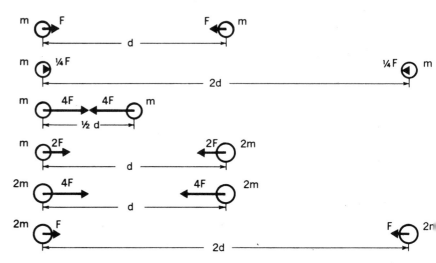

FIG. 5-4

Newton's principle of universal gravitation is fully consistent with his laws of motion. We have seen that according to his second law of motion the force required to produce a given acceleration in an object depends on the mass of the object. Thus the force of gravity of the earth on a ball falling near its surface varies directly as the mass of the ball. By Newton's third law the ball exerts a force on the earth that is equal and opposite to the force of the earth on the ball. Thus the force of gravity must vary directly as the mass of the earth.

THE GRAVITATIONAL CONSTANT

In his principle of universal gravitation Newton claimed that gravitational forces affect *all* objects. That should mean that there is a force of attraction between two apples hanging on a tree. We do not observe such a force, Newton would have argued, because it is very tiny.

About seventy years after Newton's death, a method was devised to measure such tiny forces. The English physicist and chemist Henry Cavendish reported in 1798 the results of an experiment that he had performed (Fig. 5-5). Two small masses (about 0.8 kg each) were suspended from the ends of a light bar about two metres long. The bar was suspended from its centre by a slender wire about one metre long. If the bar is rotated slightly, it will oscillate very slowly

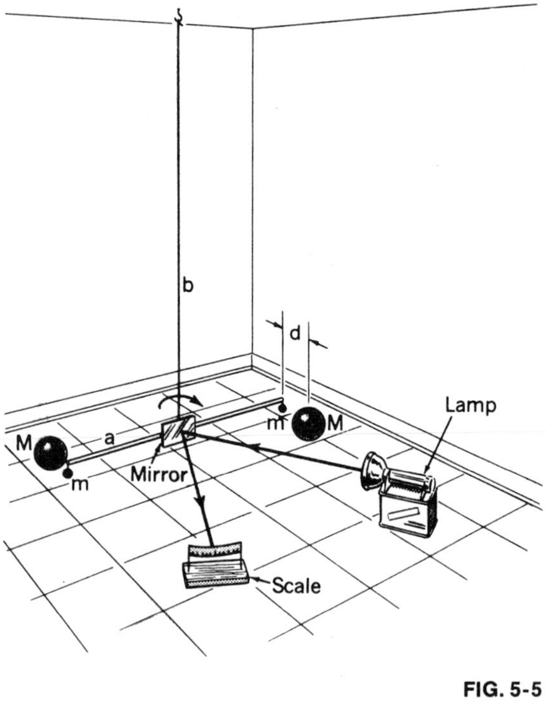

FIG. 5-5

back and forth in horizontal arcs. The time for an oscillation can be changed by the application of very tiny forces. Cavendish did that by placing two large balls of lead (m = 50 kg) near the ends of the bar, one on each side, so that their forces of attraction both caused a rotational effect in the same direction. The effect of these small forces was to change the time required for the bar to make one oscillation. From that Cavendish could calculate the size of the force of attraction. He found it to be such that if two masses, each of one kilogram, are located one metre apart, the force of attraction of each on the other is 6.67×10^{-11} N.

Newton's principle of universal gravitation can be written

$$F = \frac{Gm_1 m_2}{d^2}.$$

The symbol G represents the constant of gravitation. Its value can be shown as follows:

$$G = \frac{Fd^2}{m_1 m_2} = \frac{(6.67 \times 10^{-11} \text{ N})(1.00 \text{ m})^2}{(1.00 \text{ kg})(1.00 \text{ kg})}$$

$$= 6.67 \times 10^{-11} \text{ N·m}^2/\text{kg}^2.$$

The force of gravitational attraction between two objects depends on their masses, m_1 and m_2, the distance between them (centre to centre), d, and the constant of gravitation, G.

THE DENSITY OF THE EARTH

An interesting check of whether all of this makes any sense is to see what the numbers and relations give for the average density of the earth. It should certainly be greater than that of water (unless the earth is hollow), and probably not as much as a hundred times greater (unless the core of the earth is super-dense). We know that the force of the earth's gravity on a 1.0 kg mass at its surface is 9.8 N, and that the radius of the earth is $d = 6.4 \times 10^6$ m. From these data and the value for G we can determine the mass and volume of the earth, and hence its average density. The volume of the earth works out to 1.1×10^{21} m^3. The mass of the earth is represented by M in the following substitutions into the equation of gravitation:

The volume of a sphere of radius r is $V = (4/3) \pi r^3$.

$$F = \frac{Gm_1 m_2}{d^2}$$

$$9.8 \text{ N} = \frac{(6.7 \times 10^{-11} \text{ N·m}^2/\text{kg}^2)(1.0 \text{ kg}) \times M}{(6.4 \times 10^6 \text{ m})^2}$$

$$M = \frac{(9.8 \text{ N})(6.4 \times 10^6 \text{ m})^2}{6.7 \times 10^{-11} \text{ N·m}^2/\text{kg}}$$

$$= 6.0 \times 10^{24} \text{ kg}.$$

Now the density of the earth can be calculated:

$$D = \frac{m}{V} = \frac{6.0 \times 10^{24} \text{ kg}}{1.1 \times 10^{21} \text{ m}^3} = 5.5 \times 10^3 \text{ kg/m}^3.$$

The average density of the earth is 5.5 times the density of water. Since surface rocks are two to three times as dense as water, this means that the core of the earth must have a density probably more than ten times that of water, but not as much as a hundred times greater. This value for the density of the earth is reasonable, and should help us to accept the principles from which it was calculated.

EQUILIBRIUM

Gravity is a force that is always acting on objects on the surface of the earth. As a result, forces often have to be applied by muscles or machines simply to balance the effect of the force of gravity. There are several important mechanical situations that will help you to see how the basic principles of Newton's laws can be applied in simple practical situations.

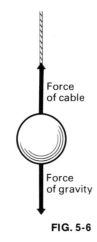

Force
of cable

Force
of gravity

FIG. 5-6

TWO FORCES

To knock down an old building, a crane is used to swing an iron ball against the walls (Fig. 5-6). The first action of the crane is to lift the ball into position. The acceleration of the upward motion does not need to be very great. The major force exerted by the crane's cable is needed to balance the force of gravity on the ball. For a ball of mass 3.0×10^2 kg, what force must be exerted by the cable?

First, calculate the force of gravity on the ball:

$$\begin{aligned}
\vec{F} &= m\vec{g} \\
&= (3.0 \times 10^2 \text{ kg})(9.8 \text{ m/s}^2 \text{ [down]}) \\
&= 2.9 \times 10^3 \text{ N [down]}.
\end{aligned}$$

With the ball just hanging on the cable, there is no motion. So, by Newton's first law, the net force must be zero. Therefore, the force exerted by the cable on the ball is 2.9 kN [up]. These two forces are equal and opposite. However, they do *not* illustrate Newton's *third* law because they both act on one object–the ball.

Any structure on earth (buildings, trees, people, elephants) must be made of materials strong enough to support the loads on them. That is, the materials must be able to exert upward forces sufficient to offset the force of gravity that acts on the masses they are designed to support.

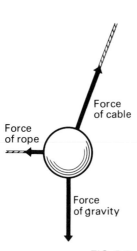

Force
of rope

Force
of cable

Force
of gravity

FIG. 5-7

THREE FORCES

Now the demolition ball is pulled aside by a rope so that the cable is no longer vertical (Fig. 5-7). The rope exerts a force of 1.1 kN [horizontal]. The ball is at rest under the action of three forces: the downward force of gravity, the horizontal force of the rope, and the oblique upward force of the crane's cable. What is the force exerted by the cable?

Since the ball is at rest, the vector sum of the three forces must be zero. Draw the two sides of the triangle formed by the vectors for the forces of gravity and the rope, head to tail as shown in Fig. 5-8. The force in the cable has to be added on to make the final sum zero. That is done by drawing the vector $\vec{F}_{cable}$ from the head of the $\vec{F}_{rope}$ vector to the tail of the $\vec{F}_{grav}$ vector. By measurement you can find that the force in the cable is 3.1 kN [21° from vertically upward].

This principle can be used to find the magnitudes of two forces, if only the force of gravity and the angle of the cable are known. For the same collision ball, what forces in the horizontal rope and the oblique cable are needed if the cable is to be pulled aside 35° from the vertical?

Start with the vector that represents the force of gravity (Fig. 5-9). Draw a line that makes an angle of 35° at the tail of the vector. Where that line crosses the horizontal will give you the point of intersection of the other two vectors. By measurement you can find that the force on the rope is 2.0 kN [horizontal] and the force on the cable is 3.5 kN [up at 35° from the vertical].

> When three or more vectors joined tail to head form a closed figure, their vector sum is zero.

> This example provides a method for calculating the magnitude of a tiny force that holds a light suspended ball a few degrees from the vertical (see Chapter 7 under *Electric potential difference*). All you need to measure are the mass of the ball and the angle of the suspension from the vertical.

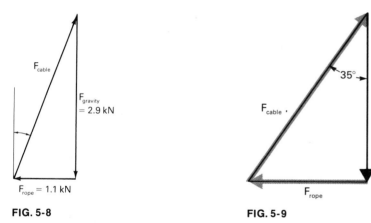

FIG. 5-8   **FIG. 5-9**

SPRINGS

There *is* a place for Newton's third law in these situations. If you call the force of the cable on the ball the action, the reaction is the force of the ball on the cable. What does the force of the ball on the cable do to the cable? Careful measurement would show a slight stretch in the cable.

To see the effect of stretching more clearly, consider a coiled spring (Fig. 5-10). A mass of about 0.5 kg on the end of a particular spring will exert a force of 5.0 N on the spring. That force will cause the spring to stretch somewhat, say 3.0 cm. A force of 10 N will cause the same spring to stretch 6.0 cm. In general, the stretch of the

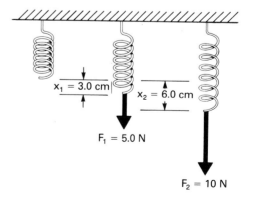

FIG. 5-10

Force is given in Hooke's law by the relation $F = kx$, where k is the spring constant and x is the distance the spring has been extended.

spring is directly proportional to the applied force. This relation, known as Hooke's law, applies to a wide range of materials, as long as they are not stretched too far.

Because of the Hooke's law relation, springs can be used to measure forces. In the example we have used, each 0.60 cm extension of the spring is the result of the application of a force of 1.0 N. If that spring was pulled so that it was extended by 9.0 cm, the applied force would be 15 N.

On the earth's surface, a force of almost 10.0 N is the force applied by gravity to a mass of 1.02 kg. For that reason a spring balance can be used to compare masses. Although the spring extension is a measure of *force*, its scale could be marked in "kilograms" if we knew it was always going to be used where the force of gravity is close enough to 9.80 N/kg. Then you could say, each 0.600 cm extension of the spring is the result of the force of the earth's gravity on a mass of 0.102 kg. An extension of 9.00 cm would indicate a mass of

$$\frac{9.00}{0.600} \times 0.102 \text{ kg} = 1.53 \text{ kg}.$$

The force of gravity of the moon on objects near its surface is about one-sixth of earth-gravity at the surface of the earth. What mass on the moon would give the same spring an extension of 9.00 cm? In the basic equation, $F = ma$, we know that

$$F = 15.0 \text{ N}, \quad \text{and} \quad a = g/6 = 1.63 \text{ m/s}^2.$$

Then $$m = \frac{F}{a} = \frac{15.0 \text{ N}}{1.63 \text{ m/s}^2} = 9.20 \text{ kg}.$$

Thus, 15.0 N is the force of earth-gravity on 1.53 kg, and it is the force of moon-gravity on 9.20 kg (measuring at the surfaces of the respective globes).

If the scale of a spring balance is marked in kilograms, it will give a correct comparison of masses only where the force of gravity is the same as at the place where it was marked. If the scale is marked in newtons, it gives the correct value of the force wherever it is used.

BALANCING ROTATIONS

So far, all the balanced forces we have considered were designed to fit Newton's first law: If the forces on an object are balanced there will be no linear acceleration. If you want to remove a nut from a rusty bolt, you will exert a force on the wrench without wanting to produce a motion that will change the bolt's location in space (Fig. 5-11). And if the turning force you exert is insufficient, you use a longer wrench.

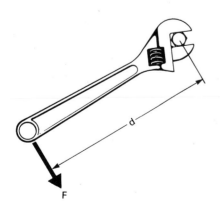

FIG. 5-11

The **torque** (T) of a turning force is proportional to the product of the applied force (F) and the perpendicular distance ($d_\perp$) from the line of application of the force to the centre of rotation. The unit of torque is the **newton metre** (N·m).

Suspend a metre-stick at its centre (Fig. 5-12). The point of suspension is called the *fulcrum*. Apply a force of 2.0 N at a point 0.30 m downward to the right of the fulcrum. What torque will be needed to keep the metre-stick from rotating? Since $T = Fd_\perp$ the torque of the first force is

$$(2.0 \text{ N})(0.30 \text{ m}) = 0.60 \text{ N·m [clockwise]}.$$

The balancing torque must be 0.60 N·m [anticlockwise]. It can be provided by applying a force on the other side of the fulcrum. Table 5-1 and the graph in Fig. 5-13 show the inverse relation between applied force and distance from fulcrum that will provide that torque.

Torque is defined as $T = Fd_\perp$.

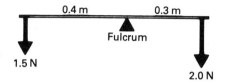

FIG. 5-12

To prevent the motion of the metre-stick through space the fulcrum must exert an upward force equal to the sum of the two downward forces.

Table 5-1

Force	Distance
5.0 N	0.12 m
4.0	0.15
3.0	0.20
2.0	0.30
1.5	0.40

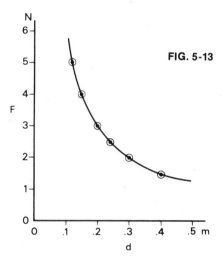

FIG. 5-13

Levers are devices by which torques can be applied to move objects. The usual advantage of a lever is that a small force can be applied on a long arm, to produce the same torque as that produced by a larger force on a smaller arm. Perhaps the simplest of all devices that use the lever principle is the equal-arm balance.

In an equal-arm balance, the distances of the applied forces from the centre are kept rigorously equal. The forces that are applied are the forces of gravity on the objects hanging from the two arms (Fig. 5-14). When there is no tendency to rotate, the torques on each side of the balance must be equal. Since the arm lengths are equal, the forces must be equal. Since the force of gravity on the masses on each arm is the same, the masses must be equal. As a result, the equal-arm balance is used to compare masses. When the arms are balanced, the unknown mass must be equal to the sum of the collection of known masses on the other arm. If you take an equal-arm balance to the moon, will you need a set of known masses different from those you use on earth?

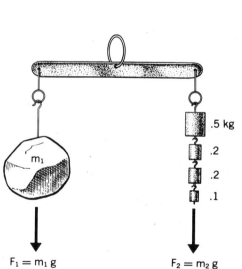

FIG. 5-14. The net torque on the equal-arm balance is zero. Thus, $F_1 = F_2$ and $m_1 = m_2$.

For the answer, turn to I at the end of the Chapter 5 Exercises.

WEIGHT

Most of the time, the word "weight" in everyday use is meant to refer to how much matter there is in the thing being weighed. As a result, the ordinary use of "weight" really means "mass," and is measured in kilograms.

In the stricter usage of physics, "weight" usually means "the force of gravity on an object." If a person is too heavy for a chair, it is because the force of gravity on him is greater than the chair can withstand. Although his mass may be large, the same chair could hold him up if the force of gravity was less. If the chair will not support loads greater than 1.6 kN, you will invite people of masses greater than 160 kg not to sit there. On the moon the same chair could still support a weight of 1.6 kN, but the person with the largest mass in the world would not weigh enough there to break it.

In most cases the word "weight" should be avoided if you want to prevent ambiguity. Instead, you say "mass" and measure in kilograms, or "force of gravity" and measure in newtons.

However, there is one instance where the word "weight" seems not to mean either "mass" or "force of gravity." Sitting on earth, the force of gravity determines how hard you press on your chair, even if you're an acrobat sitting on a chair on a high wire. If the wire breaks, you will not press down on the chair during the downward trip. Then it might be appropriate to say that you are "weightless," without meaning that either your mass or the force of gravity has suddenly become zero. Tower divers, gymnasts, and astronauts in orbit perform somersaults while falling freely (Fig. 5-15). They feel weightless, because they do not feel the force of gravity pushing them against anything. In fact, they are being accelerated toward the earth by the force of gravity.

FIG. 5-15

PRESSURE

If you rent an elephant for a bit part in your school play you'll have to be sure that the floor of the stage is well enough supported to withstand the force of gravity of perhaps 7.0×10^4 N on the elephant. That may not be too difficult, but there's another problem. When the elephant walks he may at times have all his weight supported on two feet. If the area of those two feet is 0.40 m², the *pressure* (P) of the elephant on the floor surface will be

$$P = \frac{F}{A} = \frac{7.0 \times 10^4 \text{ N}}{0.40 \text{ m}^2} = 1.8 \times 10^5 \text{ N/m}^2.$$

The SI unit of pressure is the pascal (Pa), where

$$1 \text{ Pa} = 1 \text{ N/m}^2.$$

So the pressure on the floor at the elephant's two feet is 180 kPa. That pressure is likely not enough to damage the floor, but watch out for Mary Jones in her spike heels. If she momentarily puts her weight of 450 N down on one heel that is 5 mm square, what a pressure!

$$P = \frac{F}{A} = \frac{4.5 \times 10^2 \text{ N}}{(5.0 \times 10^{-3} \text{ m})^2} = 1.8 \times 10^7 \text{ Pa,}$$

or 18 MPa, one hundred times the pressure exerted by the elephant's two feet.

Is pressure a vector? (For the answer, turn to II at the end of the Chapter 5 Exercises.)

Example: Standard atmospheric pressure is 101 kPa. A scuba diver going beneath the surface of Lake Huron will experience pressures greater than atmospheric. At what depth will the pressure be doubled?

What we want to know is the depth at which the force of gravity on the water above the diver will cause it to exert a pressure of 101 kPa. Consider a column of water that has a base of 1.00 m², and a height of x m. Then calculate (a) the volume of the column of water, (b) the mass of that water, (c) the force of gravity on the water, (d) the pressure of the water.

(a) Area = 1.00 m²   Height = x m.

$$\text{Volume, } V = \text{area} \times \text{height}$$
$$= (1.00 \text{ m}^2)(x \text{ m}) = 1.00 \, x \text{ m}^3.$$

(b) Density of water is $D = 1.00 \times 10^3$ kg/m³.

The density of water changes very little as depth increases.

$$m = DV$$
$$= (1.00 \times 10^3 \text{ kg/m}^3)(1.00 \, x \text{ m}^3) = 1.00 \times 10^3 \, x \text{ kg.}$$

(c) The force of gravity (for $g = 9.81$ m/s²) on the column is

$$F = mg$$
$$= (1.00 \times 10^3 \, x \text{ kg})(9.81 \text{ m/s}^2) = 9.81 \, x \text{ kN}.$$

This series of relations can be combined into a single one that gives the pressure at depth h in a fluid of density D ($p = Dgh$). You should check to see that the units of density, acceleration, and distance do combine to give the unit of pressure.

(d) The pressure on area of $A = 1.00$ m² is

$$P = \frac{F}{A} = \frac{9.81x \text{ kN}}{1.00 \text{ m}^2} = 9.81 \, x \text{ kPa}.$$

But the pressure is to be 101 kPa.

Therefore,

$$x = \frac{101 \text{ kPa}}{9.8 \text{ kPa}} = 10.3.$$

The total pressure is the sum of the atmospheric pressure and the water pressure.

At a depth of 10.3 m, the total pressure will be double the standard atmospheric pressure.

Exercises

Acceleration due to gravity, $g = 9.80$ m/s² (3 digits)
$= 10$ m/s² (one digit)

A

1. A half dollar coin is dropped from a height of 2.0 m. From what height should a dime be dropped at the same instant so that both coins will hit the floor at the same time? Try it.

2. Cut out a paper disc of diameter slightly smaller than that of a half dollar coin. Drop the two from the same height at the same time. Which one hits the floor first? Why? Place the coin and disc together and drop them. Explain any change that is observed.

3. Suppose a lump of steel falls from the top of the CN Tower with negligible air resistance. Calculate the speed with which it will fall at 1, 2, 3, 4, 5, 10 s.

4. A baseball is thrown vertically upward from the ground with an initial speed of 20.0 m/s. What velocity will it have at 1.0, 2.0, 3.0 s?

5. Sketch a velocity-time graph for the baseball of question 4.

6. On a foul tip, a baseball is hit vertically upward at 30 m/s. Neglecting air resistance, calculate the time that will elapse before the ball hits the catcher's glove. With what velocity will it strike the glove?

7. Charles Atlas was once a 44-kg weakling. What was the force of gravity on him then?

8. After training, Charles Atlas could lift a barbell of 180 kg. What minimum force did he have to exert to lift it?

9. The force of gravity on a baseball is 1.47 N. What is the mass of the baseball?

10. The gravitational field strength at the surface of the moon is 1.61 N/kg. What mass could an astronaut support against the moon's gravity when he can exert a force of 100.0 N?

11. At what location on the earth's surface is the value of g (a) greatest, (b) least?

12. Perhaps the variations in g over the surface of the earth should be taken into account in determining Olympic sports records. Since locations nearer the equator are farther from the centre of the earth, should it be easier to set jumping records in Moscow (latitude 55° N) or in Mexico City (latitude 20°N), other things being equal?

13. On the launching pad, a satellite experiences a force of gravity of 36×10^4 N. It is located at a distance from the centre of the earth of r (the radius of the earth $= 6 \times 10^6$ m). What will be the force of the earth's gravity on the satellite (a) at a distance of 6×10^6 m above the earth's *surface*, (b) at a distance of $6r$ from the earth's centre, (c) at a distance of $60r$ from the earth's centre?

14. The distance of the centre of the moon from the centre of the earth is about $60r$ ($r =$ radius of the earth). The force of gravity of the earth on the moon is 2.0×10^{20} N. At what distance would the force of the earth's gravity on the moon be (a) 8.0×10^{20} N, (b) 2.0×10^{22} N, (c) 2.0×10^{18} N?

15. From the information given in question 14, what is the force of the moon's gravity on the earth?

16. For each of the following statements indicate whether the word "weight" (or derivatives thereof) means

"mass," or "force of gravity." If there is ambiguity, specify the circumstances that would clear it up.
(a) How much weight did you gain last month?
(b) How much does that pot roast weigh?
(c) How much weight do you give to his argument?
(d) How much weight does that pillar support?
(e) The astronaut will weigh less on the moon.
(f) The cosmonaut will weigh the same on the moon.

17. A hunting bow approximately obeys Hooke's law for springs. If a bow requires a maximum pull of 3.0×10^2 N to be drawn back 0.80 m, calculate (a) the force required to draw the bow a distance of 0.60 m, (b) the distance the bow would be drawn by a force of 1.3×10^2 N.

18. The distance that the end of a diving board is depressed is proportional to the force applied to it. If the distance is 5.0 cm/100 N, calculate (a) the distance the board would be depressed by a girl of mass 55 kg standing at the end of the board, (b) the force exerted on the end of the board to depress it 45 cm.

19. Archie Bunker tightened the nuts on his car's wheels by standing on the wrench at a distance of 0.40 m from the centre of the bolts. His mass is 84 kg. To loosen the bolts, daughter Gloria slid a pipe of 1.0 m length over the handle of the wrench. What force would she have to exert at the end of the pipe?

20. A 630 N bucket of water is attached by a rope around an axle of radius 4.0 cm. A crank is attached to the axle. What length of crank would make a force of 70.0 N at the end of the crank just enough to raise the bucket, neglecting friction?

21. A dollar bill lying flat on the table exerts a pressure of about 1.0 Pa. The area of the bill is about 100 cm². Calculate (a) the force of gravity on the bill, and (b) the mass of the bill.

22. Standing momentarily on the toe of one skate, Toller Cranston exerts a force of 640 N on an area of 4.0×10^{-6} m². What pressure does his skate exert on the ice surface?

B

23. An elevator has a mass of 1.4×10^3 kg. Calculate the force in the cables supporting the elevator when it is
(a) at rest,
(b) accelerating upward at 1.4 m/s²,
(c) accelerating downward at 2.1 m/s²,
(d) moving upward at a constant speed of 4.0 m/s.

24. A cannon is situated on the edge of a cliff that is 78 m above the sea. A ball that is dropped straight down will hit the sea with a speed of 39.0 m/s. If the cannon fires a shell horizontally at 260 m/s, calculate
(a) the time for the shell to hit the water,

(b) the distance out from the bottom of the cliff that it will hit the water,
(c) the *velocity* with which the shell would strike a ship located at that point.

25. Draw a speed-time graph to represent the motion of an object falling freely from rest with an acceleration of g. Then calculate areas under the graph-line to determine the distance fallen at 2.0, 4.0, 6.0, 8.0, and 10.0 s.

26. If a person falls out of a flying airplane without a parachute he will achieve a terminal speed of falling of about 53 m/s after having fallen a distance of about 550 m. Use the graph of question 25 to determine the distance from which a fall without air resistance would achieve the same speed.

27. From the data in question 26, approximately how long would it take a person without a parachute to fall to earth from a height of 2.0×10^3 m?

28. During a burn of 1.50 s, a rocket motor propelling a sled on a horizontal track exerts a force of 7.89×10^5 N. The initial mass of the sled is 2.58×10^3 kg, and the final mass is 2.28×10^3 kg. Calculate
(a) the mass of the fuel expended,
(b) the average acceleration of the sled,
(c) the speed achieved by the sled,
(d) the time required for the sled to travel 5.0×10^3 m, assuming no friction,
(e) the maximum acceleration expressed as a multiple of g.

29. A small rocket on the launching pad has a mass of 5.0×10^4 kg. Its rocket motor can exert a force of 2.2 MN for 10.0 s. Calculate
(a) the vertically upward acceleration of the rocket,
(b) the upward speed achieved.

30. For the situation described in question 29 sketch a velocity-time graph that shows the increase in speed from zero to maximum after 10 s, followed by a decrease in speed at the rate of -10 m/s². Use the graph to determine the time taken and the vertical distance travelled when the rocket achieved zero velocity at the top of its trajectory.

31. A 55 kg load of bricks on a platform rests on the ground. A rope from there goes up the side of a building, over a pulley, and is attached to a second platform onto which a workman steps, making the load there 60 kg. Neglect friction in the pulley and the masses of the rope and pulley.
(a) Calculate the unbalanced force acting on the system once the man steps on the platform.
(b) Calculate the acceleration of the motion.
(c) How fast will the system be moving after 10.0 s?
(d) How far will the workman have descended after 10.0 s?
(e) If the workman was originally 35 m above the ground, how long will it take him to reach the ground, and with what speed will he hit the ground?

32. A 1.5 kg dynamics cart is fastened by a horizontal cord over a pulley at the edge of a table to a mass of 0.50 kg. The frictional resistance in wheels and pulley is 1.2 N. Calculate the acceleration of the cart.

33. A golf ball of mass 0.046 kg rests on a tee. Tom Watson swings his driver to give the ball a speed of 50 m/s after a contact interval of 4.0×10^{-3} s. The ball flies eastward at such an angle with the horizontal that its horizontal progress is made at 40 m/s. Calculate
  (a) the average force exerted by the club on the ball,
  (b) the speed of the vertical motion of the ball,
  (c) the time during which the ball was in the air,
  (d) the displacement of the ball when it lands in the sand trap and doesn't bounce or roll.

34. In an experiment a wooden block 12 cm long is dropped from rest past two photocell timers. It takes 0.43 s to fall from the first to the second light beam, and 0.028 s to pass through the second light beam. From these data calculate the value of g at the location of the experiment.

35. A ball of mass 1.0 g is hanging by a light thread. What is the magnitude of the horizontal force required to pull the ball aside so that the thread makes an angle of 10° with the vertical?

36. An automobile of mass 1.7×10^3 kg is being supported on a hydraulic hoist. The diameter of the cylinder of the hoist is 16 cm. Calculate the pressure that must be supplied to the bottom of the cylinder to support the auto. Express your answer in kilopascals, and as a multiple of atmospheric pressure.

C

37. When you are sitting on a bus on a rainy day, drops of water make vertical streaks on the window when the bus is at rest. Some streaks come from raindrops (case I) and others come from water dripping off the eaves of the bus (case II). When the bus moves (forward or backward), the streaks are inclined at an angle to the vertical. For each case, decide whether the size of the angle is a measure of the velocity or the acceleration of the bus, relative to the motion of the drop.

38. (a) An object falls from rest in time t and achieves a speed $v = gt$. In that time it falls a distance $d = \frac{1}{2} vt$. Express d in terms of g and t.
  (b) In a very accurate determination of g a metal bar is dropped from rest in a vacuum. The bar has two marks on it that are 1.000 00 m apart. A timer starts when the lower mark begins to move and stops when the upper mark passes the point from which the lower mark started. For a time of 0.45164 s, calculate the value of g for the place where the experiment was performed.

39. A fair estimate of a person's reaction time can be found by the following method. Let a metre stick hang vertically from your thumb and forefinger, and have a classmate hold his thumb and forefinger about 2 cm apart at the 50 cm mark on the stick. He watches your hand and when you release the metre stick he closes his grasp. Measure the distance the stick fell before he stopped it. Then calculate the time required for the stick to fall that distance. If the distance is 10 cm, what is the reaction time?

40. As soon as any projectile is shot it begins to fall with an acceleration of g. For that reason, the direction of shooting must be inclined upward. On a rifle, this is accomplished by adjusting the sights. If a rifle is fired from the prone position on the ground with a speed of 300 m/s for the bullet at a target 1200 m away, calculate
  (a) the time that the bullet must be in the air,
  (b) the initial vertical speed that will allow the bullet to stay in the air for that time,
  (c) the angle of the rifle above the horizontal (by vector diagram, or trigonometry).

41. In order for a projectile to be fired a maximum distance (range) the angle of inclination of the projector should be 45°, if the effect of air resistance is neglected. At 45° the vertical and horizontal speeds are equal. For greater angles the vertical component of the velocity is greater and the horizontal component is smaller. An arrow is shot at a speed of 60 m/s over several angles in the range from about 40° to 50°. The corresponding vertical and horizontal components are given in the table.

Vertical speed (m/s)	39.0	41.0	42.4	44.0	46.0
Horizontal speed (m/s)	45.6	43.8	42.4	40.8	38.5

Using $g = 10.0$ m/s², and assuming the arrow is shot from ground level, for each pair of values calculate
  (a) the time the arrow will be in the air (from the vertical speed),
  (b) the distance at which the arrow will hit the ground (from the horizontal speed).

42. If a projectile is shot at 45° with a speed v, its range is $d = v^2/g$. Calculate the speeds required to achieve the following ranges:
  (a) The homerun ball in Exhibition Park travelled 115 m.
  (b) The world record for the javelin throw is 94.6 m.
  (c) Harry Drake's footbow record range is 2005 m.

Answers to text questions

  I. As long as there is some force on the two arms of the balance, and the arms are equal in length, the balance will equalize masses whatever the magnitude of the force. Thus, the same standard masses can be used anywhere.

  II. Pressure in fluids is not a vector quantity because it is exerted equally in all directions.

CHAPTER 6

Energy
and
Conservation

In highway driving, a small car may be able to travel 100 km on 8 L of gasoline. We can call this a gasoline consumption of 8 L/100 km. Whatever the gasoline is doing for us, it is evident that we would expect to use 16 L to travel 200 km. The gasoline used is proportional to the distance travelled, for a constant speed.

What the gasoline is doing for us becomes clearer by considering that a larger automobile might have a consumption rate of 16 L/100 km. We know that the gasoline is needed to run the engine, and that to maintain a constant velocity on the highway the engine must exert a force just sufficient to compensate for the opposing frictional forces of road and air. These frictional forces are greater at greater speeds of the auto, but we can easily imagine both small and large cars having the same speed, taking one hour, for example, to travel 100 km. Since the larger car is pushing more air, it makes sense to suggest that its larger consumption of gasoline is the result of the engine having greater frictional forces to overcome. If the frictional force on the smaller car is 6.0×10^2 N, that on the larger car could well be 12.0×10^2 N. That would mean that as well as being proportional to the distance travelled, the gasoline consumption is proportional to the force exerted by the engine against friction.

The property of gasoline that enables it to drive automobile engines is called **energy** *(E)*. When the gasoline is exploded with air in the cylinders, the rapidly expanding gases impart energy to the pistons of the engine. Through geared connections the motion of the pistons imparts energy to the automobile. We say that energy is given to the auto because it is moving as a result of the force applied. Suppose you started your car with the bumper up against a brick wall. You might spin the wheels and impart energy to the road in the form of heat, but you would not move the car, and it would not make sense to say that it had received any net energy.

One of the important features of energy is that it can be changed from one form into others. In the process of changing energy from one form to another, we say that work is done. The energy in the gasoline is only potential until a squirt of it is exploded with air in the cylinder of the engine. The expanding gas exerts a force on the piston and makes it move. The energy is transferred from the explod-ing gas to the piston—work is done. Eventually, the energy is trans-ferred to the wheels to keep the car moving down the highway. More work is done. Ultimately, the energy is dissipated as heat to the road and air.

Two definitions of work ▶ **Work** is done in the transfer of energy from one form to another, when an applied force produces motion in the direction in which it is applied. Based on our example of the two cars on the highway, we *define* work (E) as the product of the force and the displacement in the direction of the force. Although both force and displacement are vectors, work and energy are scalars. That is because the same amount of energy (and gasoline) is required, no matter in which di-rection your trip takes you. Thus, we can write

$$E = \vec{F}\Delta\vec{d}.$$

This will make the unit of energy the newton metre, which is given a special name:

$$\text{one joule} = \text{one newton metre,}$$
$$1 \text{ J} = 1 \text{ N·m.}$$

Example: How much energy was transformed from the chemical po-tential of the gasoline to the energy of motion of the small car in our previous discussion? The directions of force and displacement are the same during the trip so they need not be considered further.

$$F = 6.0 \times 10^2 \text{ N} \quad \text{and} \quad \Delta d = 1.0 \times 10^5 \text{ m.}$$

$$E = F\Delta d = (6.0 \times 10^2 \text{ N})(1.0 \times 10^5 \text{ m}) = 6.0 \times 10^7 \text{ J.}$$

Thus the gasoline in the small car does 6.0×10^7 J of work in mov-ing the car 100 km.

The question of direction often does come in when the magnitude of an energy is calculated. Consider that a block of mass 1.00 kg is lying on a perfectly smooth table, that is to say, a frictionless one. Since $\vec{g} = 9.80$ m/s^2 [down], the force of gravity on the block will be $\vec{F} = 9.80$ N [down]. If now you wish to lift the block up, you will have to exert a force of 9.80 N [upwards]. To lift the mass by 2.00 m, the total work done by you will be

$$E = \vec{F}\Delta\vec{d} = 9.80 \text{ N [up]} \times 2.00 \text{ m [up]} = 19.6 \text{ J.}$$

You can feel yourself doing this work. The energy you lose is trans-ferred to the block, which is now capable of doing work itself. This can be seen by considering the action of the block first of all when it is just held in the hand at table level and secondly if it is dropped into the hand from a height of two metres.

Now consider that the block is once more on the table, but moving through 2.00 m horizontally at a constant speed along the frictionless surface as illustrated in Fig. 6-1. There are still forces acting, the gravitational force downwards and the reaction force of the table upwards, but this time no work will be done. That is,

$$0 = \text{Force [up or down]} \times 2.00 \text{ m [sideways]}.$$

No work is done if the force acting and the displacement are at right angles to one another. (In practice it is, of course, not possible to get frictionless surfaces, and therefore some work will always have to be done to overcome the frictional forces. These will always be along the same line as the displacement though in the opposite direction. In addition, some energy is required to start the motion.)

One rather surprising result of the fact that no work is done if the force and the displacement are perpendicular to each other is that it takes no energy to keep the moon rotating around the earth or the earth around the sun. To keep an astronaut circling the earth as shown in Fig. 6-2 needs only sufficient energy to overcome the slight air resistance. This is because the gravitational force between the earth and the satellite acts in the direction joining the centres of the satellite and the earth, along a radius of the orbit, while the displacement of the satellite is along the circumference of the orbit. Radii are perpendicular to the circumference of a circle, and so to the direction of the displacement, and thus no work is done.

Example: Calculate the work done (or the energy used) in moving a block a horizontal distance of 6.0 m against a constant frictional force of 4.5 N, the velocity of the block being constant at all times.

The frictional force will always be in the opposite direction to the displacement. The force of gravity will be at right angles to the (horizontal) displacement, and therefore will not enter into this problem. As there is no acceleration (the velocity is constant) there cannot be any unbalanced forces. The applied force must therefore be just equal to the frictional force, but forward instead of backward.

Since $E = F\Delta d,$

then $E = (4.5 \text{ N})(6.0 \text{ m}) = 27 \text{ J}.$

Thus, the work done was 27 J.

Example: An object of mass 5.0 kg is moved 6.0 m southwards in a horizontal plane across a frictionless surface by a force $\vec{F}$. The work done during this operation is 15 J. Calculate the force applied and the acceleration of the object.

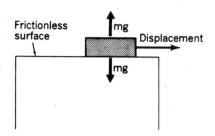

FIG. 6-1

$E = F\Delta d_{\parallel}$
In contrast to torque ($T = Fd_{\perp}$) work and energy depend on a displacement measured *parallel* to the direction of the applied force.

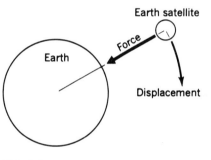

FIG. 6-2

Since $\qquad E = \vec{F}\Delta\vec{d},$ then $\vec{F} = \dfrac{E}{\Delta\vec{d}}$

$$\vec{F} = \frac{15\text{ J}}{6.0\text{ m}}\text{[South]} = 2.5\text{ N [South]}.$$

Thus the magnitude of the force is 2.5 N, and its direction will be south, the same direction as that of the displacement.

Since $\qquad\qquad \vec{F} = m\vec{a},$ then $\vec{a} = \dfrac{\vec{F}}{m}$

$$\vec{a} = \frac{2.5\text{ N [South]}}{5.0\text{ kg}} = 0.50\text{ m/s}^2\text{ [South]}.$$

Therefore, the acceleration of the object is 0.50 m/s² [South].

KINETIC ENERGY

During a slap-shot, Bobby Hull's stick exerts a force on the puck, and does work on it to increase its velocity from zero to 40 m/s [East]. If the stick is in contact with the puck for 0.0050 s, we can calculate the average acceleration of the puck, and the displacement through which the force applied that acceleration. Let the eastward direction be positive.

$$\vec{a} = \frac{\Delta\vec{v}}{\Delta t} = \frac{+40\text{ m/s} - 0}{0.0050\text{ s}} = +8.0 \times 10^3\text{ m/s}^2.$$

$$\Delta\vec{d} = \tfrac{1}{2}(\vec{v_1} + \vec{v_2})\Delta t = \tfrac{1}{2}(0 + 40\text{ m/s})(0.0050\text{ s}) = +0.10\text{ m}.$$

Acting through a displacement of +0.10 m, the stick produced an acceleration of $+8.0 \times 10^3$ m/s². The mass of the puck is 0.16 kg, so the force is

$$\vec{F} = m\vec{a} = (0.16\text{ kg})(+8.0 \times 10^3\text{ m/s}^2) = +1.3 \times 10^3\text{ N},$$

and the work done is

$$E = \vec{F}\Delta\vec{d} = (+1.3 \times 10^3\text{ N})(+0.10\text{ m}) = 1.3 \times 10^2\text{ J}.$$

As the puck slides toward the net at 40 m/s, it is reasonable to suppose that it "carries" the energy that was imparted to it by the stick. This energy of the motion of the puck is called **kinetic energy.** We can now show that the kinetic energy of the puck is completely determined by its mass and velocity and is equal to the work done on the puck. Since the initial velocity was zero, let us call the final velocity simply $\vec{v}$. The change in velocity is $\Delta\vec{v} = \vec{v} - 0 = \vec{v}$. Then we can go through in symbols the same work we did with numbers and units. Start with the formula for work,

$$E = \vec{F}\Delta\vec{d}.$$

Use $\vec{F} = m\vec{a}$ to replace $\vec{F}$:

$$E = m\vec{a}\Delta\vec{d}.$$

Use the motion relations, $\vec{a} = \Delta\vec{v}/\Delta t = \vec{v}/\Delta t$ and $\Delta\vec{d} = \frac{1}{2}\vec{v}\Delta t$, to get

For constant acceleration, the displacement during a time of Δt is the product of Δt and the average velocity. The average velocity from zero to v is $v/2$.

$$E = \left(m\frac{\vec{v}}{\Delta t}\right)\left(\frac{1}{2}\vec{v}\Delta t\right)$$

$$E_k = \frac{1}{2}m\vec{v}^2.$$

The subscript "k" represents *kinetic* energy. This formula indicates that the puck has no "memory" of anything but the amount of work done on it—if half the force had acted over twice the displacement the result would have been the same.

We should check to see that the formula gives the same result as above:

$$E_k = \frac{1}{2}(0.16 \text{ kg})(+40 \text{ m/s})^2 = 1.28 \times 10^2 \text{ kg·m}^2/\text{s}^2$$

$$= 1.3 \times 10^2 \text{ kg·}\frac{\text{m}}{\text{s}^2}\text{·m} = 1.3 \times 10^2 \text{ N·m} = 1.3 \times 10^2 \text{ J}.$$

The unit manipulation has been done to show that the unit for $\frac{1}{2}m\vec{v}^2$ is indeed the joule.

This formula provides another indication that energy is a scalar quantity. If the velocity had been –40 m/s, the effect of squaring the velocity would be to give the same result that we got with +40 m/s. Every direction for the velocity gives the same result for the energy. Therefore, the value of the energy is independent of the direction of the velocity. For that reason, we may omit the vector designation and write

$$E_k = \frac{1}{2}mv^2.$$

POTENTIAL ENERGY

So far our measures of energy have involved motion in some way. They do not provide for our sense that we should associate energy with the gasoline in the tank of a car, with the rock held by the caveman at the edge of the cliff, or with William Tell's drawn bow. In each of these situations we say that energy is *potentially* available to do work to start something moving. The energy can be thought of as being stored in the molecules of gasoline, the suspended rock, or in the stretched bow. It is called **potential energy**.

In some cases, how much energy is stored in a system can be determined from the work that was done in the process of storing the energy. To hold a crossbow fully stretched might take a continuing force of 350 N after the string has been pulled through a displacement of 0.40 m. If the string is then hooked on a trigger mechanism, the bow can be carried about with the energy stored in it, until the trigger releases the string against which an arrow has been placed. In drawing back the string the initial force required was very small. It increased uniformly to 350 N when fully loaded. Thus, the work done depends on the average force, 175 N, and the displacement:

$$E = F\Delta d = (175 \text{ N})(0.40 \text{ m}) = 70 \text{ J.}$$

Once the bowman has done 70 J of work, he can let fly whenever he wishes. When he does, the force of the stretched bow will produce a large acceleration of the arrow (and also of the ends of the bow). In a typical case the mass of the arrow is 0.060 kg, and the effective mass of the parts of the bow being accelerated is an additional 0.020 kg. Thus, the formula for kinetic energy can be used with $E_k = 70$ J and $m = 0.080$ kg.

Since $\qquad E_k = \frac{1}{2}mv^2, \qquad$ then $\qquad v^2 = \dfrac{2 E}{m}$

$$v^2 = \frac{2 \times 70 \text{ kg·m}^2/\text{s}^2}{0.080 \text{ kg}} = 1750 \text{ m}^2/\text{s}^2.$$

Therefore, $\qquad v = \sqrt{1750 \text{ m}^2/\text{s}^2} = 42 \text{ m/s.}$

The arrow will leave the bow with a speed of 42 m/s, carrying with it 75% of the energy originally stored in the bow. The other 25% stays with the bow and has to be absorbed by the bowman.

In general, potential energy is possessed by any object that is being held against forces that will cause it to move when the hold is removed. This statement applies to the chemical potential energy stored in gasoline as well as to more obvious situations. The atoms that compose the molecules of gasoline are held in place by electrical forces. When the gasoline is combined chemically with oxygen (in burning) those electrical forces do work in moving groups of atoms about. Some of the increased kinetic energy of those groups of atoms (the new molecules formed in the reaction) are transferred to the pistons of an auto engine. The increased kinetic energy of the molecules themselves is shown in the increased temperature within the cylinders of the engine. Energy that goes to heating the engine block is not available for pushing on the pistons.

GRAVITATIONAL POTENTIAL ENERGY

Energy was stored in the crossbow when work was done against the elastic force of the bow; and the potential energy was equal to the work done. In the same way, since objects near the earth are acted on continuously by the force of gravity, gravitational potential energy is stored in them when they are moved to locations farther from the centre of the earth. As a matter of convenience a zero for gravitational potential energy can be chosen at any level desired. For example, it is often useful to treat gravitational potential energy as zero at ground level, even though an object on the ground has gravitational potential energy relative to the bottom of a well.

If caveman Og carried a 25 kg rock to the top of the cliff, he would have to have exerted a force just greater than the force of gravity on it, and in the opposite direction. The force of gravity was

$$\vec{F}_{grav} = m\vec{g}$$
$$= (25 \text{ kg})(9.8 \text{ m/s}^2 \text{ [down]}) = 2.5 \times 10^2 \text{ N [down]}.$$

Og's applied force was approximately

$$\vec{F}_{appl} = -\vec{F}_{grav}$$
$$= -2.5 \times 10^2 \text{ N [down]} = 2.5 \times 10^2 \text{ N [up]}.$$

If Og carried the stone up 16 m, the work done was

$$E = \vec{F}\Delta\vec{d}$$
$$= (+2.5 \times 10^2 \text{ N})(+16 \text{ m}) = 4.0 \times 10^3 \text{ J}.$$

At a height of 16 m, a 25 kg mass has a gravitational potential energy of 4.0×10^3 J.

In symbols, we can put together the two relations:

$$E_p = -m\vec{g}\Delta\vec{d}.$$

We have taken the *up* direction to be positive, which makes $\vec{g} = -9.8$ m/s². As a result the value of E_p (gravitational potential energy) is positive when $\Delta\vec{d}$ is measured upward, which is the normal thing to do. However, since energy is a scalar, we can neglect directions, and write

$$E_p = mg\Delta d.$$

A sign *can* be attached to energy in order to show an increase (+) or a decrease (−) in the amount of energy during a certain activity.

When Og released the stone it had 16 m to fall to return to the ground. That would take 1.8 s. The velocity acquired in that time is

$$\vec{v} = \vec{a}\Delta t = (-9.8 \text{ m/s}^2)(1.8 \text{ s}) = -18 \text{ m/s}.$$

With what kinetic energy would the rock strike the ground?

$$E_k = \frac{1}{2} m\vec{v}^2 = \frac{25 \text{ kg}}{2}(-18 \text{ m/s})^2 = 4.0 \times 10^3 \text{ J}.$$

At the top of the cliff the potential energy was 4.0×10^3 J and the kinetic energy was zero. At the bottom of the cliff the potential energy was zero and the kinetic energy was 4.0×10^3 J. The work done by the force of gravity consisted of transforming the gravitational potential energy of the rock at the top of the cliff into kinetic energy at the bottom of the cliff.

(a)

(b)

FIG. 6-3

POWER

A lazy person doing a job of work and an energetic person doing the same job do exactly the same amount of work and use the same amount of energy. The difference lies in the time they take to do the job, that is, in their rate of working (Fig.6-3). In scientific language, the rate of energy transfer is called **power**, and it is defined by the equation

$$P = \frac{E}{t}.$$

That is, power is the work done divided by the time taken to do it.

The unit of power is a joule per second, which is called a **watt**. The kilowatt is a rate of working one thousand times that of the watt.

From $$P = E/t, \quad E = Pt;$$

that is, power multiplied by a time gives an energy. The joule is in fact a watt second. The **kilowatt hour**, kW·h, is the amount of energy transferred by a machine working at a rate of 1000 W for a period of 1 h. This unit is used in electrical applications and will be discussed further in Chapter 11.

Example: A man raises a 50.0 kg mass a vertical distance of 1.2 m in 0.50 s. With what power is he working?

$$P = \frac{E}{t} \quad \text{and} \quad E = mg\Delta d.$$

Therefore $$P = \frac{mg\Delta d}{t}$$

$$= \frac{(50.0 \text{ kg})(9.8 \text{ m/s}^2)(1.2 \text{ m})}{0.50 \text{ s}} = 1.2 \times 10^3 \text{ W}.$$

Therefore the man works with a power of 1.2 kW.

Example: A mass is being moved in a horizontal direction by an engine that works at a constant rate of 100 kW. It is found that the mass has a displacement of 20 m in each second, the velocity being constant. Calculate the frictional forces resisting the movement of the mass.

As there is no acceleration, the engine must exert a force just equal to the frictional forces, F.

Since $$P = \frac{E}{t} = \frac{F\Delta d}{t}, \quad \text{then} \quad F = \frac{Pt}{\Delta d}.$$

Therefore, $$F = \frac{100 \times 10^3 \text{ W} \times 1.0 \text{ s}}{20 \text{ m}} = 5.0 \times 10^3 \text{ N}.$$

Thus, the frictional forces are 5.0 kN.

THE PRINCIPLE OF ENERGY CONSERVATION

Have you ever dreamed up a scheme for saving energy such as the following? Attach four electric generators to each wheel of a bicycle. Use the electricity they can produce to run an electric motor attached to the frame and arranged to drive the front sprocket. All you have to do is get the bike going, get up some speed, and then let the generators be driven by the tires. Switch on the motor, take your feet off the pedals and away you go, with no more effort. The motor will drive the wheels, and the wheels will drive the generators. Or will they?

If a scheme such as this would work, you would have a perpetual motion machine. To keep the bike going against frictional forces would require energy to be created out of nothing. It won't work. Why not?

Many such perpetual motion schemes have been proposed over the past thousand years, but none has ever been made to work. We are now convinced that no such machine can possibly work. However, there is no way to *prove* that they will not work—that is, to deduce from other principles that perpetual motion is impossible. As a result, in conformity with long experience, the impossibility of perpetual motion has been made into a principle itself. In simple terms, the principle says that you cannot get something for nothing.

More formally, we call it the **principle of the conservation of energy:**

Within any system of inter-related parts, the total amount of energy remains constant.

When you are on a bicycle on level ground, *you* are the only source of energy for propelling the bicycle. The relevant system of related parts includes you and the bike, the ground and the air. If you do work to get the bicycle into motion your internal energy decreases—eventually to be replenished by a good meal. If you arranged for the wheels to drive generators, the energy that went into them would not be available for overcoming the friction of the air and the ground. Some fraction of the energy that goes from you to the generators could be transferred as electricity to the motor, but even if there were no losses whatever, the generator-motor combination would simply be a more complicated method of transferring energy from you to the bike.

The principle of conservation of energy contains two major ideas. One is that energy comes in many different forms. The other is that energy cannot be created or destroyed, but only converted from one form to others. If the amount of energy in one form increases, it does so at the expense of that in another form. The potential and kinetic energies that we discussed earlier in this chapter are two forms of

How has artist M.C. Escher managed to defy the principle of energy conservation here?

what is called **mechanical energy**. Heat is another form of energy that we have mentioned from time to time. We must take now a more careful look at this form; for, a satisfactory grasp of the principle of energy conservation only occurred when scientists in the nineteenth century realized that heat was a form of energy.

If you accept the principle of energy conservation, then for heat to be a form of energy, it must be true that whenever x J of mechanical energy is converted into heat, the same "amount" of heat is always obtained. The amount of heat that is transferred to an object is measured by the mass of the object, the rise in its temperature, and the nature of its material. Careful experimentation has shown that if 1000 J of energy are absorbed by 100 g of water, the temperature rise of the water is close to 2.4°C. The regularity of this relation between heat and other forms of energy has been demonstrated many times since the first such experiments were performed by James Joule in the 1840s. Today, scientists in all fields base energy calculations on their assurance of the equivalence of every form of energy. The conservation of energy is one of the major foundations of scientific investigation.

Thus, energy is conserved when you work to maintain a constant speed on your bicycle. Friction with the road and the air results in the transfer of energy from you and the bike into heat energy. And, when you brake to stop your bike, the friction of the brakes on the wheel-rims transforms the kinetic energy of you and the bike into heat energy.

> The amount of energy that is needed to raise the temperature of 1.0000 g of pure water by 1.0000°C is 4.1868 J.

AN AUTOMOBILE TRIP

Many of the ideas of this chapter can now be brought together for an energy analysis of a simple automobile trip. Starting from some basic information about the trip, we can calculate energies, powers, and the efficiency of the operation of the engine. A trip of 300 km at a speed of 90 km/h will take

$$\Delta t = \frac{\Delta d}{v} = \frac{300 \text{ km}}{90 \text{ km/h}} = 3.33 \text{ h} = 1.2 \times 10^4 \text{ s.}$$

The speed of 90 km/h is the same as 25 m/s.

Initially, the auto takes 9.0 s to get to a speed of 25 m/s. The mass of the auto is 1650 kg. The rate of gasoline consumption is 15 L/100 km. The potential energy of gasoline is about 3.6×10^7 J/L. The frictional forces of the road and air and in the mechanical connections total 1.2×10^3 N. At the end of the trip, the brakes are jammed on, bringing the car to a stop in 4.0 s.

(1) Consider first the main part of the trip at a constant speed of 25 m/s. The major energy utilization during the trip was that expended by the engine in overcoming the frictional forces. The engine had to exert a force of 1.2×10^3 N over a distance of 3.0×10^5 m. Hence, the energy transferred to heat by friction was

$$E = F\Delta d = (1.2 \times 10^3 \text{ N}) (3.0 \times 10^5 \text{ m}) = 3.6 \times 10^8 \text{ J}.$$

(2) The amount of gasoline consumed was

$$\frac{15 \text{ L}}{100 \text{ km}} \times 300 \text{ km} = 45 \text{ L}.$$

The energy content of 45 L of gasoline is

$$3.6 \times 10^7 \frac{\text{J}}{\text{L}} \times 45 \text{ L} = 1.6 \times 10^9 \text{ J}.$$

The fraction of that energy that was used to supply the force to overcome friction is the *efficiency* of the engine:

$$\text{efficiency} = \frac{3.6 \times 10^8 \text{ J}}{1.6 \times 10^9 \text{ J}} = 0.22 = 22\%.$$

Only 22% of the energy from the gasoline was used in overcoming friction. The rest went directly to heat. Of course, all the energy to drive the engine also ended up as heat. But while that happened, the car carried its passengers a distance of 300 km.

(3) The *useful* energy was that needed to keep the car moving. The power (P) of the engine to do that can be calculated:

$$P = \frac{E}{t} = \frac{3.6 \times 10^8 \text{ J}}{1.2 \times 10^4 \text{ s}} = 3.0 \times 10^4 \text{ W}.$$

The engine operated at 30 kW during the trip.

(4) Auto engines have generally much greater powers than 30 kW. The extra power is used during acceleration. Here, the additional energy in getting the 1650 kg auto to 25 m/s in 9.0 s can be found:

$$E = \tfrac{1}{2} mv^2 = \tfrac{1}{2}(1650 \text{ kg})(25 \text{ m/s})^2 = 5.2 \times 10^5 \text{ J}.$$

And the power to do that is

$$P = \frac{E}{t} = \frac{5.2 \times 10^5 \text{ J}}{9.0 \text{ s}} = 5.8 \times 10^4 \text{ W}.$$

The power required in the acceleration was 58 kW. Since resistance is somewhat less at lower speeds, we might suppose that an additional 20 kW was needed by the engine to overcome friction during the acceleration. Thus, a total power of about 78 kW was the rate of energy expenditure by the engine during acceleration.

(5) As long as the car is travelling at 25 m/s, it maintains a kinetic energy of 5.2×10^5 J. This is about half a megajoule, and hence negligible compared to the 360 MJ required for the main part of the trip. Nevertheless, that 0.52 MJ has to be absorbed in the brakes and converted to heat when the car is stopped. Thus, the power of the brakes is

$$P = \frac{E}{t} = \frac{5.2 \times 10^5 \text{ J}}{4.0 \text{ s}} = 1.3 \times 10^5 \text{ W}.$$

The brakes have to be able to take up the heat energy at the rate of 130 kW. The materials of the brakes must be such that they can withstand the temperatures that are produced.

THE LONG AND THE SHORT OF ENERGY

"Energy makes the world go round" is a *false* statement. For there is a rotational inertia that applies to spinning objects in the same way that linear inertia applies to arrows or ice pucks. The earth just keeps on rotating by itself. However, if by "world" you mean human activities, or the incessant motions of atoms, then "energy" certainly is the word to use. In this section, we will examine the use to which the idea of energy is put in two important areas. In the first, we will consider some of the dimensions of the present world-wide concern about the supplies of energy for use by people. That will involve amounts of energy in excess of exajoules (EJ). For the second, energy amounts even tinier than attojoules (aJ) are used to describe interactions among the atoms of which matter is composed.

1 EJ = 10^{18} J, and 1 aJ = 10^{-18} J.

Table 6-1

Basic life-style of population	Daily energy use per person
Hunting	2×10^7 J
Agricultural	1×10^8 J
Industrial	3×10^8 J
Technological	9×10^8 J

SUPPLYING THE WORLD'S ENERGY NEEDS

The daily energy supply per person in a primitive hunting community is about 2×10^7 J (Table 6-1). As technology has advanced, the rate of use of energy has greatly increased. From small wood fires, mankind has advanced to electrical heating derived from large nuclear installations. At the present time in Canada, the average use of energy per person is about 9×10^8 J each day, or 3×10^{11} J each year. And approximately 80% of that energy comes from petroleum and natural gas. What are the prospects for the future?

FACTORS TO BE CONSIDERED

There are four basic ingredients in any thinking about energy policies:

1. the average rate of energy use per person
2. the number of people
3. the quantity of energy available in the sources of supply

4. the efficiency of the utilization of the sources in producing energy in useful forms.

If we consider each of these items in turn, we can discover some of the major concerns that are being expressed about energy supplies today.

1. Energy use

Taking into account all industrial, heating, and transportation uses in Canada, energy is being extracted from its sources at the rate of about 3×10^{11} J per person each year. And that rate is increasing. Because of the continuing increases in the use of energy to make life more comfortable, our rate of energy use has been doubling every fifteen years or so. By about 1995, Canada's annual energy bill is expected by many to be about 6×10^{11} J per person.

The present average annual energy consumption on a world-wide basis is about one-fifth of Canada's rate, or about 6×10^{10} J per person. That rate includes more than a billion people whose energy consumption is less than a twentieth of ours in Canada.

2. Population

What would you consider to be a reasonable projection of energy use on a world-wide basis for 1995? Will the gap between rich and poor nations increase, or will it be narrowed? What the world-wide average will be then can only, of course, be a guess. Let us suppose that an all-out effort is made to improve the world rate to one-third of Canada's by 1995—i.e., to 2×10^{11} J/person. Canada's present population is about 2.3×10^7. In 15 years time it may grow to about 2.8×10^7. The present world population is about 4×10^9. At present rates of increase it will be close to 6×10^9 by 1995.

The total energy requirement is the product of the rate of use by the population size. If both factors are increasing, then the product will increase even faster. Table 6-2 shows these products, with the energy values rounded to one digit. The world use of energy in 1995 by our figures would be

$$6 \times 10^9 \text{ persons} \times 2 \times 10^{11} \text{ J/person} = 1 \times 10^{21} \text{ J.}$$

Of course, any increase of this magnitude would require gigantic investments of effort, even if we only consider the expansion in energy transformation facilities that would be needed.

3. The energy supply

Where will the required energy come from? Many mammoth studies are being carried out to find answers to that question. The current major fuel supplies are petroleum and natural gas. How much is there left underground, and how much effort will it take to get it all out? The amount of available energy left to be exploited is estimated

Table 6-2

ONE ESTIMATE OF ENERGY CONSUMPTIONS

	Population	Energy per person	Total energy
1977			
Canada	2.3×10^7	3×10^{11} J	7×10^{18} J
World	4×10^9	6×10^{10} J	2×10^{20} J
1995			
Canada	2.8×10^7	6×10^{11} J	2×10^{19} J
World	6×10^9	2×10^{11} J	1×10^{21} J

This amount is five times the present annual world use of energy.

to range from 10^{22} J to 10^{23} J. If the lower estimate is correct, these fuels could supply the world at the projected 1995 rate for 10 years.

The energy available in the known coal reserves may be as much as ten to twenty times greater than in petroleum and natural gas. However, a lot of new industry would have to be created to be able to mine the coal without ruining large tracts of land, and to use the coal in devices that now depend on petroleum products.

If you like "clean" energy, you might prefer hydroelectric plants. But that source is limited by the amount of waterflow that can be efficiently developed. The world maximum is estimated to be capable of producing about 10^{20} J annually—only 10% of what might be needed.

Nuclear energy is seen by many as the only hope to enable industry to expand and to increase the comforts of life throughout the world. Some of the concerns about the disposal of highly radioactive wastes are described in Chapter 23.

Since the sun is the actual original source of much of our current energy supplies, many people think that a large effort should be put into finding out how to make more use of solar radiation. The amount of energy that reaches the earth in a year from the sun is about 1×10^{24} J. That energy can be used to grow crops to produce fuels that can be burned. Or it might be converted directly into electrical energy. There is also the possibility of storing solar energy in the form of heat (say in large water tanks) until it is needed at a later time.

In all these instances it should be obvious that much effort and enterprise would be needed in order to meet the increasing energy demands of an increasing population.

These students are building a house designed to be heated by solar energy.

4. Efficiency

Instead of putting all our efforts into finding reliable energy sources, some people are beginning to suggest that we could make much better use of energy than we now do. For example, the insulation of homes can be improved by as much as 50%. If this were done, a Canadian population of 40 million would need no more energy for home heating than is used today.

At the present time in Canada, transportation accounts for about 30% of our annual energy use. That makes it an attractive area in which to effect improvements. Mass transportation is much more energy-efficient than private automobiles. If such systems were made convenient enough, many people might be willing to save the family car for pleasure driving. Savings can also be made by using smaller cars and more efficient engines.

Examples of this sort can be multiplied endlessly. However, you should know that many energy conversion processes create unwanted heat, which cannot be avoided. Engines that transform chemical potential energy in fuels into kinetic energy are not able to change *all* the heat energy into kinetic energy. Even in the most efficient engines, more than 50% of the heat produced when the fuel burns remains in the form of heat energy. The more such processes are used, the greater is the heat load that is put on the environment.

One of the important tasks for the future is to find ways to channel the waste heat into places which need to be heated. Dumping the heat into the air and into rivers and lakes is more than simply wasteful. It can also produce ecological problems.

One way to reduce heat waste is to use the hot water from thermal-electric generating stations to heat buildings.

OPTIMISTS AND PESSIMISTS

You should be able to conclude from the above discussion that any energy policy for Canada or the world will have to involve trade-offs. How much of our effort and resources should be devoted to each of the various programs that will help to maintain the quality of life? One such program includes the exploration for accessible reserves of uranium and fossil fuels, and improvement in the methods of extracting them. Another program involves research into methods for making use of *renewable* energy sources—how can solar energy be tapped effectively? Still another program involves the variety of ways in which energy can be used more efficiently.

Among those who are studying energy resources and energy utilization, there are optimists and pessimists. However, both of those groups agree that a very large effort is required to be able to guarantee a continuing supply of energy for the human population. Some optimists think that the world can sustain a population that is 4 times greater than at present. For the year 2080 they project a world-wide annual energy use that is about 10 times that for 1980. That would mean $10/4 = 2.5$ times the present energy use per person. However, the optimists also expect a tripling in the efficiency of energy production and use. That would be equivalent to people being on the average $3 \times 2.5 = 8$ times better off for energy than at present.

Others question the capacity of the earth to sustain such a large population. They believe that the world population should level off at about 8×10^9 people, or fewer. They put a strong emphasis on conserving energy, including improved efficiencies of the transformation processes. However, that could require some change in life-style, as we become increasingly conscious of the need not to continue to make extravagant demands on the earth's resources. Every conceivable form of recycling would be used to reduce wastage of materials and energy resources. Pessimists can conceive an annual world-wide energy use for 2080 that is no more than 4 times that at present. With a population only double the present one, that represents $4/2 = 2$ times the present energy use per person. The pessimists also conceive a possible doubling of efficiency (primarily in the use of energy rather than in its production)—so they can foresee a world-wide average improvement that is $2 \times 2 = 4$ times the present per person use of energy.

Compared to the optimists' projections, for a population 50% as

On page 40 of the September 1971 issue of *Scientific American*, Chauncey Starr wrote: "It is evident that the present rate of world population growth cannot be sustained indefinitely; sooner or later environmental restrictions will cause the death rate to increase substantially, and the least developed countries will be the first to suffer. The long-term alternative for the world is a controlled birthrate. Nevertheless, for some decades to come social trends will cause an inevitable increase in world population. In order to meet not only the food requirements but also a minimally reasonable quality of life, the contributions that can be made by the use of energy in various forms are essential. The issue therefore is *not* whether energy production for the world should be increased. It is rather how to increase it effectively with minimum deleterious side effects."

Earl Cook on page 144 wrote: "Major changes in power technology will be required to reduce pollution and manage wastes, to improve the efficiency of the system and to remove the resource-availability constraint. Making the changes will call for hard political decisions. Energy needs will have to be weighed against environmental and social costs; a decision to set a pollution standard or to ban the internal-combustion engine or to finance nuclear-power development can have major economic and political effects. Democratic societies are not noted for their ability to take the long view in making decisions. Yet indefinite growth in energy consumption, as in human population, is simply not possible."

On page 49 Chauncey Starr wrote: "Perhaps the most fundamental question of national policy is how we should allocate our present resources for the benefit of future generations. The development of new speculative energy resources is an investment for the future, not a means of remedying the problems of today. It is equally clear that the quality of life of the peoples of the world depends on the availability *now* of large amounts of low-cost energy in useful form. This being so, we must emphasize an orderly development of the resources available to us with present technology, and these are primarily power plants based on fossil fuels and nuclear fission."

large, pessimists can see 50% of the optimists' improvement by 2080 for 40% of the total energy developed per year.

Both these projections to 2080 require large efforts in technological improvement—in finding new energy sources, in building the plants to utilize them, and in improved efficiency. In other respects, they differ on where to allocate resources and research, and on how to try to influence people's attitudes. Pessimists seek population controls, while optimists think population will level off by itself. Pessimists stress efficiencies in energy use, and an increase in attitudes of conservation of natural resources, while optimists tend to put more faith in exotic technology. Of course, there are also extreme optimists who think that things will take care of themselves; and extreme pessimists who think that human attitudes and technology cannot possibly change fast enough to avert a world-wide decline in living standards.

A sample of ideas about the issues involved is given in the accompanying quotations from the "Energy and Power" issue of *Scientific American*, September 1971. Debate will continue on these matters, and the decisions that are made will affect your life. What will you do about that?

(a)

FIG. 6-4. (a) The tip of a fine tungsten needle magnified one million times.

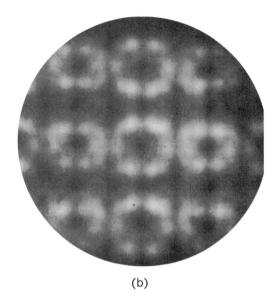

(b)

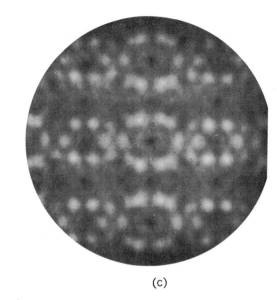

(c)

MECHANICAL ATOMS AND HEAT

The basic atomic model for matter is supported on a broad base of experimental evidence (Fig. 6-4). Without going into that evidence in detail, we can examine the main structure of the model and the energy relations it involves. The model can be called mechanical because the actions at the atomic level will be described in terms of kinetic and potential energies, and of forces. We will not enquire into the nature of the forces.

Consider a small bar of copper. If its temperature is raised, the bar will expand. At a high enough temperature, about 1100°C, the solid bar will melt into a pool of liquid copper. At a much higher temperature, about 2600°C, the liquid will boil. The liquid will be dispersed into a vapour. How can the mechanical-atomic model account for these changes?

The atomic model of matter pictures copper as consisting of large numbers of tiny atoms. The atoms in the model have a diameter of about 2×10^{-10} m, and a mass of about 1×10^{-25} kg. The atoms are always in motion. According to the mechanical theory of heat, the temperature of a collection of atoms is directly proportional to the average kinetic energy of the atoms. In the vapour state the atoms will be moving in all sorts of directions, and colliding from time to time. They will have a wide variety of speeds and kinetic energies. The many collisions will mean that any one atom will change its kinetic energy frequently.

The average kinetic energy of atoms (or molecules) in gases and vapours at room temperature has an order of magnitude of 10^{-21} J. (Room temperature is approximately 300 K.) At double the temperature (600 K = 327°C), the average kinetic energy of the atoms will be doubled.

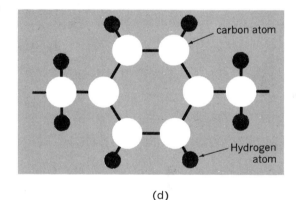

(d)

FIG. 6-4. (b) X-ray picture of xylylene molecules at 20°C. (c) X-ray picture of xylylene molecules at −190°C showing diminished atomic vibration. (d) Chemist's structural diagram of the xylylene molecule.

Degrees Celsius are the same size as kelvins, but 0.00°C = 273.15 K.

To double the kinetic energy requires a speed that is greater by $\sqrt{2} = 1.414$.

In the atomic model, solid copper consists of atoms packed together in an orderly array (Fig. 6-5). Each atom is held in place by forces of attraction exerted by the other atoms. The centres of the atoms are located at distances of approximately 2×10^{-10} m from one another. These atoms cannot move very far, but they are vibrating with frequencies of approximately 5×10^{12} Hz. The distance of vibration is much smaller than the distance between the atoms, perhaps about 1/40 as much. That makes the dimensions of the back and forth motion about 5×10^{-12} m. The force that pulls the atoms back has an average value of about 5×10^{-10} N. The work that is done by that force over such a distance is a measure of the *vibrational energy:*

$$E = F\Delta d = (5 \times 10^{-10} \text{ N})(5 \times 10^{-12} \text{ m}) = 2 \times 10^{-21} \text{ J (approx.)}.$$

The values given here are only very rough approximations. However, they show that the vibrational energy of atoms in the solid state are of the same order of magnitude as the kinetic energies of atoms in gases at the same temperature.

The usual way to raise the temperature of the copper bar is to put it in contact with some object at a higher temperature. The energies of atoms in that object (say a flame) will be greater than those of the copper. The impacts from the particles in the flame will transfer energy to the copper atoms. As a result, the atoms will vibrate over greater distances, making the copper bar expand.

When the atoms are vibrating over distances about 1/10 of their distance apart, they have enough energy to overcome the forces that are holding them together in a regular arrangement. For vibration distances of about 2×10^{-11} m, the force is about 2×10^{-9} N, making the vibrational energy about 4×10^{-20} J. This energy is available to work against the forces of attraction within the solid. When that work is done, the atoms are in the liquid state. Their *kinetic* energy will not be greater in the liquid than in the solid at the same temperature. However, their *potential* energy has been increased because of the work done against the force. The potential energy needed to convert the solid to liquid is called the *latent heat of fusion.* It is "latent" because it does not show up as kinetic energy.

As the temperature of the molten copper is increased, the atoms gain more and more energy. In order for the liquid to be vaporized, enough energy must be supplied to separate the atoms to distances of several diameters, say 1×10^{-9} m. The energy required to move an atom that distance against a force of about 1×10^{-9} N is 1×10^{-18} J. And that is a reasonable approximation of the value of the *latent heat of vaporization* per atom for copper.

This picture of the mechanical-atomic model for matter has been painted with broad, rough strokes. It has not attempted to explain why temperature remains constant during changes of state. However, you should get the basic idea of the place of kinetic and potential energies in the description of the model. More kinetic energy means

1 Hz = 1 s⁻¹ (one cycle per second).

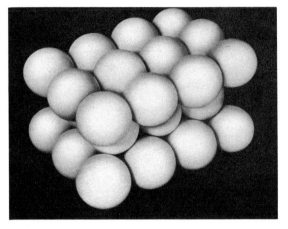

FIG. 6-5

Latent is derived from the Latin verb *latere*, meaning to lie hidden.

that the atoms move faster—the temperature increases. More potential energy means that the atoms have been moved farther apart against a force of attraction—the state of matter can thereby change from solid to liquid, or from liquid to vapour (Fig. 6-6).

Finally, you should begin to get some feeling for atomic dimensions. Distances are expressed as fractions of nanometres (or from 5 to 1000 picometres). Forces have the general order of magnitude of nanonewtons. Energies range from one to a few thousandths of attojoules. And frequencies of vibration are expressed in units of terahertz.

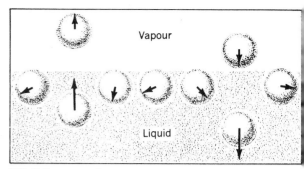

FIG. 6-6

FIG. 6-7: A NOTE ON RELATIVITY

According to the basic formula for kinetic energy, $E_k = \frac{1}{2}mv^2$, the energy of an object is directly proportional to the square of the speed of the object. Thus, the graph of v^2 against E should be a straight line. It is, but only as long as the speed is less than about one-tenth of the speed of light. Beyond that, as more energy is supplied, v^2 will increase more slowly than in direct proportion to the energy.

This effect was predicted theoretically by Albert Einstein in 1905. It was part of his *special theory of relativity*, in which he assumed that the speed of light does not change with the motions of the sources or observers of light. For very high speeds, the ideas of relative motion that we described in

Chapter 3 are subject to the limitation that no speed greater than that of light can be achieved.

The correctness of the solid line on the graph has been amply confirmed by experiments with electrons and other particles. When electrons are given high speeds in particle accelerators, their energy is related to their speed as shown on the graph. The dashed line shows the relation to be expected from $E_k = \frac{1}{2}m_0v^2$, where m_0 is the mass of the electron at rest. The solid line shows that v^2 increases progressively more slowly as more energy is supplied to the electrons. This implies that mass in fact increases with energy and speed. The speed of light in a vacuum, 3.00×10^8 m/s, is the universal speed limit for matter.

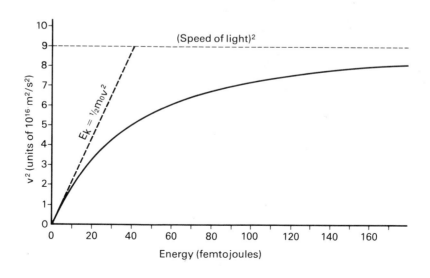

Exercises

A

1. Give several examples for each of the following situations, in which there is
   (a) displacement but no force (and therefore no work is done),
   (b) force but no displacement (and therefore no work is done),
   (c) force at right angles to the displacement (and therefore no work is done),
   (d) force and displacement along the same line (and therefore work *is* done).

2. For each of the following situations, state what form of energy is being transformed into what other form of energy:
   (a) A curling stone is slowing as it slides along the ice.
   (b) After the firing pin of a rifle strikes the shell, the bullet is accelerated along the barrel.
   (c) A baseball is slowing after being hit straight up.
   (d) An electric stove is turned on.
   (e) A skydiver is falling at constant speed.

3. List in order the various forms of energy that are involved in each of the following actions:
   (a) A box of sand suspended vertically by a rope from a tree branch begins to swing when struck by a rifle bullet.
   (b) Water falls through large pipes to drive turbines connected to electric generators which supply energy to electric lamps.
   (c) A railway engine is driven by electric motors supplied by electric generators that are driven by oil-fueled diesel engines.
   (d) Life on earth depends on nuclear processes in the sun.
   (e) After eating a hearty meal, Jean played an inspiring game of hockey.

4. In a soccer game a foot exerted an average force of 140 N on the ball, and was in contact with the ball over a distance of 0.50 m. Calculate the energy imparted by the foot to the ball.

5. Starting off on a trip to the moon, the first stage of a Saturn V rocket exerted an average force of 3.3×10^7 N over a distance of 1.3×10^5 m. Calculate the energy imparted to the rocket.

6. (a) In a hard clearing shot, a hockey defenceman applies an average force of 150 N over a distance of 0.80 m. How much energy does he impart to the puck?
   (b) If a slap-shot acts on the puck over a distance of 0.10 m, how large must the average force be to impart the same amount of energy to the puck as in part (a)?

7. On a trip of 80 km, a motorcycle motor does 3.0×10^7 J of work against frictional forces. What is the average frictional force?

8. The energy content of the food for one day in a substantial diet is 1.5×10^7 J. On a bicycle trip a cyclist exerts an average force of 50 N to overcome frictional resistance. How far could the cyclist travel if all the energy of one day's meals was expended in cycling? Express your answer in kilometres.

9. You can get some idea of the energies involved in sporting activities from the following data. In the throwing events, of course, energy is also expended in moving part or all of the body in the process of throwing the object. The data provided are based on recent records for most of the events. In each instance calculate the kinetic energy.
   (a) A curling stone of mass 18 kg leaves the skip's hand at a speed of 4.0 m/s.
   (b) Nolan Ryan pitched a baseball of mass 0.15 kg at a speed of 45 m/s.
   (c) Bobby Hull's slap-shot gave a 0.16 kg hockey puck a speed of 53 m/s.
   (d) Ivanka Khristova put the 4.0 kg shot with an initial speed of 15 m/s.
   (e) Mac Wilkins threw the 2.0 kg discus with an initial speed of 26 m/s.
   (f) Walter Schmidt threw the 7.2 kg hammer with a speed of 28 m/s.
   (g) Bob Beamon (assumed to have a mass of about 70 kg) took off from the board of a long jump pit with a speed 9.3 m/s.

10. The energy required to accelerate a train from zero to 40 m/s (neglecting frictional resistance) is 1.2×10^8 J. Calculate the mass of the train.

11. The explosive charge of a particular cannon can supply 1.8×10^8 J of energy to the projectile. What mass of projectile can that amount of energy accelerate to a speed of 1.5×10^3 m/s?

12. In an accelerator in a physics laboratory, a particle supplied with 4.1×10^{-14} J of energy achieves a speed of 7.0×10^6 m/s. What is the mass of the particle?

13. When a softball pitcher supplies 81 J of energy to the 0.18 kg ball, with what speed does the ball leave her hand?

14. A coconut of mass 0.80 kg is growing 30 m above the ground in its palm tree. The tree is just at the edge of a cliff that is 50 m above the sea. Calculate the gravitational potential energy of the coconut relative to (a) ground level, (b) sea level.

15. The major electrical generating stations on the Niagara River make use of a 90 m drop through penstocks and turbines to the river at Queenston-Lewis-

ton. Calculate (a) the potential energy that is available from 1 kg of water that falls through a penstock; (b) the energy available to each generator in one second from a water flow of 1.0×10^5 kg/s.

16. To make measurements in the upper atmosphere a Black Brant rocket delivers an instrument package of 27 kg mass to a height of 148 km above the earth's surface. Using 9.6 m/s² as the average value for g, calculate the gravitational potential energy of the instrument package at its maximum altitude.

17. Neglecting air resistance, calculate how high a baseball of mass 0.15 kg could be thrown straight up with an energy of 100 J.

18. Little John can supply 80 J of energy to an arrow. What is the maximum mass that he can deliver to the window 50 m above him in the tower where Robin Hood is imprisoned?

19. Many single actions in sports require about the same amount of energy, but occupy differing time intervals. Thus, the actions differ in their power or rate of doing work. Calculate the power for each of the following, on the basis that each action has an energy of 100 J:
    (a) The swing of a curling stone takes 0.80 s.
    (b) A baseball pitch takes 0.25 s.
    (c) A tennis racket is in contact with the ball for 0.030 s.

20. Calculate the power exerted by Vasili Alexeev in lifting 254 kg through a height of 1.2 m in a time of 1.5 s. (This is from squatting position with the masses at shoulder level to the upright position with arms extended over the head.)

21. Neglecting air resistance, what is the power required by a 1.2×10^3 kg auto to accelerate from zero to 20 m/s in 6.0 s?

22. Working at a rate of 100 W, the gardener took 20.0 min to cut the lawn. How much energy did he expend?

23. When Al Fudd set out in his motorboat on that fateful foggy day his fuel tank contained fuel with an energy content amounting to 3.6×10^8 J. His motor consumed fuel at the rate of 75 kW. For how long would the motor continue to run? Express your answer in minutes.

24. How much electrical energy is used by a 100 W electric lamp operating for 10 min?

B

25. An iron shot of mass 4.0 kg is dropped from a height of 125 m above the ground. The distance fallen at the end of each second is shown in the following table:

Time (s)	0	1.0	2.0	3.0	4.0	5.0
Distance (m)	0	5.0	20.0	45.0	80.0	125.0

Construct a table of seven columns and six rows. Put the values for time and distance fallen in the first two columns. Then calculate the following quantities (using $g = 10$ m/s²) and put their values in the other columns:
    (a) the height above the ground at each time,
    (b) the potential energy of the shot at each time,
    (c) the speed acquired by the falling shot at each time, neglecting air resistance ($v = g\Delta t$),
    (d) the kinetic energy of the shot at each time,
    (e) the total energy of the shot at each time.
Is total energy conserved during the fall?

26. A rubber-band slingshot (or catapult) shoots a stone of mass 0.025 kg. Calculate the speed with which the stone leaves the catapult when it is released after having been pulled back a distance of 0.15 m by an average force of 27 N. Neglect the mass of the rubber band.

27. A hockey puck hits the crossbar of the net and bounces straight up with a speed of 14 m/s. What height will the puck reach before starting to fall? (The mass of the puck is 0.16 kg. However, see if you can perform the calculations with x for the mass. Does the answer depend on the mass of the puck?)

28. Terry Lemus of mass 60 kg starts her trapeze act on a platform 20.0 m above the safety net. She is holding the bar of the trapeze so that its 5.0 m ropes are stretched taut horizontally.
    (a) Calculate Terry's gravitational potential energy with respect to the level of the net.
    (b) Terry then steps off the platform and swings down until the trapeze ropes are vertical. At that moment, what is her height above the net? What is her gravitational potential energy relative to the net?
    (c) At the bottom of the swing what are Terry's kinetic energy and speed?
    (d) Just at the bottom of the swing Terry's hands slip and she falls to the net. With what kinetic energy and speed will she strike the net?

29. On the midway you can win a prize if the bell rings when you strike a wooden block with a 10.0 kg hammer. The block is at one end of a lever, the other end of which drives a metal bar of mass 2.0 kg up a slide to ring the bell 9.0 m above. With what speed must the hammer strike the block in order to make the bar hit the bell?

30. The energy content of gasoline is 3.6×10^7 J/L. However, only 20% of this energy is used to drive an outboard motor. How many litres of gasoline would be needed to drive a 45 kW motor at full power for 50.0 min?

31. An auto of mass 1.2×10^3 kg is equipped with hydraulic bumpers that will bring it to a stop without damage in a distance of 0.60 m, from a speed of 3.0 m/s. What must be the average force exerted by the hydraulic system?

32. A bob of mass 2.0 kg is suspended on a cord 15.0 m long. It is pulled aside to make an angle of 14.3° with the vertical. When the bob is released, it will swing through an arc of length 7.5 m to the opposite side in a time of 3.9 s. Make a scale drawing of the pendulum so that you can measure the vertical height of the bob's highest position from its lowest. Then, calculate
  (a) the gravitational potential energy of the bob at its maximum height relative to its lowest point,
  (b) the speed of the bob at its lowest point,
  (c) the average speed of the bob in its swing from one side to the other,
  (d) the ratio of the maximum speed of the bob to its average speed.

33. To maintain a circular orbit at a height of 180 km above the earth's surface a satellite must travel at a constant speed of 7.8×10^3 m/s. In the range from the earth's surface to a height of 180 km, the average value of g is 9.5 m/s². For a satellite of mass 1.0×10^3 kg, calculate
  (a) the gravitational potential energy at a height of 180 km,
  (b) the kinetic energy at its speed of 7.8×10^3 m/s,
  (c) the total energy of the satellite.

34. A very large steam-driven turbine system drives two electric generators, which combine to produce electricity at the rate of 1.2 GW. In each 24 h period the system consumes 9.6×10^3 t of coal, which in burning produces heat energy of 2.7×10^{10} J/t. Calculate the efficiency of the system's conversion of energy from heat to electricity.

C

35. On a test track, a rocket-powered sled of average mass 3.6×10^3 kg achieved an average horizontal acceleration of 250 m/s² during the 4.0 s that the rocket motor operated.
  (a) Calculate the speed and kinetic energy achieved by the sled.
  (b) Calculate the average force (thrust) of the rocket motor, and the distance travelled during the 4.0 s burn.
  (c) The test track is 6.0×10^3 m long. What is the total length of time required for the sled to reach the end of the track?

36. During the operation of the first stage of a rocket, the average mass was 5.0×10^4 kg. Fired vertically, its motor provided a force of 2.5×10^6 N for 10.0 s. (Use $g = 10$ m/s².)
  (a) Calculate the height and velocity of the rocket at the moment the motor ceased operation.
  (b) If the next operations (separation of first stage and firing of second stage) malfunctioned, for how long would the rocket continue to climb, and what maximum height would it reach before starting to fall back to earth?

37. To lift off from the moon, astronauts used a lunar module of average mass 2.5×10^3 kg, with a fuel load that could provide them with 4.0×10^9 J of energy. To rejoin the command module in orbit they had to achieve a speed of at least 1.6×10^3 m/s. With $g = 1.6$ m/s² near the moon, what maximum height above the moon could the command module have been without having the lunar explorers miss it?

38. For a particular hunting bow, the force (F) of the draw can be expressed as $F = (700 \text{ N/m})d$, where d is the distance through which the string is pulled. For a combined mass of arrow and bow-tips of 0.091 kg, how far must the bow be drawn to achieve a speed at release of 50 m/s?

39. Electrons have a mass of 9.11×10^{-31} kg, and protons 1.67×10^{-27} kg. What is the speed of a proton that has the same kinetic energy as an electron travelling at 3.00×10^6 m/s?

40. For speeds greater than one-seventh of the speed of light, the formula, $E_k = \frac{1}{2} mv^2$, gives values that are too small by 1% or more. The variations are shown on the graph of Fig. 6-7. Use that graph to answer these questions.
  (a) For an electron of kinetic energy 40 fJ, find its (speed)² and then its speed.
  (b) If an electron has a speed of 2.0×10^8 m/s, what is its kinetic energy?
  (c) At what speed is the kinetic energy of an electron double that expected from the formula, $\frac{1}{2} mv^2$?
  (d) This graph applies to all kinds of matter. Since the mass of an electron at rest is 9.1×10^{-31} kg, what is the kinetic energy of an object having a rest mass of 1.0 kg travelling at a speed that is 88% of the speed of light?

41. (a) Estimate the power of a housefly, based on the following assumptions. The fly has a mass of 0.1 g and exerts a force that is triple the force of gravity on it in order to fly straight up a distance of 10 m in 3 s.
  (b) For how long could the fly operate at that power if it ate food of mass equal to its own mass, with the food supplying energy at the rate of 10^7 J/kg, and an efficiency of transformation into flight of 20%?

42. Estimate the amount of fuel energy that would be needed to put 10^6 people into an orbit about the earth and sustain their life for 10^3 d (three years). The mass of fuel needed to get each kilogram of payload into orbit is 10^2 kg, and the energy content of the fuel is about 10^8 J/kg. For the mass going into orbit, assume 10^2 kg per person (including personal belongings); 10^3 kg per person for equipment (including the space vessel itself); and a food supply that provides each person with 10^7 J/d of energy, coming from materials that provide 10^7 J/kg of energy per mass of substance. Add 10^2 kg of water per person, which will be continually recycled. No extra allowance is made for energy in orbit on the assumption that electricity will be generated from solar energy.

Although we have calculated a result from these data, you could get a different result if you altered some of the data to values you consider more reason-able. Then, you might wish to judge the feasibility of this method of overcoming the population problem on earth. You could try to consider adjustments needed to make the colony self-sustaining for centuries; and you might want to add in estimates of the energy required to assemble all the materials needed for the expedition.

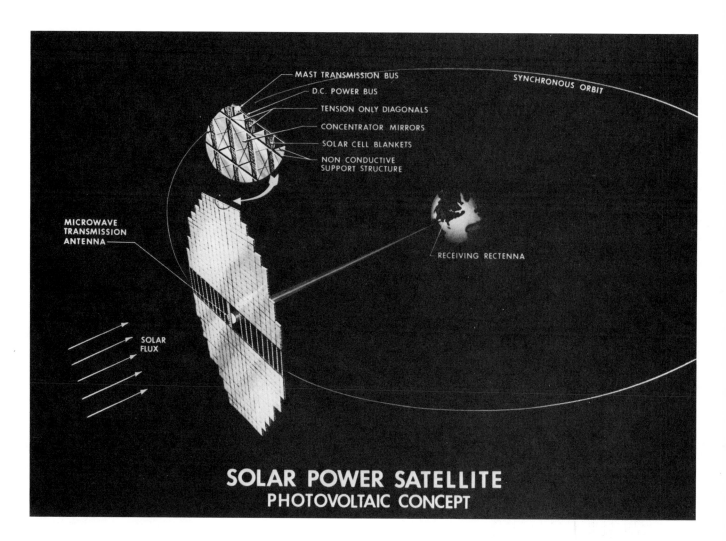

MAST TRANSMISSION BUS
D.C. POWER BUS
TENSION ONLY DIAGONALS
CONCENTRATOR MIRRORS
SOLAR CELL BLANKETS
NON CONDUCTIVE SUPPORT STRUCTURE

SYNCHRONOUS ORBIT

MICROWAVE TRANSMISSION ANTENNA

RECEIVING RECTENNA

SOLAR FLUX

SOLAR POWER SATELLITE
PHOTOVOLTAIC CONCEPT

Horse-carriage, steam engine, gaslight, coal stove— these were some of the ingredients of life in the pre-electric age. Today in industrialized countries electrical energy drives trains and trolley buses, powers factories, and provides light and heat to homes and offices. Even when electricity is not the main form of energy, as in oil-fired engines and furnaces, the control devices are operated by electricity. Wires and coils and transistors have replaced many of the gears and pulleys of an earlier age.

In this unit you will investigate the properties of electric forces and the units in which to measure them. With further units to measure the properties of electric currents you will be able to measure the properties of various electric circuits, and calculate the amounts of electrical energy used in devices such as stoves and stereos.

You will also study in this unit how magnetism is produced from electricity. By learning about electromagnetic forces and electromagnetic induction you will be able to understand the operation of electric meters and motors, and the generation and transmission of electrical energy.

Electricity and Energy

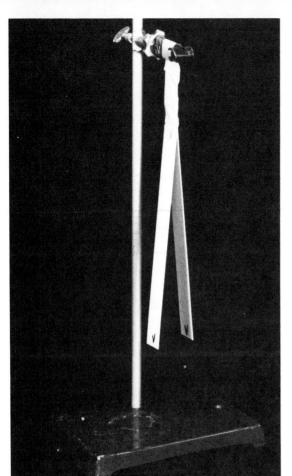

FIG. 7-1

CHAPTER **7**

Electric Forces

Forces of electric attraction show up in many places. They are particularly noticeable on cold, dry days. When you brush your hair it may spring upward towards the brush. As you pull off a woollen sweater it may tend to cling to your shirt. "Static cling" is a familiar phenomenon in clothes driers.

In contrast to gravitational forces, which are very tiny between the ordinary objects we handle, electric forces are much stronger. In addition, electric forces can be turned on and off, which cannot be done with gravity. We begin the study of electricity with an examination of some of the properties of static electric forces before considering a theory to account for them.

PROPERTIES OF ELECTRIC FORCES

Start with two light objects that can be suspended from threads. They may be two rubber balloons, or two strips of acetate. Then rub both objects with some other material. Wool would be good for rubber, and paper for acetate. As you move the two rubbed objects closer together you will find you have to push them against some force—a force of repulsion. The closer you try to bring them together, the stronger will be the repulsion. No repelling force ever shows up with gravity! The rubbing has produced a new kind of force, an electric force between electrified objects.

Two vinyl strips similarly rubbed exert a force of repulsion on each other (Fig. 7-1). Each strip is said to be *charged*. Also, two acetate strips, similarly rubbed, will repel each other. Whenever two similar objects are charged by the same process, the force between them is repulsive. But, between a charged acetate strip and a charged vinyl strip there is a force of *attraction* (Fig. 7-2). Either kind of strip will attract a wide variety of uncharged objects.

To suppose that only one kind of electrification exists would not be enough to account for both attraction and repulsion. Let us imagine two kinds of electric charge (Fig. 7-3). Call one kind **A** and the other **B**. Between two objects charged **A**, the force is repulsive. Between two objects charged **B**, the force is repulsive. This will account for the fact that between two similarly charged objects the force is al-

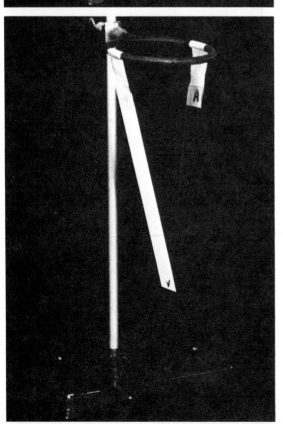

FIG. 7-2

ways repulsive. But we need two kinds of charge because two differently charged objects may attract one another. Between a charge of type **A**, and one of type **B**, there is a force of attraction.

Now, suppose a third type of charge, **C**, exists (Fig. 7-4). You can go through all the possible combinations of force that might exist between **C** and **A** or **B** and **C**, and **C**. For example, if **C** were attracted by **A** and repelled by **B**, it would mean that **C** had the same electric charge as **B**—it would be indistinguishable from **B**. The one possibility that would require a third type of charge is for **C** to attract *both* **A** and **B** and yet for **C** to repel **C**. But by trial you will find that two similar objects that attract charges of both types **A** and **B** will exert no force on each other. No other actions between charged objects are observed. You might want to call **C** a third type of charge, but it would not fit the rule that two similarly charged objects repel each other. It makes more sense to say that **C** is uncharged, or neutral.

Imagine an object made up of equal quantities of the two types of charge, **A** and **B**, all mixed up. A nearby object charged with type **A** would repel the **A**s and attract the **B**s. The two sets of forces might balance, leaving no force. This could be a model for our type **C** uncharged object; except that we know that an uncharged object is attracted by a charged one. To account for that, suppose that the **A** charge pushes away some of the **A**s in the neutral object. The result would be that in the neutral object more **B**s were closer to the charged object; and there would be a small net force of attraction.

If equal numbers of **A**s and **B**s make an object neutral, we can write

$$\mathbf{A} + \mathbf{B} = 0.$$

Then,

$$\mathbf{A} = -\mathbf{B}.$$

If a neutral object has a zero charge, then we can say that one type of charge is more positive than neutral, and the other is more negative than neutral. This is the way physicists have decided to describe electrification. Instead of the **A**s and **B**s of our preceding discussion, they use + and −. Positive charges are found on glass and acetate that have been rubbed with cloth or paper. Negative charges are found on ebonite, vinylite, and polythene that have been rubbed with cloth or paper.

To build these ideas into a satisfactory model for electrification, we need to consider some more experiences. Suspend a small piece of aluminum foil from a light thread. On a couple of glass containers support a rod or a stick of one metre length so that one end of the rod is about a centimetre from the foil. Then bring a charged object close to the opposite end of the rod (Fig. 7-5). Depending on the material of which the rod is composed you will observe an attraction of the foil to the end, and perhaps a subsequent repulsion. Use rods of different materials, including wood, plastic, and metals. The distance of the charged object from the foil is such that no effect will be seen if no rod is in place. Somehow, the electrical effect of the charged object can be transferred through the rod to the foil. This transmission is called **conduction**.

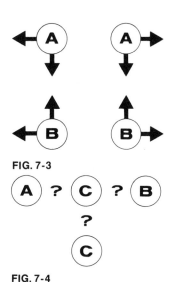

FIG. 7-3

FIG. 7-4

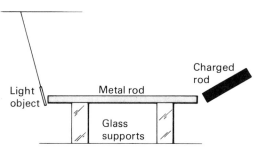

FIG. 7-5

If you shuffle your feet across a rug on a cool, dry day, you can observe a small spark when your finger is brought near a doorknob or other metal object. Sparks can also often be observed if you make momentary metallic contact between the two terminals of a flashlight battery. This provides some evidence that the static electricity we have been discussing is at least somewhat like the electricity from batteries. Sparks are less likely to be observed if you bring your finger close to non-metals, or insulators, such as glass. Evidently charges are able to move in many materials, but they move much more readily in metals. A very rough division of materials can be made between those that conduct very well and those that conduct very poorly. The poor conductors are called insulators. Metals are generally very good conductors.

A MODEL FOR ELECTRICITY

Let us summarize the basic ideas we have discussed. There are two kinds of electricity which we name *positive* and *negative*. Each kind repels its own kind, and attracts the other kind. If the two kinds of electricity are equal in an object it is neutral. Neutral objects are attracted by charged objects, whether positive or negative. At least one kind of electricity seems able to move readily in solids. It moves more easily in metallic conductors.

What we have so far is already a basic theory of electricity, since we invented the ideas of positive and negative. All that is observed in nature is a variety of motions that we see as being either attraction or repulsion. Now, we can refine the theory further, and offer a model for matter that accounts for the various electrical effects we have observed.

Many people find it easy to imagine that matter in its finest structure is composed of extremely tiny particles called atoms. However, nothing in a basic atomic theory necessarily suggests the source of electric forces. The electrical extension of the basic atomic model for matter requires that atoms have parts, some of which are positively charged and the others negatively charged. We could imagine a neutral atom having one positive part and one negative part. And initially, we have no basis for deciding whether the positive parts are easily moved, or the negative parts, or both. The following experiment is a way to find out.

The major device for this experiment is very much like a light bulb (Fig. 7-6). It is an evacuated glass globe containing a filament of tungsten. However, the filament is heated only to a dull red by a small battery. Inside the globe there is also a metal plate close to the filament, with a wire that connects it to the outside. One of the filament terminals is connected through an electric meter and a large battery to the metal plate. Depending on the way in which the large battery is connected, the plate can be made either positive or negative with respect to the filament. The meter will indicate if there is any flow of charge across the space between the filament and the plate.

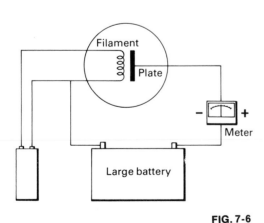

FIG. 7-6

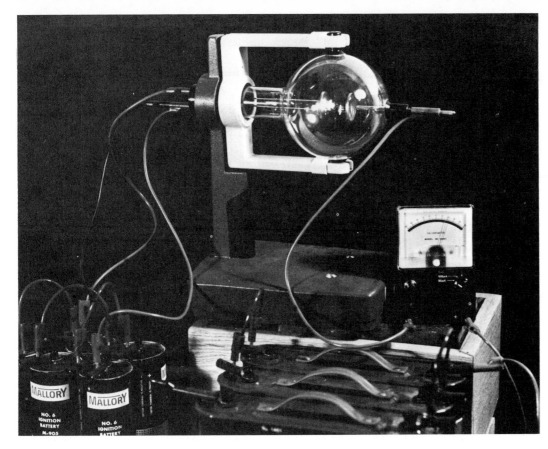

FIG. 7-7

Before the filament is heated, the large battery is connected one way and then the other between the plate and the filament. In neither case is there any reading on the meter. No net charge is passing through the space. And thus, no net charge is being emitted by either the filament or the plate.

Now, connect the small battery so that it heats the filament. Perhaps this will be a way to "boil" charged particles out of the tungsten filament. Whichever kind of charge might be boiled out, the filament would be left with a net charge of the opposite sign. The result is likely to be a "cloud" of charge surrounding the filament. If that charged cloud is positive, it should be attracted across to the plate if the plate is made negative with respect to the filament. When that is tried there is no reading on the meter.

If the charged cloud is negative, it should be attracted to the plate, when positive with respect to the filament. Try that, and the needle of the meter moves away from zero (Fig. 7-7). That indicates that a charge is now being transferred across the space. *Thus the charge that can be boiled out of a metal filament by heat is negative.*

The negatively charged particles in matter are called **electrons**. They are the ones that are most easily moved. When an electron is removed from an atom, the positive part of the atom that is left behind is called a **positive ion**—or often, just an **ion** (Fig. 7-8). Evidently the positive ions are much less easily moved than the electrons. From our study of Newton's second law, we might suggest that the ions are much more massive than the electrons.

The removal of charge from a conductor by strong heating is called *thermionic emission*. It was first noted in 1883 by Thomas Edison as he investigated the internal workings of electric lamps.

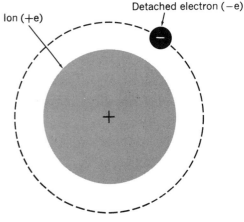

FIG. 7-8

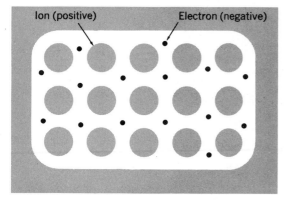

Ion (positive)   Electron (negative)

FIG. 7-9

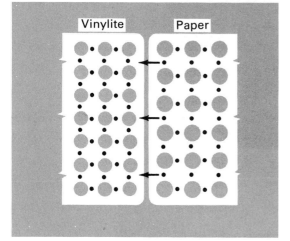

Vinylite   Paper

FIG. 7-10

Electric forces, like gravitational forces, vary inversely as the square of distance: at double distance the force is reduced to one-quarter of the original value. This relation was established experimentally by Charles Coulomb in 1785.

This experiment has been performed with filaments of many different metals, always with essentially the same results. Thus, it appears that all materials contain electrons of only one kind.

These results make it possible for us to build a satisfactory model for the electrical nature of matter (Fig. 7-9). Electrons are parts of the atoms of all materials. The charge of electrons is negative. A neutral metallic object consists of positive ions embedded in a sea of electrons.

Further, of course, we must include in the model the idea that electrons repel each other; that positive ions repel each other; and that the force between ions and electrons is one of attraction.

How will this model account for the charging process, for example when a vinylite strip is rubbed with paper? All we have to do is to suppose that the ions of vinylite have a stronger attraction for electrons than do the ions of paper (Fig. 7-10). As a result, when the two materials are very close together, a few surface electrons will be attracted from the paper to the vinylite. The paper is left with a net positive charge, and the vinylite becomes negatively charged. The rubbing that you do does not generate electricity—it only helps to provide the close contact that is needed for the electron transfer to occur. However, you do perform work. The electrical energy arises when you exert a force to pull the charged objects apart.

The model can also account for the distinction between conductors and insulators. In conductors electrons are much more mobile than in insulators. The electrons in insulators are bound quite tightly to their ions, and only a relatively small number are involved in electrostatic effects. In the very best metallic conductors, one electron per atom may be readily moved by electric forces.

Although we have said that charged objects attract uncharged ones, we do not need to consider that to be a separate effect. When a positively charged strip is brought near a neutral object, the electric force attracts electrons in the neutral object to the side of the object near the charged strip (Fig. 7-11). As a result, the uncharged object will have a temporary negative charge in the region close to the charged strip, and a temporary positive charge on the opposite side. The net force of the charged strip on the neutral object is an attraction, because the force of attraction on the negative charge, acting

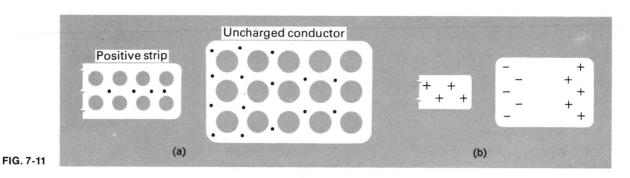

Positive strip   Uncharged conductor

(a)   (b)

FIG. 7-11

over a shorter distance, is greater than the force of repulsion on the positive charge (Fig. 7-12).

In conductors, where the electrons move about easily, we imagine that they always redistribute themselves to be as far from one another as possible.

Let us now apply the model to two final examples of electrostatic effects.

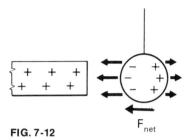

FIG. 7-12

THE ELECTROSCOPE

In an electroscope a metallized straw is pivoted at its centre about a metal pin suspended on a metal rod (Fig. 7-13). At the top of the rod is a metal plate. Usually, the rod and straw are enclosed in a metal cylinder, separated from the cylinder at the support by a ring of insulating material. Any charges on the cylinder should not affect the interior, because they exert equal forces in all directions.

Bring a negatively charged object near to the plate at the top of the electroscope (Fig. 7-14). Electrons will be repelled from the region of the plate near the charged object, and will move to the rod and straw. That will make the rod and straw negatively charged, with a surplus of electrons. The force of repulsion between the negatively charged parts will cause the straw to move away from the rod.

The straw will return to the position that indicates neutrality as soon as the charged object is removed. However, if the charged object touches the metal plate, some electrons may be conducted from the negatively charged object to the plate. That will make the whole electroscope have a net negative charge, and the straw will continue to stand out from the rod, even when the charged rod is removed. This way of charging the electroscope is called charging by *conduction*.

FIG. 7-13

CHARGING BY INDUCTION

A permanent charge can be put on a conductor by means of *induction*, which does not involve touching the conductor in question with the charged object. However, the process does involve the use of a second conductor. Often your body can serve as the second conductor. The second conductor is touched to the one to be charged while the charged object is held nearby. The touching is often called "grounding" or "earthing". The earth is a fairly good conductor and because of its size can readily give up or absorb a large number of electrons.

The approach of the positively charged strip to an electroscope causes a movement of electrons to the region of the electroscope near the strip (Fig. 7-15). When you touch your finger to the electroscope, electrons are conducted into the electroscope. Then remove your finger. Now the electrons are trapped on the electroscope. When the charged strip is removed, the electrons distribute themselves evenly over the electroscope. The positively charged strip has been used to *induce* a negative charge on the conductor.

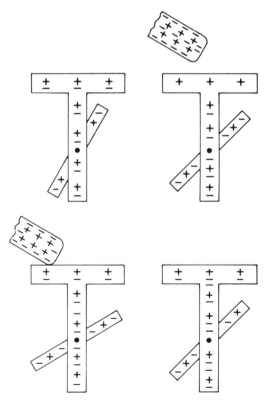

FIG. 7-14

FIG. 7-15 appears on page 92.

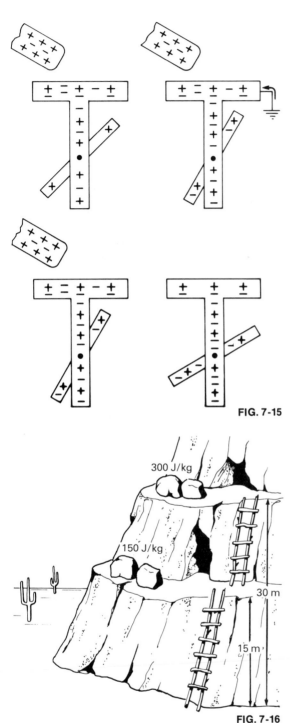

FIG. 7-15

FIG. 7-16

In charging both by induction and by conduction the charge is produced by a transfer of electrons. Throughout, the principle of the **conservation of electric charge** applies:

Whenever any amount of positive charge is produced (or lost) within a closed system, an equal amount of negative charge is also produced (or lost).

ELECTRICAL UNITS OF MEASUREMENT

Electrically charged objects exert forces on one another. When these forces move the objects they do work and transfer energy. In order to make these ideas quantitative, we need units of measurement. Although measuring instruments will be described in a later chapter, some understanding of electrical quantities should be begun here.

As far as possible, electrical quantities and units should fit with those already developed in mechanics. When an external force is applied to move an object against an electric force, the object's potential energy will be increased. This is the same as increasing the potential energy of an object by lifting it up against the force of gravity of the earth.

Cliff-dwellers, for example, can store gravitational potential energy by carrying rocks up to their ledges. For any given mass of rock, the potential energy stored is proportional to the height of the ledge above the bottom of the cliff (Fig. 7-16). Any particular rock dropped from 30 m will transfer twice as much energy to the bottom of the cliff as one dropped from 15 m. For $g = 10$ N/kg, we could describe the two levels as having *potentials* of 300 J/kg and 150 J/kg, respectively.

For electrical situations several factors are different. First, the quantity of electricity is not measured in kilograms. Second, for gravity there is only one very massive object in our vicinity, the earth. That makes calculations of gravitational potential simple. However, for electricity there are usually many attracting and repelling charges in any region. The situation is more complex, and there is no easy electrical equivalent for height. Specifically electrical quantities will have to be defined.

QUANTITY OF ELECTRIC CHARGE

Gravitational forces are directly proportional to the masses on which they act. Experiment shows that electric forces are directly proportional to electric charge. Start with three small light identical conducting spheres X, Y and Z (Fig. 7-17). Leaving Z aside for a moment, put X and Y in contact. Charge them and they will move apart. Each of X and Y will have an equal charge. Call it Q. (Q is the symbol usually used for charge—quantity of electricity.) The force of repulsion between X and Y will hold them apart with a force F. Now, keeping X charged at Q, let Y and Z touch. Sharing the charge will give Y and Z each a charge of $Q/2$. At the same distance apart as before, the force of repulsion between X and Y is $F/2$, and between Y and Z, $F/4$. This shows that the electric force between charged objects is proportional to the product of their charges.

Thus, electric charge—deficit or surplus of electrons—does for electric forces what mass does for gravitational forces. Every electron carries a negative charge that is equal to the charge on every other electron. That makes the charge on an electron a *natural* unit of charge. However, the charge on one electron is a very tiny amount. A larger unit of charge has been defined, called the coulomb (C). It takes 6.24×10^{18} electrons to make -1.00 C. Thus, the charge on one electron is -1.60×10^{-19} C.

A surplus or deficit of a few electrons makes a negative or positive charge of about 10^{-18} C. In your electrostatics experiments, the quantity of charge is of the order of nanocoulombs (1 nC $= 1 \times 10^{-9}$ C). In lightning strokes the amount of charge transferred between cloud and ground is between about 10 C and 100 C.

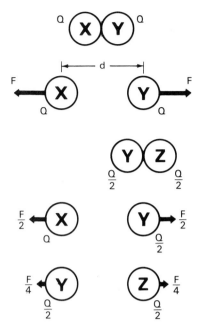

FIG. 7-17

ELECTRIC POTENTIAL DIFFERENCE

Equipped with a unit for electric charge, we can now deal with electrical energy. A metal sphere of 10 cm diameter is given a considerable positive charge. Then a small metallized ball with a negative charge of 1×10^{-8} C is held close to one side of the sphere (Fig. 7-18). There is a force of attraction between the two. Within a region of several centimetres from the sphere, the average force of attraction is found to be about 6×10^{-4} N. To move the ball away from the sphere a force slightly greater than a balancing force must be applied, and work will be done. In the process of moving the ball away against the electric force, the potential energy of the ball is increased. In moving the 5 cm from A to B, the potential energy will increase by

$$E = F\Delta d = (6 \times 10^{-4}\,\text{N})(5 \times 10^{-2}\,\text{m}) = 3 \times 10^{-5}\,\text{J}.$$

The electric potential difference (symbol V) between the points A and B is the work per unit charge needed to move the ball from A to B. Thus,

$$V = \frac{E}{Q} = \frac{3 \times 10^{-5}\,\text{J}}{1 \times 10^{-8}\,\text{C}} = 3 \times 10^{3}\,\text{J/C}.$$

The unit joule per coulomb is given the name volt (V), so

$$1\,\text{V} = 1\,\text{J/C}.$$

Thus, the electric potential difference between A and B is 3×10^{3} V.

The electric potential at B is 3×10^{3} V higher than at A, in the same way that a rock on a higher ledge has a greater potential than one on a lower ledge. For electricity, the potential is measured in

This tiny force can be calculated from the mass of the small ball and the angle of deflection from the vertical as described in Chapter 5 under *Three forces*.

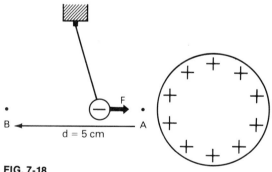

FIG. 7-18

The electric force on a charged object located between two charged parallel conducting plates is constant throughout the space between them as long as the distance between the plates is much less than the linear dimensions of the plates.

joules per coulomb (volts), rather than the joules per kilogram that are appropriate in the gravitational situation. Since the zero of potential is arbitrary in both cases, our attention is mainly concentrated on potential *differences* between specified locations.

Example: In a globe like the one in Fig. 7-7, electrons are accelerated through a potential difference of 1.0×10^2 V. (a) The charge on an electron is 1.6×10^{-19} C. Calculate the energy imparted to each electron. (b) The mass of an electron is 9.1×10^{-31} kg. Calculate the speed at which electrons strike the positive plate.

(a) The energy of each electron can be found from the charge and the potential difference:

$$E = QV = (1.6 \times 10^{-19} \text{ C})(1.0 \times 10^2 \text{ V}) = 1.6 \times 10^{-17} \text{ J}.$$

(b) The electron has energy 1.6×10^{-17} J, mass 9.1×10^{-31} kg, and speed v.

Since
$$E_k = \tfrac{1}{2} mv^2,$$

then,
$$v^2 = \frac{2E}{m} = \frac{2 \times 1.6 \times 10^{-17} \text{ J}}{9.1 \times 10^{-31} \text{ kg}} = 3.5 \times 10^{13} \text{ m}^2/\text{s}^2.$$

Therefore,
$$v = 5.9 \times 10^6 \text{ m/s}.$$

The speed with which electrons strike the plate is almost 2% of the speed of light. Because of relativistic effects (see page 79), this formula will not apply to electrons for potential differences greater than about 10 kV.

Electrostatic potential differences in school laboratories range up to hundreds of kilovolts. Since the charges involved are of the order of nanocoulombs, energies range from microjoules to millijoules. By contrast, lightning strokes may traverse potential differences of up to twenty megavolts. With charges of ten coulombs or more, you can see that lightning can transform up to hundreds of megajoules of energy along its path. The energy produces light in the flash, sound in the thunder, and new chemical compounds as well as heat.

Exercises

A

1. Compare electric and gravitational forces by listing the respects in which they are alike, and those in which they are unlike.

2. Describe what you would expect to see in the following situations:
   (a) Two bars of wax are rubbed with a paper towel. One bar is suspended so that it can move freely and the second bar is brought close to it.
   (b) Two bars of bakelite (a solid non-conductor) are rubbed with soft paper. When one bar is brought toward the suspended wax of part (a), the wax moves toward the bakelite. The other bakelite bar is suspended, and the first bakelite bar is brought close to it.
   (c) A rubbed bar of wax is brought near the rubbed suspended bar of bakelite.

3. When rods made of the following materials are rubbed with a paper towel, state the sign of the charge that is produced on the rod: (a) vinyl, (b) acetate, (c) ebonite, (d) polythene, (e) glass.

4. Describe what you would expect to see in the following situations:
   (a) A smooth metal cylinder is held in your bare hand and rubbed vigorously with soft paper. It is then brought near a suspended light graphite-coated ball.
   (b) A cylinder similar to that in (a) is held by a hand that is encased in thick rubber. The cylinder is rubbed with soft paper and brought near a light moveable ball as in part (a).

5. (a) What is the direction of transfer of electrons when an acetate strip becomes positive when rubbed with paper?
   (b) What should be the charge state of the paper after rubbing it on an acetate strip?

6. Describe the sequence of events when a negatively charged rod is brought near a light graphite-coated ball that is free to move. Include the result of the ball and rod coming into contact. Explain the events by means of the idea of electron transfer.

7. The charge cloud around the heated filament of a vacuum tube is negative. How is the cloud affected when the nearby plate carries a charge that is (a) negative, (b) positive?

8. Use a series of diagrams to illustrate the charging of an electroscope by conduction using a positively charged plastic strip. What is the final charge on the electroscope?

9. Use a series of diagrams to illustrate the charging of an electroscope by induction using a negatively charged plastic strip. What is the final charge on the electroscope?

10. For each of (a) conduction and (b) induction state how the sign of the final charge compares to that of the charge on the charging strip.

11. (a) A neutral sodium atom can easily lose one electron. What is the magnitude of the electric charge of the positive ion formed when that happens?
    (b) A neutral chlorine atom can easily accept a single electron. What is the magnitude of the electric charge of the negative ion so formed?

12. The magnitude of charge on one electron is 1.6×10^{-19} C. What is the charge in coulombs (with sign) on an object which has
    (a) a surplus of 1.0×10^5 electrons,
    (b) a deficit of 5.0×10^{10} electrons?

13. What is the electronic condition (that is, whether surplus or deficit of how many electrons) of an object with a charge of (a) $+3.2 \times 10^{-8}$ C, and (b) -8.0×10^{-13} C?

14. (a) What is the potential difference between two points if it takes 84 J of energy to move 7.0 C of charge from one point to the other?
    (b) What is the potential difference between your finger and a charged strip in which a charge of 3.0×10^{-9} C carries an energy of 1.5×10^{-6} J just before a spark jumps between your finger and the strip?

15. What is the order of magnitude of the energy involved in an electrostatic generator where there is a transfer of about 1 nC of charge through a potential difference of about 10^2 kV?

B

16. Describe how to identify the charged state of a light suspended graphite-coated sphere, supposing that someone might have charged it before you arrived on the scene. The difficulty that you have to get around is that a neutral object is attracted by both positive and negative charges, while unlike charged objects also attract each other.

17. Two smooth metal cylinders on insulating stands are in contact. Then a negatively charged strip is brought near the left end of the pair. While the strip is held there, you move the right-hand cylinder a few centimetres to the right, touching only the insulating stand.

Then the charged strip is removed.

(a) Draw three diagrams to illustrate the distribution of charges on the two cylinders through the course of the above actions.

(b) What is the sign of the final net charge on each of the two cylinders?

(c) How do the magnitudes of the charges on the two cylinders compare?

18. Suppose the outside package of a 90 V battery has been damaged so that you cannot tell which terminal is positive. Describe how to use a sensitive electroscope to find out.

19. (a) Consider molecules of vinyl to be cubes about 1×10^{-9} m along each edge. What is the area in square metres of one face of such a cube?

(b) What is the surface area in square metres of a strip of vinyl that is 2 cm wide and 5 cm long?

(c) How many molecules of the vinyl are in the top surface layer of the strip?

(d) Suppose that when the strip is rubbed with a piece of paper towel the charge produced on it is -1.6×10^{-8} C. How many surplus electrons are on the surface of the strip?

(e) What is the ratio of the number of molecules in the surface of the strip to the number of surplus electrons in the charge on the surface?

C

20. In a demonstration of electrical potential difference, two square metal plates with sides about 30 cm long are set on insulating stands 0.15 m apart. The plates are then connected to a high voltage source. Then a light graphite-coated ball hanging on a thread from an insulating rod is allowed to touch one of the plates and pick up charge from it. Without allowing the ball to touch the other plate, the demonstrator holds the rod so that the ball is close to the centre of the space between the two plates. The thread now makes an angle of 10° with the vertical. If you know that the charge on the ball is 1.0×10^{-8} C, that the mass of the ball is 1.0×10^{-3} kg, and that $g = 10$ N/kg, calculate

(a) the magnitude of the electric force on the ball,

(b) the energy that would be required to move the ball from one plate to the other,

(c) the potential difference between the two plates.

21. Charge placed on metal spheres above the surface of the earth causes a potential difference between the surface of each sphere and the earth. The larger the charge on a single sphere, the greater is the potential difference. Since the same charge on two spheres of different sizes will be spaced out more on the larger sphere, its potential difference with respect to the earth will be smaller than for the same amount of charge on the smaller sphere.

These two factors (amount of charge and potential difference) determine a property of conductors (metal spheres in this case) that is called *capacitance*. The capacitance (C) of a conductor is defined by the relation $C = Q/V$. The SI unit of capacitance is the farad (F), and one farad = one coulomb per volt. The capacitance of many types of electroscopes is about 1 pF.

(a) What potential difference relative to the earth will a 1 pF electroscope acquire if 1 nC of charge is put on it?

(b) How much charge is needed for a 1 pF electroscope to have a potential difference of 10 V relative to the earth?

(c) A metal sphere of radius 5 cm is raised to a potential difference of 10 kV relative to the earth by a charge of 50 nC. What is its capacitance?

(d) The capacitance of the sphere of a laboratory Van de Graaff generator is 10 pF. What charge is needed to give it a potential difference of 500 kV?

(e) What is the capacitance of a cloud in which a charge of 10 C creates a potential difference relative to the earth of 10 MV?

22. (a) Find out about and describe *Faraday's ice-pail experiment.*

(b) How are the results of this experiment used in electrostatic shielding? In Van de Graaff generators?

23. The sphere of a Van de Graaff generator is raised to a high potential difference by adding charge to it continuously from the circulating belt. Once the sphere begins to be charged, progressively more work is needed to add additional charge to it (against the force of repulsion of the charge already on it), although very little work was needed to put the first charge on the sphere. (This should remind you of the way that force increases as a bowstring is pulled back.) Calculate the energy stored in a 10 pF sphere that is charged to a potential difference of 100 kV relative to the earth.

24. An important practical application of electrostatics is electrostatic printing, known as *xerography*. Find out and explain how a xerographic printer works.

25. Outdoor TV receiving antennas are always fitted with lightning arrestors. Find out what such a device consists of and how it functions.

26. (a) Find out how lightning rods function.

(b) Why do you suppose that lightning rods are rarely installed on steel frame buildings such as apartment buildings and office blocks?

Current Electricity

FIG. 8-1

Static electricity is one form of energy. By the action of mechanical forces working against electric forces in matter, we can build up charges on objects. The transformation is from mechanical energy to electrical energy. Various other forms of energy can also be transformed to electrical energy.

Flashlight cells and automobile storage batteries are examples of *voltaic cells* (Fig. 8-1). In them, chemical potential energy is transformed into electrical energy. In any one cell, plates of two dissimilar materials (often metals) have between them a liquid or paste that is either acidic or alkaline. The chemical action in the cell has the effect of separating charges by pushing a surplus of electrons onto one plate (or *electrode*) and leaving a deficit of electrons on the other electrode. Within a single cell the chemical activity is able to maintain a continuous potential difference of 1 to 2 V between the electrodes, depending on the materials used.

In contrast to most electrostatic operations, the voltaic cell can maintain a continuous transfer of charge through a conductor joining the two electrodes externally. As a voltaic cell operates, it transforms chemical potential energy into electrical energy. Chemical changes degrade the materials gradually until the activity diminishes greatly. Then the cell must be either recharged, or replaced.

Heat energy can be transformed into electrical energy in *thermocouples*. Wires of two different metals are twisted together to form a junction. If a temperature difference is maintained between the junction and the rest of the apparatus, a potential difference of a few millivolts is maintained between the other ends of the wires. The potential difference in this transformation depends on the nature of the materials and the magnitude of the temperature difference.

Photovoltaic cells are devices for transforming light energy into electrical energy (Fig. 8-2). A surface of the metal selenium is covered with a very thin layer of another material. When light strikes the interface between the two materials, electrons pile up on one side of the interface, leaving a deficit on the other. Depending on the nature of the materials and of the light, potential differences of a few tenths of a volt are created.

FIG. 8-2. Electricity is supplied to this Soviet Soyuz spacecraft by the two solar panels protruding from the instrument module. The photograph was taken from above against a cloud background with a camera in an American Apollo spacecraft.

When certain crystals, such as quartz, are squeezed a potential difference is produced across them. This is known as the *piezoelectric effect*. Such crystals are used in some microphones to transform sound energy into electrical impulses. In the tone-arm cartridges of many inexpensive record players the vibrating needle squeezes a piece of crystal to produce an electrical signal that can be amplified. The reverse effect of applying a changing voltage to a crystal to make it change its shape (that is, to vibrate) is used to generate the sound in the inexpensive earphones that come with portable radios.

Today's electrical industry is founded on the transformation of mechanical energy into electrical energy using *electromagnetism*. Potential differences from 1 V to 25 kV can be maintained in the electrical generators that are described in Chapter 11.

Like the other devices mentioned, generators produce continuous charge separation, as long as the external energy source continues to operate. If an external conductor is connected between the points where the potential difference is being maintained, there is a continuous passage of electrons through the conductor—an **electric current**. Depending on what they encounter in their passage, the electrons can do work, and produce a transformation from electrical energy to some other form. For the moment we can consider a simple electric *circuit*—a closed conducting path connecting one terminal of a generator or voltaic cell to the other terminal. A light bulb in that circuit might provide the transformation of electrical energy into heat and light energy (Fig. 8-3).

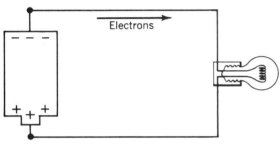

FIG. 8-3

SIMPLE ELECTRIC CIRCUIT

A copper wire consists of an orderly array of positive ions embedded in a cloud of electrons. Each ion has a charge of $+e = +1.6 \times 10^{-19}$ C. The number of electrons and positive ions is equal. When the wire is connected to a dry cell there is a potential difference of about 1.5 V between the ends of the wire. The negative electrode of the dry cell has a surplus of electrons exerting forces of repulsion on one another. When the wire is connected, the electrons will be jostled along the wire by that force of repulsion. They will also be attracted by the net positive charge on the other electrode of the cell. To keep the electrons moving along, the energy provided to them by the cell has to overcome the forces of attraction of the positive ions in the wire. In the process, the energy of the motion of the electrons is transferred to the positive ions, causing them to vibrate more rapidly. Electrical energy is thus transformed to heat energy. In a light bulb, the temperature rise is enough to make the filament glow.

VOLTAGE RISE AND VOLTAGE DROP

The amount and rate of energy transfer can be found from certain electrical measurements in this circuit. The energy per unit charge supplied by the chemical activity of the dry cell is the potential difference, or **voltage rise** in the cell. The *rate* at which charge is transferred through the circuit is the **electric current**. Its magnitude depends on the nature of the conductor. Some conductors offer more *resistance* to the passage of charge than others. Every conductor has some resistance, in which electrical energy is transformed to heat energy. The energy per unit charge that is given up in some portion of a circuit by transferring the kinetic energy of the moving electrons to heat energy can be called the **voltage drop** in that part of the circuit.

Definitions and units for these quantities can be given by comparison with a mechanical circuit. In Fig. 8-4, a man lifts bowling balls to a height of about 1.5 m, giving each one a gravitational potential energy determined by the mass of each ball, the height each is lifted, and the force of gravity. The balls roll down a gentle slope until they fall off into a cylinder of oil. Friction with the oil keeps the balls from accelerating. As they fall, their potential energy is transformed into heat in the oil. A trapdoor device (not shown) lets the balls out at the bottom to roll back to the man's feet. When they arrive there, they have lost all the potential energy that he gave them. The process continues until the man has to renew his supply of energy. The circuit is kept full of balls; the faster they move, the faster the man has to work. They will not move through the circuit as quickly if the oil is very thick, thus permitting the balls to move through it only very slowly.

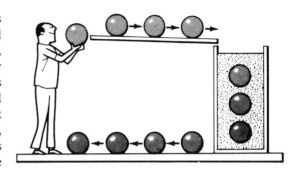

FIG. 8-4

No matter how quickly or slowly the balls traverse the circuit, the man always supplies exactly the same amount of potential energy to each ball. In electricity, the potential energy supplied is measured in volts. The voltage rise through a standard dry cell is 1.5 V. From that, we can calculate the energy supplied to each electron of charge 1.60×10^{-19} C.

Recall from Chapter 7 that 1 V = 1 J/C.

Since $V = \dfrac{E}{Q}$, $E = VQ = (1.5 \text{ V})(1.6 \times 10^{-19} \text{ C}) = 2.4 \times 10^{-19} \text{ J}.$

When each electron drifts into the positive electrode of the cell, it has given up that same amount of energy in the circuit (Fig. 8-5). When the cell is connected to a light bulb, the voltage drop represents the transformation of electrical energy into heat energy.

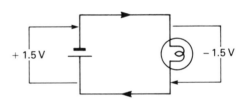

FIG. 8-5

In drawing circuits we use the symbols shown in Fig. 8-6 to represent the various components that are connected together. The symbol for a resistor can be used to represent any element that impedes the free passage of electrons through the resistor. Usually, the connecting wires are assumed to have no resistance.

The voltage relations in a circuit are consistent with the principle of energy conservation. The energy given up by an electron as heat in the resistance of a circuit is equal to the energy that it received in the dry cell. Thus, the sum of all the voltage drops throughout any circuit must be equal to the sum of all the voltage rises in the circuit.

ELECTRIC CURRENT

The faster the man works (Fig. 8-4), the greater will be the number of balls passing a point in a given interval of time. In the electrical case, the rate of passage of charge is the *current* (*I*):

$$\text{current} = \frac{\text{charge}}{\text{time}}.$$

In symbols,

$$I = \frac{Q}{t}.$$

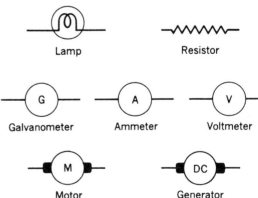

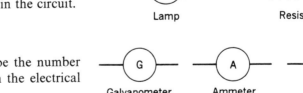

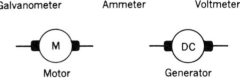

FIG. 8-6

In units, one ampere = one coulomb per second

$$1 \text{ A} = 1 \text{ C/s}.$$

In many typical light bulbs, the current is about 1 A. Brighter lamps require currents up to 10 A or more.

If the potential difference between two points is increased, the electric forces per charge are also increased in proportion. As a result, when the potential difference of a source is greater it makes the electrons drift along more rapidly. In fact, if everything else is held constant, the current is directly proportional to the potential difference.

Whenever electrons are separated from an ion, the positive charge that remains must be equal in magnitude to the negative charge removed. The sum of all charges must remain always constant. The sum is zero since the sum of positive charges equals the sum of negative charges. Thus, since charge cannot disappear in a circuit, it follows that the current in any single loop circuit will be the same at every point in the loop.

ELECTRIC RESISTANCE

Various metals differ in the ease with which electrons can move through them. An iron wire, for example, offers a greater resistance to the passage of electrons than one of copper of the same dimensions. As a result, for the same applied potential difference, the current in the iron wire will be smaller than in the copper wire. That means that the current in a circuit is inversely proportional to the **resistance** of the circuit.

With current directly proportional to potential difference, and inversely proportional to resistance, we can write $I = kV/R$. If we choose proper units,

$$I = \frac{V}{R}.$$

To do that, the SI unit of resistance is defined to fit the relation

$$R = \frac{V}{I}.$$

The unit of resistance is the ohm, defined by

$$1 \text{ ohm} = 1 \text{ volt per ampere}$$
$$1 \, \Omega = 1 \text{ V/A}.$$

Ω is the capital Greek letter *omega*.

There is a resistance of 1 Ω in a portion of a conductor if with a voltage drop of 1 V between the ends of that portion, there is a current of 1 A through it.

ELECTRICAL ENERGY AND POWER

A flashlight lamp has a resistance of 3.0 Ω (Fig. 8-7). It is connected to a cell with a potential difference of 1.5 V between its terminals. From the relation above, we can calculate the current (the rate at which that potential difference can push electrons through a conductor with that resistance).

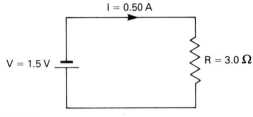

FIG. 8-7

$$I = \frac{V}{R} = \frac{1.5 \text{ V}}{3.0 \text{ Ω}} = \frac{1.5 \text{ V}}{3.0 \text{ V/A}} = 0.50 \text{ A}.$$

The dry cell supplies energy to the electrons, which give it up to heat the filament of the lamp. The energy transfer is given by the relation

$$E = VQ.$$

From the definition for current, we know that

$$Q = It.$$

Therefore, we can substitute that for Q in the previous equation:

$$E = VIt.$$

Energy is transferred to the lamp as time passes, and more and more energy is transformed from chemical potential energy in the cell to heat and light in the lamp. If the flashlight is switched on for 20 s the energy transfer can be calculated. The units will be written out in expanded form to show that the result really is a measure of energy.

$$E = (1.5 \text{ V})(0.50 \text{ A})(20 \text{ s})$$

$$= (1.5 \times 0.50 \times 20)(\frac{\text{J}}{\text{C}} \times \frac{\text{C}}{\text{s}} \times \text{s}) = 15 \text{ J}.$$

In 20 s, the flashlight transformed 15 J of energy.

Since power is energy per unit time, we have

$$P = \frac{E}{t} = \frac{VQ}{t} = VI.$$

From the above example it should be clear that the regular unit for power, 1 W = 1 J/s, fits here. If you know the voltage and current in any circuit, their product gives the power, or *rate* of energy transfer.

THE SI BASIS FOR ELECTRICAL UNITS

The foregoing relations give the basic ideas needed for the investigation of simple electric circuits. The following sections will go into more detail on a couple of important issues, as well as summarizing what has been done so far.

To begin, it is important for you to know that in SI units, the ampere is a base unit. So far, we have not considered it such, because its definition depends on electromagnetic relations you have not yet studied. For that reason, charge and the coulomb were introduced first. However, now we can review the basic electrical relations, starting from the ampere. A precise experimental technique exists for defining the ampere as a base unit. Once that is done, the coulomb can be defined from the relation

$$Q = It \qquad 1 \text{ C} = 1 \text{ A·s.}$$

The coulomb is the quantity of electricity transported in one second by a current of one ampere.

Then the volt can be defined in a form equivalent to the earlier definition:

$$V = \frac{P}{I} \qquad 1 \text{ V} = 1 \text{ W/A.}$$

The volt is the difference of electric potential between two points of a conductor that is carrying a constant current of one ampere when the power dissipation between these points is equal to one watt.

The definition of the ohm is the same as that given previously, 1 Ω = 1 V/A. The ohm is the electric resistance between two points of a conductor when a constant difference of potential of one volt applied between these two points produces in the conductor a current of one ampere.

COMBINATIONS OF ELEMENTS

Several dry cells and several lamps can be connected together into circuits more complicated than the simple circuit considered so far. To be able to analyze such circuits, you need to know how to extend the principles that have already been established. Various combinations of elements will be discussed.

CELLS IN SERIES

One flashlight cell will give an electric potential energy of 1.5 J to each coulomb of charge that passes through it. If several cells are connected together with the negative terminal of one joined to the positive terminal of the next, the connection is said to be in *series*. If

each such cell produces a potential difference of 1.5 V, then four cells connected in series will produce a potential difference of 4 × 1.5 V = 6.0 V (Fig. 8-8). Each cell supplies 1.5 J of energy to each coulomb of charge.

By means of the series connection, batteries of cells can be combined to produce potential differences of 100 V or more. Typical automobile batteries consist of six cells of 2.0 V each connected in series, to make a 12 V potential difference. If you remove the casing from various dry batteries you will find small cells connected in series.

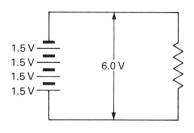

FIG. 8-8

OHM'S LAW

The major electrical measurements that can be made in a circuit are voltage and current. Current is measured with an ammeter which is connected directly into the circuit. The ammeter is designed to offer virtually no resistance to the passage of charge. The voltage (or potential difference) between two points in a circuit is measured by a voltmeter. The voltmeter is connected across the two points. It is designed to take a minimal current from the circuit.

Suppose that a coil of copper wire of 100 m length is connected in a simple circuit with an ammeter and one or more dry cells (Fig. 8-9). A voltmeter is connected across the ends of the coil. As different numbers of cells are connected into the circuit, the current and potential difference are recorded. The result is shown in Table 8-1 and on the graph in Fig. 8-10.

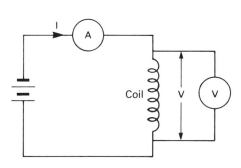

FIG. 8-9

Table 8-1

TABLE FOR OHM'S LAW

Voltage (V)	Current (I)	V/I
1.5 V	0.18 A	8.3
3.0	0.34	8.8
4.5	0.52	8.7
6.0	0.69	8.7
	Average	8.6

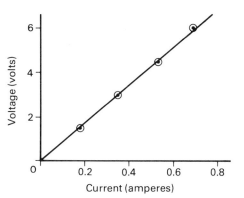

FIG. 8-10

From the definition we know that resistance is the ratio voltage/current. Table 8-1 and Fig. 8-10 show that the ratio is constant throughout this experiment. Thus, resistance is more than a calculated quantity. It is an apparently constant property of the coil of wire, over a wide range of voltages and currents.

This experimental result is known as **Ohm's law:**

The resistance of many conducting materials is constant and independent of voltage and current, as long as the temperature remains constant.

There are in fact many conductors for which the ratio V/I is not so constant. Ohm's law applies to common metals such as copper, silver, gold, aluminum and iron. They are called ohmic conductors. Ohm's law does not apply to gases, some liquids, and some alloys. They are called non-ohmic conductors.

To design a resistor made of an ohmic conductor you have to take account of three main factors that will determine its resistance. These are the cross-sectional area of the conductor, its length, and the nature of its material. The influence of each of these factors can be seen in the electron-ion model for metals. For each factor consider two wires each connected to a single 1.5 V dry cell. Since resistance is inversely proportional to current, whichever wire has the greater current will have the smaller resistance.

First consider two copper wires of the same length, one of a larger diameter than the other. The number of electrons available to be acted on by the electric force of the cell is directly proportional to the cross-sectional area of the wire. The thicker wire will have more electrons moving through it, and thus a greater current. The resistance of a conductor is therefore inversely proportional to the cross-sectional area.

Second, consider a copper wire of length 3.0 m connected to the 1.5 V cell. The energy per unit charge dissipated in the wire is 1.5 J/C. Since $E = F\Delta d$, the force per unit charge in the wire can be obtained by dividing the energy per unit charge by the displacement, which is the length of the wire. The average force per unit charge acting over the length of the wire is

Recall from Chapter 6 that 1 J = 1 N·m, so that 1 J/m = 1 N.

$$\frac{F}{Q} = \frac{1.5 \text{ J/C}}{3.0 \text{ m}} = 0.50 \text{ N/C}.$$

Then, in a copper wire of the same diameter, but only 1.0 m long, connected to the 1.5 V cell, the force per unit charge is 1.5 N/C. Thus, in the shorter wire electrons experience a greater force and will accelerate to greater speeds. As a result the current (the *rate* of motion of charge) is greater in the shorter wire. The greater current in the shorter wire means that it has a smaller resistance. Resistance is directly proportional to the length of the conductor.

Finally, consider two wires of the same length and diameter, one of copper and the other of iron. The ions of iron exert a stronger attraction on electrons than do the ions of copper. As a result, the electric force of the cell is able to accelerate electrons more against the weaker force of the copper ions. The result is a greater current in the copper, and thus a smaller resistance. The property of materials that determines their resistance because of the ionic forces is called *resistivity*. The resistivity of materials is expressed as the resistance of a block of the material one metre long, and one square metre in cross-sectional area. From the foregoing discussion, we have that the resistance of a conductor (R) is directly proportional both to its resis-

Table 8-2

Metal	Resistivity at 20°C
Silver	1.6×10^{-8} Ω·m²/m
Copper	1.7
Aluminum	2.8
Tungsten	5.5
Iron	9.5
Mercury	96.0

tivity (ρ) and its length (l), and inversely proportional to its cross-sectional area (A).

Thus $$R = \frac{\rho l}{A} \quad \text{and} \quad \rho = \frac{RA}{l}.$$

ρ is the Greek letter *rho*.

This last relation shows that the appropriate SI unit for resistivity is the ohm square metre per metre. Values for the resistivities of common conducting materials are shown in Table 8-2.

The table for resistivities specifies a temperature of 20°C. This suggests that resistance varies as temperature changes. Indeed, the electron-ion model indicates that should be so. For, at higher temperatures the ions will vibrate over greater distances, and electrons are likely to encounter ions more frequently. As a result, resistivity (and resistance) is likely to be higher at higher temperatures. The variation of resistivity with temperature for a few metals is shown on the graph in Fig. 8-11.

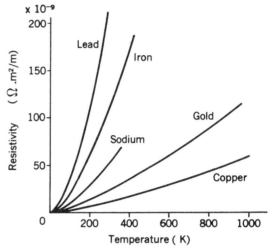

FIG. 8-11

CELLS IN PARALLEL

When cells are connected in series, every electron that moves through the circuit goes through every cell. In the parallel connection illustrated in Fig. 8-12, there are three parallel paths. The three cells have their positive terminals connected together to receive electrons, and their negative terminals connected together to expel electrons. If the three cells are identical, electrons will be randomly directed to each of the three positive terminals. Whichever path an electron takes, it will go through a potential rise of 1.5 V. If the total current in the external circuit is 1.0 A, the current through each cell will be 0.33 A.

The only advantage of this kind of connection of cells is that the work is shared among them and they will last longer. This parallel connection is the one that is used to boost a car battery on a cold day. When the starter motor needs a large force to move the engine with cold viscous oil in it, a single battery may not be able to supply charge at a great enough rate. The two batteries can share the load.

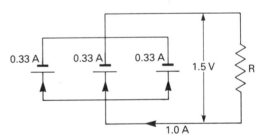

FIG. 8-12

RESISTANCES IN SERIES

Lamps or other appliances may be connected either in series or in parallel. In the series connection they are joined end to end. That makes a single loop circuit. Suppose that we know the values of the resistances of two appliances, determined by measurement in a simple circuit. If they are connected in series, what will be the value of the combined resistance?

Two appliances of resistance R_1 and R_2 are connected in series across a battery of potential difference V_T (Fig. 8-13). The voltage drops across the resistances will be V_1 and V_2, respectively. Throughout the circuit there will be a current I. The usual relations among

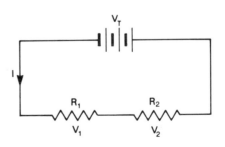

FIG. 8-13

electrical quantities can be applied both to the whole circuit and to parts of it. Because of the conservation of energy, we have

$$V_T = V_1 + V_2.$$

Then substitute for the V's from $V_1 = IR_1$, $V_2 = IR_2$, $V_T = IR_T$,

to get
$$IR_T = IR_1 + IR_2.$$

Then, divide through by I, and get the relation

$$R_T = R_1 + R_2.$$

When appliances are connected in series, their total resistance is equal to the sum of the individual resistances.

RESISTANCES IN PARALLEL

Two resistances are connected in parallel as shown in Fig. 8-14. At their junction the current I_T from the battery divides, with I_1 being the current in R_1, and I_2 the current in R_2. The voltage drop is the same, V, across both resistances. Since there is charge conservation,

$$I_T = I_1 + I_2.$$

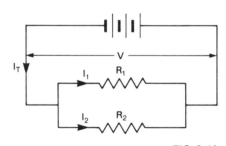

FIG. 8-14

Then substitute for the I's from $I_1 = V/R_1$, $I_2 = V/R_2$, and $I_T = V/R_T$

to get
$$\frac{V}{R_T} = \frac{V}{R_1} + \frac{V}{R_2}.$$

Divide through by V:

$$\frac{1}{R_T} = \frac{1}{R_1} + \frac{1}{R_2}.$$

The reciprocal of the total resistance of resistors in parallel is the sum of the reciprocals of the individual resistances.

Example: A toaster of resistance 10 Ω and a mixer of resistance 15 Ω are connected in parallel across a 120 V supply. What is the combined resistance of the two appliances; and what is the current that must be supplied to the combination?

(a) Substitute the values of the two resistances in the equation for parallel resistances:

$$\frac{1}{R} = \frac{1}{10 \ \Omega} + \frac{1}{15 \ \Omega} = (0.10 + 0.067)/\Omega = 0.167/\Omega.$$

Notice that the resistance of a parallel combination of resistors is always less than that of any one of them.

Now, invert: $R = \dfrac{1}{0.167/\Omega} = 6.0 \ \Omega.$

The combined value of the two resistances is 6.0 Ω.
(b) The current drawn by the combination is

$$I = \frac{V}{R} = \frac{120 \ V}{6.0 \ \Omega} = 20 \ A.$$

Exercises

A

1. Name four forms of energy that can be transformed into electrical energy, and name the device that is used to effect the transformation for each.

2. In the bowling ball circuit (Fig. 8-4) the person lifts each ball through a height of 2.0 m, exerting a force of 60 N.
   (a) How much energy is supplied to each ball?
   (b) If in 1.0 min 12 balls are lifted, how much energy is supplied in that time to the oil through which the balls drop?

3. An automobile battery is rated at 12 V.
   (a) How many joules of energy does it supply to each coulomb of charge that passes through it?
   (b) How much energy does the battery supply to each electron that passes through it?

4. A small walkie-talkie transmitter is operated for 20 s. In that time, the charge that passes through the 9.0 V battery is 6.0 C.
   (a) What is the current in the set?
   (b) How much chemical potential energy was transformed into electrical energy?

5. While a flashlight is on for 3.5 min, the current in the bulb is 0.75 A. How much charge passes through the bulb in that time?

6. A car battery is advertised as having a "cold cranking power" of 450. This is the current in amperes that the battery can deliver at a sufficient voltage to operate the starter motor for 30 s at a temperature of 0°C. How much charge will such a battery deliver in that time?

7. The lamp of a battery-operated lantern is rated at 0.50 A and 4.7 V.
   (a) Calculate the resistance of the lamp.

   (b) If the lamp is connected to a fresh 6.0 V battery, what current would it draw if its resistance did not change?

8. An electric razor motor operates at 4.5 V and 0.20 A. What is its effective resistance?

9. What is the power used by the electric motor in question 8?

10. An electric kettle operating at 120 V draws 12.5 A. What is the power used by the kettle?

11. Show that the following two definitions of volt are equivalent: 1 V = 1 J/C, and 1 V = 1 W/A.

12. A current of 10 mA is maintained through a 10% solution of sodium chloride in water by a potential difference of 15 V. Calculate the resistance of the solution.

13. At its operating temperature, the element of an electric stove has a resistance of 32 Ω. What current will it draw from a 240 V electric supply?

14. A certain electric lamp filament will melt at currents greater than 2.5 A. Its resistance is 56 Ω at its operating temperature. What is the maximum supply voltage to which it can be safely connected?

15. Battery packs for large hand-held lanterns consist of eight 1.5 V cells. Some of these batteries are 12 V and others are 6 V. Describe how the internal connections differ for the two types.

B

16. In a lightning flash, 20 C of charge pass through a potential difference of 1×10^8 V in an interval of 1×10^{-2} s. Calculate (a) the average current, and (b) the energy dissipated.

17. The chemicals in a flashlight cell are able to supply energy to 2.0×10^3 C of charge during the cell's lifetime at an average potential difference of 1.2 V. What is the amount of energy stored in a fresh cell?

18. A 12 V storage battery is rated at 100 A·h. That means that it could deliver 100 A for 1 h, or 1 A for 100 h, or any equivalent combination. Calculate (a) the charge that the battery is able to transfer, and (b) the total energy that is available from the battery without recharging it.

19. A microwave oven draws 12 A with a voltage drop of 120 V. When the oven operates for 15 min, calculate
(a) the total charge that is delivered to the oven,
(b) the energy that is transformed by the oven.

20. To toast two pieces of bread in 15 s, an electric toaster requires 9.0×10^3 J of energy. If the potential difference across the toaster is 120 V, calculate the current in its heating element.

21. The following measurements were made in an experimental investigation of Ohm's law for a coil of aluminum wire:

Voltage across coil	Current in coil
24 V	2.0 A
37	3.0
62	5.0
88	7.0
102	8.0

Do these data support Ohm's law?

22. A coil of copper wire was immersed in running water to maintain its temperature at 26°C. The following measurements were made:

Voltage	Current
6.20 V	0.200 A
12.48	0.400
15.36	0.500
21.88	0.700

Do these data confirm Ohm's law?

23. Describe the appearance of a graph of current plotted against voltage for an ohmic conductor. State two simple ways in which the graph of current against voltage could be different for a non-ohmic conductor.

24. (a) What properties of a metallic conductor determine its resistance?
(b) How would the resistance of the conductor change as a result of a decrease (one by one) of each of the factors in your answer to part (a)?

25. There is a current of 2.0 A in two small electric motors connected in series with a battery. The voltage drop across motor A is 8.0 V, and across motor B 12.0 V.
(a) What is the total voltage drop across the two motors?
(b) Calculate the combined resistance of the two motors.
(c) Calculate the separate resistances of A and B and compare them to the value of the combined resistance of the motors.

26. In one kind of Christmas-tree decoration, eight lamps are connected in series to a 120 V supply. The resistance of each lamp is 30 Ω. Calculate
(a) the total resistance of the eight lamps connected in series,
(b) the current in the circuit,
(c) the voltage drop across one lamp.

27. A lamp of resistance 3.0 Ω is designed to carry a current of 1.5 A. Calculate
(a) the current that the lamp would draw if connected to a 6.0 V battery,
(b) the value of the resistance that would have to be added in series with the lamp in order to limit the current to the value for which the lamp was designed.

28. When two resistors A and B are connected in series to a 5.0 V battery, the current is 0.25 A. When A is connected to the battery by itself, the current is 0.33 A. What would be the current if B were connected to the battery by itself?

29. Two small electric motors are connected in parallel across a 12 V battery. The current in motor A is 3.0 A, and in motor B 2.0 A.
(a) What is the total current supplied to the two motors?
(b) Calculate the combined resistance of the two motors.
(c) Calculate the separate resistances of A and B and compare them to the value of the combined resistance of the motors.

30. Two lamps are designed each to operate at 3.0 V. One has a resistance of 6.0 Ω and the other of 1.5 Ω.
(a) What is their combined resistance when connected in parallel?
(b) What current will the combination draw from a 3.0 V supply?

31. (a) What is the resistance of two resistors in parallel, having individual resistances of 10 Ω and 100 Ω?
(b) What is the combined resistance of the parallel connection of resistors of values 300 Ω, 400 Ω, and 600 Ω?

32. An electric toaster of resistance 10 Ω is connected in parallel with an electric iron of resistance 20 Ω across a 120 V supply. Calculate the total current supplied to the two devices.

33. A certain type of electric lamp of resistance 12 Ω is designed to operate across a supply of 6.0 V.
(a) Calculate the current in the lamp when it is connected to a 6.0 V battery.
(b) Calculate the current if two such lamps are connected in series to a 6.0 V battery.
(c) Calculate the total current if two such lamps are connected in parallel to a 6.0 V battery.

34. Convenient Christmas-tree lamp strings can have ten lamps connected in parallel with the 120 V supply,

each lamp having a resistance of 200 Ω.
(a) What is the combined resistance of the ten lamps?
(b) What is the total current drawn by the string?
(c) What is the current in one lamp?
(d) Why is a lamp string such as this more convenient than a series string?

35. Find out more about thermocouples and thermo-electric effects. Specifically, what is the difference between the Peltier effect and the Seebeck effect?

C

36. Examining the rate of motion of mass along a highway (in automobiles) can help you to understand how to calculate the speed of electrons in a wire. Assume that the mass of each car travelling at the same speed along a highway is 1.0×10^3 kg.
(a) Suppose that you stand by the side of the highway for one hour counting the number of cars that pass you. If the cars are equally spaced travelling at 90 km/h, and if you count 1800 in an hour, how many cars are there per kilometre along the highway?
(b) At another time the rate of transfer of mass along the highway is 8.0×10^5 kg/h. The number of equally spaced cars per kilometre of highway is 80. Calculate the speed of the cars.

37. The calculations of question 36 can now be modified to suit the motion of electrons in a wire. The magnitude of the charge of each electron is 1.6×10^{-19} C. In a copper wire having a diameter of about 1 mm, there are about 10^{21} free electrons per centimetre of length (according to the model of one free electron per atom). A wire of this diameter can safely carry a current of about 1 A. Electrons have a rapid random motion, on which a steady drift is superposed when an electric field is present. Calculate the speed of the electron drift in centimetres per second for a current of 1 A.

38. (a) Find out what is meant by *superconductivity*.
(b) What practical applications have been made of this phenomenon?

39. Small plates of platinum, dipping into a solution of hydrochloric acid in water, are connected in series with an ammeter and a variable direct current source. A voltmeter is connected between the leads to the platinum plates. The following pairs of readings are recorded.

Voltage	Current
2.2 V	10 mA
3.0	20
3.8	30
4.6	40
5.4	50

(a) Plot a graph of current against voltage for these data.
(b) Calculate the resistance of the solution for the first and last pairs of values.
(c) The graph does not pass through the origin because an internal voltage is developed between the two plates as a result of electrochemical action. The solution could be treated as an ohmic conductor if that voltage could be eliminated. One way to do that is to define resistance as the change in voltage divided by the change in current. Use that definition to calculate several values for the resistance of the solution. Do those values conform to Ohm's law?
(d) What is the value of the internal voltage?

40. So far in this chapter we have neglected the fact that dry cells possess a small internal resistance. When a high resistance voltmeter is used to measure the potential difference of a cell, the internal resistance has a negligible effect on the measurement, since the current supplied to the voltmeter is extremely low. The reading on the voltmeter is called the no-load voltage of the cell.

However, the internal resistance can have an appreciable effect in a circuit which has a relatively small resistance connected to the cell. For example, two cells with a combined no-load voltage of 3.0 V and a total internal resistance of 0.3 Ω are connected in series with a resistance coil and an ammeter of negligible resistance. A high-resistance voltmeter is connected across the ends of the coil. Calculate the readings of the ammeter and voltmeter if the resistance of the external coil is (a) 9.7 Ω, (b) 0.70 Ω.

41. The no-load voltage of a single dry cell is 1.50 V. When a resistance coil and an ammeter of negligible resistance are connected in series with the cell, the reading of the ammeter is 3.00 A and the voltage drop across the coil is 1.20 V. Calculate the internal resistance of the cell.

42. (a) Calculate the resistance of an aluminum wire 1.0 km long with a cross-section area of 1.0 cm².
(b) Calculate the resistance of a column of mercury, 20 cm long, with a cross-section area of 1.0 mm².

The ship attached to this compass has a heading of 6° east of north (magnetic).

For both magnetic and electric forces, likes repel and unlikes attract.

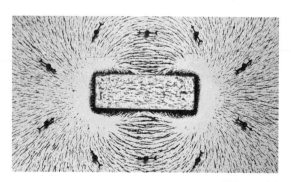

FIG. 9-1 (a)

Magnetism and Electricity

MAGNETIC FORCES

A magnetic compass may not keep you from getting lost in the woods, but it will give you a good indication of which way north is. Magnetic forces have several features that distinguish them from both gravitational and electric forces. You can investigate these in the laboratory.

One of the first things you will discover is that magnetic forces seem to be confined to a small number of materials. The major substances in which magnetic forces are easily seen are the metals iron, nickel, cobalt, and gadolinium. Some mixtures of these with other substances may also be magnetic—many steels are, but stainless steel is not. If you hold a Canadian nickel, dime or quarter close to either end of a magnetic compass needle, the needle will move toward the coin. Any object that affects the needle that way is composed of magnetic material.

The end of a magnetic compass needle that points northward is called the *north-seeking* (or just *north*) *pole*. If you test the ends of two such needles against one another, you will find that north-seeking poles repel each other, south-seeking poles repel each other, and a north-seeking pole attracts a south-seeking one. Like electric force, magnetic force seems to come in two varieties. But, unlike electric force, no way has been found to create an isolated pole of one variety, either only north or only south.

Whenever an object has a north pole somewhere on it, it must have a south pole somewhere else. Indeed, that is why the word "pole" has been used to describe magnets. For magnets are best described as having ends that are different; and a pole (or rod) is an object whose shape most readily displays ends.

When you bring the north end of a bar magnet near a compass needle, the north end of the needle is repelled and the south end attracted. The effect of the pair of magnetic forces is to cause the needle to turn. The net force is too small to cause a translational motion. However, the magnetic forces do produce a noticeable torque on the compass needle.

Since magnetic forces always come in pairs, they are not as easily described as gravitational or electric forces. For, gravitational and electric forces are directed along lines radiating from the centre of the force (either the gravitational mass or the electric charge). No such simple centre can be found for magnetic forces.

The net direction of the magnetic force at any point near a bar magnet can be shown by the direction of the north pole of a small compass needle at that point. A number of such needles could be used to trace out the force directions all around the bar magnet (Fig. 9-1). If iron filings are sprinkled on a card placed on top of the bar magnet, they will clump into clear lines that curl in towards the poles of the bar magnet. They picture the way the magnetic force is distributed about the magnet. The distribution of magnetic force in the region of a magnet is called the **magnetic force field**. The lines of iron filings, or a drawing of them, are called **field lines**. The field lines show the direction of the magnetic force about the magnet.

The card over the magnet marks only one plane through the magnetic field. You should imagine the field filling a volume of space. If the plane of the card is rotated about the axis of the magnet, you can imagine each position showing the same pattern of field lines that the horizontal position shows.

The advantage of such a picture is that we can use it to describe magnetic forces even when we cannot get at the poles of a magnet. This is in fact the case with the earth. The directions of magnetic compasses all over the earth trace out the earth's magnetic field. You might suppose that this means that there is a gigantic magnet within the earth. However, it is better to say simply that the earth is a magnet. The field lines of the earth's magnetic field shown on the map in Fig. 9-2 indicate that compass needles do not generally point exactly north.

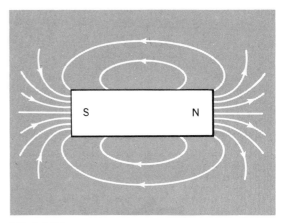

FIG. 9-1 (b)

Or, rotate the magnet under the card.

Other planets and the sun and stars also have magnetic fields.

FIG. 9-2

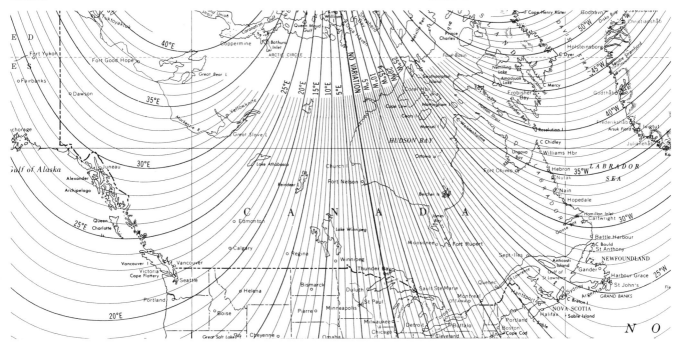

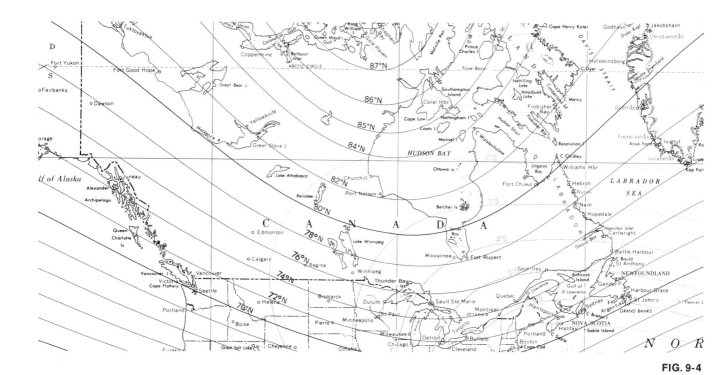

FIG. 9-4

FIG. 9-3

When a magnetized needle is pivoted on a vertical pin it can move only in the horizontal plane. Thus, it only shows the direction of the magnetic field in that plane. If the needle is pivoted on a horizontal pin, it can show the field direction in the vertical plane (Fig. 9-3). That plane must contain the direction of the horizontal needle. Such a dipping needle will have its north pole pointing downward from the horizontal in the northern hemisphere. In southern Ontario the angle of dip is between 70° and 75° from the horizontal (Fig. 9-4). At the magnetic equator the angle of dip is zero—the needle is horizontal.

A MODEL FOR MAGNETISM

Imagine a bar of soft iron of dimensions 1 cm by 1 cm by 10 cm. Consider it composed of about ten million clumps of atoms, each clump consisting of about 10^{17} atoms. The clumps are called *domains*. Each domain is totally magnetized, but when the bar is unmagnetized, the orientations of magnetization of the domains are random (Fig. 9-5).

If the bar is placed in a magnetic field, some of the domains will have their magnetization direction shifted in response to the force of the field. The stronger the force, the larger the number of domains that will line up with it.

Magnetic materials differ in the ease with which their domains will switch direction. They switch easily in soft iron, and much less so in hard steel. If the domains do switch easily in the presence of a field, they will easily switch back again when the influence of the field is removed. A material's ability to stay magnetized is called **retentivity**. Steel has a larger retentivity than soft iron. Thus, steel makes better permanent magnets than soft iron does.

An interesting test of this model can be made with a rod of soft iron. Hold it horizontally in an east-west direction and strike it sharply a few times with a light hammer. When it is tested against a compass needle, both of its ends should attract both ends of the needle. That indicates that the rod is not magnetized. Then, hold the rod parallel to the earth's magnetic field—that is, tilted downwards towards the north at about 75°. Strike it sharply with the hammer, and test each end again by bringing it slowly towards each end of the magnetized compass needle. One end should now repel one end of the compass needle. The striking is done in order to give the domains a chance to overcome their tendency to remain locked in place. When the rod is not aligned with the magnetic field lines of the earth, the striking tends to shake the domain magnetizations into directions across the rod's width. When the rod is aligned with the earth's field lines, more of the domains have their magnetization along the length of the rod.

A more effective way to magnetize a bar is to draw the south pole of a permanent magnet along the bar from one end to the other. Repeated a number of times, this procedure can align a number of the domains in the material with their north poles pointing in the direction of motion of the south pole of the magnet.

This procedure is more effective when the magnet you use is stronger. You should note that both the methods of magnetization could be called **induction**. Unlike electrical induction, whether the effect is permanent or not depends more on the material than the method of treatment.

When you sprinkle iron filings on a card above a bar magnet, the individual filings are magnetized by induction. Even if a filing may have been slightly magnetized before, the strength of the nearby magnet may be enough to switch the magnetization of its domains. The same effect may be seen if you quickly bring the north pole of a bar magnet toward the north pole of a compass needle. The force that is displayed may not be repulsion.

MORE ABOUT FIELD LINES

Magnetic field lines have been used to show the *direction* of the magnetic force about a magnet. They can also be used to give an indication of the *strength* of the magnetic force. All the field lines are closed loops that pass through the magnet. Outside the magnet they spread out as shown in the photograph of the iron filing patterns (Fig. 9-1). The field lines are closest together within the magnet. And just off the ends of the magnet, the field lines are closer together than at greater distances. Since the magnetic force is greatest at the ends of the magnet, the concentration of field lines is a measure of the

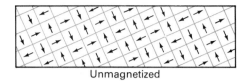
Unmagnetized

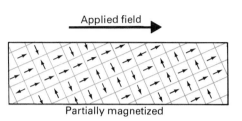
Applied field

Partially magnetized

FIG. 9-5. The boundaries between domains are by no means as regular as they appear in these sketches of the magnetic domain model.

This was the earliest method of magnetization. In ancient times, the iron ore magnetite was often found to be magnetized. Such a natural magnet was then rubbed along steel needles to magnetize them.

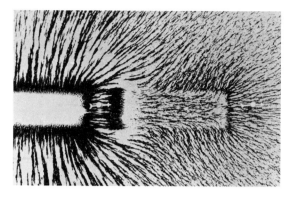

FIG. 9-6

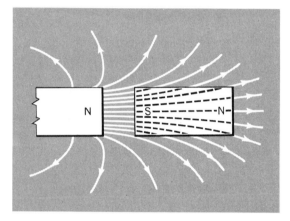

FIG. 9-7

strength of the magnetic force. Where the field lines are farther apart the magnetic force is weaker.

The photograph of Fig. 9-6 shows the iron filing pattern in the vicinity of the north pole of a bar magnet when a piece of soft iron is located there. The effect is to concentrate the magnetic field lines into a smaller space than they would occupy if there was air in that region instead of iron. The compass needles indicate that the right end of the iron bar has the properties of the north pole of a bar magnet. The soft iron bar, placed in the field of the bar magnet, has been induced to be a magnet. The effect on the magnetic field lines is illustrated in the diagram of Fig. 9-7.

Whenever any material is placed in a magnetic field it changes the magnetic field strength in the space it occupies. The change that a material can make in the magnetic field strength in a volume of space can be defined numerically by a quantity named **permeability**. Numerically a material's permeability is the ratio of the magnetic force with the material present to the magnetic force if the material was not present.

The symbol for permeability is μ, the Greek letter *mu*. For most substances (such as air or wood or copper) the permeability differs only very slightly from 1. For the usual magnetic materials, the permeability has values in the hundreds or thousands. Some special alloys have permeabilities as great as 100 000.

The magnetic field lines of two magnets can also be used to show the direction of the force between the magnets (Fig. 9-8). When two bar magnets are placed side by side, with north poles at the same end, their field lines are parallel. The force between the magnets is repulsion. Thus, when field lines are parallel they depict a force of repulsion. If one of the magnets is reversed, the force will be one of attraction. Now the field lines point in opposite directions, and can be said to be anti-parallel. Thus, when field lines are anti-parallel, they depict a force of attraction.

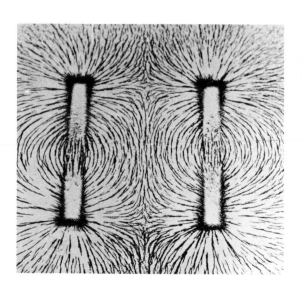

FIG. 9-8(a). Bar magnets side by side with *like* poles opposite.

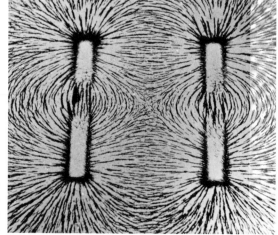

FIG. 9-8(b). Bar magnets side by side with *unlike* poles opposite.

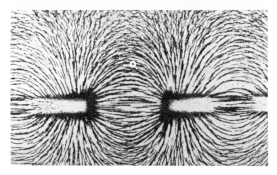

FIG. 9-8(c). Bar magnets with *unlike* poles end to end.

These rules are fine for magnets that are side by side, but they need modification when magnets are placed end to end. With unlike poles end to end, the field lines of the two magnets can be joined together. That makes them parallel, yet the force is one of attraction. Keeping this exception in mind, you will be able to use the rules when you know the directions of field lines but are not able to identify poles.

THE MAGNETIC FIELD OF ELECTRICITY

Arrange a copper wire so that it is slightly above a compass needle and parallel to it. Then connect the ends of the wire to a dry cell. The compass needle will swing round to align itself more or less perpendicular to the wire. Electric currents have magnetic fields associated with them. In Fig. 9-9 the pattern of the magnetic field about the current carrying conductor is shown by iron filings and compass needles.

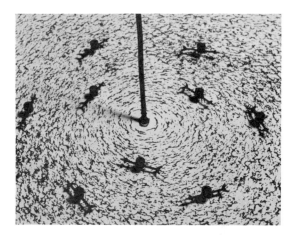

FIG. 9-9

A fuller representation of the magnetic field of the current can be shown in a three-dimensional drawing. Fig. 9-10 represents a rectangular volume of space around a section of wire in which electrons are flowing. The directions of electron motion and of the field lines are indicated by arrows. When viewed from the end, an arrow is either receding or approaching. If the arrow points away from you it is represented by a cross (×), and if it points toward you, by a dot (·). This is a map of the magnetic field due to the current in the wire.

The relation between the direction of electron motion and the direction of magnetic field lines can be described simply by a left-hand rule:

Grasp the conductor in your left hand with the thumb pointing in the direction of electron motion. The fingers, curled about the conductor, point in the direction of the magnetic field lines.

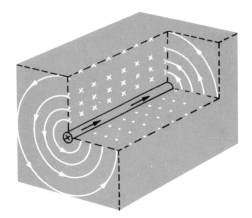

FIG. 9-10

To draw three-dimensional diagrams often requires considerable effort, and a cross-sectional diagram would be easier. Yet the left-hand rule requires some indication of space relations, since the field lines occupy a plane and the wire is perpendicular to that plane. In a cross-sectional diagram, it is often convenient to represent the wire perpendicular to the plane of the page. The direction of electron flow is shown by a cross or a dot. The magnetic field lines are then concentric circles about the wire. In Fig. 9-11, diagram (a) shows the relation when the conductor in (b) is viewed from the left end, and dia-

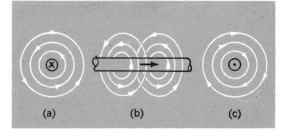

(a)   (b)   (c)

FIG. 9-11

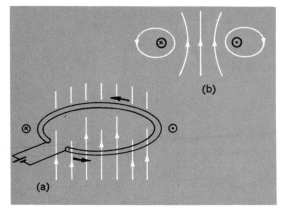

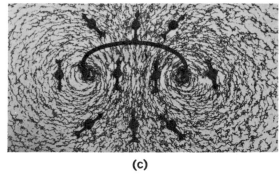

(b)

(c)

FIG. 9-12 (a)

gram (c) shows the relation when it is viewed from the right end. The left-hand rule is followed in all three diagrams.

The magnetic field in a section of space can be strengthened by looping the conductor around the space, as shown in Fig. 9-12. Diagram (a) shows the three-dimensional relations; (b) is a cross-section when viewing the loop from the edge; (c) is a photograph that confirms the prediction of the left-hand rule. Notice that each segment of the loop produces a magnetic field in the same direction within the loop.

THE MAGNETIC FIELD AROUND COILS

A magnetic field can be further strengthened by combining the effects of a number of loops, close together. The diagram and photograph in Fig. 9-13 illustrate the magnetic field of a conductor that has been coiled into the shape of a helix. This coil has eleven turns (or loops).

The direction of the magnetic field lines due to a current in a coil can be related to the direction of electron motion by the left-hand rule for coils:

Grasp the coil in your left hand with the fingers pointing in the direction of electron motion. The extended thumb points in the direction of the magnetic field lines within the coil.

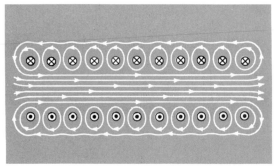

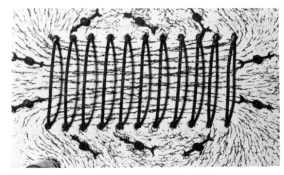

FIG. 9-13   a   b

Both left-hand rules illustrate that magnetic field lines are perpendicular to the direction of electron motion.

The magnetic field around the coil is very similar to the magnetic field around a bar magnet. As a result, you will find that there are many applications in which a magnet produced by an electric current can be used in place of a permanent bar magnet. However, we need to be able to make such an electromagnet stronger than it is in the situation we have just examined. There are three factors that determine what the strength of an electromagnet will be.

1. We have already seen that the number of turns has an effect on the magnetic field strength of a coil. More precisely, it is the number of turns per unit length that affects the magnetic field strength of a coil. Ten turns spread over a kilometre will have a very much weaker field than ten turns in one centimetre.

2. If a magnetic field is associated with each moving electron, then the magnetic field would be expected to depend on the number of electrons moving, and on the speed with which they move. Thus the magnetic field strength of a coil should depend on the current in the coil.

3. If the coil is wound on a core material with a high permeability, that should increase its magnetic field strength.

The magnetic field strength of a coil is found to vary directly as the permeability of the core (μ), the number of turns per unit length in the coil (N), and the current in the coil (I).

The effect of each of these factors on the magnetic field of a coil is illustrated in the diagrams of Fig. 9-14. To indicate a stronger magnetic field the field lines are closer together and thus more numerous.

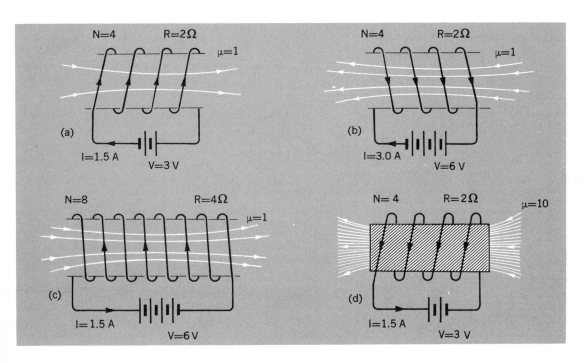

FIG. 9-14

Exercises

A

1. In what ways are magnetic forces (a) similar to and (b) not similar to electric forces?

2. The head of a large nail is brought toward the south pole of a compass needle from the side. Describe the action that you would observe if
   (a) the nail is iron, but unmagnetized,
   (b) the nail head is a magnetic north pole,
   (c) the nail head is a magnetic south pole.

3. Suppose you have two identical looking bars of metal. One is a magnet, the other is unmagnetized iron. How could you tell which was which (a) without using any other object, (b) by using a third object?

4. If you were to construct a small model of the earth so that tiny compass needles would seem to point on the model as they do on the earth, how would you orient the bar magnet that you insert to produce the magnetic field of the model?

5. In Ontario, how does the angle of dip at any given place compare to the latitude there?

6. Do you suppose that the magnetic equator of the earth coincides with the geographic equator?

7. Draw a diagram with a series of short arrows to show the directions of magnetization of the domains of (a) an unmagnetized iron bar and (b) an iron bar that is fully magnetized ("saturated").

8. What characteristics of retentivity and permeability would be best for (a) a permanent magnet, (b) the material of a device in which the magnetization has to be altered frequently?

9. (a) What kind of force exists between side-by-side magnets whose field lines are parallel (pointing in the same direction)?
   (b) What kind of force exists between side-by-side magnets whose field lines are anti-parallel (pointing in opposite directions)?

10. Draw two sets of three concentric circles side-by-side in your notebook. Let the innermost circle in each set represent a conductor in which electrons are moving.
    (a) Put a dot at the centre of one set to represent electrons travelling toward you, and put arrow heads on the outer two circles to show the direction of the magnetic field lines about the conductor.
    (b) Put a cross (×) at the centre of the other set to represent electrons travelling away from you, and put arrow heads on the outer two circles to

show the direction of the magnetic field lines about the conductor.
    (c) If the two conductors were quite close together, would the magnetic force between them be one of attraction or repulsion?
    (d) When two conductors close together are carrying electrons in the same direction is the magnetic force between them one of attraction or repulsion?

11. In the following sketch, a conductor is carrying electrons northward. The dashed lines represent possible orientations of compass needles that are above and below the conductor. Draw the sketch in your notebook and fill in the correct orientation of the two compass needles.

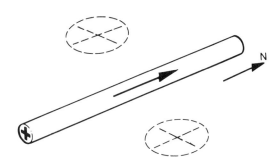

12. The following sketches for this problem show magnetic field lines about two conductors. Copy the sketches into your notebook and complete them to show the direction of motion of electrons in each conductor.

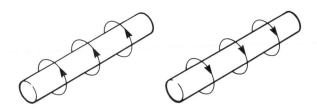

13. Copy the following four sketches into your notebook, and complete them so that the polarities of the magnetic coil (N and S), and of the battery (+ and −), and the direction of electron motion, are shown in all four sketches.

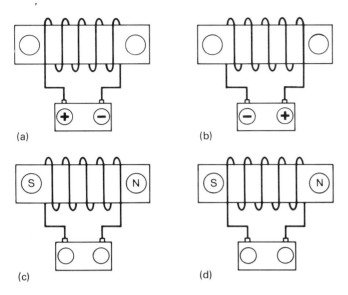

(a)

(b)

(c)

(d)

14. Insulated copper wire is wrapped with its turns close together in a single layer around a cardboard cylinder. A soft iron bar fits snugly into the cylinder. The ends of the copper wire are connected to two dry cells in series. The electromagnet so constructed can exert a force of 1.0 N at its end. What change would you expect in that force if
(a) the coil was connected to four dry cells in series,
(b) the soft iron bar was removed,
(c) a nickel bar was used as the core instead of the soft iron?

B

15. A compass needle is pointing in its usual north-south direction. In what direction must electrons move in a conductor beneath the compass so that the compass needle does not move?

16. A coil of 750 turns is wound using 200 m of copper wire. Connected to a 6.0 V battery, the coil with a soft iron core can support a load of 3.0 N. What load could be supported using the same battery if
(a) 375 turns were removed from the coil, but the 100 m of wire unwound remained in the circuit,
(b) the 100 m of wire was cut off so that the circuit contained only the 100 m of wire of the 375 turns that remain?

17. Describe the details of the attraction of a permanent magnet for a soft iron nail in terms of domains and magnetic induction. (Recall the similar argument for electric charges in Chapter 7.)

18. (a) If a steel ship is built with its bow pointing north, the hammering during construction often results in the ship being magnetized. Which end will have a north polarity?
(b) Draw a quick sketch of a ship magnetized as in (a), with a few turns of a wire coil about it that could tend to offset the magnetization. Show the direction of electron motion.

C

19. Ferromagnetic materials used as cores for electromagnets exhibit a property known as *magnetic hysteresis*.
(a) Find out and explain in a sentence or two what this means.
(b) Which would exhibit greater magnetic hysteresis, soft iron or hardened steel?
(c) Explain your answer to (b) in terms of the domain model.

20. Look up and explain the differences between paramagnetic, diamagnetic, and ferromagnetic substances.

CHAPTER 10

Electromagnetic Forces

While there are a number of applications for permanent magnets, electromagnets have proved to be much more versatile. An electromagnet can be energized by the flick of a switch, and de-energized by another flick. In addition, electromagnets can be made with magnetic fields many times stronger than any permanent magnet. In this chapter we shall consider applications in which electromagnets exert forces on magnetic materials, and then go on to applications in which the electromagnet is a coil moving in a magnetic field.

ELECTROMAGNETS

Electromagnets are designed to produce an intense magnetic field in the working area. The lifting electromagnet illustrated in Fig. 10-1 has a core made of soft iron or of a high-permeability low-retentivity alloy. The magnetic field lines are largely confined within the core except on the bottom surface where the magnetic force is exerted. The space within the core is filled with a coil of many turns of copper wire. The resistance of the wire will influence the current in it. Thicker wires have less resistance and therefore allow more current to pass, but they each occupy more space. A compromise choice of wire size is made to make the product of the number of turns and the current as large as possible. Electromagnets of this design may be able to support loads that are hundreds of times the weight of the magnet.

A horseshoe of iron with coils on its legs is used effectively in the devices illustrated in Fig. 10-2. In each of the diagrams there is a movable bar of iron called the **armature,** which is mounted on a pivot. When the electromagnet is energized by closing the switch the armature is drawn toward the magnet. When the switch is opened, a spring pulls the armature away from the magnet. In Fig. 10-2(a), closing the switch causes the armature to strike gong A. When the switch is opened, the armature is pulled back and strikes gong B. This can give you a two-note door chime.

In Fig. 10-2(b) the armature has been made the switch in a second circuit. Such a device is called a *relay*. When the switch S is closed the armature closes the *relay circuit* to light the lamp. The relay

(a)

Core

Coil

(b)

FIG. 10-1

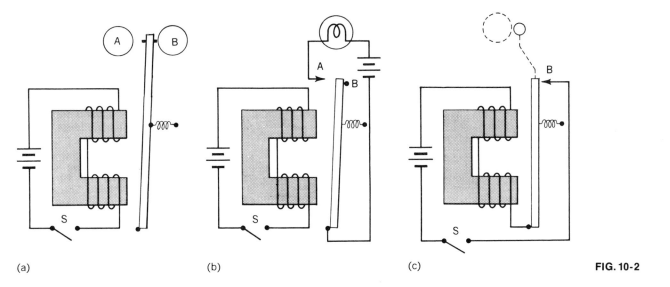

(a) (b) (c) **FIG. 10-2**

circuit could be arranged with the contact at B instead of A so that the lamp will be alight as long as switch S is open. Relays are widely used in electrical circuitry in an application akin to amplification (see Chapter 20). A sensitive electromagnet circuit can be arranged to actuate the armature switch for currents in the coil of 1 mA or less. The current in the relay circuit, on the other hand, might be 1 A or more. With a relay a small current can control a much larger one.

In Fig. 10-2(c), the armature switch is made a part of the electromagnet circuit. When the main switch is closed the armature moves towards the electromagnet, and breaks the contact at B. With the electromagnet de-energized the spring pulls the armature back to contact B. Once more the magnet is energized, the armature pulls away, and the cycle is repeated. As long as the main switch is closed, the armature vibrates back and forth. This is the basic circuit of an electric buzzer, or, with hammer and gong attached, of an electric bell.

A CONDUCTOR IN A MAGNETIC FIELD

A conductor with an electric current in it has a magnetic field around it. If the conductor is placed in the magnetic field of a horseshoe magnet (either a permanent magnet or an electromagnet), there might be expected to be a force between the two magnetic fields. From the discussion in Chapter 9 we should be able to predict the direction of the force. Fig. 10-3 represents a cross-section of a horseshoe magnet with a conductor perpendicular to the line between its poles. Electrons in the conductor are moving into the page. (A small number of field lines has been used to make the deduction clear.) The field about the conductor is anticlockwise, according to the left-hand rule. On the left the field lines of conductor and magnet are

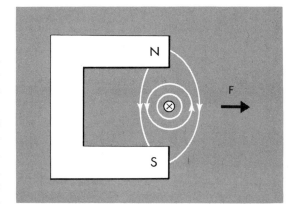

FIG. 10-3

FIG. 10-4

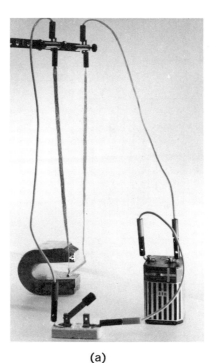

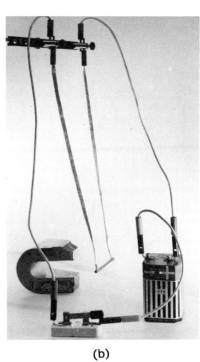

(a)   (b)

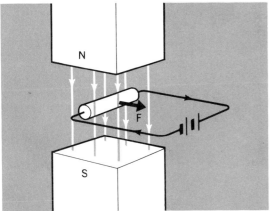

FIG. 10-5

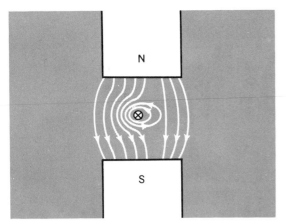

FIG. 10-6

parallel (in the same direction) and on the right they are anti-parallel (that is, parallel, but pointing in opposite directions). Thus, we can predict that the conductor will experience a force to the right. The prediction can be checked using the apparatus shown in Fig. 10-4. Photograph (a) shows the location of the conductor when the current is zero. The effect of the force between the magnet and the conductor when there is current in the conductor is evident in (b). The directions in the photograph agree with the prediction from Fig. 10-3.

The three-dimensional nature of the arrangement is made clear in Fig. 10-5. The force between magnet and conductor is strongest when the conductor is perpendicular to the magnet's field lines, and the force is exerted in a direction perpendicular both to the conductor and to the field lines. The existence of a force on a conductor in a magnetic field is often called the **motor principle**:

A conductor in which electrons are moving perpendicular to an external magnetic field experiences a force which is perpendicular both to the conductor and to the magnetic field lines.

The directional relations can be illustrated and remembered by a left-hand palm rule. Hold your left hand with the fingers together and the thumb at right angles to them. Now orient your hand so that the fingers point in the direction of the magnetic field and the thumb in the direction of motion of electrons. The direction of the force of the magnetic field on the moving electrons is in the direction in which your palm pushes. You will see that this rule applies to Figs. 10-4 and 10-5.

The actual shape of the magnetic field lines in this situation is illustrated in Fig. 10-6. Note that the conductor moves in the direction away from the concentrated field lines.

Careful measurements have shown that the force between a conductor and a magnet varies directly as the magnetic field strength and the current in the conductor. The dependence of the force on the current is used in a direct application of the motor principle. Fig. 10-7 illustrates the basic structure of a radio speaker. A coil of fine wire of small mass is centred within the circular gap of a permanent magnet. This voice coil is wound on a thin cylindrical form to which is attached a paper cone. A varying electric current in the voice coil results in a varying force between the magnet and the coil. As a result the coil moves back and forth parallel to the axis of the magnet. Thus the speaker cone is made to vibrate in step with the current supplied to the voice coil. Chapter 21 describes the basis of the system by which a radio produces a varying electric current corresponding to the sounds in the broadcasting studio. From this varying current the speaker in your living room is able to reproduce the sound in the studio.

The force on a conductor carrying a current I in a magnetic field B is
$$F = IIB_\perp$$
where I is the length of the conductor in the field and $B_\perp$ means that the directions of conductor and field are perpendicular. B is measured in teslas (T) where 1 T = 1 N/A·m. The magnetic field strength of the earth is about 50 μT, and of a bar magnet about 5 mT. Very powerful electromagnets may produce fields up to about 5 T.

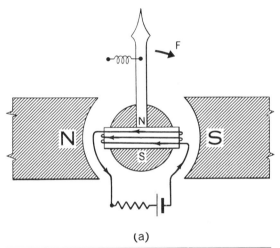

(a)

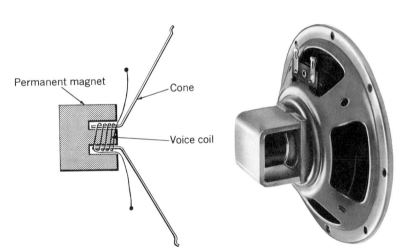

FIG. 10-7

ELECTRIC METERS

If a coil is located in a magnetic field in the position shown in Fig. 10-8(a), a current through the coil will result in a force between the magnet and the coil. The force varies directly as the current in the coil. The top of the coil has a north polarity, and the bottom has a south polarity, so that the force on both ends tends to produce a clockwise rotation of the coil. In the photograph of Fig. 10-8(b) the flat coil spring provides a variable force to oppose the magnetic force. The spring acts to measure the magnetic force, in the same way that a spring balance is used to measure gravitational forces.

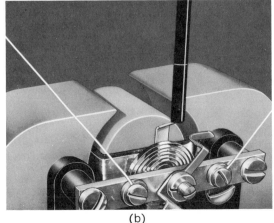

(b)

FIG. 10-8

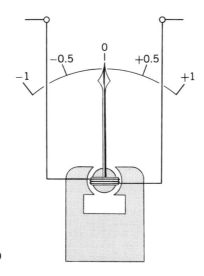

FIG. 10-9

The amount of rotation varies directly as the current in the coil. This arrangement forms the basis of the current measuring device called a **galvanometer**. Within the coil is a stationary soft iron cylinder, which serves to increase the magnetic field strength within the coil.

The complete arrangement of a galvanometer is shown in Fig. 10-9. This meter is also called a milliammeter because the needle is deflected from 0 to 1 when the current in the coil is 1.0 mA. With the needle in the centre of the scale for no current in the coil, the needle will deflect to the right for electrons moving in one direction through the coil, and to the left for electrons in the opposite direction. The galvanometer is thus able to indicate both the magnitude of small currents and the direction of the electron motion.

A current of 2.0 mA provides enough force to move the needle of the galvanometer from one side of the scale to the other. This meter movement is then said to have a full-scale deflection of 2.0 mA. The resistance of the meter is 50 Ω. These two measurements are used to identify the characteristics of any meter. Moving coil galvanometers constructed like the one in Fig. 10-9 provide the basic movement (or structure) for electric meters used to measure currents or voltages over a wide range. But in all cases the current limitation of the meter's coil must be recognized. In the particular meter we are considering, 2.0 mA is the maximum current that may be applied to the coil.

For a circuit of fixed resistance, the voltage across any part of the circuit varies directly as the current through the circuit. How can a galvanometer be modified to give a deflection that varies directly as the voltage across its terminals?

In Fig. 10-10 a galvanometer in series with a resistor R_v is connected across a 1.0 Ω resistance that is connected to a dry cell of 1.0 V. The resistor R_v must be chosen so that the current through the galvanometer will not exceed the 2.0 mA current that its coil can

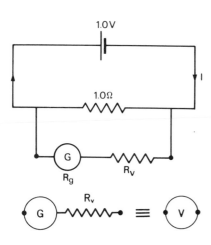

FIG. 10-10

handle. The value of R_v can be calculated according to the following example.

Example: A galvanometer having a resistance of 50 Ω has a full-scale deflection of 2.0 mA. Calculate the value of the series resistor that will give full-scale deflection when meter and resistor are connected across two points between which there is a potential difference of 1.0 V.

The current in the galvanometer is to be

$$I = 2.0 \text{ mA} = 2.0 \times 10^{-3} \text{ A}.$$

The potential difference across meter and resistor is

$$V = 1.0 \text{ V}.$$

The resistance of resistor and galvanometer has to be

$$R = \frac{V}{I} = \frac{1.0 \text{ V}}{2.0 \times 10^{-3} \text{ A}} = 5.0 \times 10^2 \ \Omega.$$

Since the resistance of the galvanometer is 50 Ω, the resistance of the series resistor is

$$R_v = (500 - 50) \ \Omega = 450 \ \Omega.$$

Therefore the resistor is required to have a resistance of $4.5 \times 10^2 \ \Omega$.

As shown in Fig. 10-10, a **voltmeter** consists of a galvanometer in series with a high resistance. In Chapter 8 we saw that a voltmeter is connected across two points to measure the potential difference between them. Now we have found that a voltmeter must have a high resistance to protect the coil of the galvanometer movement. In addition, the high resistance of the voltmeter means that it will take only a small fraction of the current in the circuit. (It must be noted that any type of voltmeter requires *some* current to produce a reading.) Thus the connection of a voltmeter into a circuit changes the circuit. The higher the resistance of the voltmeter, however, the smaller is its effect on the circuit.

The measurement of the current in a circuit requires an **ammeter** connected into the circuit in series. For it to have a minimum effect on the circuit its resistance should be as small as possible. What arrangement can be made to reduce the resistance of a 50 Ω galvanometer? From the discussion of parallel resistors in Chapter 8, it is evident that the parallel combination of the galvanometer with a resistor having 1% of its resistance would have a total resistance just less than 1% of the galvanometer's resistance. A low resistance connected in parallel with a galvanometer is called a *shunt resistance.* The shunt lowers the effective resistance of the galvanometer, and it will carry most of the current, thus protecting the moving coil. The

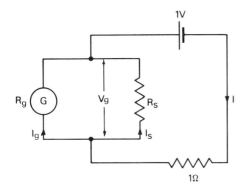

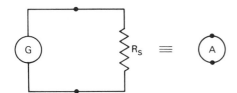

FIG. 10-11

arrangement in Fig. 10-11 shows the adaptation of a galvanometer to measure larger currents than the 2.0 mA that its coil can withstand. The value of the shunt resistance R_s can be calculated according to the following example.

Example: A galvanometer having a resistance of 50 Ω has a full-scale deflection of 2.0 mA. Calculate the value of the shunt resistor that will give full-scale deflection when meter and resistor are connected in a circuit carrying 1.0 A.

In the circuit illustrated in Fig. 10-11, a coil of wire of resistance 1.0 Ω is connected to a dry cell of potential difference 1.0 V. The current in the circuit is

$$I = V/R = 1.0 \text{ A}.$$

The current that the galvanometer may carry is

$$I_g = 2.0 \text{ mA} = 2.0 \times 10^{-3} \text{ A}.$$

The resistance of the galvanometer is

$$R_g = 50 \text{ Ω}.$$

The voltage drop across the galvanometer for full-scale deflection is therefore

$$V_g = I_g R_g = (2.0 \times 10^{-3} \text{ A})(50 \text{ Ω}) = 0.10 \text{ V}.$$

In the parallel connection, the voltage drop across the shunt resistor is also

$$V_s = V_g = 0.10 \text{ V}.$$

For conservation of charge, the current in the shunt must be the difference between the total current and the current in the galvanometer. It is

$$I_s = I - I_g = 1.000 \text{ A} - 0.002 \text{ A} = 0.998 \text{ A}.$$

The resistance of the shunt is

$$R_s = \frac{V_s}{I_s} = \frac{0.10 \text{ V}}{0.998 \text{ A}} = 0.10 \text{ Ω}.$$

Therefore the required resistance of the shunt is 0.10 Ω.

Because of the accuracy of the quantities, the resistance of the shunt must be expressed simply as 0.10 Ω, and the net resistance of galvanometer and shunt in parallel is 0.10 Ω for all practical purposes. Notice that connecting the ammeter to measure the current increases the resistance of the circuit from 1.0 Ω to 1.1 Ω and therefore the current measured is no longer 1.0 A. The accuracy with which a measurement can be made depends upon the influence that the measuring process has on the quantity being measured: the smaller the influence, the greater is the accuracy obtainable.

THE DIRECT CURRENT MOTOR

A galvanometer coil could be arranged so that its winding is almost vertical when there is no current. With the north pole of the coil next to the north pole of the magnet, the coil will rotate clockwise when a current flows (Fig. 10-12). If the force of the opposing spring is small enough the coil could rotate almost a full 180° until the north pole of the coil is opposite the south pole of the magnet. The rotation could be continued if at that moment the direction of the current within the galvanometer coil could be reversed so that the north and south poles in the coil were reversed. Subsequent reversals of the current at each 180° rotation of the coil could maintain the circular motion of the coil.

Such regular reversals of the current direction can be accomplished by a device attached to the axis of the coil. A cylinder of copper is split into two segments of almost 180° each. One end of the coil is connected to each of the segments of the **commutator**—the device for converting current directions (Fig. 10-13). Connections from the segments to a battery are provided by carbon brushes which maintain electrical contact with the segments as they slide by. With the proper orientation of the segments and brushes, the current direction can be reversed at exactly the appropriate moments. The complete arrangement of commutator, brushes, coil, and magnet constitutes an electric motor. An **electric motor** is a device that transforms the kinetic energy of electrons into mechanical kinetic energy.

Since the current from a voltaic cell is continuous it is called **direct current**—in contrast to alternating current, described on page 138. The basic parts of a simple direct current (DC) motor are illustrated in Fig. 10-14. The armature consists of a coil of copper wire wound onto a soft iron core. The armature is mounted on an axle perpendicular to the page. The magnetic field is provided by the field magnet, which may be a permanent magnet, or an electromagnet as illustrated in Fig. 10-14. The supplies to the armature magnet and the field magnet are shown here as separate. In practice, the two may be supplied from a single battery, connected to them either in parallel or series. The motion of electrons in the coil makes the armature an electromagnet strengthened by the iron core. The rotation of the armature is produced by the magnetic forces between the poles of the field magnet and the poles of the armature.

The action of the commutator in reversing the current can be followed through a series of steps shown in Figs. 10-15a to 10-15d. Throughout the cycle electrons arrive at the armature coil from Brush A. In Fig. 10-15a, we can use the left-hand rule to show that the marked pole of the armature is north. It is repelled by the N pole of the field magnet, and it moves around in a clockwise direction. In

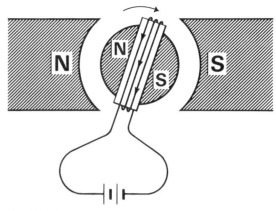

FIG. 10-12

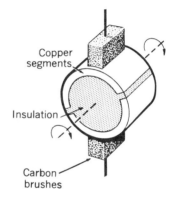

FIG. 10-13

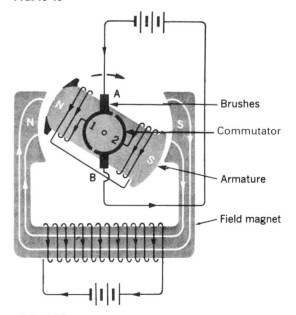

Brushes

Commutator

Armature

Field magnet

FIG. 10-14

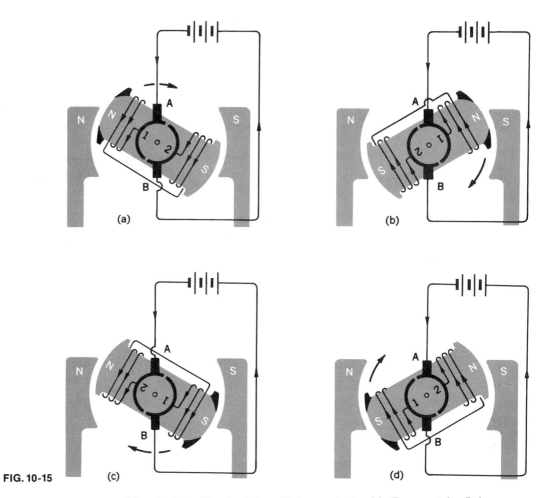

FIG. 10-15

(a) (b) (c) (d)

Fig. 10-15b, Brush A is still in contact with Segment 1 of the commutator, and electrons move in the same direction as in Fig. 10-15a. The marked pole, still north, is attracted by the S pole of the field magnet. Without the commutator the motion would cease when the armature became horizontal. The inertia of the armature is sufficient to carry it past the horizontal. In Fig. 10-15c, Brush A contacts Segment 2 of the commutator, causing the direction of the electrons in the coil to reverse. The marked pole becomes south and is repelled by the S pole of the field magnet: rotation continues. In Fig. 10-15d, the marked pole is still south and is attracted by the N pole of the field magnet. Continuing the cycle from Fig. 10-15d to Fig. 10-15a involves another reversal of electron motion and armature polarity, as in going from Fig. 10-15b to Fig. 10-15c. Rotation continues cycle after cycle: the kinetic energy of moving electrons in the coil has been translated into the kinetic energy of rotation of the armature.

Practical electric motors have a number of coils, each associated with its own pair of oppositely located commutator segments. An armature might have as many as 16 such coils. Electricity is supplied to one or two coils at a time, at the moment that the coil is oriented so

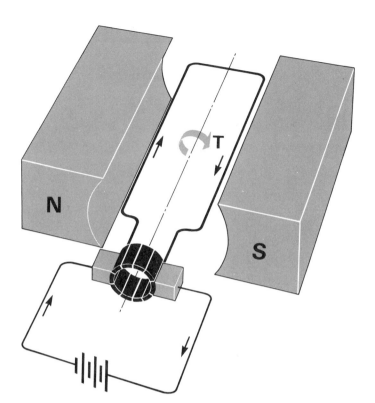

FIG. 10-16

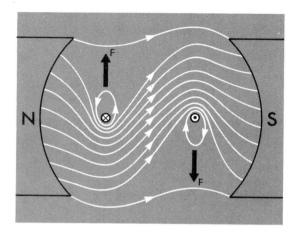

FIG. 10-17

that the torque on it is a maximum. Fig. 10-16 shows one loop of such a coil connected to one of four pairs of segments in á commutator. There should be three other such coils, but they are not shown. Each coil will be energized over a 45° arc centred on the axis of the poles of the field magnet. The magnetic force between the field magnet and the armature will be strongest in this region where the magnetic field lines of the field magnet are most strongly concentrated. Then, as one coil moves out of that region, its commutator segments lose contact with the brushes, while those of the next coil make contact. This next coil is then energized through the same region that the previous coil was. The pattern of field lines that gives rise to the magnetic force is shown in Fig. 10-17.

The photograph of an electric streetcar motor (Fig. 10-18) shows the armature removed from the casing that holds the field magnets. This motor operates on 300 V, and delivers a power of about 40 kW.

FIG. 10-18

Exercises

A

1. Draw a diagram of a horseshoe electromagnet, with windings arranged to make one leg a north pole and the other a south. Include a battery in the circuit and show the direction of electron motion in the coil on each leg.
   (a) Sketch in a few field lines to show the magnetic field in the region at the ends of the legs.
   (b) Repeat the original sketch, but now include a soft iron bar near the ends of the legs perpendicular to them, about a centimetre from their ends, and sketch a few magnetic field lines for this new situation.

2. A sketch of a small number of magnetic field lines is sufficient to deduce the direction of the force between a horseshoe magnet and a conductor in which there is a current. Make such a sketch for an end-on view of the poles of the magnet with a conductor between them. In the conductor show the electron motion toward you out of the page, with the north pole of the horseshoe magnet on the left and the south pole on the right. In which direction will the conductor tend to move?

3. A horseshoe magnet is lying on the table with its open end toward you, north pole on the left. A rectangular loop of wire is situated in a horizontal plane between the legs of the magnet.
   (a) Make an end-on sketch to show the direction that electrons will have to move (into or out of the page) so that the left part of the loop will experience an upward force, and its right side a downward force.
   (b) If the loop is pivoted so that it can rotate about an axis parallel to the legs of the magnet, in what direction will it tend to move?

4. Use the following diagram of a bar of iron pivoted between the legs of a horseshoe magnet for the following questions.
   (a) Show the direction of electron motion in the coil that will make the upper end of the bar north. In which direction will the bar tend to move?
   (b) Show the direction of electron motion in the coil that will tend to make the bar rotate in a counterclockwise direction.

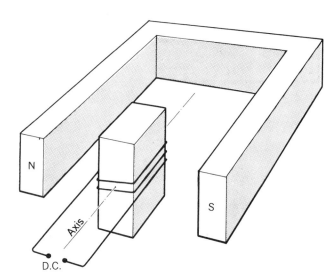

5. A galvanometer having a resistance of 50.0 Ω has a full-scale deflection of 2.00 mA. Calculate the value of the series resistor that will give a full-scale deflection when the meter and resistor are connected across two points between which there is a potential difference of 10.0 V.

6. (a) Calculate the value of the combined resistance of 100.0 Ω in parallel with 1.00 Ω.
   (b) The two resistors are connected in parallel to a 10.0 V battery. What is the current in (i) the 1.00 Ω resistor, (ii) the 100.0 Ω resistor?

7. A galvanometer of 50 Ω resistance has a full-scale deflection of 2.0 mA. Calculate the value of the shunt resistor that will give full-scale deflection when the meter and the shunt connected in parallel to it are connected in a circuit carrying a current of 10.0 A.

8. Trace the actions that produce rotation in a direct current motor during one complete rotation of the armature for a battery connection that is opposite to the one shown in the diagrams in Fig. 10-15.

B

9. (a) A cylinder of soft iron is suspended from a spring balance so that its lower end is just inside the top of a coil of wire of many turns. Draw a diagram showing the magnetic field lines to describe the action when there is a current in the coil.
   (b) Describe how this apparatus might be used as an ammeter.

(c) How effectively would the apparatus continue to work as an ammeter if the direction of electron motion in the coil was reversed frequently, so that the current value alternated from $+2$ A to -2 A?

10. Draw a diagram to determine the direction of the force on a conductor in a magnetic field with field lines directed leftward when the direction of electron motion in the conductor is upward.

11. Here is an analogy to illustrate the operation of shunts in ammeters. Imagine that between two cities there is a wide, straight toll highway. Just before the entrance to the toll gates there is access to a second route between the cities, a narrow, winding road. On the average, for every thousand cars that enter the highway, three take the road. (The highway has a considerably smaller "resistance" than the road.) During four hours on a Friday evening in summer, sitting at a point along the road, you count 24 cars going by. What was the current (in cars per hour) on the highway?

12. A galvanometer has a full-scale deflection of 1.0×10^{-4} A and a resistance of 1.0×10^2 Ω. Calculate
(a) the value of the series resistor needed to convert the galvanometer to a voltmeter for potential differences up to 10.0 V;
(b) the value of the shunt resistor needed to convert the galvanometer to an ammeter to measure currents up to 5.0 A.

13. In certain radio circuits there are currents in the range from 40 mA to 80 mA. You have two meters available, one with a full-scale deflection of 1.0 A, and the other 10 mA. Assuming that you have the equipment to make suitable shunt resistors, which meter would you use?

14. Many DC motors of more than flea-power size have an electromagnet for the external (or stator) field. Draw a diagram of a motor to show the connection of both the field winding and the brushes to the commutator with a single battery,
(a) to put the field and armature coils in series,
(b) to put the field and armature coils in parallel (called a shunt connection).

C

15. Find out what is meant by the earth's *magnetosphere*, and why it is given that name.

16. Find out what a ballistic galvanometer is and what it is used for.

17. (a) Use the relation $F = IlB_\perp$ to calculate the force on a 30 cm length of wire carrying a current of 2.0 A in a uniform magnetic field of 0.5 T at right angles to the wire.
(b) What would the force be if the same wire were aligned perpendicular to the earth's magnetic field of 60 μT?

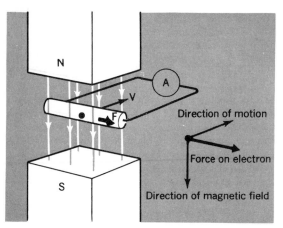

FIG. 11-1

Electromagnetic Induction and Energy

MAGNETIC FORCE ON ELECTRONS

We know that the motion of electrons through a wire (an electric current) creates a magnetic field around the wire, and we know that when electrons are moving in a wire located in a magnetic field there is a force on the wire. When the wire is perpendicular to the magnetic field lines, the force on it is perpendicular both to the wire and to the magnetic field lines. In earlier discussions, the electron motion resulted from a voltage applied across the ends of the wire. But the effect is completely general: *whenever* an electron moves in a magnetic field it experiences a force.

Fig. 11-1 illustrates a wire being pulled through a magnetic field. Since electrons are moving with the wire they experience a force. But the force, being perpendicular to the direction of motion, is along the wire. The electrons will move along the wire as a result of this force, and their motion is an electric current. The diagram of Fig. 11-1 illustrates the relations between the directions. When a conductor is moved broadside through a magnetic field perpendicular to it, there is a current induced in the conductor. This effect is **electromagnetic induction**.

For there to be a current the circuit must be complete. Even if it is not a complete circuit, there will still be an induced voltage.

DEMONSTRATION OF ELECTROMAGNETIC INDUCTION

A powerful magnet and a sensitive galvanometer are needed to show electromagnetic induction with a single conductor. The effect is much greater when a coil of many turns is used. If such a coil is connected to a galvanometer, as in Fig. 11-2, there will be an indication of current each time a bar magnet is thrust into the coil, or removed from it. Current is indicated only when there is relative motion between the coil and the magnet. After trying a number of variations, we can conclude:

Whenever the magnetic field within a closed circuit changes, there will be a current induced in the circuit.

This conclusion can be tested in a number of ways:

FIG. 11-2

(a) In Fig. 11-1, the closed loop is being drawn through the magnetic field so that the fraction of the magnetic field within the loop is decreasing, inducing a current.

(b) When a bar magnet is thrust into a coil as shown in Fig. 11-2, the magnetic field within the coil is increasing, inducing a current.

(c) When the bar magnet is withdrawn from the coil the magnetic field is decreasing, inducing a current.

(d) If the bar magnet is held motionless, the magnetic field within the coil is unchanged. No current passes through the coil.

(e) If the bar magnet is held part way into the coil and then moved back and forth in a direction perpendicular to the axis of the coil, the magnetic field within the coil is unchanged, and no current passes through the coil.

(f) If the loop in Fig. 11-1 is moved about without changing the magnetic field within it, there is no current in the wire.

The English scientist Michael Faraday's first observation of electromagnetic induction in 1831 involved changing the magnetic field within a coil in a way different from any so far discussed. He had two coils of insulated wire wound around an iron ring with no electrical connection between the two coils. As shown in Fig. 11-3, Coil A was connected in series with a switch and a battery. Coil B was connected to a galvanometer. At the moment of closing the switch, Faraday observed "immediately a sensible effect on the needle" of the galvanometer. From the direction of the deflection of the needle he could deduce the direction of the current. Then, "when the contact with the battery was broken the motion of the needle was as if a current in the opposite direction existed for a moment."

In this experiment Faraday was changing the magnetic field within Coil B by using Coil A as an electromagnet, which he turned on and

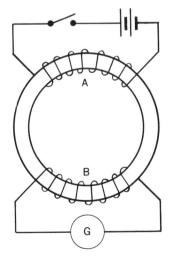

FIG. 11-3

off. When the switch is closed electrons flowing in Coil A produce a magnetic field in the iron ring. As this field builds up from zero to its final value, it is changing within Coil B and a current is induced. When the magnetic field reaches a steady value, there is no current in Coil B. When the switch is opened the electrons in Coil A cease to flow and the magnetic field in the iron ring collapses to zero. As the magnetic field within B decreases, there is an induced current in Coil B. The electrons move in the opposite direction this time, which is to be expected from observations using bar magnets.

MAGNITUDES IN ELECTROMAGNETIC INDUCTION

The magnitude of a current in a circuit depends on the potential difference provided by the source and on the resistance of the circuit. Thus the magnitude of the induced current in a coil connected to a galvanometer will depend on the resistance of the coil and galvanometer. To avoid having to consider the resistance when describing induction, it is usual to speak of the **induced potential difference** between the ends of a coil in which there is a changing magnetic field (since the potential difference is not affected by the resistance in the coil and galvanometer). Of course, as long as there is no change in the resistance of the complete circuit, the induced current varies directly as the induced potential difference. Accurate measurements confirm the following relation between the quantities in electromagnetic induction:

When the magnetic field within a coil changes, the induced potential difference varies directly as the product of the number of turns in the coil and the rate of change of the magnetic field.

We can look upon this process, then, as a source of electrical potential difference, and just as a voltaic cell can maintain a potential difference between its terminals, so a potential difference can be maintained between the terminals of a coil as long as there is a changing magnetic field within the coil. The voltaic cell transforms chemical potential energy into the energy of moving electrons. In Faraday's apparatus of Fig. 11-3, the electrons in Coil A have kinetic energy that is transformed to magnetic energy in the iron ring. The magnetic energy is then transformed into the kinetic energy of electrons in Coil B. If you move a magnet in and out of a coil, then you are providing the energy. The induced electrical energy comes from whatever energy source is used to change the magnetic field.

DIRECTIONS IN ELECTROMAGNETIC INDUCTION

Moving a magnet within a coil of wire is a means for transforming energy from some other form into electrical energy. Then we should expect the principle of the conservation of energy to apply to the transformation. Imagine a long bar magnet on wheels being pushed into a long coil of wire, as illustrated in Fig. 11-4. The changing magnetic field within the coil will cause a motion of electrons through the coil. That motion will provide the coil with its own magnetic field. The coil's magnetic field has its field lines along the axis of the coil.

Suppose that as the magnet is inserted in the coil the induced electron motion is in the direction that produces field lines in the same direction as those of the bar magnet. The initial motion of the magnet would induce a small current and that would produce a small magnetic field within the coil. With field lines in the same direction there would be a force of attraction between the coil and the bar magnet. That force would move the magnet faster, inducing a greater current, giving the coil a greater magnetic field, producing a stronger force of attraction on the bar magnet, making it move faster, inducing a greater current, . . . and the apparatus would continue to move by itself without further pushing. Such a state of affairs is contrary to experience and to the principle of energy conservation. It would be a perpetual motion machine.

But the total of the kinetic energy of the electrons and the bar magnet cannot exceed the initial kinetic energy of the bar magnet. The supposition in the preceding paragraph was wrong, so the direction of the field lines of the coil must be opposite to the field lines of the bar magnet. And the direction of electron motion conforms to the left-hand rule of Chapter 9.

The principle of energy conservation makes us confident to suggest that the magnetic field of the induced electron motion opposes the change in the inducing magnetic field. So if the north pole of the bar magnet is withdrawn from the coil, the induced magnetic field opposes the withdrawal, which means that the two sets of field lines are in the same direction. This requires a reversal in the direction of electron motion from the preceding example, which is consistent with observations. The two situations are illustrated in Fig. 11-5.

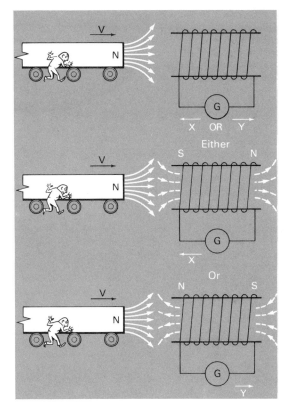

FIG. 11-4

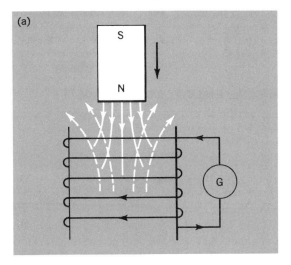
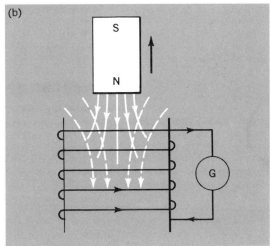

FIG. 11-5

To summarize:

(a) When the magnetic field strength within a coil changes there is an induced potential difference between the ends of the coil.

(b) The induced potential difference varies directly as the product of the number of turns in the coil and the rate of change of the magnetic field.

(c) When the ends of the coil are connected through a circuit there is an induced current in the coil. The electrons moving in the coil produce an induced magnetic field of their own.

(d) *The electrons of an induced current move in the direction that produces a magnetic field to oppose the inducing action.*

This last statement is called Lenz's law. The relation was discovered in 1834 by Heinrich Lenz in Russia. The application of Lenz's law involves the following steps:

(a) Determine the nature of the change in the magnetic field that produces the electromagnetic induction.

(b) Choose the direction for the induced magnetic field that opposes the change.

(c) Apply the left-hand rule to determine the direction of electron motion from the direction of the magnetic field.

When the magnetic field within a coil is initially zero, an increase in the magnetic field will be opposed by the induced magnetic field, attempting, one might say, to keep the magnetic field zero. On the other hand, if a steady magnetic field within a coil begins to decrease, the induced magnetic field acts to oppose the decrease, in an attempt to keep the field at its original value. This effect has some similarity to inertia, and in electrical theory there is in fact a place for such an idea. In any event, it can be seen that the induced magnetic field is truly conservative: it opposes change.

It should be mentioned that there is no energy transformation in electromagnetic induction until there is a complete circuit. In the same way, a dry cell is ready to transfer its chemical potential energy to the kinetic energy of electrons, but does not do so until there is a complete circuit. When the circuit is completed, electrons are supplied with kinetic energy, and in their impacts with the metallic ions in the wire increase the internal energy of the wire.

CONVERTING MECHANICAL ENERGY TO ELECTRICITY

An **electric generator** is a device that transforms mechanical kinetic energy into the kinetic energy of electrons. To apply electromagnetic induction to the generation of electricity, a method is needed for producing a continuous inducing action. A bar magnet, connected to the piston of a steam engine, might be moved back and forth within a coil. Or a coil could be rotated between the poles of a horseshoe magnet; but the wires connected to the coil would very soon be wrapped around the shaft. An early solution was to keep the coil stationary and rotate the magnet, but a powerful generator needs a large magnet, and too much energy is needed to overcome friction in

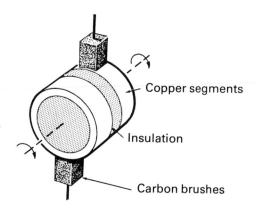

Copper segments

Insulation

Carbon brushes

FIG. 11-6

keeping a massive magnet moving. The problem was finally solved by connecting the ends of a coil to rings of copper mounted on the axis of rotation. A sliding contact was made with these **slip rings** by **brushes**, fixed pieces of metal to which the external circuit was connected (Fig. 11-6). Thus a rotating coil could be used without any tangling or twisting of the connecting wires.

A complete model of an electric generator is shown in Fig. 11-7. Its basic structure is the same as that of the DC motor described earlier.

As the armature is rotated there is a continuous change in the magnetic field within the coil. Thus, by electromagnetic induction, electrons are made to move continuously through the voltmeter.

Although the electrons are always moving in a regular way, their direction of motion reverses once during each half revolution of the armature. Lenz's law and the left-hand rule can be used to follow the cycle of changes illustrated in Fig. 11-8. In (a) the marked pole of the armature is being pulled away from the N pole of the field magnet. To oppose the change there must be an induced attraction between the armature and field (Lenz's law). The marked pole is therefore south, and the direction of electrons is as shown (left-hand rule). When the marked pole approaches the S pole of the field in (b), Lenz's law requires repulsion. The marked pole continues to be south, and the electron direction remains unchanged.

As the marked pole passes the central point of the S pole of the field magnet, motion towards the pole is replaced by motion away from the pole. To oppose the movement away, shown in (c), there must be attraction between the poles of armature and field: the marked end of the armature must change from south to north. To produce the change the electrons must move in the opposite direction. The voltmeter, which had indicated a positive voltage during the first half revolution, now swings negative. The progression from (c) to (d) is similar to that from (a) to (b). The next cycle begins as the armature rotates from (d) to (a); the electron direction again reverses as it did in the rotation from (b) to (c).

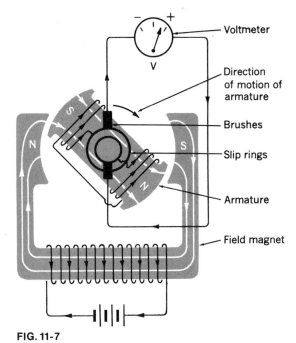

FIG. 11-7

FIG. 11-8

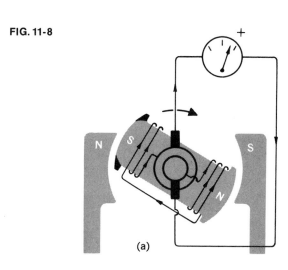

(a)

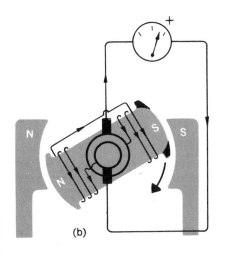

(b)

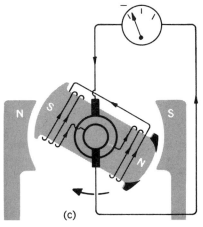

(c)

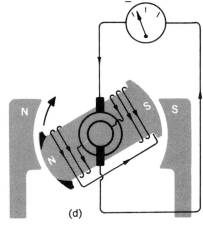

(d)

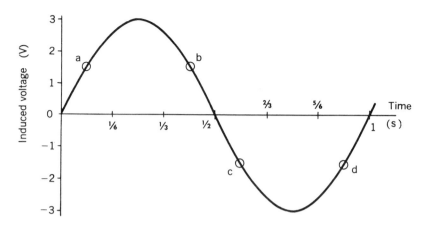

FIG. 11-9

ALTERNATING CURRENT

The direction of motion of the electrons in the armature circuit is reversed, or alternated, once during each half revolution. For that reason, the output from the generator is called **alternating current** (AC). The term AC is normally used in a way that neglects the fact that C is an abbreviation for current; for example, it is quite proper to speak of an AC voltage.

The graph of Fig. 11-9 shows the changes in the readings of the voltmeter of Fig. 11-8 as the armature is rotated. The meter is designed for use with direct current (DC), and will respond only to slow alternations. In the model generator a rotation of one revolution per second produces AC with a frequency of 1 Hz. As the armature rotates through its cycle the voltage increases smoothly from zero to a maximum, then decreases smoothly to zero, reverses direction, becomes more negative to a minimum, then increases to zero, and the cycle is repeated.

The time required for one complete cycle is called the period (symbol T). Its relation to the frequency of rotation (f) is

$$T = \frac{1}{f}.$$

Electricity supplied by electric energy companies in North America is usually AC of frequency 60 Hz. Then one complete cycle takes 1/60 s. One terminal of a 60 Hz AC supply is positive for 1/120 s, then negative for 1/120 s, then positive again, etc. In AC the average voltage is zero, and that is the reading one would find on a DC voltmeter. However, the energy transferred is not zero, and instruments have been designed specifically for measurements in AC circuits.

THE DIRECT CURRENT GENERATOR

Initially, scientists saw no use for the alternating current from early generators. So they sought a way to avoid the alternation in the di-

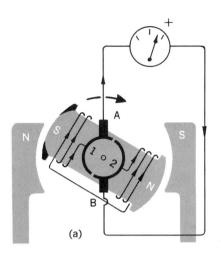

(a)

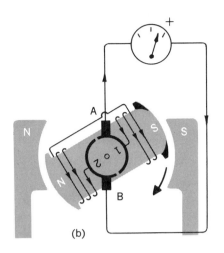

(b)

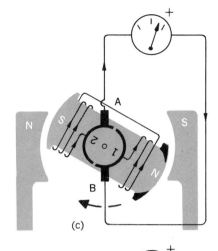

(c)

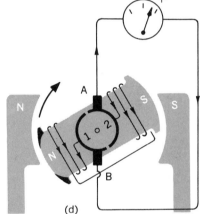

(d)

FIG. 11-10

rection of electron motion in the external circuit. There are reversing switches that could be operated manually each half cycle to keep the electrons moving in the same direction in the external circuit. But it would be difficult to keep in step with the alternations, and almost impossible to operate the switch 120 times a second. The commutator described for electric motors on page 127 is exactly suited for this task. In fact, it was invented about 1835 for use with generators.

The operation of the DC generator is illustrated in Fig. 11-10. The commutator segments are numbered 1 and 2; and the two brushes are identified by the letters A and B. In (a) and (b) electrons move from Segment 1 into Brush A. In all other respects the operation is like that in (a) and (b) of Fig. 11-8 for the AC generator. But when the polarity of the marked pole of the armature is reversed in passing from (b) to (c), the gaps between the segments pass under the brushes. As the direction of electrons in the coil reverses, Brush A loses contact with Segment 1 and begins to contact Segment 2. When the electrons reverse direction they begin to move out of Segment 2. So they continue to move into Brush A and the direction of electrons in the voltmeter is the same as before. The brushes exchange segments every half revolution, as the direction of the electrons and the polarity of the armature are reversed.

The way that the voltage changes as the armature of the DC generator rotates is shown in Fig. 11-11. The shape of each half cycle is the same as in Fig. 11-9 for the AC generator, but every half cycle here is positive. We say that the alternating current, which is still

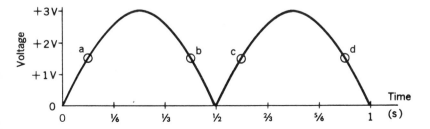

FIG. 11-11

present within the armature coil, has been *rectified*. Of course, this graph is quite different from the voltage variation with time that would be obtained from a voltaic cell. The graph of Fig. 11-11 shows a form of direct current that might best be called pulsating, or varying, unidirectional current. The waves in the graph would be less pronounced if the armature were rotated more rapidly. Another way to smooth the output would be to wind a number of separate coils on the armature, each connected to a pair of segments on the commutator.

ELECTRICAL SYSTEMS

The armature of an electric generator can be rotated by a water-wheel or a gasoline engine, or by rubbing along a bicycle tire. Wires can be run from the generator to motors, lights, or heating devices. As long as the generator is near the place where the electricity is to be used, we can neglect the resistance of the connecting wires.

However, with large generator installations near waterfalls, it becomes necessary to connect the generators by long lines to the places that use the electricity. The resistance of the lines will result in energy losses to heat. We should investigate how much energy loss is involved, and try to find some way to reduce it.

ENERGY AND POWER

In any machine that changes energy from one form to another, the longer the machine operates, the more energy is transformed. Since the amount of energy transformed is proportional to the time, the important property of the machine is its power, or *rate* of transforming energy. A certain garden cultivator is operated by a 6.0 kW gasoline engine. Working at full power for 300 s, the energy transformed by the engine is

Recall the definition of power, $P = E/t$.

$$E = Pt = (6.0 \text{ kW}) (300 \text{ s}) = 1.8 \text{ MJ}.$$

1 W·s = 1 J.

Over a million joules of energy were expended by the engine in 5 min.

Electrical devices, too, have specific (rated) powers; but they must also carry a specification of the voltage at which they are designed to operate. Common household appliances are rated for 120 V. Very large modern generators are able to convert mechanical to electrical energy at rates up to about one-half gigajoule per second. Thus, the power of such a generator is one-half gigawatt, or 500 MW. Late on a cold winter afternoon, you may hear a news report that the full electrical generating capacity of a system is in use. The amount will be specified in gigawatts, or millions of kilowatts. The amount of electrical energy that is consumed will depend on the length of time that the system has to deliver at that rate. For example, 16 GW for 24 h will produce an energy of

$$E = Pt = (16 \text{ GW})(24 \text{ h}) = 3.8 \times 10^{11} \text{ W·h}$$

$$= (3.8 \times 10^{11} \text{ W·h}) (3.6 \times 10^3 \text{ J/W·h}) = 1.4 \times 10^{15} \text{ J}.$$

1 W·h = 3.6 × 10³J.

If the system operated at 16 GW for a whole day, it would produce 1.4 PJ of energy.

Example: The heating element of an electric kettle has a resistance of about 10 Ω. When it is connected to the voltage for which it was designed, 120 V, it will draw a current (*I*) of

$$I = \frac{V}{R} = \frac{120 \text{ V}}{10 \text{ Ω}} = 12 \text{ A}.$$

From the current and the voltage, we can calculate the power of the kettle when it is connected to 120 V. (If it was connected to a higher voltage, more current would result, and the kettle would be damaged.)

$$P = VI = (120 \text{ V})(12 \text{ A}) = 1.4 \text{ kW}.$$

Frequently, manufacturers specify the power of the device at its rated voltage. Thus, energy consumed can be calculated directly from the power and the time of operation. If you want to know either current or resistance for the device, they can be calculated from the power and the voltage.

POWER LOSS IN TRANSMISSION

The dimensions and materials of a transmission line determine its resistance. For example, 20 km of copper wire of 0.50 cm diameter has a resistance of 17 Ω. The usual way to determine the rate of energy loss in such a resistance is from the values of current (*I*) and resistance (*R*). Substitute *IR* for *V* in $P = VI$, and get

$$P = I^2R.$$

The power lost in a resistance *R*, carrying a current *I*, is equal to the square of the current times the resistance.

Example: A small electrical system generates 1.0 MW of electricity at 10 kV. The system is connected by 20 km of copper wire, of resistance 17 Ω, to the community that uses the electricity. Calculate the power lost in transmission, and express it as a percentage of the total power generated.
(a) From the power and voltage, calculate the current.

$$I = \frac{P}{V} = \frac{1.0 \times 10^6 \text{ W}}{1.0 \times 10^4 \text{ V}} = 1.0 \times 10^2 \text{ A}.$$

The current in the circuit is 100 A.

(b) Calculate the power lost in the line of resistance 17 Ω.

$$P = I^2R = (100\ \text{A})^2 \times 17\ \Omega = 1.7 \times 10^5\ \text{W}.$$

(c) The percentage of the generated power that is lost in the line is

$$\frac{1.7 \times 10^5\ \text{W}}{1.0 \times 10^6\ \text{W}} \times 100\% = 17\%.$$

A power loss in the lines of 17% is larger than we would like. How could it be reduced? Since power loss is proportional to the square of the current, any reduction in the current in the line would result in a reduced power loss. To transmit energy at the same rate (same power) the current could be reduced if the voltage was increased, since $P = VI$.

Since about 1895, electrical engineers have been able to transmit electricity at high voltages, even though it is generated at a low voltage, and used by consumers at even lower voltages. It can be done using alternating current and electromagnetic-induction devices called **transformers**. They make it possible to change AC voltages so that transmission lines can operate at potentials of 500 kV or more. The higher the voltage of the transmission line, the lower the current for the same power transfer, and the less power is lost in the lines.

What would be the percentage of power loss in the line for a transmission voltage of 100 kV? (See I at the end of Chapter 11 Exercises.)

In 1891 AC transmission at 25 kV over a distance of 170 km was achieved in Germany. The eight 4 MW generators installed at Niagara in 1895 to supply Buffalo were designed by George Forbes of Britain and manufactured by the Westinghouse Company in the United States.

TRANSFORMERS

The principle of transformer operation is that alternating current supplied to one coil (the primary) on an iron ring induces a current in the circuit connected to the other coil (the secondary) as shown in Fig. 11-12. The induction of current in the secondary depends on changes in the magnetic field within the iron core. That is produced by the alternating current in the primary. No such simple device exists for converting large quantities of energy from one DC voltage to a different DC voltage.

A model transformer for laboratory use is shown in Fig. 11-13. It consists of a U-core of iron onto which coils of different numbers of turns may be slipped. The magnetic linkage is completed by a short iron bar that fits across the top of the U. The properties of the transformer can be studied using the circuit shown in Fig. 11-14. Throughout this work, the subscript 1 is used to identify properties in the primary circuit, and the subscript 2 to identify those in the secondary.

The series of photographs in Fig. 11-15 shows a transformer in operation connected to an AC supply of 75 V. In all three photographs, the primary coil has 600 turns. The secondary coil in successive photographs has 600 turns, 1200 turns and 300 turns. The secondary

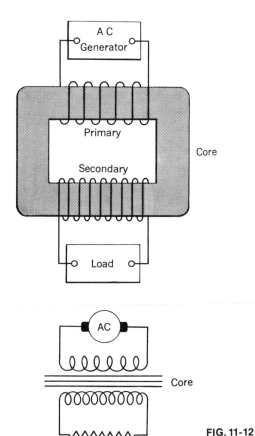

FIG. 11-12

FIG. 11-13

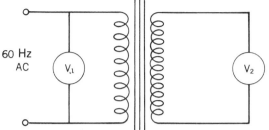

FIG. 11-14

voltages can be read from the meter. From a table of these and other measurements, a basic relation for transformer operation can be deduced. Using the symbols V for voltage, and N for the number of turns in the coils, it is found, within the limits of experimental variation, that

$$\frac{V_2}{V_1} = \frac{N_2}{N_1}.$$

That is, the ratio of voltages in the secondary and primary of a transformer is equal to the ratio of the number of turns in the secondary and primary coils.

Example: A model electric train operates at 12 V. To supply it from the 120 V AC line requires a transformer. The transformer available has 500 turns in the primary. How many turns should there be in the secondary?

The following quantities are given:

$$V_2 = 12 \text{ V}; \quad V_1 = 120 \text{ V}; \quad N_1 = 500 \text{ turns.}$$

Since $\dfrac{V_2}{V_1} = \dfrac{N_2}{N_1}$,

then $N_2 = \dfrac{V_2}{V_1} \times N_1 = \dfrac{12 \text{ V}}{120 \text{ V}} \times 500 \text{ turns} = 50 \text{ turns.}$

Therefore the secondary coil of the transformer should have 50 turns.

APPLICATIONS OF TRANSFORMERS

In a modern electrical home, step-down transformers are used to operate doorbells and electric trains. Step-up transformers are used to start oil burners, and to supply the high voltages needed in the cathode-ray tube of a television set. Transformers are also widely used in circuits where the electrical energy has much higher frequencies

(a)

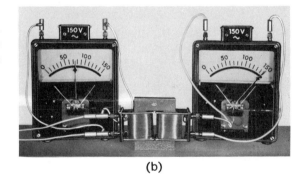

(b)

(c)

FIG. 11-15

than 60 Hz. In radios, television sets, and stereos, there are electric transformers that operate in the audio-frequency range from 20 Hz to 20 kHz. In radio-frequency circuits there are transformers with air cores that operate at frequencies of millions of hertz.

The principle of the transformer is used with direct current sources, such as batteries, in a device called an **induction coil**. Induction coils are used as step-up transformers in high voltage applications. Ignition or spark coils in automobiles provide the energy to ignite the gasoline-air mixture in the cylinders. The electrons from the auto battery are started and stopped by the operation of a switch, connected mechanically to the rotation of the crankshaft. The primary circuit must have such a device for interrupting the electron motion. The primary circuit of induction coils used in school laboratories is interrupted by including in it the elements of an electric buzzer circuit. The primary coil and iron core of the induction coil are the electromagnet of the buzzer. The electron motion in the secondary is in one direction when the circuit is closed, and in the other when it is opened. It has been found that the induced voltage on opening the circuit is several times greater than that when the circuit is closed.

THE DISTRIBUTION OF ELECTRICAL ENERGY

Large transformers operating at 60 Hz are important components in the system by which electrical energy is supplied to homes and industries. Mechanical energy is transformed to electrical energy in generating stations where the generators produce electricity at voltages ranging from 14 kV to 24 kV. To transmit the energy over long distances, the voltage is stepped up at the generating station to 115 kV, or 230 kV, or 500 kV. Then, near the locations where the energy is to be utilized, there are transformer stations that step down the voltage to 44 kV, or 28 kV, or 14 kV. At these voltages, the electricity is distributed to substations where transformers step down the voltage to 4.0 kV for transmission along our streets and roads. A pole transformer near your home steps down the voltage from 4.0 kV to 120 V and 240 V for the lines that enter your home. The diagram of Fig. 11-16a shows the four transformers through which the energy passes from the generating station to your home.

FIG. 11-16 appears on pages 146-7

It is interesting that in the transmission of billions of kilowatt hours of electrical energy, no single electron need ever make the complete trip from generator to consumer. In fact, with separate circuits linked magnetically through the cores of the transformers, there is no complete conducting path from generator to consumer. But even between two transformers we do not expect the continuous motion of any one electron around the loop. For, in alternating current electrons move one way for 1/120 s and then the other way for 1/120 s. And in each of these intervals an electron is not likely to travel more than about one micrometre.

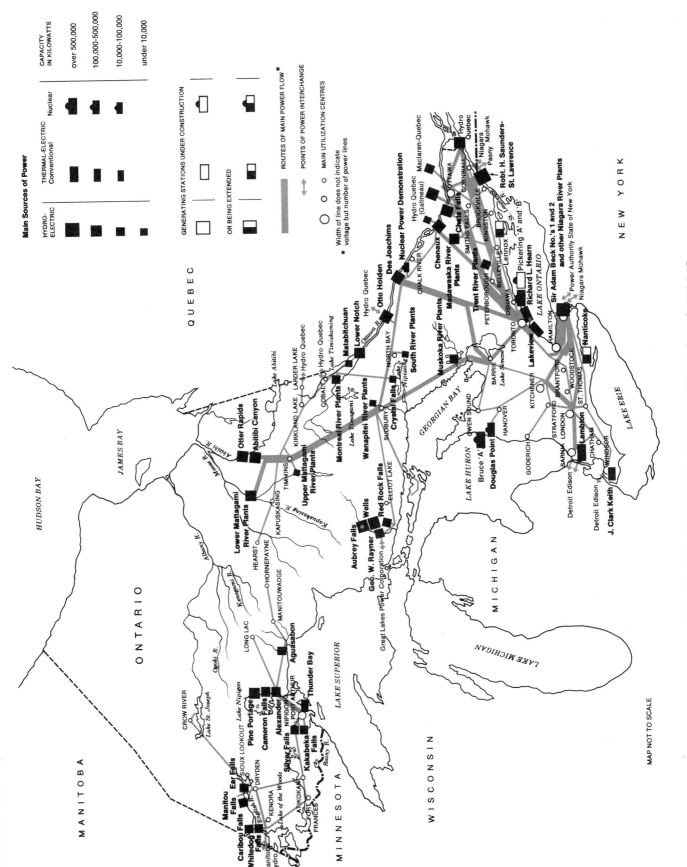

THE MAJOR ELECTRICAL ENERGY ROUTES IN ONTARIO

MAP NOT TO SCALE

Main Sources of Power

	HYDRO-ELECTRIC	THERMAL-ELECTRIC Conventional	Nuclear	CAPACITY IN KILOWATTS
				over 500,000
				100,000-500,000
				10,000-100,000
				under 10,000

GENERATING STATIONS UNDER CONSTRUCTION

OR BEING EXTENDED

ROUTES OF MAIN POWER FLOW *

POINTS OF POWER INTERCHANGE

○ ○ ○ MAIN UTILIZATION CENTRES

Width of line does not indicate voltage but number of power lines

* Main power flow

FIG. 11-16. (a) The various voltages that are used in a modern electrical distribution system. (b) The structure of a hydroelectric generating station. (c) The structure of a coal-fired thermo-electric generating station. (d) The structure of a nuclear thermo-electric generating station. (e) On the Niagara River the Adam Beck generating stations at Queenston (on the left) and the Robert Moses station at Lewiston have a combined generating capacity of 4.2 GW. (f) When these turbine blades are struck by high-pressure steam they drive the generator rotor at high speed. (g) Workmen installing the stator of a new generator. (h) A 500 MW turbine and generator (in the foreground) installed in a modern thermal plant. (i) This transformer has a power rating of 750 MW.

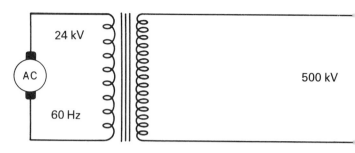

Generating station

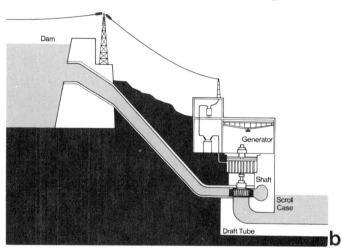

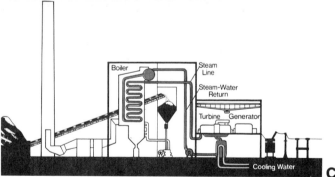

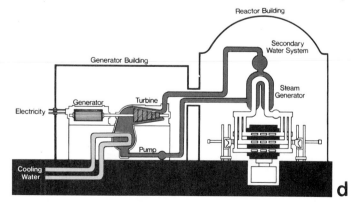

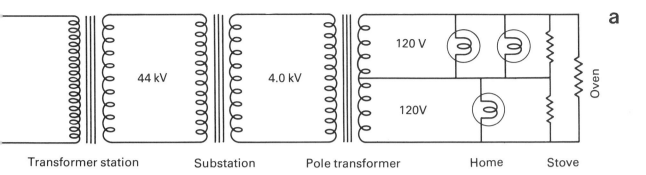

44 kV   4.0 kV   120 V   120V   Oven

Transformer station   Substation   Pole transformer   Home   Stove   **a**

g

h

i

POWER IN TRANSFORMERS

With no moving parts (except electrons) a transformer can be designed to be a very efficient translator of energy. Energy losses are quite small. They result from the heat developed in the coils (when electrons collide with the metal ions), and from induced currents within the iron core. By careful design these losses can be reduced to as little as one per cent of the total energy passing through the transformer. Thus practical transformers conform very closely to ideal transformers. In the following discussion we shall consider an ideal transformer in which there are no energy losses.

Currents induced in the iron core are called *eddy currents*. They can be reduced by breaking up the conducting paths in the iron. This is done by building up the core with strips of iron (called *laminations*) insulated from one another by varnish. If a commercial transformer is available, you may be able to see the laminations of the core. If a dissectible transformer is available, see how the brightness of a light bulb in the secondary circuit is affected when part of the laminated core is replaced by a solid iron bar of the same dimensions. Why does the change occur? (See II at the end of Chapter 11 Exercises.)

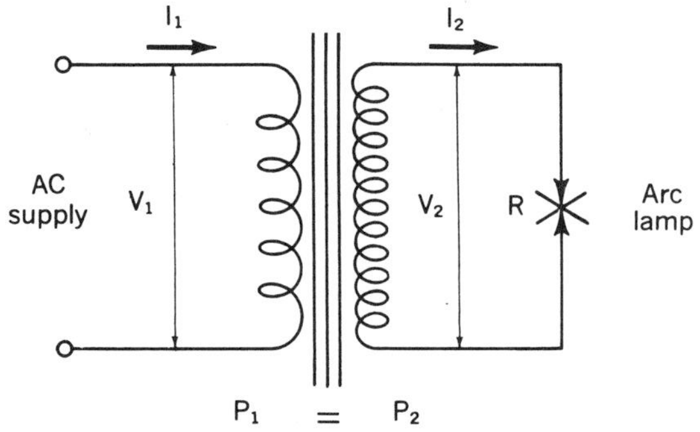

FIG. 11-17

In an ideal transformer the energy supplied to the primary (E_1) is equal to the energy available from the secondary (E_2). The rate at which energy is transmitted through the transformer is the power, so we would expect that $P_1 = P_2$. Earlier in this chapter we considered the voltage relations between the primary and secondary. Now we should consider the power and current relations in a transformer. The given quantities in the following example are the ones that would, in practice, be known. The ones we calculate might be called the dependent quantities.

Example: In Fig. 11-17, a sodium vapour arc lamp having a resistance of 160 Ω is designed to operate on 240 V. It is operated from a transformer that is supplied with alternating current at 100 V. Calculate the power transferred and the current in the primary.

In the secondary circuit:

$$V_2 = 240 \text{ V} \quad \text{and} \quad R = 160 \text{ Ω}.$$

The secondary current is

$$I_2 = \frac{V_2}{R} = \frac{240 \text{ V}}{160 \text{ Ω}} = 1.5 \text{ A}.$$

The power in the secondary circuit is

$$P_2 = V_2 I_2 = (240 \text{ V}) (1.5 \text{ A}) = 360 \text{ W}.$$

For an ideal transformer the power in the primary is

$$P_1 = P_2 = 360 \text{ W}.$$

The primary voltage is

$$V_1 = 100 \text{ V}.$$

Therefore the primary current is

$$I_1 = \frac{P_1}{V_1} = \frac{360 \text{ W}}{100 \text{ V}} = 3.6 \text{ A}.$$

Thus, the primary current is 3.6 A, which is 2.4 times the secondary current. Energy passes through the transformer at the rate of 360 W.

THE COST OF ELECTRICAL ENERGY

Like any other form of energy, electricity has to be paid for. The costs include the price paid for the fuel used to create steam when thermal energy is used to produce the motion of the generators. In hydroelectric stations, the water is free. However, the construction and maintenance of equipment for generation and transmission has to be paid for. As of 1977, the average cost of electrical energy to Ontario homes is between 2.5 and 3 cents per kilowatt hour.

The cost of operating a lamp can be found simply from its power rating and the time during which it operates. If a 100 W lamp is on for 10 h, the energy it uses is

$$E = Pt = (100 \text{ W})(10 \text{ h}) = 1 \text{ kW·h}.$$

At 2 cents per kilowatt hour, the cost of the energy is 2 cents.

Sometimes the nameplate of an appliance does not list the power rating. Instead it will give the voltage and the current. A toaster may be rated at 120 V, 10.5 A. Its power rating is easily calculated:

$$P = VI = (120 \text{ V})(10.5 \text{ A}) = 1260 \text{ W} = 1.3 \text{ kW}.$$

If the toaster is operated for 20 min, the cost at 2.5 cents/kW·h is:

$$\text{Cost} = (Pt)(2.5 \text{ cents/kW·h})$$
$$= (1.3 \text{ kW})(20 \text{ min} \times \frac{1\text{h}}{60 \text{ min}})(2.5 \text{ cents/kW·h}) = 1.1 \text{ cents}.$$

FUSES AND SAFETY

In household wiring, there are usually several separate electric circuits. To maintain safety, no circuit should carry more current than its wires are designed for. Depending on the cross-sectional area of the wires, the maximum safe current may be between 15 A and 25 A. Beyond the safe current, the temperature rise resulting from the I^2Rt energy loss in the wires may start a fire in the insulation or other materials. In order to prevent currents that are too high for the wires, each circuit is equipped with a fuse or circuit breaker.

FIG. 11-18

Fuses contain a short section of a conductor with a low melting point (Fig. 11-18). The cross-section of the conductor is designed to cause it to melt when the current in it exceeds the value for which it was designed. If the fuse wire melts, the circuit is broken and current ceases. The fuse must be replaced. It is dangerous to insert a 25 A fuse in a circuit that was designed for 15 A; for, some other part of the circuit may get too hot before the fuse-wire melts. A circuit-breaker is an electromagnetic device (Fig. 11-19). When the current exceeds its rated value, the magnetic force of the current overcomes a mechanical restraining force to cause a switch in the device to open. As soon as the cause of the excessive current is removed the circuit breaker can be reset by pushing the switch.

Most household appliances are designed to operate properly at 120 V. As a result, household circuits are connected in parallel, so that the potential difference at each socket is 120 V. If several sockets are on a single fused circuit, the current through the fuse is the sum of the currents in each appliance. From that it can be shown that the

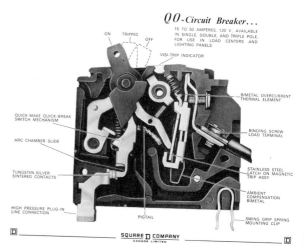

FIG. 11-19

powers of the individual appliances add together when they are connected in parallel. Appliances of powers P_1 and P_2 have currents of I_1 and I_2 respectively. The potential difference across each is V. For each, $I = P/V$. Then, since the total current is

$$I_T = I_1 + I_2$$

$$\frac{P_T}{V} = \frac{P_1}{V} + \frac{P_2}{V}$$

Therefore, the total power is $P_T = P_1 + P_2$.

The major error that leads to overloading a circuit consists of connecting too many appliances into a single circuit. Somebody living in one room might try to get breakfast by connecting the electric kettle and the toaster into sockets attached to the light fixture. The 1.5 kW kettle and the 1.3 kW toaster have a combined power drain of 2.8 kW. On a 120 V supply, the current is

$$I = \frac{P}{V} = \frac{2.8 \times 10^3 \text{ W}}{1.2 \times 10^2 \text{ V}} = 23 \text{ A}.$$

If the circuits in the house are fused at 15 A, there will clearly be an overload. If the 15 A fuse is replaced by a 25 A fuse to save blowing a fuse every morning, the fire risk in the wiring can be alarming.

Exercises

A

1. Sketch an end-on view of the poles of a horseshoe magnet with its north pole on the left and south pole on the right. Draw a narrow vertical rectangle between the poles to represent a section of a conductor in the magnet's field. If the conductor is being pulled forward toward you out of the page, in what direction will electrons in the conductor tend to move?

2. (a) What is the essential physical relation that must exist between a coil of wire and a permanent bar magnet in order for a potential difference to be induced between the ends of the coil?
   (b) What other arrangement has to be ensured so that the electrons in the wire will continue to move in some regular way while the conditions of (a) are maintained?

3. A coil of 500 turns of copper wire is connected to a millivoltmeter. An electromagnet within the coil can be energized by different currents and brought to maximum strength in various times.
   (a) The current in the electromagnet is increased uniformly from zero to 4.0 A. What is the rate of change of current (and thus, by a constant factor, the rate of change of the magnetic field strength within the coil) when the time for the current to reach 4.0 A is (i) 1.0 s, (ii) 2.0 s, (iii) 0.50 s?
   (b) Repeat part (a) for a current increasing 2.0 A in the electromagnet.
   (c) A current of 1.0 A reached in 1.0 s in the electromagnet produces a maximum potential difference of 50 mV in the coil. Make a table to show the maximum readings to be expected on the millivoltmeter for each of the situations described in parts (a) and (b).

4. When a bar magnet is plunged into a coil having 200 turns, the induced voltage between the ends of the coil is 0.10 V. If the same magnet is plunged at the same rate into a coil having 500 turns, what will be the induced voltage between its ends?

5. Make sketches in your notebook like those in the following figure. To complete each one to conform to Lenz's law, fill in the blanks to show the magnetic polarity induced in the coil (and use arrows to show the direction of electron motion), or the polarity of the moving magnet or the direction of its motion.

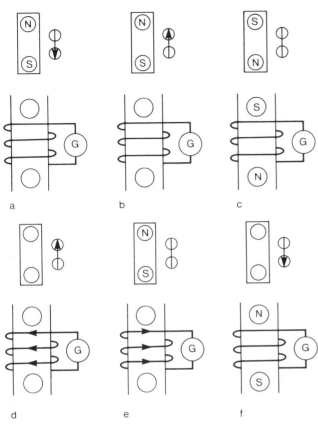

a   b   c

d   e   f

6. For each of the following devices state the form in which energy is supplied to the device, and the form into which the device changes the energy.
   (a) electric generator
   (b) electric toaster
   (c) dry cell
   (d) electric motor
   (e) radio loudspeaker
   (f) photovoltaic cell
   (g) electric refrigerator
   (h) steam engine
   (i) television picture tube
   (j) incandescent electric lamp
   (k) crystal microphone
   (l) television camera tube.

7. On the basis of the principles of electromagnetic induction, what properties of the induced voltage in an AC generator would be affected by an increase in the rate of rotation of the armature? Would they be increased or decreased?

8. (a) For the diagrams of Fig. 11-8 indicate the position of the armature relative to the poles of the field magnet when the induced voltage is (i) zero, (ii) maximum.
   (b) For the diagrams of the Fig. 11-8 indicate during which parts of the rotation cycle the induced voltage is (i) increasing, (ii) decreasing.

9. Draw a graph of induced voltage versus time for three complete revolutions of the armature of a model AC generator tuning at 1.0 Hz. Make the maximum induced voltage 5.0 V.

10. Draw a graph of voltage against time for an interval of 1.0 s for
    (a) an AC generator having a frequency of 2.0 Hz and a maximum induced voltage of 6.0 V,
    (b) a 6.0 V auto battery,
    (c) a DC generator having a two-pole armature and a two-segment commutator, rotating 3.0 times per second, with a maximum induced voltage of 6.0 V.

11. A colour television set rated at 330 W operates for 5.0 h during the evening. How much energy does it consume in that time? Express your answer in (a) watt hours, (b) kilowatt hours, (c) megajoules.

12. A room air conditioner is rated at 1.4 kW. During July it operates 10 hours a day for 25 days. How much energy does it consume? Express your answer in (a) kilowatt hours, (b) megajoules.

13. An electric clock is rated at 2.0 W. For a thirty-day month, calculate the electrical energy it uses (a) in kilowatt hours, (b) in megajoules.

14. What is the power rating of a portable tape recorder that draws a current of 300 mA from a 6.0 V supply?

15. What is the current in a 100 W light bulb operating at 120 V?

16. An electric blender takes 8.33 A when connected to the 120.0 V supply. What is its power rating?

17. What is the current required to supply energy at the rate of 6.0×10^3 W in a circuit for which the supply voltage is (a) 120 V, (b) 1200 V?

18. Calculate the power loss in a conductor having a resistance of 3.0 Ω when it carries a current of (a) 11 A, (b) 1.1 A.

19. Number 8 gauge copper wire has a resistance of 2.08 Ω/km and can carry currents up to 70.7 A. Calculate the power loss in 1.00 km of this wire when carrying the maximum current.

20. (a) A coil of wire of 300 turns carrying a current of 2.0 A produces a magnetic field strength of 17 units. What is the magnetic field strength of a second coil carrying the same current, identical in all respects to the first coil except that it has 600 turns?
    (b) A certain rate of change of magnetic field strength within a coil of 700 turns induces in the coil a voltage of 43 V. What voltage would the same rate of change produce in a coil like the first one in all respects except that it has 350 turns?

21. An AC voltage of 120 V is supplied to the primary coil of a transformer having 600 turns. What is the voltage across the terminals of the secondary coil of

the transformer if it has (a) 1200 turns, (b) 300 turns, (c) 6 turns, (d) 12 000 turns?

22. A transformer to supply the various voltages required in an electronic apparatus has 300 turns in its primary coil which is connected to the 120 V supply. Calculate the number of turns required in the secondary coils designed to supply (a) 600 V, (b) 400 V, (c) 5.0 V, (d) 6.3 V.

23. The normal alternating current supplied to householders has voltages of 120 V and 240 V. Devices that require potential differences other than these often employ transformers. List four such devices that might be found in a home, indicate whether a step-up or step-down transformer is required, and, if possible, the voltage at which the device operates.

24. Consider the cost of electrical energy to be 3.0 cents per kilowatt hour. For each of the following devices calculate the cost of operation for the time specified:
(a) a 100 W lamp for 10 h,
(b) a 12.5 kW range for 2.0 h,
(c) a 1.15 kW portable hair dryer for 15 min a day for two months.

B

25. A coil of copper wire has a resistance of 20 Ω. A bar magnet plunged into the coil can induce a potential difference of 1.0 V. Calculate the induced current when the coil is connected to a galvanometer having a resistance of (a) 30 Ω, (b) 80 Ω.

26. A coil is lying with its axis horizontal on a desk. It is connected to a galvanometer. A bar magnet is passed right through the coil. As the south pole enters at one end the galvanometer needle moves to the right. In what direction will the galvanometer needle move as the north pole is withdrawn from the other end of the coil?

27. (a) Copy the diagram of Fig. 11-3 onto a sheet of paper and indicate the direction of electron motion in the coil connected to the battery when the switch is closed, the direction of the magnetic field lines within the iron ring, and the direction of the induced electron motion in the coil connected to the galvanometer as the magnetic field is increasing in the ring.
(b) Repeat the procedure of part (a) for the situation that occurs as the switch is opened after having been closed for a minute.

28. Three coils, A, B, and C, have the number of turns and resistance indicated in the following table. They are connected in series with one another and with a galvanometer having a resistance of 60 Ω. One end of a bar magnet is plunged at the same rate into each coil in turn, producing a reading on the galvanometer.

When the end of the magnet is plunged into Coil A the maximum reading on the galvanometer is 1.0 mA.

Coil	Number of turns	Resistance
A	300	2.0 Ω
B	600	8.0
C	1200	30.0

(a) What will be the maximum reading of the galvanometer when the magnet is plunged into (i) coil B, (ii) coil C?
(b) Calculate the value of the induced voltage when the magnet is plunged into each coil.
(c) In this demonstration of the effect of the number of turns on an induced current, why should the three coils be connected in series to the galvanometer?
(d) If coil C was connected by itself to the galvanometer and the magnet plunged into the coil at the same rate as before, what would be the maximum reading on the galvanometer?

29. Summarize the argument by which Lenz's law is deduced from the principle of the conservation of energy, indicating the principles and laws upon which the argument is based.

30. A coil of wire with many turns is wound in the form of a ring with a diameter of about 25 cm. The coil is rotated about an axis in the plane of the coil — i.e., on a diameter of the circle that the coil forms. When the coil is connected to a galvanometer the effect of rotating it in the magnetic field of the earth can produce an observable deflection. What should be the direction of the axis of rotation relative to the direction of the magnetic field lines of the earth's field in order to produce (a) a maximum reading on the galvanometer, (b) a minimum (or zero) reading?

31. Draw a diagram to illustrate two coils of wire, one wound around each leg of an iron U-shaped core. With a battery and switch connected to the coil on the left, and a galvanometer connected to the coil on the right, indicate the direction in which electrons would move in the right-hand coil,
(a) when the switch is closed,
(b) when the switch is opened,
(c) when a bar of soft iron is placed across the open end of the U while the switch is closed,
(d) when the bar of soft iron is removed, while the switch remains closed.

32. Make a quick sketch of the graph that was described in question 9. Along the time axis mark the locations at which the axis of the armature coil is (a) parallel, and (b) perpendicular to the straight line joining the poles of the field magnet.

33. Trace the steps in the production of a voltage in a DC generator during one complete revolution of the armature in an anti-clockwise direction — that is, in

the direction opposite to that used in Fig. 11-8.

34. By what means could the voltage-time graph of a DC generator be made smoother — that is, with "ripples" that are less pronounced?

35. (a) Let E be the energy dissipated in a conductor of resistance R in time t, when the voltage across the conductor is V. Derive an expression for E in terms of V, R, and t.
(b) Express power P in terms of the voltage drop V across a resistance R.

36. An electric motor has a resistance of 14 Ω when it is operating on a 120 V supply. It is connected to the supply by a line having a resistance of 1.0 Ω. Calculate
(a) the total resistance of the circuit,
(b) the current in the circuit,
(c) the power loss in the line.

37. Electricity is to be supplied to a group of cottages 15 km from the nearest power line. The maximum load is to be 60 kW and the resistance in the line is 8.0 Ω. Calculate the power loss in the line if the supply voltage at the cottages is (a) 2.4×10^2 V, (b) 4.0 kV.

38. (a) Suppose that the current in the primary coil of the transformer of question 22 is 2.0 A. What is the power in the primary circuit?
(b) Assuming that no energy is lost in the core of the transformer, what is the power in the secondary circuit?
(c) For each of the secondary coils of question 22, calculate the current in the coil if that in the primary is 2.0 A.

39. A transformer has 80 turns in the primary and 560 turns in the secondary. The secondary circuit has 3.0 A at 9.0×10^2 V. Calculate the voltage and current in the primary circuit.

40. A spot-welding machine operates with a current of 75 A at 55 V. It is supplied from a transformer whose primary is connected to 550 V. Calculate (a) the power in the secondary, (b) the current in the primary.

41. A 1.0 kW electric toaster is designed to operate on 120 V, and has a built-in fuse rated at 15 A. It is sent as a present to Britain, where the standard household voltage is 220 V. When the toaster is plugged in there, will it
(a) work efficiently,
(b) work, but with a very low heat output, or
(c) blow the fuse?

42. In return for the gift in question 41, a 1.5 kW kettle made in Britain for the domestic market is sent to Canada. It is plugged into 120 V here in a circuit fused for 20 A. Will the kettle
(a) work efficiently,
(b) work, but with a very low heat output, or
(c) blow a fuse?

C

43. The dynamic or moving-coil microphone uses electromagnetic induction to produce electrical signals from sound waves.
(a) Find out how this device is constructed and how it works.
(b) In many intercom systems, there is no microphone and the loudspeaker doubles as a microphone. How can this be?

44. (a) A changing magnetic field induces a current in a coil. Find out how this is used in the playback mode of operation of tape recorders.
(b) In order to record and play back the very high frequencies used in television without having an extremely high tape speed, many video tape recorders use what is called helical scan. Find out how this works.

45. If the current to an electric motor and the potential drop across it are monitored with meters, it is found that both are largest when the motor is starting, and decrease significantly as the speed of rotation increases. (You can try this in the lab if time permits — students who come across it unexpectedly are often quite surprised by the effect.)
(a) This effect is often explained by saying that a *back voltage* or a *counter voltage* has been induced in the armature. Explain how this could be and why it depends on speed.
(b) A more basic understanding of the effect can be gained by trying to explain the phenomenon by means of rotational inertia and the energy per second (power) needed to overcome it. Do so.

46. Which would be more difficult to turn, the armature of a generator connected to a light bulb, or the armature of a generator that is not connected to anything? Why? (If a generator with a hand crank is available, try it.)

47. (a) A coil of many turns of wire wrapped around an iron core is connected to a 1.5 V dry cell, and the current is found to be 3 A. What is the coil's resistance?
(b) If the coil is now connected to a transformer secondary giving 1.5 V AC, the current is found to be 30 mA. What is the coil's effective AC resistance (its *impedance*)?
(c) Find out and explain why the (b) answer (the impedance) is so much more than the (a) answer (the resistance).

Answers to text questions

I. With $V = 100$ kV and $P = 1.0$ MW, $I = 10$ A; and $I^2R = 1.7$ kW. Thus, the line-loss is 0.17%—1/100 of the loss is achieved for a 10 times increase in the voltage.

II. Energy that goes into the eddy currents in the solid iron is not available to heat the lamp.

This boy wonders how to rock the boat.

This boy knows how.

A toy boat in a pond can be made to move by dropping a stone into the water at a distance from the boat. The stone moves the water it touches. Ripples that spread out from there will rock the boat. But the water that rocks the boat is not water that had been in contact with the stone. The energy has been transmitted across the water by *wave motion*. This method of energy transmission can be contrasted with your throwing a shoe at a ball lodged in a tree. The shoe applies a force to the ball as the result of the kinetic energy you gave to it. The shoe, a material object, travelled the whole distance from you to the ball. On the other hand, in wave motion no material substance makes the whole trip from the stone to the boat.

In this unit you will examine the basic properties of vibrations and waves, and apply them to investigations in sound and light. From the wave nature of sound you will be able to see the basis for the design of such musical instruments as horns and clarinets. From the wave nature of light you will be able to analyze the refraction of light, and apply it to the lenses that are used in cameras, microscopes, and telescopes.

Energy in Waves

CHAPTER 12

Ear
156-162
p 168 - 16
Ultra sound

Vibrations
and
Waves

Imagine a man basking in the sun at a lakeside summer cottage. Music from a nearby radio falls on his ears; a few feet away water splashes against a dock; a flag over his cottage ripples in the breeze; suddenly he is aroused by a tremor in the earth due to a passing train. He sits up with the realization that he is surrounded. He is surrounded by waves: light waves from the sun, radio waves from a broadcasting studio, sound waves from his radio, water waves in the lake, patriotic waves in the flag and shock waves from the passing train. If you look around you, you can find all sorts of examples of waves and of the vibrations from which the waves originate. This chapter deals with mechanical examples of vibrations and waves, which will lead to a clearer understanding of sound and electromagnetic waves.

VIBRATIONS

The "tick-tock" of a mechanical clock or watch is controlled by the regular to and fro motion of a pendulum or balance wheel. Any object that repeatedly moves back and forth or up and down has a motion that is called a **vibration**. When some of the joints in the frame of an automobile are not tight, the jiggling motion of the engine can cause them to vibrate. Sometimes in an older car a driver can become quite expert in judging his speed on the highway by the sounds from various vibrating parts.

If you hold your tongue toward the roof of your mouth and then blow air past it, your tongue will vibrate. The muscular force you exert tries to hold the tongue steady, so that it pushes against the force of the air, overshoots, and relaxes. The air then pushes the tongue back and the cycle is repeated. This type of action is common in vibrating objects where a restoring force (the tongue muscles) alternately overcomes an external force (the blown air), and then is overcome by that force. For a springy material the restoring force is provided by the material's internal elastic forces—the forces that hold the material together.

For a simple pendulum, such as a stone swinging on the end of a string, the restoring force is provided by gravity (Fig. 12-1). In this

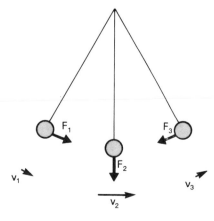

FIG. 12-1

case, we use energy conservation to account for the continuation of motion past the vertical position. With gravity acting always downward, the stone experiences a force opposing its motion as soon as the vertical position is passed. The work then done against gravity gradually transforms the kinetic energy of the moving stone to gravitational potential energy. When the kinetic energy has been reduced to zero, the stone begins to swing back. Gravity, now acting in the same direction as the motion, does work to transform the gravitational potential energy to kinetic energy. The tendency of the force of gravity is to restore the string to the vertical position.

There are three different types of vibration that can be distinguished. For any vibrating object you should examine the direction of the vibratory motion relative to the long axis of the object. This can be done for the three types of shock absorbers in autos. For the leaf-spring (Fig. 12-2) the direction of motion is perpendicular to the long axis. This is **transverse vibration**—the motion is *across* the axis.

For coiled springs (Fig. 12-3) and hydraulic shock absorbers (Fig. 12-4) the direction of motion is *along* the axis—**longitudinal vibration.** In a torsion-bar suspension the motion is *around* the axis—**torsional vibration.**

The physical description and measurement of vibratory motions requires the introduction of several new quantities. These quantities are based on the fact that vibrations are repeated back and forth motions.

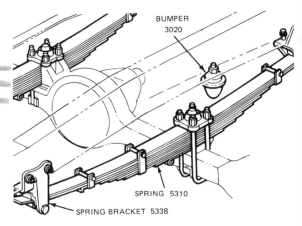

FIG. 12-2

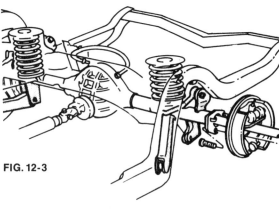

FIG. 12-3

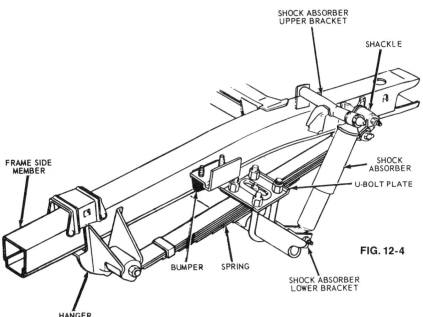

FIG. 12-4

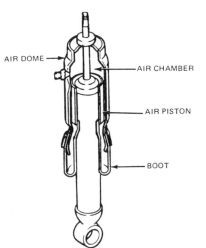

How much time is required for a pendulum to complete a cycle, i.e., one full vibration? Fix your attention on any point through which the bob of the pendulum passes. As it passes that point in one direction, start a stopwatch. Stop the watch when the bob next passes the *same* point in the *same* direction. The motion you have timed

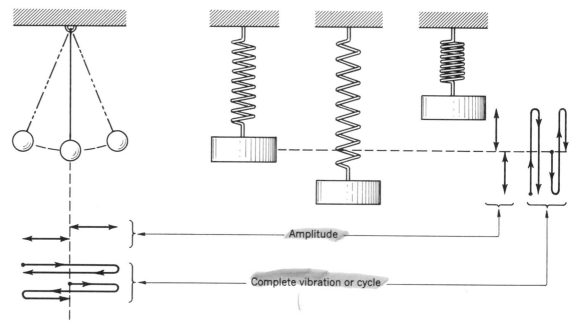

Amplitude

Complete vibration or cycle

FIG. 12-5 is one full vibration or **cycle** (Fig. 12-5). The time-interval required to complete one vibration or cycle is called the **period** (*T*). A simple pendulum 1.0 m in length has a period of 2.0 s. For a period of 1.0 s, the length is 0.25 m.

Relatively slow vibrations are commonly identified by their periods. However, since much more rapid vibrations have periods of small fractions of a second, it is usual to identify them by their frequencies. The **frequency** (*f*) of a vibration is the number of cycles completed per second. The unit of frequency, one cycle per second, is the hertz (Hz). The pendulum of period 2.0 s has a frequency of 0.50 Hz. And our usual electrical supply, of frequency 60.0 Hz, has a period of 0.0167 s. Large frequencies have small periods, and small frequencies have large periods. In fact, there is an inverse variation between period and frequency. Their product is 1. Thus,

$$fT = 1, \quad f = \frac{1}{T}, \quad \text{and} \quad T = \frac{1}{f}.$$

When a pendulum hangs at rest it is in its equilibrium position. Pull it through a distance of 15 cm and let go. Except for the effect of friction with the air, the pendulum bob will continue to move back and forth a distance of about 15 cm on either side of the equilibrium position. The **amplitude** of any vibration is the distance from the equilibrium position to either of the extreme positions (Fig. 12-5). For longitudinal vibrations the amplitude is measured in the standard units of length, e.g., 15 cm for a load on a coiled spring that vibrates 15 cm above and below the equilibrium position. For transverse vibrations, too, the amplitude is measured in standard units of

The gradual decrease in amplitude resulting from frictional resistance is called *damping*.

length, this time along the line perpendicular to the long axis of the vibrating object. The amplitude of a transverse vibration can also be expressed by angular measure. For example, a 1.0 m simple pendulum is pulled aside so that its bob is 15 cm from the vertical position, measured horizontally. Swinging back and forth through that point means that its amplitude is 15 cm. The amplitude could also be expressed by the maximum angle that the string makes with the vertical, in this case 8.6°. For torsional vibrations, amplitude is most commonly measured angularly.

During the course of a month the appearance of the moon goes through a cycle of changes—first quarter, full moon, last quarter, new moon; this cycle is then repeated (Fig. 12-6). These are called the phases of the moon. For a vibration, **phase** indicates the part of the cycle in which a vibrating object is located. The notion of phase is most often used to compare two vibrations having the same frequency. If each is in the same part of its own cycle as the other, the two are *in phase*. The two vibrations can be out of phase, or have a *phase difference* by any fraction of a period between 0 and 1. Fig. 12-7 is a sketch to represent one cycle of a vibration of period 0.8 s. The locations of the points are shown at each 0.1 s through the cycle. Examples of phase differences are: from A to C is $T/4$, from A to E is $T/2$, from A to F is $5T/8$, and from D to H is $T/2$.

Now that you are equipped with the ideas of cycles, period, frequency, amplitude, and phase, we can turn to an examination of the motions in waves.

WAVES

When one point in a material is set into vibration, its connections with other parts of the material can result in its communicating motion to them. If the other parts are free to move, the motion that is communicated to them will set them into vibration. A **wave** can be defined as a disturbance or vibration travelling along or through a medium, transmitting energy in succession to the particles or material parts of the medium. The resulting transmission of energy through the material medium is called a **wave motion**. A major feature of wave motion is that while energy is transmitted through the medium the material parts merely undergo vibrations; the medium itself does not travel. This can be contrasted with the transferring of energy to a bowling pin by rolling a ball at it.

The most vivid image aroused by the word "waves" is likely to be of breakers crashing in on a beach. Unfortunately, that is not a good first image to have, because the motions in water waves are too complex. Instead, begin with a long coiled steel spring (a slinky) stretched over three or four metres along the floor. Grasping a small number of coils at one end, you can make a sharp side-to-side motion with your hand. A single vibration of your hand will cause the transmission of a single **pulse** along the length of the spring (Fig. 12-8). Timing the passage along the spring of pulses of various sizes and

For a simple pendulum, the amplitude affects the period according to a complicated rule, with larger amplitude swings having a longer period than shorter ones. For amplitudes up to about 10° the effect is very tiny. About 1583 Galileo was the first to notice the relative independence of period and amplitude for small amplitudes.

First quarter | Full moon | Last quarter | New moon | First quarter

FIG. 12-6

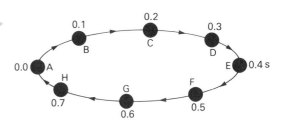

FIG. 12-7

FIG. 12-8

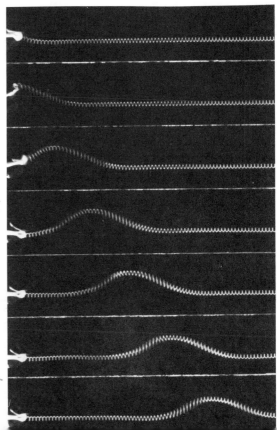

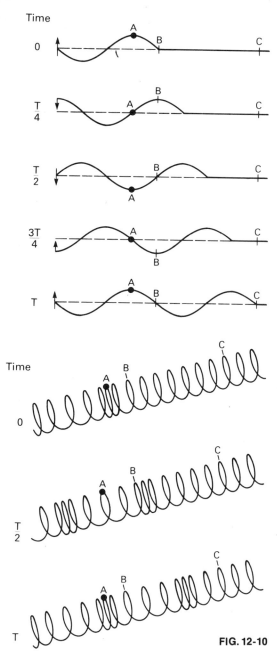

Time
0

$\frac{T}{4}$

$\frac{T}{2}$

$\frac{3T}{4}$

T

Time
0

$\frac{T}{2}$

T

FIG. 12-10

FIG. 12-9

shapes would reveal that the speed of travel seems to depend only on the spring. If you change the stretch of the spring, you get a different speed of travel.

A **wave train** or a travelling wave consists of a continuing series of pulses in a medium. This can be produced in the coiled spring by continuing to swing your hand back and forth. Initially, you will see the spring take a series of shapes like those shown in Fig. 12-9. Before long, a different shape is likely to appear as a result of the waves being reflected back from the other end. The standing wave that is thereby produced is described on page 165. The diagrams of Fig. 12-9 show the shape of the spring for a time-interval equal to one period of the vibrating source. If you consider the motion of the point A on the spring (marked ●) you will see that during this same time interval, it too completed a full cycle of motion. As a wave passes points in a medium, it sets them into a vibration with a frequency the same as that of the source of the wave.

These pulses and waves in the coiled spring involve motions of the particles of the medium that are perpendicular to the direction of travel of the disturbance. Waves that exhibit this feature are called **transverse waves**. The coiled spring can also be used to create **longitudinal waves** in which the direction of vibration of the particles of the medium is parallel to the direction of travel of the wave. To produce a longitudinal wave train in the coiled spring on the floor, swing your hand back and forth along the direction in which the spring is stretched. The appearance of the spring after a short time will be similar to the diagrams in Fig. 12-10. As for the transverse wave, the point A undergoes one complete vibration in the same period as the source of the vibration. In a **torsional wave** the direction of motion of the particles of the medium is around the direction of travel of the wave, as illustrated in Fig. 12-11. Although torsional vibrations are not usually easy to see, Fig. 12-12 shows one spectacular example. The suspension bridge over the Tacoma Narrows in the State of Washington, USA, was completed in 1940 with a main span 850 m long. Four months later a 68 km/h gale set the bridge into vibration with waves both transverse and torsional travelling along the span. Within several hours the bridge was torn apart and crashed into Puget Sound below.

FIG. 12-12

The complexity of water waves results from the fact that the motion of the particles of water is a combination of transverse and longitudinal vibrations. The cycle of each particle has a circular or elliptical shape. In relatively deep water the motion is quite circular. As a wave disturbance approaches shallower water, the motion is impeded by the bottom of the sea or lake, and becomes elliptical with the long axis in the longitudinal direction. As result, near a beach swimmers can be struck by a veritable wall of water or heavy surf (Fig. 12-13). Nonetheless, it is true that a surfer riding on the leading edge of a wave crest is always travelling through "new" water—the wave motion is continually being transmitted from particle to particle by the forces that hold the water together. The result of the friction with the sea bottom is that the speed of the wave motion is smaller in shallower water.

The language of water waves has come to be applied to transverse waves, even though water waves are not transverse. In Fig. 12-14 the parts of a wave above the axis are called **crests**, and those below are called **troughs**. For longitudinal waves, other names are used. The region where the spring is compressed more than normal is called a **condensation**. The region where the spring is spread out (or rarefied) more is called a **rarefaction** (Fig. 12-15).

To summarize, the following facts should be noted in each case of wave motion discussed:

1. A vibrating source and a medium are both necessary for the propagation of a wave.
2. Particles of the medium vibrate in succession because adjacent particles exert forces on each other.
3. The frequency of vibration of each particle in the medium equals that of the source.
4. Energy is transmitted from the source through the medium at a definite speed.

THE WAVE EQUATION

The distance between two successive crests in a transverse wave is called the **wavelength**. The symbol for this quantity is λ, the Greek letter *lambda*. Of course, as shown in Fig. 12-14, the wavelength is equally the distance between two successive troughs, two successive rarefactions in a longitudinal wave, etc. The wavelength is the distance from any point in a periodic wave to the next point that is in phase with it. Wavelength is measured in standard length units.

The **period** (*T*) of a wave motion is the time required for one complete cycle of a wave to pass a single point in the medium. As you can see from Fig. 12-9, the period of the wave is the same as that of the vibratory motion of the point A, and of the vibrating source of the wave. In the first sketch a crest is at A, in the third a trough, and in the fifth the next crest. Also, then, the **frequency** (*f*) of a wave is the number of complete cycles that pass a point per second. As for vibrations, the period of waves is measured in seconds and frequency in hertz.

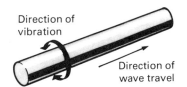

FIG. 12-11

FIG. 12-13

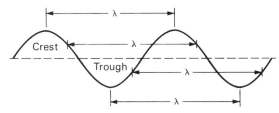

FIG. 12-14

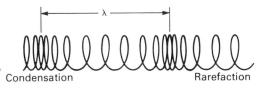

FIG. 12-15

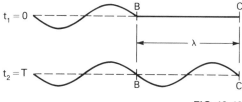

FIG. 12-16

Calculating speeds of wave motions requires only the simple distance-time relation discussed at the beginning of Chapter 2.

The **amplitude** of a wave is the maximum displacement of a particle in the medium from its undisturbed position.

Fig. 12-16 contains the first and fifth sketches from Fig. 12-9. During a time interval of one period the disturbance on the coiled spring travelled from B to C. Since those two locations are at successive points in the same phase in the wave, the distance BC is one wavelength. Referring back to the first equation for speed (v) in Chapter 2, we can substitute λ for d and T for t in the relation:

Since
$$v = \frac{d}{t}, \quad \text{then} \quad v = \frac{\lambda}{T}$$

The speed of travel of a wave is equal to its wavelength divided by its period. Also,

since
$$v = \left(\frac{1}{T}\right)\lambda \quad \text{and} \quad \frac{1}{T} = f, \quad \text{then} \quad v = f\lambda.$$

The speed of travel of a wave is equal to its frequency times its wavelength. With the wavelength measured in metres, period in seconds, and frequency in hertz, the speed will be expressed in units of metres per second. Although the two equations for the speed of a wave are equivalent, the latter one, $v = f\lambda$, is used more frequently than the other. It is called the (universal) **wave equation**.

Example: One end of a long rope is vibrated at a rate of 20 Hz. The wavelength (distance between successive crests) is found to be 0.15 m. What is the speed of the waves along the rope?

Since $f = 20$ Hz and $\lambda = 0.15$ m,

then $v = f\lambda = (20 \text{ Hz})(0.15 \text{ m}) = 3.0$ m/s.

The waves travel along the rope at 3.0 m/s.

The wave equation can be applied to a wide variety of waves. Whenever two of the quantities are known, the third can be calculated.

Example: In a microwave oven, a device called a magnetron generates electromagnetic waves (see page 224) with a frequency of 2.45 GHz. The speed of the waves is 3.00×10^8 m/s. Calculate the wavelength of the microwaves.

Since $f = 2.45$ GHz $= 2.45 \times 10^9$/s,

$$v = 3.00 \times 10^8 \text{ m/s}, \quad \text{and} \quad v = f\lambda,$$

then $\lambda = \dfrac{v}{f} = \dfrac{3.00 \times 10^8 \text{ m/s}}{2.45 \times 10^9 \text{/s}} = 1.22 \times 10^{-1}$ m.

The wavelength of the microwaves is 0.122 m or 12.2 cm.

RIPPLE TANKS

So far we have concentrated our attention on waves travelling in a single dimension (i.e., along a line). Wave disturbances can also spread out in two dimensions over plane surfaces, and in three dimensions in extended media. Although the latter are the most important they are difficult to visualize. We can get some notion of them, however, by examining ripples on the surface of water in a shallow tank. That can provide a two-dimensional picture. Then you use your imagination to try to visualize waves spreading out in space.

A ripple tank is a horizontal tray with a transparent bottom, frequently rectangular, measuring 60 to 70 cm on a side. The tank (Fig. 12-17) is mounted on legs 50 cm or so long, with a white screen on the table beneath it, and a source of light suspended above. The tank contains water to a depth of about 1 cm. Since the water is shallow, the speed of ripples over the surface will depend on the depth of the water—the speed is less in shallower water.

When there are ripples on the surface of the tank, their action on the light passing through them is to make crests appear as bright lines on the screen. If you let a droplet of water fall a short distance to the centre of the tank, a circular pulse will spread out from the point where the drop strikes. Fig. 12-18 is a drawing to show two successive locations of a single pulse. It shows that the direction of travel of the pulse is perpendicular to the line of the pulse. The energy spreads out along radii from the centre, uniformly in all directions. If a vibrating source is located at the centre, a circular wave disturbance spreads outward as shown in Fig. 12-19. The wavelength (distance between successive crests) is marked.

At a very great distance from a point source of energy, the circular crests have a very small curvature. They are almost straight lines. Although circular ripples are fine for regions near a source, straight rip-

FIG. 12-17

Ripples on the surface of water travel at a maximum speed of about 30 cm/s, whereas ocean waves have been observed travelling at 20 m/s.

From geometry we know that any radius of a circle is perpendicular to the circumference at the point where the two intersect.

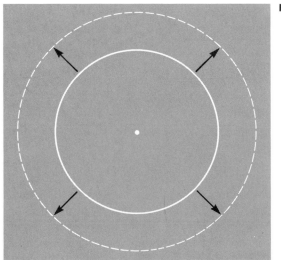

FIG. 12-18

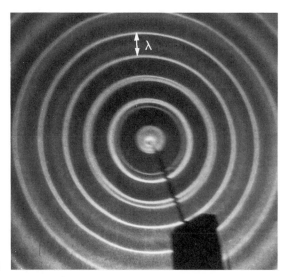

FIG. 12-19

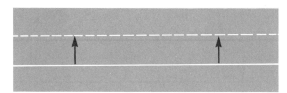

FIG. 12-20

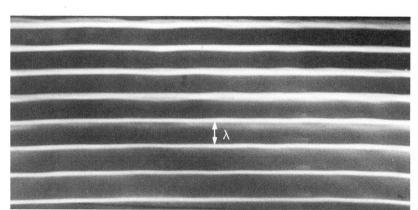

FIG. 12-21

ples are better to represent wave crests in regions far from a point source. In the ripple tank straight pulses can be produced by rolling a wooden dowel about a quarter-turn at one end of the tank. Fig. 12-20 pictures a straight pulse at two successive instants, showing that the direction of travel of the pulse is again perpendicular to the line of the pulse. This is also true of straight waves, such as those in Fig. 12-21. These are generated by a bar of wood vibrating at one end of the ripple tank.

INTERFERENCE OF PULSES AND WAVES

When two or more waves travel through the same region of a medium at the same time, they jointly affect the motions of the particles of the medium. The displacement of any particular particle that is so affected will be the vector sum of the displacements it would undergo from each wave separately. This is called the **principle of superposition**. The net result of the waves moving through the medium at the same time is called **interference**.

The medium takes on an appearance that is different from that when a single wave is travelling through it. The net motions of the particles when waves are interfering create a pattern called an **interference pattern**. Here, we shall examine several different patterns of interference.

INTERFERENCE IN ONE DIMENSION

In the photographs in Fig. 12-22, a coiled spring is shown with pulses moving from opposite ends toward the centre. The left-hand pulse produces an upward displacement of the spring, and the other a downward displacement. In the third photo the two pulses are beginning to overlap in the centre. In the fourth photo the spring is almost straight in the centre, as the two pulses tend to urge it to move in opposite directions. When the addition of a second wave into a region *decreases* the motions of the particles of the medium, the result is called **destructive interference**. Notice that the two pulses continue to

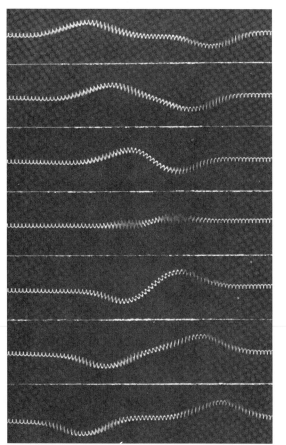

FIG. 12-22

move along the spring, so that in the seventh photo they are approaching the ends opposite their starting places.

In the series of photographs in Fig. 12-23, the two pulses both produce upward displacements of the spring. The two pulses are interacting in photos 3 to 7. With both pulses tending to urge the spring in the same direction the displacement when they are exactly superimposed is equal to the sum of their amplitudes. If the two pulses have the same amplitude, the displacement of the "super-pulse" is double the displacement of the individual pulses. This is shown in the fifth photo. When the addition of a second wave into a region *increases* the motions of the particles of the medium, the result is called **constructive interference**. Here again the pulses continue to move along the spring after having passed through each other.

STANDING WAVES

Pulses provide a chance to see the effects of constructive and destructive interference separately. However, we are often more interested in waves than in pulses. Imagine two continuous waves travelling in opposite directions along the length of a coiled spring (Fig. 12-24). The straight line AG represents the spring before the waves appear. Then, at a given instant one wave AXU and another PYG are both exerting their influence on AG at the same time. The vector sums of the displacements of the two waves at various points combine to give the net effect shown by the heavy line, PQRDSTU.

At points A, C, E, and G along the spring, the displacement of one wave is zero. Thus, the sum will equal the displacement of the other wave. That gives the points P, R, S, and U respectively along the resultant wave. At points B and F, the two waves cross, so that their displacements are equal. Hence, the resultant displacements at Q and T are simply double either single displacement. Finally, between C and E, the resultant wave must cross the zero axis at D. The symmetry of the situation indicates that D should be midway between C and E. And it should be evident that the two waves have equal and opposite displacements at that point.

Now, consider a section of a coil spring with waves travelling along it in opposite directions (Fig. 12-25). The two waves are identical in all respects except their direction of travel. As shown in the first drawing, the spring is 1.5 λ in length, and both waves of wavelength λ are providing identical displacement instructions. As a result, the actual displacement of the spring at this moment will be double what it would have been with one wave alone.

Then, after one-sixth of a period ($T/6$) has elapsed, the solid wave has moved λ/6 to the right, and the dotted wave λ/6 to the left. Some destructive interference is replacing the constructive interference of the first diagram. The displacement of the points marked with open circles has diminished. The displacement of the points marked with solid circles remains zero. After another one-sixth of a period (at $T/3$), the resultant wave-form has been reversed from the

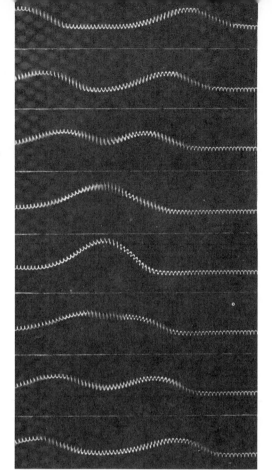

FIG. 12-23

Recall vector addition from Chapter 3.

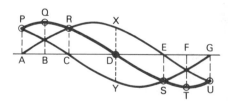

FIG. 12-24

FIG. 12-25 appears on page 166.

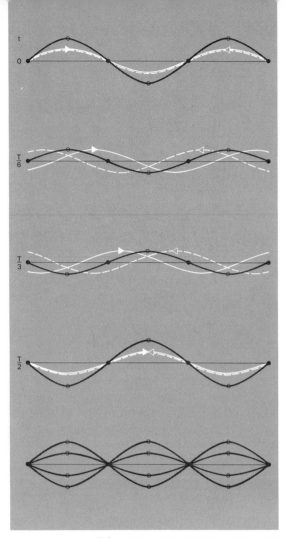

FIG. 12-25. Standing waves produced by the interference of two identical waves travelling in opposite directions.

preceding one. Finally, after half a period has elapsed, the resultant has attained maximum displacement on the opposite side of the spring from the first diagram.

Now the four resultants are put together in a single diagram. This shows the variation in displacement of the points marked with open circles, and the continuing zero displacement of the points marked with solid circles. You should see that an interference pattern has been set up in the spring. This constant pattern is called a **standing wave**, to distinguish it from a travelling wave in which *all points* in the spring undergo regular changes in displacement. In the standing wave pattern the points that always have zero displacement are called **nodes**. The points that undergo maximum displacement, midway between the nodes, are called **antinodes**. Some people use the word "loop" to mean the same as antinode, while others use "loop" to mean the whole region between the nodes.

An important feature of standing waves is that the distance between successive nodes is one-half a wavelength; that is, $\lambda/2$, where λ is the wavelength of the travelling waves whose interference creates the standing wave. A standing wave like the one we have described is shown in the long-exposure photograph of Fig. 12-26. The waves travelling in one direction are generated by the boy. The waves travelling in the other direction result from the reflection of the energy from the fixed end.

INTERFERENCE IN TWO DIMENSIONS

The pulses, waves, and nodes along one dimension have the appearance of a cross-sectional view of waves in a ripple tank. They have allowed us to examine the details of simple interactions. Now, we look at an image of the *surface* of the ripple tank. A vibrator at one end of the tank is arranged to make two small spheres move up and down at the surface of the water. The spheres are a couple of centimetres apart. As they vibrate, each sphere is the source of a set of circular waves that spread out across the surface of the water.

FIG. 12-26

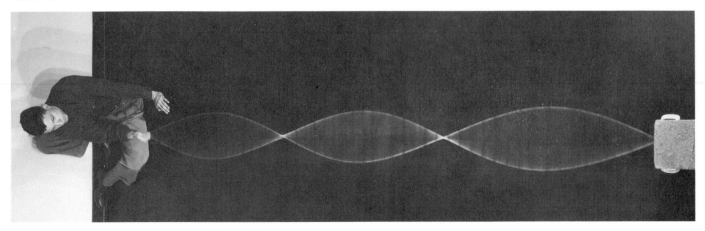

Because the waves spread out into the same region, they will interfere. If you look at the image of the surface projected onto a screen (Fig. 12-27) you will see that a constant pattern is set up on the surface of the water. The two diagrams of Fig. 12-28 will show how this pattern is created. A and B are the two point sources of circular wave fronts. The crests and troughs from each source are represented

FIG. 12-27

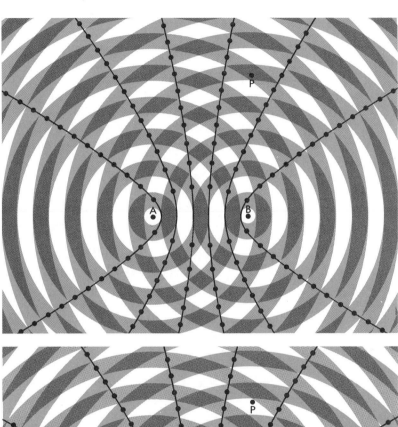

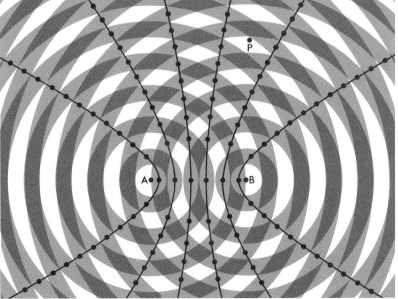

FIG. 12-28. Drawings of the interference pattern from two point sources in phase, separated by a time-interval of about half a period. The stationary point P marks a super-trough in the upper drawing and a super-crest in the (later) lower drawing. P is thus located along a line of maximum disturbance in the interference pattern, whereas the six nodal lines mark the regions of *minimum* disturbance in the pattern.

by alternating circular bands of white and grey. Since *both* sets of waves cover the surface, the pattern that you see is the result of their interference. The white regions in Fig. 12-28 are the locations of the constructive interference of two crests. The darkest regions are the result of the constructive interference of two troughs. The grey regions are relatively still, because of the destructive interference of crests from one source coinciding with troughs from the other one.

The two diagrams in Fig. 12-28 are separated by a time-interval that is about one-half of the period of vibration of the sources. Yet, you can see that the locations of the various regions of interference are essentially unchanged. The lines joining the nodal points are in exactly the same location in both diagrams. This demonstrates that the result is a stationary pattern, despite being created by two sets of travelling waves. The *nodal lines*, that is, the set of all nodal points, are a permanent feature of the pattern. And, between the nodal lines are regions that are subjected to alternating super-crests and super-troughs as a result of the constructive interference there. This pattern demonstrates standing waves in two dimensions.

Suppose there is a series of small floats at the end of the ripple tank opposite the location of the point sources of the two waves. Floats located in the regions of the nodal lines would hardly move at all; whereas the floats in between would bob about quite vigorously. Thus, at the end of the ripple tank away from the source of the two waves, there is an alternating pattern of regions of no disturbance separated by regions of considerable disturbance. The production of this kind of pattern by two point sources is typical of every wave phenomenon. Whether sound or light are wave phenomena can be tested by setting up two point sources and seeing whether you can find such alternating regions of sound and quiet, or of light and darkness.

By contrast, imagine two fire hoses emitting a fine spray of water side-by-side, directed toward a wall a few metres away. You would find it very surprising if the result was that there were alternating bands of wet and dry on the wall. The water sprays are not a wave phenomenon.

> For a vibrating string of fixed length only certain wavelengths can produce standing waves. The string length l must be a whole number of half wavelengths. Thus, $l = n\lambda$, or $\lambda = 2l/n$ (for $n = 1, 2, 3, \ldots$). This restriction of the wavelength to particular values is called *quantization*. You will meet this idea again (in Chapter 18) in the quantized energy levels of electrons in atoms.

Exercises

A

1. Classify each of the following examples as a transverse, longitudinal, or torsional vibration:
   (a) a child bouncing up and down on a pogo stick,
   (b) a needle on a sewing machine while in use,
   (c) the rotary agitator in a washing machine while in use,
   (d) a child swinging on a swing in a playground,
   (e) an object attached to the end of a long, vertical, twisted string,
   (f) a tree swaying in the breeze.

2. What is the average period, in seconds, of each of the following examples of motion?
   (a) A child skipping jumps off the ground 40 times in 1.0 min.
   (b) An adult shovels topsoil into a truck, working at the rate of 12 shovelfuls per minute.
   (c) An electric metronome clicks 50 times in 30 s.
   (d) An athlete has a pulse rate of 120 beats in a minute after running a race.
   (e) The moon travels round the earth five times in 136.6 d.

(f) Electrons move back and forth across the face of a television picture tube 60 times every second.

3. What is the average frequency, in hertz, of each of the following?
(a) A stenographer takes dictation of 610 words in 5.0 min.
(b) An adult walks 5 paces every 10 s.
(c) A photocell, electronic counter, and accurate stopclock are used to determine that a xenon stroboscope flashes 10 times in 0.125 s.
(d) An automatic facing and cancelling machine at the post office can handle an average of 30 000 pieces of mail in an hour.

4. What is the period of vibration of objects which have the following frequencies: (a) 25 Hz, (b) 0.50 Hz, (c) 3.0×10^2 Hz, (d) 104.5 MHz?

5. What is the frequency, in hertz, corresponding to each of the following periods: (a) 0.10 s, (b) 4.0 s, (c) 1.25×10^{-2} s, (d) 5.0 ms?

6. (a) If the bob of a long pendulum has an amplitude of 8.0 cm, what distance does it travel in 5 vibrations?
(b) The end of a 512 Hz tuning fork has an average amplitude of 1.0 mm for 3.0 s. Through what distance does the end of the fork travel during this time?
(c) What is the amplitude of a rotary agitator in a washing machine that makes a three-quarter turn before reversing?

7. Draw a diagram of an object vibrating on a long spring when the object is at the bottom of its vibration and just starting to come upward. Draw a second diagram for each of the following cases to show the location and direction of motion of an identical object on an identical spring, but with a phase difference of: (a) one-quarter period, (b) one-half period, (c) three-quarters of a period, (d) zero.

8. Longitudinal waves with a frequency of 0.50 Hz are being generated at one end of a long spring. How many (a) rarefactions, (b) compressions, would someone halfway down the spring observe passing in 4.0 s?

9. (a) Use the idea that a gas consists of a collection of free-moving molecules that are well separated by empty space to explain briefly how a longitudinal wave could travel through a gas.
(b) Why would it be very difficult to generate a transverse wave in a gas?

10. Draw a diagram of a transverse wave train containing four waves with an amplitude of 2 cm and a wavelength of 3 cm travelling to the right. On the diagram indicate (a) the direction of motion of the wave, (b) the direction of motion of some particle of the medium, (c) two successive particles which are in phase (but not ones at the top of crests or the bottom of troughs or on the equilibrium line of the medium).

11. The period of the sound emitted by a siren is 2.5 ms. Calculate the wavelength of the sound if the speed of sound is 340 m/s.

12. The speed of sound in carbon dioxide gas at 0°C is 260 m/s. The wavelength of a sound wave travelling through this medium is 65 cm. What is the period of the wave?

13. Determine the unknown quantity for each of the following waves which have frequency f, wavelength λ and speed v.
(a) $f = 20$ Hz, $\lambda = 6.5$ m, $v = ?$
(b) $f = 256$ Hz, $v = 332$ m/s, $\lambda = ?$
(c) $\lambda = 50$ cm, $v = 0.75$ km/s, $f = ?$

14. Calculate the speed of sound in air if a sound wave has
(a) a frequency of 125 Hz and a wavelength of 2.68 m,
(b) a frequency of 12 kHz and a wavelength of 28.5 mm.

15. What is the frequency of a sound wave if its speed and wavelength are
(a) 342 m/s and 0.5 m respectively,
(b) 400 m/s and 85 cm respectively?

16. Determine the wavelength of a wave which has
(a) a speed of 8 m/s and a frequency of 4.5 Hz,
(b) a speed of 3×10^8 m/s and a frequency of 1.5×10^{15} Hz.

B

17. When a spring is stretched, it has elastic potential energy. The top photograph in Fig. 12-22 shows two pulses on the spring, that is, two places on the spring where the spring is stretched more than normal, and thus where the spring has elastic potential energy. The fourth photo shows the spring with almost zero amplitude and hence almost zero elastic potential energy. Where do you suppose all the potential energy went? Is there any indication in the fourth photo that would support your hypothesis?

18. Draw a diagram similar to Fig. 12-26 showing a string 12 cm long with the number of nodes specified in each of the following. Then calculate the wavelength of the interfering waves in each case.
(a) two nodes (that is, one at each end)
(b) three nodes
(c) four nodes
(d) five nodes.

19. Would it be possible to set up standing waves on the string of question 20 with waves of wavelength 5 cm? Explain why or why not.

20. A long coil lies on a smooth surface. Each end of the coil is held by a student. Each student vibrates his or her end of the coil through one cycle sending a single pulse to the opposite end of the coil. Describe what

would be observed when the two waves coincide at the middle of the coil when the students vibrate the coil (a) in phase, and (b) with a phase difference of one half period. What type of interference does each case illustrate?

21. A vibrating point in a ripple tank produces a complete wave every 0.10 s. By the use of a stroboscope which apparently stops the motion of the waves, the difference in radii between the 1st and 6th circular crests is found to be 12 cm.
    (a) What is the wavelength?
    (b) What is the frequency of the waves?
    (c) What is the speed of the waves?

22. A 360 Hz source emits waves having a wavelength of 24 cm. In what time will this disturbance travel a distance of 144 m?

23. Standing waves are produced in a string by two sources each having a frequency of 120 Hz. The distance from the 2nd node to the 6th is 72 cm. Determine the wavelength and speed of the original travelling waves.

24. A vibrating loudspeaker at one end of a horizontal column of air in a tube vibrates at 1.2 kHz. Fine cork dust is sprinkled along the bottom of the tube. The end of the tube opposite the loudspeaker is closed. The standing waves in the air in the tube cause piles of cork dust to form at the nodes. The distance from the 1st pile to the 5th is 58 cm. What is the speed of the wave in the column of air?

C

25. Draw two points A and B 5 cm apart on the same horizontal line about one-quarter way from the bottom of a piece of metric graph paper, and centred in the left and right direction. With the aid of a pair of compasses draw an interference pattern produced by the point sources as follows. With first A and then B as centre, draw concentric circles of radii 2 cm, 4 cm, 6 cm, 8 cm, and so on, to represent the crests of the waves generated by A and B. Draw dotted circles midway between the solid circles to represent the troughs. Fill up most of the page with these circles. Then go over the entire drawing and put a black dot at every point of destructive interference, and a small cross at every point of constructive interference.
    (a) What distance on the drawing is used to represent one wavelength?

    (b) Draw the right bisector of AB. What type of interference occurs along this right bisector?
    (c) Draw a line on each side of this bisector joining the rows of black dots nearest to the bisector. What name is given to this type of line? Draw other similar lines crossing AB and passing through rows of black dots between which there are rows of crosses.
    (d) Find a point P which is 3 cm from A and 4 cm from B, a point Q which is 5 cm from A and 6 cm from B, and a point R which is 7 cm from A and 8 cm from B. What characteristic is common to P, Q, and R?
    (e) (i) For any point X on either of the first nodal lines (first meaning nearest to the right bisector), what is the magnitude of the path difference XA - XB (ii) for any point X on either of the second nodal lines, (iii) for any point X on either of the nth nodal lines?
    (f) What are the corresponding equations for points on the antinodal lines?

26. A pendulum 100 cm in length swings with a period of approximately 2 s. Its 200 g bob has an amplitude of about 1 cm. State how each of the following changes would affect the frequency f of the pendulum.
    (a) The length is decreased to 50 cm.
    (b) The length is increased to 150 cm.
    (c) The amplitude is increased to 2 cm.
    (d) The mass of the bob is increased to 400 g.

27. The engineer in a diesel locomotive sounds the horn, which has a frequency of 280 Hz. The speed of sound in air is 348 m/s that day. An observer hears the sound while travelling in a train towards the engine at a speed of 20.0 m/s.
    (a) What is the wavelength of the sound emitted by the whistle?
    (b) Knowing the speed of the emitted sound relative to the air, calculate the speed of sound relative to the observer in the train when the train is (i) approaching the engine, (ii) going away from the engine.
    (c) Knowing the wavelength of the sound of the whistle and the speed of the sound relative to the observer in the train while approaching and receding from the engine, calculate the frequency of the sound heard by the observer (i) approaching the engine, (ii) receding from the engine.
    (d) Describe in words what the observer would actually hear. (This phenomenon is known as the *Doppler effect.*)

CHAPTER 13

Sound Waves

A timber wolf howls a signal to his pack; Wolfman Jack growls out a gusty song; and Elizabeth Taylor bawls, "Who's afraid of Virginia Woolf?" Sound is a widespread means of expression and communication. Sound waves travelling through the air strike your ears. Your eardrums are vibrated by the waves, and nerves convey messages to the brain to be interpreted.

But, how can you tell that sound consists of waves? The most immediate evidence is that sound originates from vibrating sources. Sound comes from the vibrations of a plucked guitar string or of air blown over a clarinet reed. If the air molecules then rushed through space to your ear, you might expect to feel the wind. Since loud sounds don't blow you over, it makes sense to consider sound as the transmission of energy from molecule to molecule through the air to a receiver such as the human ear. Later in this chapter we shall consider another kind of evidence for the wave nature of sound.

CHARACTERISTICS OF SOUNDS

The chief characteristics of sounds are pitch, loudness and quality. They can be related to various features of sound waves. The principal features of any wave motion are its speed, frequency, and amplitude. That the speed of sound is small compared to that of light can be readily observed. Suppose you are a hundred metres away from the starting-point of a foot race. The starter's gun is fired, and you *see* the puff of smoke before you *hear* the "crack" of the report.

The speed of sound depends on the material through which it travels. In still dry air the speed of sound is about 340 m/s. When sound travels through media other than air, it has a different speed. The speed of sound in any medium is a characteristic of the medium (see table in the Appendix). The speed of sound also depends on the temperature of the medium.

PITCH

The frequencies of sounds generally audible to humans range from about 20 Hz to 20 kHz. Sounds of the higher frequencies are recognized as being of higher **pitch**. The relation between the pitch of two

The speed of sound in still, dry air at 0 °C is 332 m/s. It increases by 0.6 m/s for each 1 °C rise in temperature. The rate of increase is called the *temperature coefficient* of the speed of sound in air.

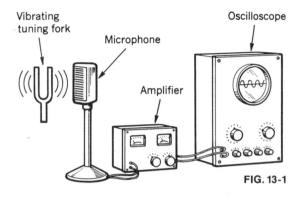

Vibrating tuning fork · Microphone · Amplifier · Oscilloscope

FIG. 13-1

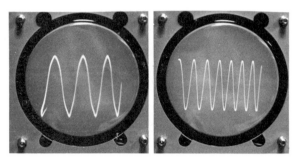

FIG. 13-2

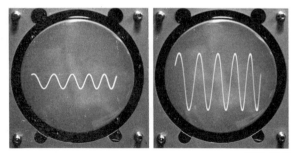

FIG. 13-3

sounds is normally expressed in terms of octaves. Each doubling of frequency represents an increase of one **octave** in the pitch. The frequency of the standard "A" in music is 440 Hz. Thus, the "A" one octave higher has a frequency of 880 Hz, and the "A" two octaves higher, 1760 Hz. The highest frequency we can hear is about 1000 times the lowest. Since $1000 = 2^{10}$ (approximately), human hearing covers a range of about 10 octaves.

You have seen that whenever speed and frequency are known, wavelength can be calculated. From the relation $v = f\lambda$ you can calculate that the wavelengths of audible sounds range from 17 m to 17 mm. The linear dimensions of musical instruments are closely related to the wavelengths of the sounds they produce. High-pitched instruments are generally smaller than low-pitched ones.

Different frequencies of sound can be illustrated using a cathode-ray oscilloscope. The apparatus of Fig. 13-1 can be used to show the pattern of the vibrations of a source of sound. The photographs of Fig. 13-2 show the patterns of two sounds of different frequency.

LOUDNESS

The sensation of **loudness** depends on the intensity of the sound wave which reaches the listener's ear. The intensity decreases quite rapidly as the distance of the wave from the source increases. Apart from any energy absorption by the medium, the intensity received varies inversely as the square of the distance between the source and ear. If the distance is doubled the intensity is reduced to one-quarter of its original strength. If the distance is trebled the intensity is reduced to one-ninth of its original strength.

The photographs of Fig. 13-3 show the patterns of two sounds of different loudness.

The intensity is defined as the rate of flow of energy (power) per unit area. The area is that of a cross-sectional surface through which the sound wave may penetrate. For instance, a joule of energy per second may flow through a square window which measures one metre by one metre. At this window the intensity received would be one joule per second per square metre (written as 1 J/s·m²). This unit of intensity is equal to 1 W/m².

The intensity received by the ear depends mainly on the amplitude of vibration of the source. The amplitude of sound waves is indicated by changes in the pressure of the air where the waves pass. Where the pressure changes are greater, the amplitude is greater. These pressure variations cause your eardrums to vibrate with greater or lesser amplitudes. The result is more or less loudness in the sound you hear.

Human ears are wonderfully sensitive detectors of pressure variations within the range of audible frequencies (Fig. 13-4). At a frequency of 3 kHz, an acute ear will detect a sound with a pressure variation of only about twenty micropascals (20 μPa). The intensity of such a sound is about 1×10^{-12} W/m^2 (1 pW/m^2). Yet your ear's structure is sturdy enough to respond also to sounds that are 10^{12} times as intense! Beyond an intensity of about 1 W/m^2 the sensation in your brain is one of *pain*, not sound.

The very large range of sound intensities has led to a special scale for measuring them. Instead of using the intensities themselves, physicists and engineers use the *index* (exponent) of the power of ten of the intensity. The new unit is called a **decibel** (dB), with 0 dB starting at the threshold of hearing.

$$0 \text{ dB} = 1.0 \text{ pW/m}^2$$
$$10 \text{ dB} = 1.0 \times 10^1 \text{ pW/m}^2$$
$$20 \text{ dB} = 1.0 \times 10^2 \text{ pW/m}^2.$$

Actually, the index itself gives the intensity in bels, so that decibels are ten times the index of the power of ten of the intensity. Intensities for some familiar sounds are shown in Table 13-1.

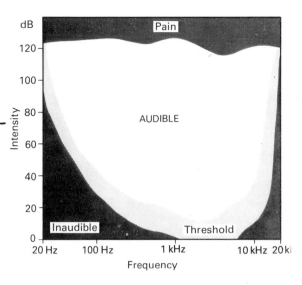

FIG. 13-4. The intensity of the minimum sound you can hear depends on the frequency of the sound.

Table 13-1

VARIOUS SOUND INTENSITIES

Sound level	Sounds	Intensity
0 dB	threshold of hearing	1 pW/m^2
10	rustle of leaves	10
20	whisper at 1 m	10^2
30		10^3
40	night noises in a city	10^4
50	auto engine at 10 m	10^5
60	conversation at 1 m	10^6
65		
70	very busy traffic	10^7
80	very close to Niagara Falls	10^8
90	pneumatic drill	10^9
100	riveter at 10 m	10^{10}
110	jet takeoff at 60 m	10^{11}
120	threshold of pain	10^{12}

QUALITY

A trumpet and a clarinet can both produce a sound with the same pitch and the same loudness. Yet you can tell the two sounds apart. The vibrations and wave patterns of the two sounds must differ in some way other than frequency and amplitude. The difference is in the complexity of the vibration pattern.

Many vibrators are able to generate complex wave patterns because their shape and size determine a specific set of frequencies that are natural to each vibrator. Usually, natural frequencies are whole-

The complexity of the vibration pattern is called *quality,* or *timbre*, or *tone colour*.

A rapid variation in pitch of from two to five times per second is called *vibrato*. Violinists, for example, produce vibrato by vibrating their fingers back and forth a tiny distance on the violin strings.

A rapid variation in loudness occurring at the rate of two to five times a second is called *tremolo*. Singers often produce a combination of tremolo and vibrato to give added colour to their singing.

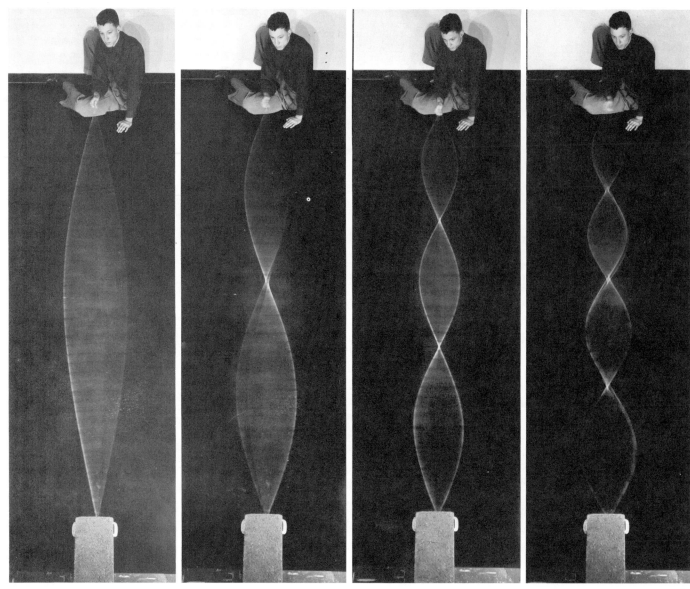

FIG. 13-5

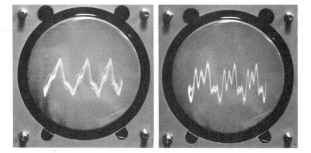

FIG. 13-6

number multiples of the lowest frequency the vibrator produces. Our friend in the photographs in Fig. 13-5 is shaking the rubber tube at different frequencies. The frequencies are 1.5, 3.0, 4.5, and 6.0 Hz. In musical terms, the lowest frequency is called the *first harmonic* of the vibrator. The second harmonic has twice that frequency; the third, three times the lowest frequency, and so on.

For the rubber tube only one harmonic is being produced at a time. However, in most musical instruments, a variety of harmonics are produced together. Which harmonics are strongest depends on the structure of the instrument. As a result, when their effects are added together, the wave-form of a sound from one instrument will be different from that of another (Fig. 13-6).

Fig. 13-7 shows two wave-forms of different frequency, with their amplitudes represented by a series of vectors. In the third diagram, the vectors are shown being added. Joining the points representing the individual vector sums produces the wave-form that results from the addition of the two individual waves.

SOUND WAVES

The demonstration of interference among sound waves will provide conclusive evidence that sound is indeed a wave phenomenon. Here, we shall examine several kinds of interference in sound. Their study will enable you to understand the construction of wind instruments and how to tune them.

SILENT REGIONS NEAR A TUNING FORK

The interference patterns discussed in the last chapter arose from two sources with the same frequency. If the two sources have a constant phase relation, they will produce a persistent interference pattern. Although a tuning fork appears to be a single source of sound, it actually is a kind of double source. The reason for that is that each tine of the fork creates compressions in the air on the side toward which it moves, and rarefactions on the side away from which it moves (Fig. 13-8). Thus, while a compression is being produced between the two tines, a rarefaction is produced on their outer sides. Then, when the tines move outward, the pressure changes are reversed. Waves from between the tines are always out of phase with those outside the tines. Where the compressions and rarefactions coincide, there is destructive interference and a minimum of sound intensity (Fig. 13-9).

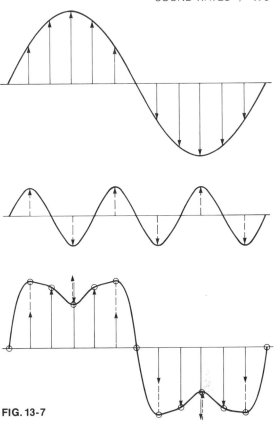

FIG. 13-7

Tuning forks are said to have been invented by the Chinese, who discovered that the tone of a small bell could be made purer by cutting two oppositely placed slits in the side of the bell. They found that the wider the slits, the purer the tone. Eventually, the slits became so wide that they got what is known as a tuning fork.

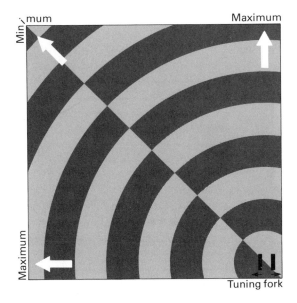

FIG. 13-9

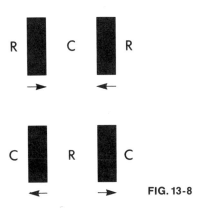

FIG. 13-8

The variation in sound intensity can be heard if a sounding tuning fork is rotated slowly near your ear. At a distance of one or two metres from the fork, the sound you hear is the average of the sounds spreading out from the whole region where the fork is located. Now, suppose that the fork is held in front of a slot about the width of a tine cut in a heavy card. Now, only the direct wave from one tine will be heard at a distance of a couple of metres. The destructive interference is suppressed, and you hear only the direct wave from the tine at the slot. As a result, the sound of the fork is louder when the slot is in place than when it is not.

PRODUCTION OF BEATS

Now consider the interference of wave fronts generated by two sources of slightly different frequencies sounded simultaneously. Two identical tuning forks are mounted on wooden boxes that make the sound more audible. Very small metal clamps are then attached to the prongs of one fork, thus increasing the mass of the prongs, and therefore their inertia. This results in slower motion causing the loaded fork to vibrate with a slightly lower frequency than the unloaded fork. (In place of the small metal clamps the addition of a little wax or plasticine is satisfactory.) When the two forks are sounded simultaneously the sound that is heard is alternately loud and soft, repeatedly rising and falling in intensity. The periodic changes in intensity are called **beats**.

The waves generated by the forks may reach the ear in phase at some particular instant. This occurs when two compressions or two rarefactions, one from each fork, meet at the ear together. They reinforce each other producing a maximum intensity. Since the frequencies are unequal, more waves per second reach the ear from the unloaded fork than from the loaded one. The waves gradually become

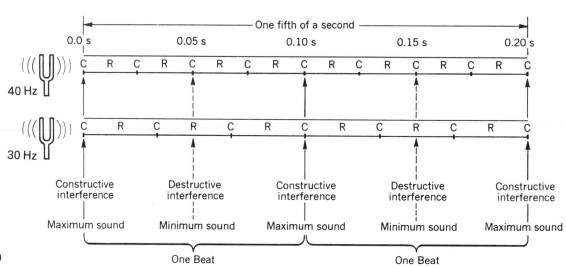

FIG. 13-10

more and more out of step with each other until they arrive at the ear in opposite phase. At this instant a compression from one fork and a rarefaction from the other meet at the ear. They cancel each other producing a minimum intensity. Each cycle of intensity from maximum to maximum or from minimum to minimum may be considered to form one beat.

In Fig. 13-10 the upper line represents a wave train produced by a fork vibrating at 40 Hz for one-fifth of a second. In this time it generates eight waves. Each wave is represented by the distance between the mid-point of one compression C and the mid-point of the next C with a rarefaction R halfway between. The lower line represents a wave train produced by the loaded fork vibrating at 30 Hz. This latter fork generates only 6 waves in the fifth of a second. The two wave trains are in phase at the 0.0 s mark, where two compressions reinforce each other producing a sound of maximum intensity. A little later, in 0.05 s, the two wave trains are in opposite phase, a compression interfering with a rarefaction, producing minimum intensity. In 0.10 s maximum intensity occurs again, then a minimum in 0.15 s, and so on. The period of a beat may be considered as the time between two successive maximum or minimum sounds. In this case the period of the beat is 0.10 s and in one-fifth of a second two beats will be formed. The beat frequency is the number of beats per second and here it is 2 beats per fifth of a second or 10 beats per second. Note that the difference between the frequencies of the two tuning forks is 10 Hz.

Fig. 13-11 shows a transverse wave representation of two wave trains generated by forks having frequencies of 30 and 27 Hz over a period of one second. At A, C, E, and G the waves are in phase, interfering constructively to produce maximum intensity. At B, D, and F they are in opposite phase, interfering destructively to produce minimum intensity. The resultant wave pattern (shown below the separate wave patterns) is formed by the addition of the two waves and represents the sound which is actually heard by the ear. Here the beat frequency is 3 beats per second as is evident from the diagram.

A beat frequency of more than about 10 Hz sounds rough and unpleasant to most people. We say that the two beating frequencies are *dissonant*. If the frequency difference continues to increase however, the beat frequency becomes less dissonant. The beat sound will seem specially pleasant or *consonant* when the two frequencies have such simple ratios as 2/1, 3/2, 4/3, 6/5, etc. In music, such frequencies are said to form *chords*.

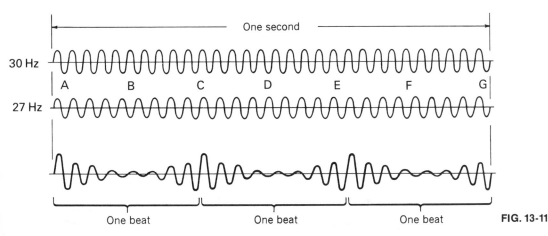

FIG. 13-11

Again, note that the difference between the frequencies of the forks is 3 Hz. In general it is found that the beat frequency equals the difference in frequency of the two forks.

The application of beats simplifies the problem of tuning musical instruments or of comparing the frequency of a stretched string with that of a tuning fork, such as tuning a guitar. The string's tension may be varied until beats occur when the string and fork are sounded together. Further adjustment of the tension can be made to reduce the beat frequency until the beats are eliminated. The pitch of both fork and string are then known to be equal.

INTERFERENCE FROM TWO IDENTICAL SOURCES

An audio-frequency generator and an amplifier may be connected in parallel to two loudspeakers. The speakers are connected to the same source and therefore generate identical wave patterns which travel from the speakers in spherical waves. The waves from the two sources interfere with one another in a manner similar to the waves produced in the ripple tank by two point sources as in Fig. 12-27. In the neighbourhood of the speakers there are regions of comparative silence along the nodal lines and regions of maximum intensity about midway between them.

This will not work well in a small room with strong reflections from hard walls.

MECHANICAL RESONANCE

A large person sitting in a swing can be set into vibration by a small person who applies comparatively small impulses of force at the proper times. If the small person pushes the large one at intervals which are too close together or too far apart he cannot build up a large amplitude of swing. The impulses of the small person must synchronize with the natural frequency of the swinging person.

A car which is stuck may often be rocked out of a depression in the ground by a series of properly timed pushes which synchronize with the natural frequency of the car. These properly timed pushes are each much smaller than the single steady force needed to haul the car out of the depression.

A column of marching soldiers can set a bridge into violent vibration if the frequency of their marching happens to equal the natural frequency of the bridge structure. It is generally customary for columns of soldiers to "break step" when marching across a bridge.

A rattle in the family car may be noticeable at a certain speed but not at lower or higher speeds. The loose part which vibrates excessively has a natural frequency which equals the frequency generated by the motor when moving at a particular speed. At other speeds the impulses of the motor act on the loose part but with frequencies which do not match its natural frequency and which are therefore ineffective unless they are unusually large.

These examples illustrate the phenomenon called **resonance** which is the response of an object to the action of a periodic force which has the same frequency as the natural frequency of the object. Large vibrations are built up by the repeated application of small impulses which synchronize with the natural frequency of the resonating object. If forces are applied to an object causing it to vibrate at a frequency other than its natural frequency, the forces must be comparatively large and the object vibrates with the forced frequency, not the resonant frequency.

A simple demonstration of resonance may be given using a length of elastic rubber and a small block of wood. The rubber should be about four yards in length, rather thin and very elastic. At its midpoint is attached a small block of wood. One end of the rubber is attached to a fixed point and the other is held in your hand so that the rubber is approximately horizontal as in Fig. 13-12. First, vibrate your hand in a direction parallel to the rubber, but do so very slowly in an attempt to make the wood vibrate back and forth in the same direction as the hand. Second, vibrate your hand very rapidly. Finally, vibrate your hand at the natural frequency of the system. This frequency may be felt or sensed by using a very small amplitude of the hand, and timing its vibrations to match those of the block.

In the first case, the hand's frequency is below the natural frequency of the block and in the second case it is above. Either case results in a small amplitude of vibration of the block even though the energy supplied by the hand appears to be considerable. However, in the last case, small vibrations of the hand timed to synchronize with the natural frequency of the system cause large vibrations of the block. The block is resonating with the hand. Thus when energy is applied periodically in small pulses synchronized with the natural frequency of a system, the system is set in vibration, and in general the vibration has a comparatively large amplitude.

The vibrations of the Tacoma Narrows Bridge (page 160) were the result of the bridge *resonating* with certain of the periodic fluctuations in the whirls of air caused by the wind blowing through Puget Sound.

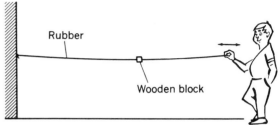

Rubber

Wooden block

FIG. 13-12

ACOUSTIC RESONANCE

Periodic impulses necessary for producing resonance may be transmitted by sound waves. If the sustaining pedal (sometimes called the loud pedal) of a piano is held down, all the strings inside are free to vibrate. Then if a person sings a note of frequency 260 Hz into the open piano, the middle C string may be set into vibration and may be heard after the singer stops. The middle C string has a natural frequency of 260 Hz and responds in resonance to the energy impulses of the sound waves striking the piano. The other strings in the piano fail to respond to the sound wave since the frequency of the sound wave does not equal their natural frequencies. In this example the middle C string is said to vibrate in sympathy with the sound wave, and its vibrations may be referred to as *sympathetic vibrations*.

Consider two identical tuning forks, mounted on resonance boxes, and placed on a table with their open ends facing each other some distance apart. If the first is set into vibration for a second or two and then stopped, the second fork is found to be vibrating with sufficient strength to be heard easily. The first fork, aided by its resonance box, sets the neighbouring air into vibration by means of longitudinal waves. This energy is then transferred to the second resonance box and its tuning fork until the latter responds to the small but properly timed impulses and vibrates strongly. If the second fork is loaded with a small weight, such as plasticine or wax, and the experiment is repeated, it is found that the second fork does not respond to the energy impulses from the first. Its new natural frequency does not match the frequency of the periodic impulses, and resonance no longer occurs.

THE NATURAL FREQUENCY OF AIR COLUMNS

A column of air in a tube has a natural frequency. This fact is used in the construction of a number of musical instruments such as woodwinds and horns. When an air column is vibrating at its natural frequency, there are standing waves in the tube.

When a compression approaches the closed end of such a tube the particles of air in contact with the solid end of the tube are not free to vibrate and so the closed end of a tube is a node. If a compression approaches the open end of a tube it suddenly breaks out into the open and the particles of air which were compressed rush apart leaving a partial vacuum or rarefaction. The particles at the open end, therefore, experience a maximum amplitude of vibration and the open end of the tube is an antinode.

Air column ⟶

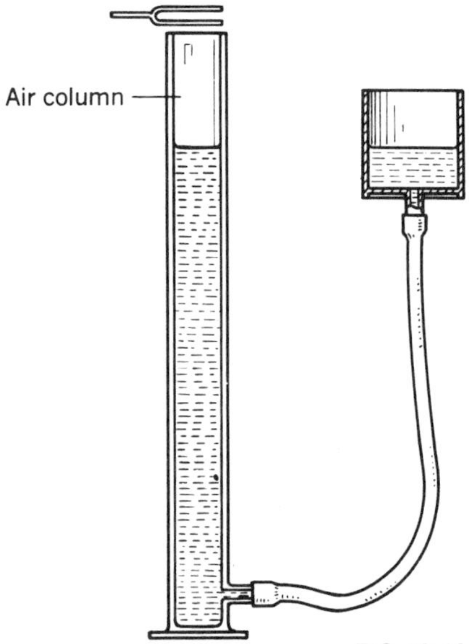

FIG. 13-14

Resonant lengths are those at which resonance occurs. In general the natural frequencies of linear vibrating systems, such as strings and air columns, form a full series of harmonics when the two ends of the system are the same. When the end conditions are different, as in an organ pipe which is closed at one end, the even-numbered harmonics are missing.

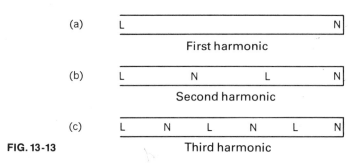

FIG. 13-13

(a) L — N
First harmonic

(b) L — N — L — N
Second harmonic

(c) L — N — L — N — L — N
Third harmonic

Remembering that two successive nodes or antinodes are half a wavelength ($\frac{1}{2}\lambda$) apart we can draw diagrams of various modes of vibrations of air columns. For a pipe, closed at one end only, the first resonant length has a node at the closed end and its adjacent antinode at the open end. Its length must then equal $\frac{1}{4}\lambda$ as in Fig. 13-13a. The second resonant length is similar but must have an additional node and antinode between the ends as in b, and so on for succeeding modes of vibration as in c. For the second resonant length, the tube length must be $\frac{3}{4}\lambda$, for the third resonant length the length must be $1\frac{1}{4}\lambda$, and so on.

Suppose that we hold the sounding tuning fork over a column of air as shown in Fig. 13-14. This column is open at the top, closed at the bottom and is adjustable in length. As the water in the tube is moved up and down, by the raising or lowering of the reservoir, it is noticed that the sound heard is more intense at certain definite lengths of the air column. These are resonant lengths in which the air resonates with the tuning fork. The shortest resonant length has the greatest intensity and is found to be ¼λ in length. The next is ¾λ, the next 1¼λ and so on. The wave patterns in Fig. 13-15 show how a standing wave naturally fits the conditions that have been stated for the modes of vibration of the various resonant lengths, namely, that there is a node at the closed end and a loop, or antinode, at the open end.

For a tube which is open at both ends, the resonant lengths of the air columns within it must be such that a loop exists at each end as in Fig. 13-16. The first resonant length must then be ½λ, the second is λ, the third is 1½λ, and so on. This again agrees with experimental results. The first harmonic is produced when there are the fewest possible nodes and loops within the air column.

Fig. 13-17 shows a policeman's whistle, 10 cm in length from the blowhole to the open end. If it produces its fundamental frequency there will be a loop at the blowhole and another at the open end with only one node between. That is, from blowhole to open end equals ½λ which is 10 and hence λ = 20 cm = 0.20 m. If the speed of sound is 340 m/s we can determine the fundamental frequency of the whistle since frequency equals speed divided by wavelength. That is,

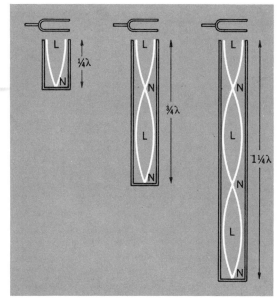

FIG. 13-15

$$f = \frac{v}{\lambda} = \frac{340 \text{ m/s}}{0.20 \text{ m}} = 1.7 \times 10^3 \text{ Hz}.$$

FIG. 13-16

Thus the open whistle has a frequency of 1.7×10^3 Hz. If the open end is plugged, as in Fig. 13-18, there is a loop at the blowhole and a node at the plug. Here ¼λ = 10 cm, λ = 40 cm and

$$f = \frac{v}{\lambda} = \frac{340 \text{ m/s}}{0.40 \text{ m}} = 8.5 \times 10^2 \text{ Hz},$$

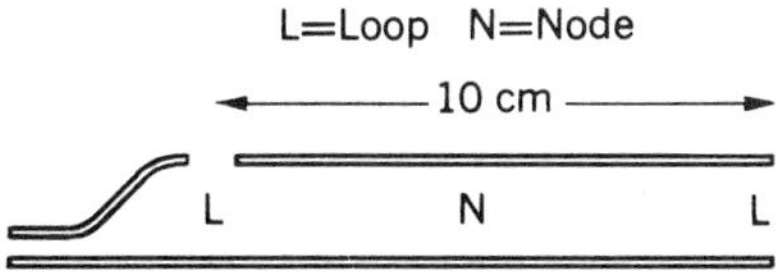

L=Loop N=Node

— 10 cm —

L   N   L

FIG. 13-17

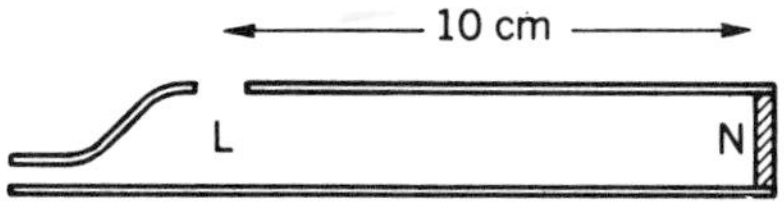

— 10 cm —

L   N

FIG. 13-18

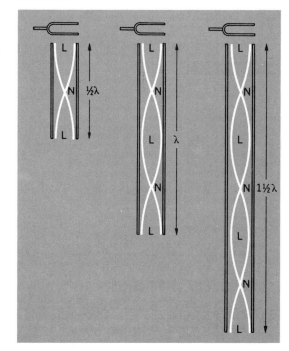

so that the plugged whistle has a fundamental frequency of about 8.5 × 10² Hz. Musically speaking, this means that by plugging the end of the whistle we lower the pitch of the note by an octave.

WIND INSTRUMENTS

Musical instruments, such as organs, woodwinds and horns, are based on the principle of resonant lengths of air columns. A means of vibrating the air within the instrument must exist. This is accomplished by compressed air which rushes into a column and strikes a lip or reed. The lip or reed causes variations in pressure in the air and hence the air column is set in vibration as in a system of organ pipes. Each pipe or air column resonates at a certain fundamental frequency determined by its length. Harmonic structures also occur in the pipes, adding greatly to the rich quality of the sounds produced by an organ. The flute and piccolo depend on the vibration of the player's lip to set the air in motion, while the clarinet, bassoon, saxophone and oboe depend on the vibration of one or more reeds. In brass instruments, such as the trombone, cornet and trumpet the air column is set in vibration by vibrations of the lips of the player, the lips acting as a double reed.

In wind instruments differences in pitch are normally obtained by altering the length of the air column. This is done in woodwinds by opening and closing holes or valves in the instrument to alter its effective length. In brass instruments, the length of the air column is changed either with valves which close off various sections of the tube as in the cornet, or in the trombone by sliding the U-shaped telescopic part of the tube. In all these instruments the phenomena of resonance and harmonic structure play an important part in the production of musical sound.

Exercises

A

1. For each of the following, state the part that causes the air to vibrate when sound is produced:
   (a) a bass drum,
   (b) an acoustic guitar,
   (c) a person speaking,
   (d) a card held against a rotating toothed wheel,
   (e) a chirping cricket,
   (f) a record player.

2. What is the speed of sound in air at (a) 25°C, (b) −10°C?

3. Calculate the distance travelled in air by a sound wave in 25 s when the temperature is 30°C.

4. Use the table in the Appendix to find which of the following transmits sound at the greatest speed and which at the lowest speed: air, aluminum, copper, and lead. For each of your two answers, calculate how far a sound would travel in 0.010 s.

5. A man and a woman each hum a musical note.
   (a) In what three characteristic ways may the notes differ?
   (b) State which characteristics of sound are controlled primarily by (i) the tension in the vocal cords, (ii) the rate of flow of air from the lungs, (iii) the shape and size of the nasal and mouth cavity.

6. The lowest tone of a violin has a frequency of 196 Hz. What is the frequency of a tone which is (a) three octaves higher, (b) two octaves lower?

7. State the approximate change in intensity of a sound

as heard by a listener if his/her distance from the source is (a) doubled, (b) halved, (c) quadrupled.

8. (a) In most jurisdictions which set noise limits, 90 dB is currently the upper limit above which employees must not be required to work without the provision of earmuffs or other protective devices. (Exceptions are Alberta and Sweden, both of which currently set the upper limit at 85 dB.) What is this expressed as picowatts per square metre?
   (b) Sound of intensity 160 dB may cause instantaneous perforation of the tympanic membrane (eardrum). What is this expressed as pW/m^2?

9. Sound becomes painful at about 1 W/m^2. What is this in decibels?

10. A worker in Britain is considered to have had his or her hearing injured by noise if a hearing loss of 40 dB can be measured when he or she is tested by listening to six pure tones between 0.5 and 6 kHz. What would the average threshold of hearing be in such a person, taking the average normal threshold to be 1 pW/m^2?

11. (a) Describe briefly how a stretched string, such as that on a violin or guitar, may be made to vibrate at different frequencies by plucking it, without altering its length, tension, diameter or density.
    (b) If the lowest natural frequency of a string is 120 Hz, state the next three frequencies with which it may readily be made to vibrate. Name the harmonic of each frequency.

12. The frequency of a stretched string in its first harmonic is 160 Hz.
    (a) What is the frequency of the sound produced by the string if it vibrates with six nodes in the string, including the node at each end?
    (b) In what harmonic is the string vibrating in part (a)?

13. How many octaves above the first harmonic is (a) the second harmonic, (b) the fourth harmonic?

14. State the regions, if any, near the tuning fork shown in Fig. 13-8 where there is an occurrence of (a) destructive interference, (b) constructive interference.

15. Two tuning forks having frequencies of 256 Hz and 254 Hz are sounded at the same time. What beat frequency will be heard?

16. A tuning fork having a frequency of 256 Hz is sounded together with a note produced by an acoustic guitar. If the beat frequency heard is 3 Hz, what are the possible frequencies produced by the guitar?

17. A third fork of unknown frequency is sounded in turn with each of the forks mentioned in question 15. What is the frequency of this fork if
    (a) 8 beats are heard in 8 s with each fork,
    (b) 8 beats are heard in 8 s with the 254 Hz fork and 24 beats are heard in 8 s with the 256 Hz fork?

18. A piano tuner sounds a pitch pipe which has a frequency of 32 Hz at the same time that he strikes a note on the piano which should emit a sound of 32 Hz. However, he hears 2 beats per second. He then increases the tension in the corresponding string to raise its frequency, repeats his test but observes 3 beats per second. Should he then further increase or decrease the tension in the piano string?

19. A vibrating string is sounded with a 256 Hz tuning fork and 15 beats are counted in 5 s. The tuning fork is then loaded with a small amount of plasticine and ten beats are counted in 5 s.
    (a) What is the frequency of the string?
    (b) What is the frequency of the loaded fork?

20. Two loudspeakers, A and B, face each other and are 24 m apart. They are connected to the same amplifier so that they emit identical, in-phase waves. An observer who walks from A to B hears a sound of maximum intensity every 3.0 m. Determine the frequency of the sound waves when the speed of sound is 342 m/s.

21. The floor of a room vibrates because of a laundry dryer in action. For certain speeds of rotation of the dryer, *stationary* concentric ripples are observed on the surface of a glass of water standing on a table in the same room. Explain.

22. A musical note is heard when a person blows across the open end of a test tube. If the test tube is removed and the person blows again no musical sound is heard. Account for the difference between the two cases.

23. When a tall thin tumbler is gradually filled with water there is a rise in the pitch of the pouring sound heard. Explain why this is so.

24. What is the longest wavelength of a note produced by a resonating tube, 50 cm in length, if the tube
    (a) is open at both ends?
    (b) is closed at one end only?

25. A vibrating tuning fork is held above the open end of an adjustable air column the other end of which is closed. The length of the column is allowed to increase gradually. The first occurrence of resonance is observed when the column is 20 cm in length.
    (a) What is the wavelength of the sound wave produced by the fork?
    (b) What is the frequency of the fork if the speed of sound in air is 340 m/s?

26. The air in a narrow tube, 34 cm long and closed at one end only, resonates with a 256 Hz tuning fork. Calculate the speed of sound in air.

27. A marine siren consists of a resonance cylinder 72 cm in length closed at one end. For sound travelling through the air at 336 m/s determine the lowest frequency of the siren.

28. The third resonant length of an air column, open at both ends, is 72 cm. Determine the first and second resonant lengths.

29. A 190 Hz tuning fork is held near one end of an adjustable, horizontal air column which is open at both ends. Determine the first and second resonant lengths of the air column if the speed of the sound in air is 332 m/s.

B

30. A ship's depth sounder sends a sound wave to the bottom of the ocean in water through which the speed of sound is 1400 m/s. It takes 0.450 s for the echo to return to the depth finder after the production of the sound. How deep is the water?

31. Some teenagers swimming under water hear a boat collision. They hear the same collision again 2.65 s later, when their heads are then above water. If the speed of sound is 3.40×10^2 m/s in air and 1.40×10^3 m/s in water, determine the distance of the crash from the teenagers.

32. Over water, the air closest to the water is usually cooler than the air further up. Consider a sound wave travelling both close to the water and higher up. What would eventually happen to its overall direction of travel? What has this to do with the fact that sound usually carries much better over water than over an equal distance of open land in daytime?

33. A vibrating string has a first harmonic at 140 Hz. It is 120 cm in length and vibrates in air which has a temperature of 30°C.
   (a) What is the speed in air of the sound wave produced?
   (b) What is the wavelength of the sound wave in air?
   (c) What is the wavelength of the sound wave produced in air when the string is vibrating in its fifth harmonic?
   (d) What is the distance between successive nodes in the string when it is vibrating in its fourth harmonic?

34. If the air temperature is 20°C and a 200 Hz tuning fork causes air to resonate in a tube which is open at both ends, determine the shortest length possible for the tube.

35. The second resonant length of an adjustable tube, closed at one end only, is 2.0 m. The tube resonates with an applied frequency of 140 Hz. From this data determine the speed of sound in air.

36. On a day when the speed of sound is 340 m/s, a saxophonist adjusts the keys of his instrument so that the distance from the reed to the first open hole is 85 cm. In operation, sound waves are reflected from the reed as from a fixed surface, so that the saxophone behaves like a pipe closed at one end. What are the frequencies of the first, second, and third resonant lengths?

37. A tube, closed at one end and 40 cm in length, resonates with a 220 Hz tuning fork held near its open end. Determine the speed of sound in air.

38. A signal whistle is 8.0 cm long from the open end to the blowhole. If the speed of sound is 336 m/s, determine the first harmonic of the whistle when the open end (a) is left open, (b) is plugged.

C

39. (a) In an elastic medium, the speed of sound =
   a constant $\times \sqrt{\dfrac{\text{the elasticity of the medium}}{\text{the density of the medium.}}}$

   From this formula and the information in the table in the Appendix, determine which of two balls, one brass and the other steel, will bounce to a greater height if dropped from the same point. State your reasoning. (Hint: brass and iron do not differ greatly in density.)
   (b) As air becomes warmer its elasticity does not change appreciably. Explain why the speed of sound in air increases as the temperature rises.

40. The natural frequency of a stretched string varies inversely as the length of the string, inversely as the diameter of the string, inversely as the square root of the density of the material of which the string is made, and directly as the square root of the tension in the string.
   (a) A piano string has a frequency of 240 Hz. A piano tuner changes its tension from 90 to 160 N. What will the new frequency be?
   (b) A string 80.0 cm long has a frequency of 420 Hz when under a tension of 96 N. What frequency does the string have when its length is increased to 100 cm and its tension reduced to 72 N?

41. A resonance tube is 28 cm in length. Calculate the lowest possible frequencies of the tuning forks which will cause resonance in this tube when the temperature is 30°C and (a) the tube is open at both ends, (b) the tube is open at one end only.

42. A whistle consists of two tubes 2.50 cm and 2.75 cm in length. Each tube is closed at one end and open at the other. When blown, each tube emits sound of the natural frequency corresponding to its length. However, the frequency of the sound that is heard is primarily that of the beat frequency produced by the two tubes. If the speed of sound in air is 341 m/s, determine the frequency of the so-called difference tone heard.

   (Difference tones are relied on in the use of small loudspeakers in radios and televisions. Being small, such loudspeakers do not readily reproduce low frequencies. However, many speech and music wave patterns carry second, third, and higher harmonics which *are* reproduced. The difference tones generated by these harmonics will thus include the first harmonic, so that you will hear it even though the loudspeaker may not be capable of generating it directly!)

CHAPTER 14

Light
Waves
and
Reflection

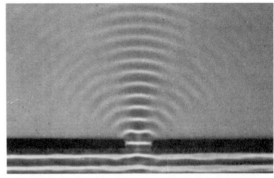

FIG. 14-1

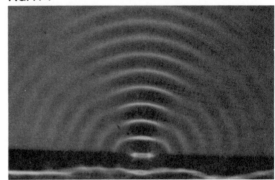

The universe is full of light. From a vast number of stars, light spreads throughout space. Light from our own local star, the sun, makes it possible for us to see the brilliant plumage of birds and the many blues and greens of sea and sky. So important is sight to us that we assist it with eye-glasses and extend it with telescopes, microscopes, spectroscopes, and cameras.

Your study of light will concentrate on the basic properties of reflection and refraction, to enable you to understand the principles of various optical instruments. But first, we should see if we can demonstrate that light has a wave nature. This is not as obvious for light as it is for sound, because there is no direct evidence that light originates in vibrating sources. Also, you will not observe interference patterns from two small flashlight bulbs side by side. However, there is another wave property that can help us to begin to see the wave nature of light.

THE DIFFRACTION OF LIGHT

When straight waves in a ripple tank encounter a small opening in a barrier, they spread out into the space beyond the barrier. As shown in Fig. 14-1, the waves beyond the barrier are not confined to the width of the narrow opening. The second photograph shows that this spreading out past the opening is more pronounced when the wavelength is longer relative to the width of the opening. This spreading out of waves as they pass a barrier is called **diffraction**. It is this wave property of diffraction that enables you to hear sounds around a corner. But, you cannot *see* around corners.

Diffraction is less pronounced for shorter wavelengths. This suggests that if light is a wave, the wavelengths of light are very short. Thus, to be able to demonstrate diffraction in light, we need to use very narrow openings, or slits. In Fig. 14-2, slits of less than one millimetre width are used. A photographic film was exposed directly to red light that had passed through the slits. As the width of the slit diminished from 0.7 mm to 0.1 mm, the light spread out more and more in passing through the slit. This provides a clear visual demonstration of the diffraction of light. It shows that light has a wave nature.

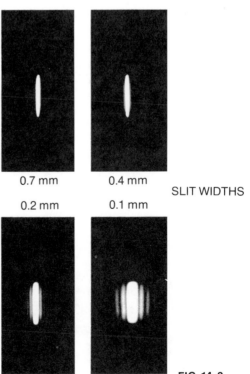

0.7 mm   0.4 mm

SLIT WIDTHS

0.2 mm   0.1 mm

FIG. 14-2

For sound, frequency determines the pitch we hear. For light, frequency determines the colour we see. The wavelengths of visible light range from about 7×10^{-7} m for red light to about 4×10^{-7} m for violet light. Since the speed of light is 3.0×10^8 m/s, the corresponding frequencies can be calculated from

$$v = f\lambda.$$

For violet light,

$$v = 3.0 \times 10^8 \text{ m/s}, \quad \text{and} \quad \lambda = 4 \times 10^{-7} \text{ m}.$$

The frequency is

$$f = \frac{v}{\lambda} = \frac{3.0 \times 10^8 \text{ m/s}}{4 \times 10^{-7} \text{ m}} = 8 \times 10^{14} \text{ Hz}.$$

Thus, the frequency of violet light waves is 8×10^{14} Hz. The frequency of red light waves is 4×10^{14} Hz.

THE INTERFERENCE OF LIGHT

The picture of the 0.1 mm slit in Fig. 14-2 shows more than the simple diffraction of light. The alternate bands of dark and bright are evidence of the interference of light. At the dark nodal regions, waves from one side of the slit are arriving out of phase with those from the other side of the slit. The result is destructive interference.

The production of a continuing interference pattern requires a constant phase relation among the wave sources. Two flashlights shining on the same spot do not produce such a pattern because the light they produce is coming out in a whole scramble of phases. Such light is said to be incoherent. Light that is coherent in bursts of about 10^{-9} s can be obtained from a very small source, either an illuminated slit or a narrow filament. When such light is then allowed to illuminate two narrow slits fairly close together, an interference pattern should be formed.

Coherent light is produced in a continuous stream by lasers (see Chapter 19).

The photograph of Fig. 14-3 was made from a coherent light source that passed through two narrow parallel slits, separated by a distance approximately equal to their width. The pattern consists of a series of alternating bands of bright and dark. Notice that all the bright bands are of approximately the same width. These narrow bands are the regions of constructive interference of the light coming from the two slits. However, the outer bands are not as bright, and the dark spaces are not all of uniform width. The reason for this is that the photograph represents the effect of the interference from the two slits combined with the individual interferences of the diffraction of light through the single slits.

FIG. 14-3

The combined effect of interference and diffraction can be shown by constructing graphs of the two effects separately. Fig. 14-4 is a graph of the variation in light intensity to be expected from two *point* sources of light in phase. But the two slits are not points. The variation in light intensity obtained in the diffraction of light through a *single* slit is shown in Fig. 14-5. When light passes through two such slits, close together, the resultant intensity is the product of the separate intensities as shown in Fig. 14-6. The intensity variations in this graph are a fairly good representation of those in the photograph of Fig. 14-3.

The two-source interference of light was first shown by Thomas Young in 1803. He used sunlight passing through one pinhole in a card to illuminate two adjacent pinholes in a second card to produce the effect. Interference provides conclusive evidence that light has a wave nature. Thus, diagrams for light radiating outward from a source can be imagined to be like ripple-tank waves from a vibrating point (Fig. 14-7).

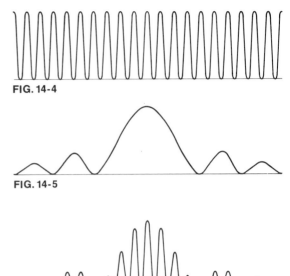

FIG. 14-4

FIG. 14-5

FIG. 14-6

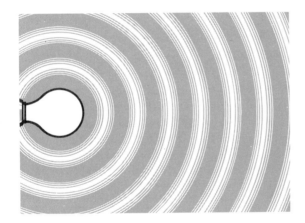

FIG. 14-7

THE REFLECTION OF LIGHT WAVES

In a ripple tank, circular waves spread out in all directions. However, straight waves can be generated that travel forward in a single direction. When each single straight pulse runs into a barrier, its direction of travel is changed. Measurement of the angles between the two directions of travel and the barrier shows that they are equal (Fig. 14-8). Light and other kinds of waves can be expected to reflect in the same manner.

A narrow beam of light will be reflected from a polished surface. Since the wavefront of the beam is very narrow, we concentrate our attention on the line of travel of the light. The line along which the light travels defines a ray of light. A light ray is only a fiction. It is an

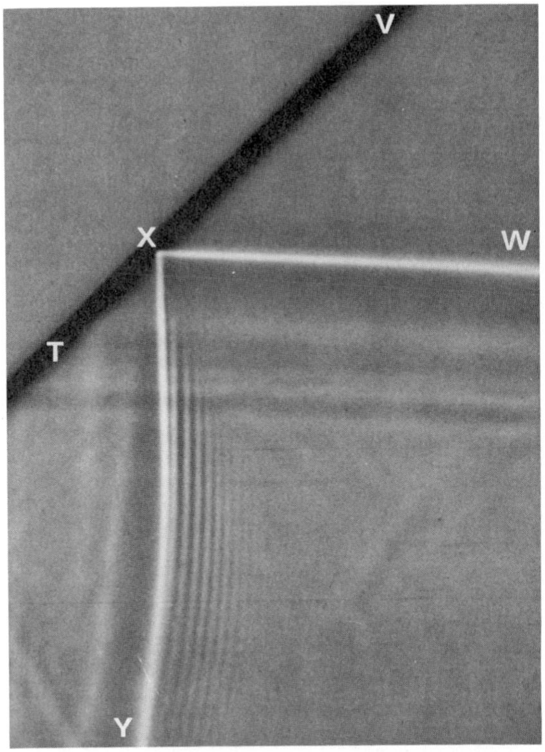

FIG. 14-8. Straight pulse WX moves toward the oblique barrier VT. The reflected pulse XY takes the direction that makes $\angle$TXY = $\angle$VXW.

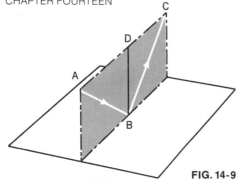

FIG. 14-9

The two laws of reflection ▶

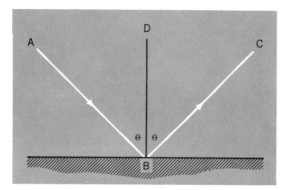

FIG. 14-10

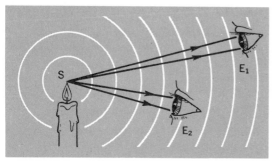

FIG. 14-11

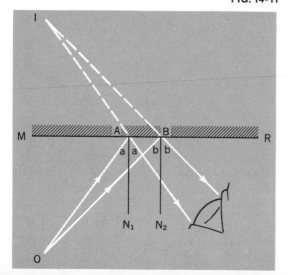

FIG. 14-12

element in the optical diagrams that we draw, an ideal straight line, but light rays do not exist in nature. Rays simply identify the path that light follows in any particular situation. In practice we can only produce narrow beams, or "pencils" of light.

Light is *reflected* from a smooth, mirror-like surface according to the diagrams in Fig. 14-9. The ray AB that strikes the surface is the **incident ray**, the ray BC that leaves the surface is the **reflected ray**, and line BD perpendicular to the surface at B, the point of contact, is the **normal**.

Two features are evident in the reflection of light. The first is that the incident ray (AB) and the reflected ray (BC) and the normal (BD) lie in one plane. The second feature of the reflection of light is that the angles of the two rays with the normal are equal. In Fig. 14-10, $\angle ABD = \angle DBC$. More formally, we say that in reflection, the angle of incidence is equal to the angle of reflection.

Although the reflection of light is a simple idea, it is not what strikes us most readily when we look at a polished surface. Perhaps you remember the myth of Narcissus who "drowned seeking the beauty he saw" reflected in a pool of water. How can the laws of reflection account for the appearance of images in mirrors?

LOCATING OBJECTS

Light is radiated in all directions from the tip of a candle flame. The light by which an observer sees it travels in a small cone with its apex at the tip of the flame and its base at the observer's eye. The limits of this cone, in a two-dimensional diagram such as Fig. 14-11, are straight lines extending from the source, S, to the edges of the pupil of the eye. We define *locating rays* as the straight lines between which the light travels in passing from an object to an observer. An object is seen at the point from which rays of light diverge (or spread apart) to one's eyes.

One of the clues which we get about the distance from a viewer to an object is provided by the locating rays. Since the eye E_1 in Fig. 14-11 is farther from the source than the eye E_2, the angle between the locating rays to E_1 is smaller than the angle between the locating rays to E_2. The more distant you are from a source, the more nearly parallel are the locating rays from the source to your eye.

IMAGES BY REFLECTION IN A PLANE MIRROR

In Fig. 14-12 the mirror, MR, is perpendicular to the page. An object, O, and an eye are in the plane of the page. Two rays from O, in the same plane, strike the mirror at A and B and are reflected to the eye. The normals, AN_1 and BN_2, are perpendicular to the mirror. The rays from A and B are locating rays to the eye. The eye then locates the point from which the rays seem to diverge. Since vision does not follow the direction change at A and B, the light appears to have diverged from I. The point I, having the appearance of the object, is called the **image**. An image in a plane mirror is **virtual** because the light only seems to diverge from the point I.

The location of an image in a plane mirror relative to the object can be deduced from the laws of reflection. In Fig. 14-13, the angles of reflection equal the angles of incidence: $\angle CAN_1 = \angle OAN_1$, and $\angle DBN_2 = \angle OBN_2$. Angles that can be deduced to be equal by elementary theorems in geometry are marked in the figure. The triangles IAB and OAB can then be shown to be congruent (two angles and one side). Then, IA = OA. Join IO. Then triangle IAG is congruent to triangle OAG (two sides and the included angle), and hence IG = OG, and $\angle OGA = 90°$.

Since Fig. 14-13 is a general application of geometry and the laws of reflection, a general rule for locating images in plane mirrors can now be stated: draw a perpendicular OG from the object to the mirror; on OG produced, cut off GI = OG; I is then the location of the image.

A complete ray diagram to show an eye looking at an extended object would require a pair of rays to the eye from each point on the object. However, it is convenient to represent objects by straight lines, and then it is only necessary to draw rays from the ends of the object. Fig. 14-14 illustrates the rays by which an eye sees the image of an object in a plane mirror. In drawing this diagram the image is drawn first in the location prescribed by the rule stated above; that is AB = BC, and FG = GH. Then the locating rays from the ends, C and H, of the image are drawn to the eye. These rays are dotted behind the mirror because light does not actually travel along that path. Finally, the rays are drawn from the ends of the object A and F to the intersections of the locating rays with the mirror.

From the diagram in Fig. 14-14 the image can be seen to be (i) erect (the same way up as the object), (ii) virtual, (iii) the same height as the object, (iv) the same distance from the mirror as the object. As we proceed to study images in curved mirrors and in lenses, we shall want to identify these four characteristics of each image: (i) its attitude, (ii) its kind, (iii) its height, (iv) its distance from the mirror or lens.

REFLECTION FROM CURVED MIRRORS

The image-forming property of plane mirrors has found a large variety of uses. However, reflection is also very useful for concentrating light. If a scene is being illuminated from one side by a source of light, the light that travels away from the scene could be reflected back onto the scene by a mirror (Fig. 14-15). A plane mirror reflects parallel rays so that they remain parallel, but there are many applications in which it is desirable to focus the light, to produce intense illumination in a small space. The solar cooker illustrated in Fig. 14-16 is one example of such an application.

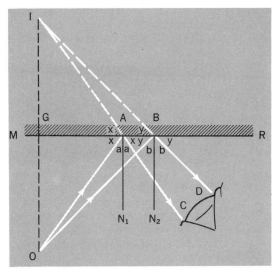

FIG. 14-13

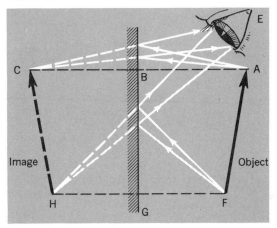

FIG. 14-14

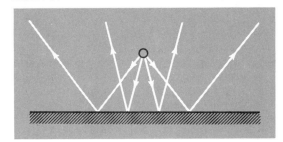

FIG. 14-15

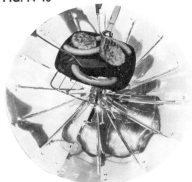

FIG. 14-16

FIG. 14-18

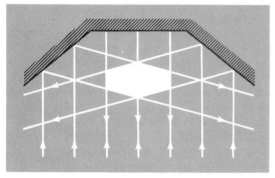

FIG. 14-17

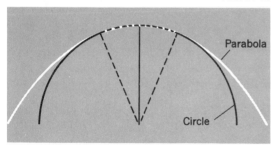

Parabola

Circle

FIG. 14-19

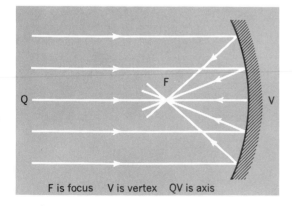

F is focus   V is vertex   QV is axis

FIG. 14-20

If the ends of a plane mirror are tilted as shown in Fig. 14-17, parallel rays of light can be made to cross in a fairly small area. If a series of narrow plane mirrors is arranged to focus the light into as small a region as possible, as shown in Fig. 14-18, the mirrors will be lined up along a smooth curve. The shape of the curve followed by the plane mirrors is called a **parabola**. It is illustrated in Fig. 14-19 with a circle for comparison. Notice that the two curves coincide in their central portions. If the curves represent sections of cylindrical mirrors the light will be focused along a line perpendicular to the plane of the page. To focus the light to a point the mirrors must be curved in all planes. Rotating a curved line about an axis to its centre produces a *surface of revolution*. For a circle, such a surface is a section of a sphere. For a parabola, it is called a paraboloid of revolution. If a sufficiently small section of a sphere is used it will provide a close approximation to point focusing, but for very accurate focusing, a parabolic mirror is necessary.

A smooth parabolic mirror will cause the convergence to a point of parallel rays striking its concave surface; this is illustrated in Fig. 14-20. The central point, V, on the mirror surface is called the **vertex**; the normal to the surface at V, the line QV, is called the **principal axis**. Rays of light parallel to the principal axis are reflected through the **principal focus**, the point F on the principal axis. The distance FV is the **focal length** of the mirror. The effect of a concave mirror on parallel rays of light is conveniently demonstrated with an optical disc. It is shown in the photograph of Fig. 14-21 where rays parallel to each other, but not to the axis, are reflected to cross at a point below the principal focus. (The point of intersection of the rays in Fig. 14-21 is sometimes called a focus. However, in this text we shall only use the term "focus" as a short form for "principal focus." Similarly, we shall refer to the principal axis as the axis. Thus in Fig. 14-20, F is the focus and QV is the axis.)

If a small source of light is located at the focus of a concave parabolic mirror, its rays after reflection will travel parallel to the axis, as shown in Fig. 14-22. Notice that the ray paths in Figs. 14-20 and 14-22 are identical in all respects except direction. In all situations light can travel in either direction along a ray path. The actual direction depends solely on the position of the source. The light rays are reversible, and this behaviour of light is often found to be useful in ray diagrams.

A concave mirror provides one method of producing a beam of light that consists of parallel rays. As illustrated in Fig. 14-23, the mirror changes the curvature of the waves from a source at the focus, so that when the rays are reflected parallel to the axis, the wave fronts are straight lines perpendicular to the axis. It should be apparent that when a wave front is a straight line (a plane in space) the rays are parallel.

Waves from a point source become progressively more plane at great distances from the source. This is illustrated in Fig. 14-24, where the change in wave curvature can be seen by comparison with the straight lines AB and CD.

IMAGES IN A CONCAVE MIRROR

A parabolic concave mirror is the principal focusing device in large astronomical telescopes. The largest of these, in the Hale telescope on Mount Palomar in California, is more than five metres across (Fig. 14-25). There can be little doubt that light from a distant star, after travelling more than 10^{16} m, will have a plane wave front. Therefore, the image of the star will be located at the focus of the mirror if the telescope is pointing directly at the star. Since light rays

FIG. 14-21

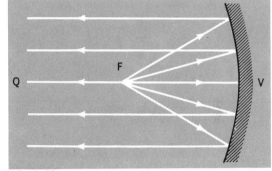

FIG. 14-22

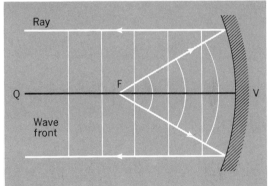

FIG. 14-23

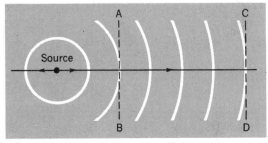

FIG. 14-25   FIG. 14-24

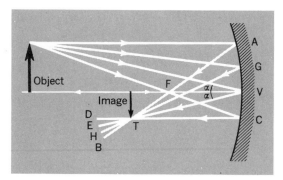

FIG. 14-26

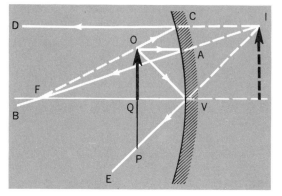

FIG. 14-27

actually arrive at the focus, the image of the star is said to be **real**; a photographic film placed at the focus would record the star's image. (In contrast, a photographic film placed at the virtual image location in a plane mirror would not record the virtual image.)

If an object is located relatively close to a concave mirror, where is its image located? The image of any point on the object is located where rays from the point converge after being reflected. We can use the previous ray diagrams to follow the reflection of certain rays in Fig. 14-26: (i) a ray from the top of the object parallel to the axis is reflected from the mirror at A through F to B; (ii) following the idea of reversibility, a ray from the top of the object through F is reflected from C parallel to the axis to D; (iii) since the axis is normal to the mirror at V, a ray from the top of the object to V will be reflected to E, making the angle of reflection equal the angle of incidence (α). The point at which these three rays intersect is the image of the top of the object. In practice, any two rays are sufficient to locate the image of a point. Once the image has been located, any other reflection path can be drawn, like the one from the top of the object, reflected from G to H.

If an eye was located at EH, the rays TE and TH would be locating rays for it. The light seems to diverge from the point of intersection of the rays, the top, T, of the image. The light actually does diverge from that point, even though it did not originate there. For that reason this is a real image. The characteristics of the image are: (i) it is inverted, (ii) it is real, (iii) it is smaller than the object, (iv) it is closer to the mirror than the object is.

Men sometimes use concave mirrors when shaving so that they can see every whisker. When the mirror is used in this way the object is located between the focus and the mirror. The ray paths to locate the image are shown in Fig. 14-27. (i) OAB is a ray parallel to the axis reflected through the focus. (ii) OCD travelling in the direction from the focus to the mirror is reflected parallel to the axis. (iii) To make the angle of reflection equal to the angle of incidence for ray OVE, make triangle VQP congruent to triangle VQO as shown. The rays AB, CD and VE are seen to diverge away from the mirror, seeming to start from the point I. The image at I is (i) erect, (ii) virtual, (iii) larger than the object, (iv) farther from the mirror than the object. It is the third factor which gives the concave mirror its magnifying properties in these circumstances.

OTHER APPLICATIONS OF CURVED MIRRORS

Parabolic concave mirrors find wide application as reflectors for light sources. Searchlights, flashlights, and automobile headlights all make use of parabolic mirrors to produce parallel beams of light. The lamp is located at or near the focus.

Radio waves have a longer wavelength than light waves, but otherwise they have much the same behaviour. Large radio telescopes have been built to receive radio waves from stars and from the gas of interstellar space. One of the largest, located at Jodrell Bank in England, is shown in the photograph of Fig. 14-28. The receiving antenna for the radio waves is located at the focus of the mirror. The whole assembly is mounted on railroad wheels so that it can be steered to point to any part of the sky.

Images can be formed in convex mirrors, though the images are always virtual and smaller than the objects. That happens because a convex mirror causes a parallel beam of light to diverge. For that reason one can get a view of a very wide area in a convex mirror. It can be seen in the convex surface of polished metal vessels. Automobile rearview mirrors are sometimes made convex in order to enlarge the driver's area of vision.

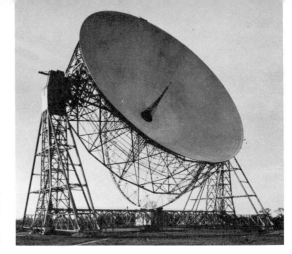

FIG. 14-28

FIG. 14-29: MEASURING THE SPEED OF LIGHT

(a) In 1676 Ole Römer found a value for the speed of light by observing a moon of Jupiter. The moon is not visible while passing through Jupiter's shadow from C to D. Römer measured the orbital

a

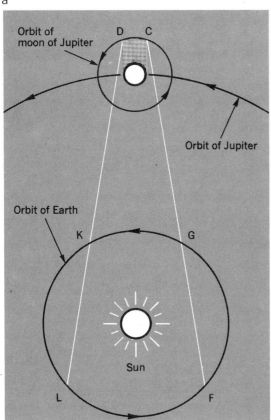

period of the moon by timing successive appearances at D. As the earth moved from K to L the moon seemed to take longer to return to D. As the earth moved from F to G the time seemed to get shorter. After the earth had travelled 230×10^6 km from K to L, the moon's return to D occurred about 16 min later than expected. Römer attributed the delay to the time required for the light from Jupiter's moon to traverse the extra distance KL. This gave him a value for the speed of light of about 2.4×10^5 km/s.

(b) In the 1920s A.A. Michelson used a rotating mirror (K) to measure the speed of light. After reflection from *a* the light travelled 35.0 km to the mirror at L and was reflected back. When mirror K was still, the light reflected from *c*. The mirror was then set into rotation at such a rate that by the time the light returned, *b* had moved to the place of *c*. The mirror was then rotating 535 times per second. The time for the light to travel 70.0 km was that needed for the mirror to make one-eighth of a revolution. These figures give a value for the speed of light of 3.00×10^5 km/s.

b

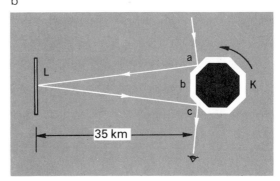

Exercises

A

1. (a) Which would undergo more diffraction in passing through a typical doorway: low-pitched sound of wavelength 1.5 m or high-pitched sound of wavelength 3 cm? Why?
   (b) In which direction, horizontally or vertically, would the most diffraction of the sound you chose in (a) part occur? Why?

2. What wave property of light determines (a) the colour of the light (b) the brightness of the light?

3. In an interference pattern what happens to the energy that is "missing" in the black bands?

4. Observe a single bright light at a distance through a linen handkerchief or other sheer material. Should the effect that is observed be attributed to reflection, diffraction, interference, or some other phenomenon?

5. What are the two laws that hold for reflection in any mirror, plane or curved?

6. If a person walks toward a plane mirror at a steady speed of 2 m/s, at what speed is he/she approaching his/her image in the mirror?

7. Draw a sketch to show how a mirror could be used to conduct an eye examination in a room 4 m long, although the person being examined must be 6 m from the vision chart.

8. The image in a plane mirror can be characterized by the following equations: $h_i/h_o = 1$, $d_i = -d_o$, where the subscripts "i" and "o" refer to the image and the object respectively. Interpret each equation in words.

9. Why are parabolic mirrors usually preferred to spherical mirrors?

10. Where must an object be located for rays of light from it to form an image at the principal focus of a concave mirror?

11. The reflector of the sealed beam unit of an automobile headlamp has a parabolic shape.
    (a) Where should a filament be located to produce a horizontal beam of parallel rays pointing straight ahead?
    (b) Where should a second filament be located to produce a beam of parallel rays that will strike a point in the road about 30 m in front of the auto?

12. Draw a ray diagram to locate the image of an object 15 cm from a concave mirror of focal length 5.0 cm. Make the object 5.0 cm tall, with its lowest point on the axis. State the four characteristics of the image.

13. Determine by means of a ray diagram drawn to scale the location of the image of an adult 2.0 m tall in a concave mirror of focal length 1.5 m, when the person is (a) 6.0 m, (b) 3.0 m from the mirror. State how many centimetres on the page represent one metre in the problem. In each case determine the height of the image.

14. The focal length of the reflector of the 5 m diameter telescope on Mount Palomar is 18 m. The distance from the earth to the sun is 1.5×10^{11} m, and the diameter of the sun is 1.4×10^9 m. (a) Where will the image of the sun appear relative to the mirror? (b) What will be the diameter of the sun's image?

15. Convex mirrors are sometimes used as auxiliary rearview mirrors on vehicles because they give a larger field of view than a plane mirror.
    (a) Compare the properties of the image of a car in a convex mirror with those of the image of the same object in a plane mirror.
    (b) Sometimes drivers used to plane mirrors dangerously underestimate how close a following vehicle is when they first use a convex mirror. Which of the properties in (a) might account for this?

B

16. For a circle or a sphere, a mathematical theorem states that radii to the circumference are at right angles to it, that is, are normal to it. Draw a semicircle of radius 5 cm at the right side of your page, opening to the left. Draw seven horizontal rays, 1 cm apart, going to the semi-circle, which represents a spherical mirror. Draw normals to the points of incidence of the rays and use the law of reflection to draw the reflected rays.
    (a) What do you notice about the reflected rays? (This effect is called *spherical aberration*.)
    (b) How can this effect be avoided?

17. Using the following measurements, draw a scale diagram to show the path of a ray of light from a lamp reflected by a plane mirror to a person's eye. The person is standing 2.0 m from the mirror with his/her eyes 1.5 m above the floor. The lamp is 4.0 m directly behind the person, located 2.5 m above the floor.

18. A plane rearview mirror in an automobile is 20 cm long, and located 45 cm from the driver's eye. Through what width of rear window can the driver see by looking into the mirror, if the window is located 140 cm behind his eye?

19. A girl whose eyes are 150 cm from the floor is standing 2.0 m from a plane mirror with its top edge 2.0 m above the floor and its bottom edge 1.0 m above the floor.
    (a) Show by means of a diagram how much of herself the girl will be able to see in the mirror.
    (b) Could she see more by moving to a distance of 1.0 m from the mirror?

20. Draw a ray diagram to locate the image of a face 20 cm long in a concave shaving or makeup mirror of focal length 50 cm, when the face is 30 cm from the mirror. What is the length of the image? By how much is the face magnified?

21. (a) If the concave side of a spherically shaped soup spoon has a focal length of 3.0 cm, where is your image when you are 20 cm from the vertex of the spoon?
    (b) If the convex side of the spoon is viewed from the same distance, where is the image now?

22. A famous illusion involves a real flowerpot and flower fastened upside down within a box, below the axis of a large concave mirror at twice the focal length from the mirror, and screened from the view of anyone farther from the mirror. People looking into the mirror see a lifesize real image which appears to be a flowerpot and flower sitting in midair in front of the mirror. However, when they go to touch the flower, there is nothing but air there. Draw a ray diagram to illustrate this illusion for a concave mirror of focal length 20 cm. What is the size of the image relative to the object? State the other characteristics of the image.

23. A student stands 50 cm from a large concave mirror with a focal length of 35 cm.
    (a) Draw a ray diagram to locate the image of the student, and state the characteristics of the image.
    (b) Why does the student see nothing but a blur rather than his or her image?
    (c) Draw a ray diagram to show what would happen if a *convex* mirror of the same focal length were used.

24. A small 20 W carbon filament lamp is placed upright (a) 3.0 m, (b) 50 cm, (c) 30 cm, (d) 20 cm, (e) 15 cm, (f) 5.0 cm from a concave mirror of focal length 15 cm. Determine the magnification, h_i/h_o, of the image in each case.

C

25. (a) In what circumstances is an image in a plane mirror erect?
    (b) Use a diagram to show how it is possible for an image in a plane mirror to be inverted.

26. (a) Draw a diagram to illustrate what is meant by lateral inversion in a plane mirror.
    (b) Show how two mirrors can be arranged to produce an image that is not laterally inverted.

27. All colours can be characterized by three quantities — hue, saturation, and brightness. Hue corresponds to the predominant wavelength in the light. Saturation corresponds to how much of the light energy occurs at the predominant wavelength compared to how much occurs as white light. Brightness corresponds to the intensity of the light. What would be the most significant difference between the characteristics of each light in the following pairs:
    (a) a 40 W yellow light and a 60 W yellow light,
    (b) a green traffic light and an amber traffic light,
    (c) a pastel blue and another blue?

28. Waves reaching a stationary observer from a moving source are shifted to shorter wavelengths if the source approaches the observer, and to longer wavelengths if the source recedes from the observer. This is known as the Doppler effect. For example, the roar of a racing car seems to shift to a higher pitch (shorter wavelength) as the car approaches, and to a lower pitch as the car recedes.
    (a) It is found that light from all the stars is shifted toward the red end of the spectrum. This is called the *red shift*. Are the stars approaching or receding from us?
    (b) Assuming that the earth holds no special place in the universe, what does the red shift indicate about the universe as a whole?

29. Some cars have a rearview mirror with a switch on it for night driving. When the switch is thrown, the brightness of the lights of following vehicles is greatly diminished. How does this work? (Consult reference books, an auto mechanic, or any other knowledgeable source.)

30. The fact that light is a wave is established by producing interference with light. The fact that the light wave is a *transverse* wave is established by showing that light can be *polarized*.
    (a) Find out and explain in terms of rope waves what polarization means.
    (b) Explain how the fact that two crossed polaroid filters produce darkness proves that light is transverse.

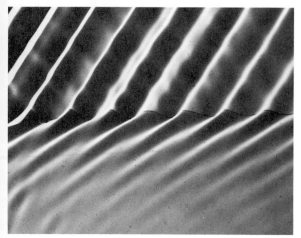

CHAPTER 15

Refraction and Lenses

FIG. 15-1

When light strikes a glass surface at a large angle of incidence (just grazing the surface), most of the light is reflected. As the angle of incidence is decreased, a larger proportion of the light is transmitted through the medium; at very small angles of incidence 96% of the light is transmitted. The light that is transmitted is bent or **refracted** as it passes into the glass. In refraction, as in reflection, the incident ray, the normal, and the reflected ray lie in one plane. To determine how light is refracted, we shall first examine wave refraction in a ripple tank.

REFRACTION OF WAVES

In Fig. 15-1, a series of plane waves on water are shown as they pass into a region where their speed is less. In relatively shallow water the speed of waves on the surface depends on the depth of the water. The speed is decreased by having the waves pass into a shallower region. With the frequency unchanged, the decrease in speed is made apparent by the decrease in wavelength when the waves pass into the shallower region (remember that $v = f\lambda$).

Why do waves bend as they pass from one region to another? In the diagram of Fig. 15-2, the boundary between the two regions is located along the line CF. For water waves, CF separates two regions of different depth. We can speak of CF as the boundary between two media: a second transmission medium is one in which waves travel at a different speed. The particular values chosen for the diagram can be obtained for water waves in a ripple tank. In the first medium the speed is $v_1 = 30$ cm/s, and in the second medium the speed is $v_2 = 20$ cm/s. Since $\lambda = v/f$, the frequency $f = 5.0$ Hz leads to wavelengths $\lambda_1 = 6.0$ cm and $\lambda_2 = 4.0$ cm.

While Fig. 15-2 could be considered to be a snapshot like Fig. 15-1, it can also illustrate the successive positions of a single wave crest at AB, CD and EF, each separated by time-intervals of one period. Recall that the period $T = 1/f$, so in this case $T = 1/5$ s. The crest begins at the location AB. One period later it is at CD, 6.0 cm distant. The side of the crest at C has reached the boundary and the side at D has another 6.0 cm to go. In the next period the side at D

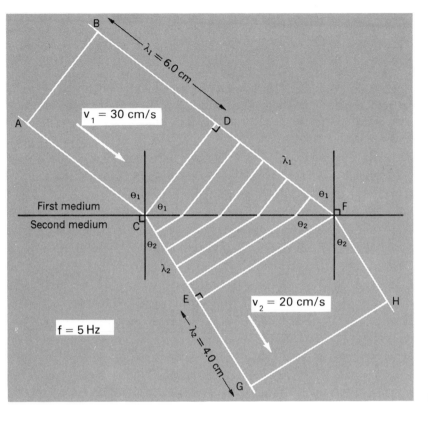

First medium

Second medium

$v_1 = 30 \text{ cm/s}$

$\lambda_1 = 6.0 \text{ cm}$

$\lambda_2 = 4.0 \text{ cm}$

$v_2 = 20 \text{ cm/s}$

$f = 5 \text{ Hz}$

FIG. 15-2

moves a distance λ_1, 6.0 cm, to F, but the side at C moves a distance λ_2 in the second medium to E, a distance of only 4.0 cm. The wave crest is retarded along CE, so that the side travelling along DF swings around, changing the direction of travel. One period later the whole crest has travelled 4.0 cm to GH. Thus, when the speed is reduced, waves are refracted towards the normal.

A diagram like Fig. 15-2 can be drawn by constructing a circle with CF as diameter. Since a diameter subtends right angles at the circumference, D and E are located on the circumference by making FD = 6.0 cm and CE = 4.0 cm. You can make this construction for other speeds in two media and for various angles of incidence. From several diagrams it becomes apparent that for equal angles of incidence the greater the change in speed, the greater the change in direction. If waves pass into a medium where their speed is increased they refract away from the normal. If waves cross a boundary in the direction of the normal they are not refracted because the change in speed affects both ends of each crest at the same instant.

It is thus apparent that a change in the speed of waves can change their direction, that is, cause refraction.

INDEX OF REFRACTION

The change in direction of waves on refraction depends on a change in speed. Since the amount of refraction depends on the amount of the change in speed, the ratio of speeds is used as a measure of the degree of refraction. The **index of refraction** (symbol n) of waves passing from one medium to another is defined as the ratio of the speeds of the waves in the two media. In symbols,

$$n = \frac{v_1}{v_2}.$$

Since $v_1 = f\lambda_1$, and $v_2 = f\lambda_2$, and since the frequency f is unchanged, then

$$n = \frac{v_1}{v_2} = \frac{f\lambda_1}{f\lambda_2} = \frac{\lambda_1}{\lambda_2}.$$

Therefore, in the example illustrated in Fig. 15-2,

$$n = \frac{30 \text{ cm/s}}{20 \text{ cm/s}} = \frac{3}{2}, \quad \text{or} \quad n = \frac{6.0 \text{ cm}}{4.0 \text{ cm}} = \frac{3}{2}.$$

The index of refraction, n, is a pure number since the units divide out. Although two media are involved in refraction, and therefore properly both should be stated when quoting a refractive index (e.g., n from air to glass), it is common to speak of n from air to glass simply as the refractive index of glass.

How to determine the index of refraction of substances for light is described below. The value for three substances relative to air is given in Table 15-1. A more complete list may be found in the Appendix. When the index of refraction is known, the speed and wavelength of light in one medium may be calculated using the preceding relations if the speed and wavelength in another medium is known.

Table 15-1

INDEX OF REFRACTION

Medium	Index of refraction relative to air
Water	1.3
Glass	1.5
Diamond	2.4

Example: The speed of light in air is $c = 3.00 \times 10^8$ m/s. The wavelength of yellow light in air is $\lambda = 5.89 \times 10^{-7}$ m. Calculate the speed (c_s) and wavelength (λ_s) of yellow light in sulfur. (The rhombic form of crystalline sulfur has an index of refraction of 1.96 for yellow light.)

Use the relations,
$$n = \frac{c}{c_s} = \frac{\lambda}{\lambda_s}.$$

For sulfur
$$n = 1.96$$
$$c = 3.00 \times 10^8 \text{ m/s}$$
$$c_s = \frac{c}{n} = \frac{3.00 \times 10^8 \text{ m/s}}{1.96} = 1.53 \times 10^8 \text{ m/s}$$

$$\lambda = 5.89 \times 10^{-7} \text{ m}$$

$$\lambda_s = \frac{\lambda}{n} = \frac{5.89 \times 10^{-7} \text{ m}}{1.96} = 3.01 \times 10^{-7} \text{ m}.$$

Therefore the speed of yellow light in sulfur is 1.53×10^8 m/s, and its wavelength is 3.01×10^{-7} m. When light travels from air into sulfur its speed is reduced from 300 Mm/s to 153 Mm/s. When the light passes from sulfur back into air its speed is restored to 300 Mm/s.

REFRACTION OF LIGHT RAYS

Since waves change direction when they enter a new medium, it should be evident that the angle of refraction is not equal to the angle of incidence. What is the relation between the two angles? For many centuries scientists were unable to find a completely valid relation. Then, early in the seventeenth century a regular relation was established between the angles of light rays refracted from one medium to another. It will be possible for us to show that this relation leads to the same value, for any particular index of refraction, as does the ratio of the speeds of light.

Angles of incidence and refraction can be measured by using a semi-circular block of glass on an optical disc. The centre of the flat face of the block is fixed at the centre of the disc (Fig.15-3). Because the radii of circles are all perpendicular to the circumference, any ray of light within the glass that strikes the centre of the disc will be along a normal to the curved surface and will not be refracted. Thus angles of incidence in the air (θ_1) and corresponding angles of refraction in the glass (θ_2) can be read from the markings at the edge of the disc. A set of corresponding pairs of such angles is provided in Exercise 15-6. It can be seen that regular increases in the angle of incidence do not produce regular increases in the angle of refraction. However, if each pair of angles is used to draw a diagram like the one in Fig. 15-4 a regular relation can be found.

In the circle, the line X'OX represents the surface between air above and glass below, and the line YOY' represents the normal. The incident ray is LO and the refracted ray is ON. Perpendiculars are drawn from L and N to meet the normal at K and M respectively. The line LK = z_1 and the line MN = z_2; since these are half the lengths of chords of the circle they may be called semi-chords.

If a diagram like Fig. 15-4 is drawn for each pair of angles, it is found that the ratio z_1/z_2 has approximately the same value each time. This relation is called Snel's law; it can be stated that:

When light is refracted from one medium into another, the ratio of the semi-chord in the first medium to the semi-chord in the second medium is constant.

That is, the ratio does not change with different angles of incidence.

We can now show that the ratio z_1/z_2 is equal to the index of re-

FIG. 15-3

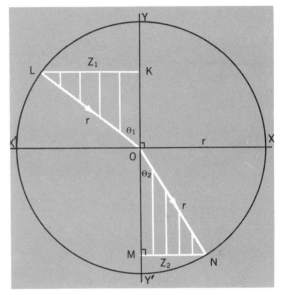

FIG. 15-4

Willebrord Snel formulated this relation (in a somewhat different but equivalent form) in 1621. In Latin his name is written Snellius. Taking it out of the Latin has often led to the mis-spelling Snell.

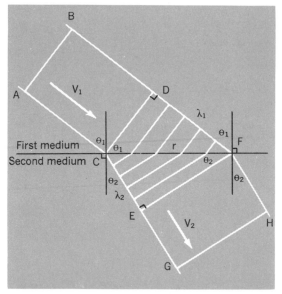

FIG. 15-5

FIG. 15-6

fraction as previously defined. The wave diagram of Fig. 15-2 has been redrawn in Fig. 15-5, with the length of the line CF equal to the radius r of the circle in Fig. 15-4. The angles θ_1 and θ_2 are the same in all three diagrams. Then the right-angle triangles FCD and LOK are congruent, as are the right-angle triangles CFE and NOM. The index of refraction equals λ_1/λ_2 as previously defined. But due to the congruence of the two pairs of triangles in Fig. 15-4 and Fig. 15-5, $\lambda_1 = z_1$ and $\lambda_2 = z_2$. Therefore $\lambda_1/\lambda_2 = z_1/z_2$. This means that the ratio of the semi-chords is equal to the index of refraction,

$$z_1/z_2 = n.$$

This relation can be established using similar triangles instead of congruent triangles, but the mathematics is more complicated.

The diagram of Fig. 15-4 can be used as the basis for a method to find an angle in refraction when the other angle and the index of refraction are known. The known angle is drawn on the diagram, and its semi-chord constructed and measured. The other semi-chord is then calculated from Snel's law, using the values of the index of refraction and the measured semi-chord. The length of the calculated semi-chord is measured along the surface from the point of incidence, and a perpendicular is constructed from the point so reached to the circumference of the circle. The diagram is then completed and the required angle is measured.

TOTAL INTERNAL REFLECTION

Light striking the flat face of the semi-circular glass block from air is bent toward the normal in the glass. When the angle of incidence in air is almost 90°, the angle of refraction in the glass is only about 40°. Now, let the light beam strike the face of the block from within the glass (Fig. 15-6). As the angle of incidence in the glass ranges from 0° to 40°, the angle of refraction in the air increases from 0° to 90°. What will happen for angles of incidence in the glass greater than 40°? The light cannot be refracted into the air, so it is *reflected* within the glass—and the angle of reflection is equal to the angle of incidence.

When light in one medium strikes the surface of another medium of a smaller index of refraction, there is a range of angles of incidence for which the light will not enter the other medium. The light is totally reflected internally. The largest angle of incidence at which there is any refraction into the other medium is called the **critical angle**. When the angle of incidence in the medium with the greater index of refraction is at the critical angle, the angle of refraction in the other medium is 90°.

We use subscript "1" for the medium having the smaller index of refraction (where the speed of light is greater); and "2" for the medium having the larger index of refraction (where the speed of light is less). When the angle in the first medium is $\theta_1 = 90°$, then $z_1 = r$, the radius of the circle in the construction of Fig. 15-4. As a result, the semi-chord of the critical angle (θ_2) will be

$$z_2 = r/n.$$

Whenever light strikes the surface between two transparent media, some of the energy is reflected. Sometimes, of course, the fraction of energy reflected is too small to be very noticeable. Fig. 15-7 shows light originating within water, and being refracted and reflected at the surface of the air. The three narrow beams on the right of the photograph are sketched in Fig. 15-8. For angles of incidence x and y, the internally reflected beams have been omitted. Angle x is clearly less than the critical angle; y is just smaller than the critical angle. Since angle z is greater than the critical angle, this third beam is *totally* reflected internally. The other two are *partially* reflected internally.

The principle of total internal reflection is often used in optical instruments to provide reflection with a minimum of absorption. Periscopes used in submarines and tanks employ prisms with a cross-section in the shape of an isosceles right-angle triangle. This application is illustrated in the photograph of Fig. 15-9. Smaller amounts of energy are lost in totally reflecting prisms than in metallized mirrors and therefore visibility is improved.

FIG. 15-7

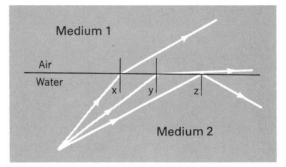

FIG. 15-8

Silvered glass, polished silver, and special alloys can reflect back just over 90% of the incident light. Other polished metal surfaces reflect 75% or less of the incident light. *Total* internal reflection is essentially 100%.

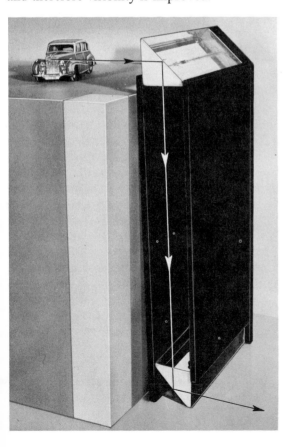
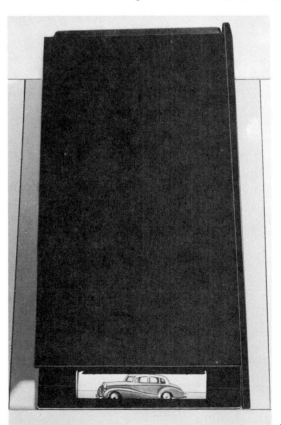

FIG. 15-9

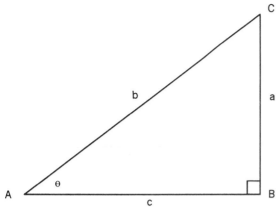

FIG. 15-10

REFRACTION CALCULATIONS

It is possible to relate the angles of incidence and refraction without using semi-chords in a geometric construction. It can be done by using the sine relation defined in trigonometry. In a right-angle triangle, the ratio of the length of the side opposite one angle to the length of the hypotenuse is defined as the sine of that angle. That is, in triangle ABC (Fig. 15-10), with a right angle at B, and

$$\angle BAC = \theta,$$
$$\sin \theta = \frac{a}{b}.$$

It is evident that the definition of the sine of an angle leads to the relation that the length of the side opposite an acute angle is equal to the product of the length of the hypotenuse and the sine of the acute angle;

$$a = b \sin \theta.$$

This relation can be used to restate Snel's law. In Fig. 15-2, triangles FCD and CFE have right angles at D and E respectively. The sides opposite the angles of incidence and refraction are equal to the wavelengths in the two media. Then,

$$\lambda_1 = CF \sin \theta_1, \quad \text{and} \quad \lambda_2 = CF \sin \theta_2.$$

But, $$n = \frac{\lambda_1}{\lambda_2} = \frac{CF \sin \theta_1}{CF \sin \theta_2}.$$

Therefore, $$n = \frac{\sin \theta_1}{\sin \theta_2}.$$

Snel's law was put into this form by Descartes in 1637. It can be used to find an angle in one medium when the angle in the other medium and the index of refraction are known. There is a table of sines in the Appendix.

Example: The index of refraction of heavy flint glass is 1.67. A ray of light in air strikes a flint glass surface at an angle of incidence of 40.0°. Calculate the angle of refraction in the flint glass.

The angle of incidence in air, $\theta_1 = 40.0°$.
From the table of sines, $\sin 40.0° = 0.6428$.
The index of refraction, $n = 1.67$.

From $$n = \frac{\sin \theta_1}{\sin \theta_2},$$

$$\sin \theta_2 = \frac{1}{n} \sin \theta_1 = \frac{1}{1.67} \times 0.6428 = 0.3849.$$

From the table of sines, $0.3849 = \sin 22.6°$.

Therefore the angle of refraction in the flint glass is 22.6°.

Example: Calculate the index of refraction of ethyl alcohol for which the critical angle into air is 47.2°.

The angle in the alcohol, $\theta_2 = 47.2°$.
The angle in air, $\theta_1 = 90.0°$.
From the table, $\sin 47.2° = 0.7737$.
From the table, $\sin 90.0° = 1.000$.

The index of refraction of the alcohol

$$n = \frac{\sin \theta_1}{\sin \theta_2} = \frac{1.000}{0.7737} = 1.363.$$

Therefore alcohol with a critical angle of 47.2° has an index of refraction of 1.36.

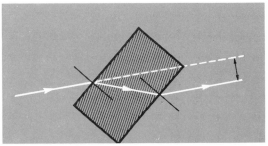

FIG. 15-11

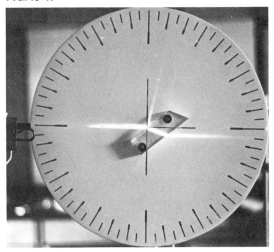

DISPERSION

No consideration has so far been given to the possibility that the speed of waves in a medium depends on their frequency. In fact, it is only in a vacuum or in air that all frequencies of light travel at the same speed. In other media, colours of different frequencies travel at different speeds. This dependence of the speed of light in a medium on the frequency of the light waves is called **dispersion**. Any medium in which dispersion occurs is called a dispersive medium. The spreading of white light into its component colours (or frequencies) after passing into a glass prism occurs because glass is a dispersive medium. The effect can also be accounted for by saying that since the speed of light in the glass depends on the frequency, the index of refraction of the glass must depend on the colour of the light.

No dispersion of white light is noticed when light passes obliquely through a parallel-sided block of glass. As shown in Fig. 15-11, the result of the two refractions at the surfaces of the glass is merely a lateral displacement of the ray of light—the direction of travel remains unchanged. There is no net dispersion because the two refractions are in opposite directions. However, when light passes through a triangular prism, there is a change in the direction of travel of the ray (Fig. 15-12). The angle that is marked in the diagram shows the extent of the change in direction. It is the sum of the changes in direction at each refraction, and these refractions are now both in the same direction.

The two refractions in the same direction have the effect of in-

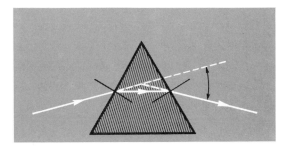

FIG. 15-12

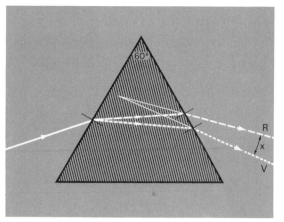

FIG. 15-13

creasing the dispersion of the white light. In Fig. 15-13, a small dispersion is shown at the first refraction. It is increased at the second refraction. The angles in the diagram have been exaggerated to show the effect more clearly. If the prism is made of crown glass, the angle of dispersion (x in the diagram) is about 1.8°.

Example: A narrow beam of white light strikes the plane surface of a block of crown glass at an angle of incidence of 82.0°. The index of refraction of crown glass is 1.51 for red light and 1.53 for violet light. Calculate (a) the angle of refraction in glass for each colour, (b) the speed in glass for each colour.

(a) Air is the first medium.

Angle of incidence, $\theta_1 = 82.0°$.
$$\sin \theta_1 = \sin 82.0° = 0.9903.$$

Glass is the second medium.

The index of refraction, $n = \dfrac{\sin \theta_1}{\sin \theta_2}$.

Therefore, $\sin \theta_2 = \dfrac{1}{n} \sin \theta_1 = \dfrac{1}{n} \times 0.9903.$

For red light $n = 1.51.$

Therefore, $\sin \theta_2 = \dfrac{1}{1.51} \times 0.9903 = 0.6558.$

Therefore, $\theta_2 = 41.0°.$

Therefore the angle of refraction for the red light is 41.0°.

For violet light $n = 1.53.$

Therefore, $\sin \theta_2 = \dfrac{1}{1.53} \times 0.9903 = 0.6473.$

Therefore, $\theta_2 = 40.3°.$

Therefore the angle of refraction for the violet light is 40.3°.

Since they are refracted at different angles the two colours are dispersed—the light is spread out through an angle of about 0.7°.

(b) Air is the first medium.

Speed, $c_1 = 3.00 \times 10^8$ m/s.

Glass is the second medium.

Speed, $c_2 = \dfrac{1}{n} \times c_1.$

For red light $n = 1.51$.

Therefore, $c_2 = \dfrac{3.00 \times 10^8 \text{ m/s}}{1.51} = 1.99 \times 10^8 \text{ m/s}$.

Therefore the speed of red light in crown glass is 1.99×10^8 m/s.

For violet light $n = 1.53$.

Therefore $c_2 = \dfrac{3.00 \times 10^8 \text{ m/s}}{1.53} = 1.96 \times 10^8 \text{ m/s}$.

Therefore the speed of violet light in crown glass is 1.96×10^8 m/s.

The dispersion of the white light is the result of the slowing of the red light to 1.99×10^8 m/s, and of the violet light even more, to 1.96×10^8 m/s.

WAVE REFRACTION BY LENSES

Fig. 15-14 shows the action of a flat glass block with a curved edge on a train of plane waves. The waves strike the flat edge normally and are not refracted, but the speed of the waves is reduced. At the curved edge the ends of the wave fronts leave the glass before the centres do, and travel at an increased speed in the air. The refraction has the effect of bending the ends inward. Since the edge of the glass is curved, each wave is bent smoothly, so that when the waves leave the glass they have the curvature shown.

Recall that curvature is related to the distance from the source, and that a plane wave has zero curvature. As waves leave the right side of the block their curvature indicates that they were converging to a point beyond the block. *Convex* transparent surfaces have a *converging* or focusing effect on light. This can be demonstrated on the optical disc.

A transparent object with curved surfaces is called a **lens**. A block of glass with flat sides and curved edges, as used on the optical disc, is a **cylindrical lens**. It focuses light to a line. Since it is often more useful to focus light to a point, most lenses are curved in all directions. When they have surfaces that are sections of spheres, they are called **spherical lenses**. A variety of spherical lenses is represented in Fig. 15-15.

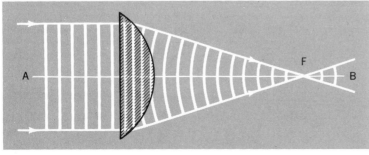

FIG. 15-14

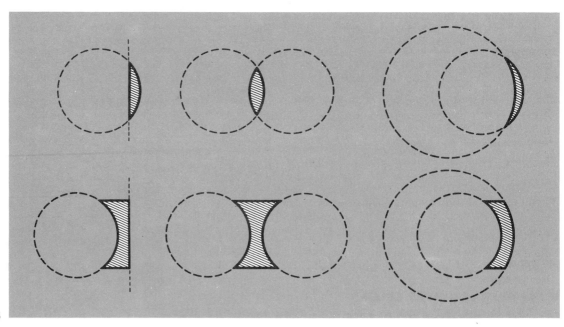

FIG. 15-15

The extent to which a lens bends light is called its *power*, and is calculated by $P = 1/f$. With the focal length f in metres, the unit of lens power is the dioptre (1 D = 1 m^{-1}). A lens of short focal length is more powerful in that it brings the light to a focus closer to the lens than does one of longer focal length. (However, do not confuse power with magnification—they are different ideas and thus different quantities.)

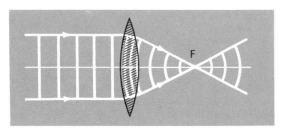

FIG. 15-16

Lens diagrams represent cross-sections of spherical lenses and show what happens on a central plane through the lenses. The line AB in Fig. 15-14 which passes through the centre of the lens perpendicular to both surfaces is called the **axis** of the lens. The direction of wave travel in that diagram is parallel to the axis. The waves converge to the point F on the axis to the right of the lens. The point to which light travelling parallel to the axis is converged after refraction is called the **focus**. The distance from the centre of the lens to the focus, along the axis, is called the **focal length**, f. Any beam of plane waves will converge to a point that lies on the **focal plane**, which is the plane perpendicular to the axis through the focus. It is indicated in Fig. 15-18(b).

The plane surface of the lens in Fig. 15-14 did not affect the curvature of the waves. When both surfaces are curved there is a double effect on the curvature (Fig. 15-16). If a lens is thin (when the distance between surfaces along the axis is less than $f/10$), the effect of the two surfaces can be considered to be combined into a single refraction at the middle of the lens. This is shown in Fig. 15-17 where the source is $3f$ from the lens. The lens changes the curvature of the waves so that they converge to a point $3f/2$ from the lens.

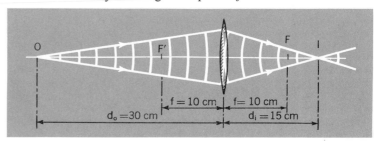

FIG. 15-17

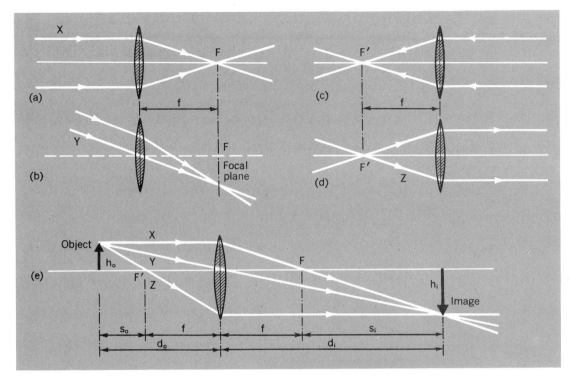

FIG. 15-18

RAY DIAGRAMS FOR CONVEX LENSES

The lenses you will use in experiments are likely to be thin lenses. The diagrams in Fig. 15-18 should correspond very closely to the results of your experiments. Rays are shown instead of waves to make the drawing simpler. A ray indicates the direction in which waves are travelling. Each of the diagrams in Fig. 15-18 illustrates a principle, as follows:

(a) The rays are refracted at the mid-plane of the lens. Incident rays parallel to the axis are refracted through the focus.

(b) Rays parallel to each other but not parallel to the axis converge to a point on the focal plane. The ray passing through the centre of the lens is not bent. The sides of the lens near the centre are practically parallel to each other so the direction of the ray is not changed. Since the lens is thin the lateral displacement of the ray is negligible.

(c) If rays come from the opposite direction (that is, from the right in the figure) parallel to the axis they are refracted through a point that is at a distance f from the lens. A thin lens has two focuses, equidistant from the lens, on either side of it. F is the focus for rays parallel to the axis approaching the lens from the left, and F' for rays parallel to the axis approaching from the right.

(d) Because of reversibility, incident rays that pass through a focus are refracted parallel to the axis.

(e) The image of a point that a lens produces can be located by tracing rays that refract in a known way. The three rays, X, Y, and Z are identified in the preceding diagrams. Any two of the three rays are sufficient to locate the image. It is usual to pick the two that can be drawn most easily.

In Fig. 15-18(e) distances from the object and image to the focuses are labelled s and to the lens, d. The subscripts o and i refer to object and image respectively. Heights are labelled h. You can pick out the similar triangles in which

$$\frac{h_i}{h_o} = \frac{d_i}{d_o}.$$

The relative heights of image and object can be found if the ratio of distances to the lens is known. The ratio h_i/h_o is called the **magnification**. Relations between distances and focal length are developed in Exercise 15-11.

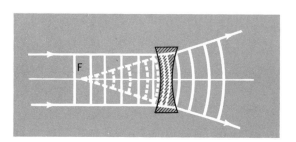

FIG. 15-19

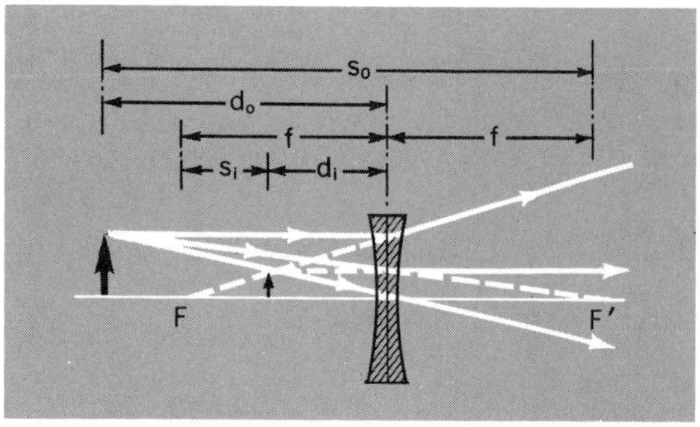

FIG. 15-20

That is, for light coming from the left.

CONCAVE LENSES

Because of its effect on a beam of parallel rays (plane waves) a convex lens is called a *converging* lens. In Fig. 15-19 you can see the *diverging* effect of a concave lens. A concave lens changes the curvature of plane waves so that they appear to be travelling outward from the point F. F is a **virtual focus** because rays do not pass through it, but only appear to have passed through it.

When the differences between convex and concave lenses are kept clearly in mind, you can deduce the effect that a concave lens has on several rays, as was done for convex lenses. Then rays can be traced to locate an image in a concave lens as shown in Fig. 15-20. The labelling here should be compared with that in Fig. 15-18. When the same distinction between F and F' is used, it is apparent that F is on the left of a concave lens, although it is on the right of a convex lens. For a concave lens the s distances are measured to the same focuses as for a convex lens.

RAY DIAGRAMS AND OPTICAL INSTRUMENTS

When you know the focal length of a lens you can find the image location for any object by drawing a diagram. There are also several ways to calculate the position of the image. If the unit of length in a ray diagram is the focal length of the lens, as in Fig. 15-21, the relation between image and object distances is independent of the actual value of the focal length.

Various optical instruments are designed for specific locations of the object, to produce a desired magnification. The ray diagrams of Fig. 15-21 are typical for the different optical instruments indicated.

The design and use of most of these instruments is described in Chapter 16. Notice that the images in (a), (b), (c), and (d) are real. The image in (f) is virtual.

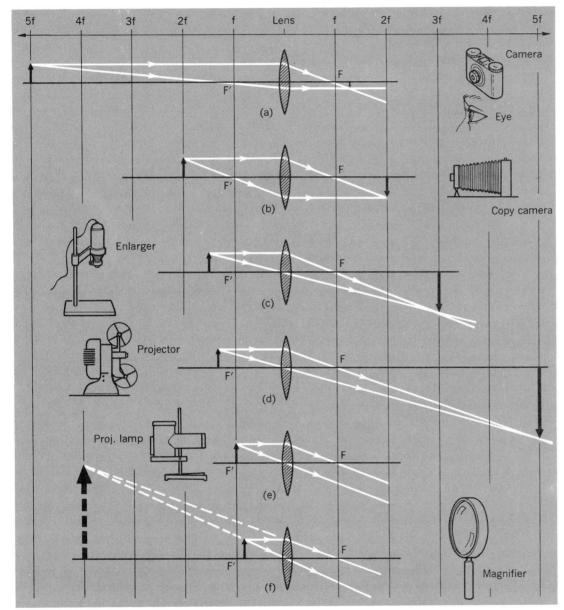

FIG. 15-21

FIG. 15-22: THE RAINBOW

Some aspects of the formation of the primary rainbow can be explained with this diagram. The rainbow is only seen when the sun is behind the observer on a day when the atmosphere is heavily laden with water droplets. The white light is dispersed as it enters a droplet at A. At B, internal reflection (not necessarily total) occurs. At B the order of colours reverses. Refraction and more dispersion occur at C.

In this diagram only the red ray enters the eye. A similar droplet lower in the sky will send a violet ray to the eye. Thus the spectral colours are separated, and red appears to be highest in the sky.

Other features of rainbows such as the shape of the bow in the sky, the appearance of the dimmer secondary bow higher than the primary bow (with colours reversed relative to the primary bow), the dark region of the sky between the primary and secondary bows, additional arcs and related phenomena have not been explained here. They could make interesting topics for library research.

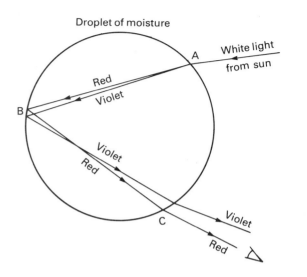

Exercises

A

1. When light passes from air into a medium such as glass or water, what happens to (a) its speed, (b) its wavelength, (c) its frequency?

2. (a) A tracked vehicle such as a bulldozer has no steering wheel. The direction of travel is controlled by brakes and throttles acting on each track individually. If a bulldozer is travelling at a constant speed of 10 km/h across a field, describe the action necessary to turn it to the right.
   (b) Why do waves bend as they pass from one medium to another? (Hint: an answer not exceeding one sentence is expected.)

3. The speed of light in air is 300 Mm/s, and in sea water 224 Mm/s. Calculate the index of refraction for sea water relative to air.

4. (a) The index of refraction of ruby relative to air is about 1.75. Calculate the speed of light in ruby.
   (b) The wavelength of yellow light in air is about 590 nm. Calculate the corresponding wavelength in water.

5. Calculate the index of refraction of a sound wave travelling from air into water, using the values for the speed of sound found in the table in the Appendix.

6. The following table gives corresponding values for the angle of incidence in air (θ_1), and the angle of refraction in flint glass (θ_2), as found with a ray box and a semi-circular glass block. Employ circle diagrams like Fig. 15-4 to determine an average value for the index of refraction of flint glass. (Hint: Making the circles large permits greater accuracy to be obtained.)

θ_1 (Degrees)	θ_2 (Degrees)
0	0
10.0	6.2
20.0	12.4
30.0	18.2
40.0	23.7
50.0	28.6
60.0	32.8
70.0	36.0
80.0	38.0

7. What is the magnitude of the angle of refraction when the angle of incidence is at the critical angle in (a) water, (b) glass?

8. Two fish are in a pond with steep sides, about 2 m beneath the surface; one is almost at the edge of the pond and the other about 7 m from the edge. A

fisherman stands on the bank directly above the first fish, with his eyes about 1.5 m above the surface of the water. Draw a sketch to show: (a) one ray by which the fisherman sees the first fish, (b) another ray to show how the fisherman sees the second fish, with the angle of incidence of the light in the water at about 45°, and (c) a third ray by which the first fish sees the second one if a large rock intervenes on the direct line between the two fish. (d) Indicate the apparent position of the second fish as seen by the fisherman, and (e) as seen by the first fish.

9. Reflection, refraction, diffraction, and dispersion all refer to the bending of light. Distinguish clearly between the four terms.

10. Draw full-size ray diagrams to locate the images in a convex lens of focal length 3.0 cm of an object that is successively 12.0, 9.0, 6.0, and 4.5 cm from the lens. Any convenient height of object is satisfactory.

11. (a) Construct a table with seven columns with space for entries on four lines. The first two columns should be headed *Distance from object to lens* (d_o), the first one in units of centimetres, the second in units of the focal length used in question 10 ($f = 3.0$ cm) e.g., $d_o = 12.0$ cm $= 4f$. The third and fourth columns should be headed *Distance from image to lens* (d_i), using the same units as the first two columns respectively. Fill in the first four columns with the object and image distances from the diagrams of question 10.

(b) Subtract $1f$ from each item in columns 2 and 4 in the table and enter the results in columns 5 and 6 respectively. Head these latter columns *Distance from object to focus F'* (s_o) and *Distance from image to focus F* (s_i).

(c) Multiply each pair of values s_o and s_i and enter the results in column 7 (*Product $s_o s_i$*). Notice that this product is the same for each row in the column. Express this result as an equation. (This equation is called the *Newtonian lens formula*. It may be used instead of ray diagrams to locate images, provided that you always remember that s_o and s_i are measured from the focal points, not from the lens.)

12. (a) Prove the triangles ABF' and F'DE in the following diagram are similar, and that triangles CDF and FGK are similar.
(b) Hence what is true for h_o, s_o, f, and h_i in the

first pair of triangles, and for h_o, f, s_i, and h_i in the second pair?

(c) Rearrange each of the proportions you found in (b) part to get ratios that are equal to the ratio h_i/h_o. (What you have just derived are known as the *Newtonian magnification formulas*. They may be used instead of ray diagrams to find the height of images, provided that you always remember that s_o and s_i are measured from the focal points, not from the lens.)

13. Make a scale diagram to locate the image of a book 20 cm tall that is 60 cm from a convex lens of focal length 15 cm. Describe the characteristics of the image. Tell how many centimetres on the page represent 1 cm in the problem. Check your results by calculation.

14. Make a scale diagram to locate the image of a pole 150 cm tall that is 225 cm from a convex lens of focal length 75 cm. Describe the image's characteristics. Check your results by calculation.

B

15. Given that the index of refraction of a material relative to air is 2.0, and that the angle of incidence in air is 75°, determine the angle of refraction in the material.

16. Determine the index of refraction of a medium relative to air when the angle of incidence in air is 60° and the angle of refraction in the medium is 30°.

17. Determine the angle of refraction in air for an angle of incidence in water of 45°.

18. Determine the angle of refraction in air for an angle of incidence in ordinary crown glass of 50°.

19. Determine the critical angle for (a) diamond, (b) water.

20. Determine the index of refraction of (a) chloroform, with a critical angle of 44°, (b) zircon, with a critical angle of 31.5°.

21. (a) What is the index of refraction relative to air of a material if the angle of incidence in air is 64° and the angle of refraction in the material is 30°?
(b) What is the angle of refraction in a medium whose index of refraction relative to air is 1.60, when the angle of incidence in air is 53°?
(c) What is the angle of incidence in a medium when the angle of refraction in a second medium is 45°, and the index of refraction of the second medium relative to the first is 1.30?
(d) What is the angle of refraction in a medium when the angle of incidence in a second medium is 50° and the index of refraction of the first medium relative to the second is 1.70?
(e) What is the index of refraction of a material for which the critical angle is 44.5°?

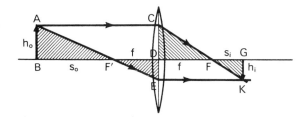

(f) What is the critical angle in a material for which the index of refraction relative to air is 1.76?

22. The index of refraction relative to air of ethyl cinnamate, a highly refractive and pleasantly non-toxic liquid, is 1.55 for red light and 1.60 for violet light. Determine the angle of refraction of each of these colours in ethyl cinnamate for an angle of incidence in air of 64.0°. What is the angle of spread between the two refracted rays? What is the name of the effect illustrated by this problem?

23. In a movie projector the film, acting as the object, is located 2.0 cm from focus F' of the convex lens of focal length 50 cm. What is the distance from the focus F of the lens to the image on the movie screen?

24. The convex lens of a camera has a focal length of 5.0 cm. The film of the camera must be located where the image is sharply focused. Where must that be to take a picture of a hockey goalkeeper who is 10 m from focus F' of the lens?

25. Draw an accurate ray diagram to locate the image of an object that is 15 cm from a convex lens of focal length 20 cm. Check your results by calculation.

26. (a) Draw a ray diagram to locate the image of an object that is 60 cm from a concave lens of focal length 15 cm.
    (b) Repeat for an object of the same height located (i) 30 cm, and (ii) 15 cm, from the same lens. Check your results by calculation in each case.

27. A tree 20 m high is located 40 m from focus F' of a convex lens of focal length 8.0 cm. What is the height of the image of the tree?

28. The image of a newspaper is focused by a convex lens of focal length 50 cm onto a film that is 1 cm from the focus F of the lens. The distance between adjacent grains on the film is about 10^{-4} cm. What is the distance between two dots on the newspaper that are focused onto adjacent grains on the film?

29. A normal human eye has a focal length of about 2.3 cm. If you look with your normal eye at the tip of a pencil 55.3 cm from your eye, where is the image assuming that the focal length of the eye does not change?

30. A slide projector has a lens of focal length 10.0 cm and casts an image on a screen 4.0 m from the focus F of the lens.
    (a) Where should the slide be located?
    (b) If the slide is 35 mm by 35 mm, what size is the image on the screen?

C

31. Red light has a shorter wavelength in water than in air. However, if you look at a red light under water, it does not appear orange or yellow or green. Suggest a reason for this.

32. A ray of red light strikes an equiangular, flint-glass prism at such an angle that the refracted ray in the glass is parallel to the base of the prism. The index of refraction of flint glass relative to air is 1.66 for red light.
    (a) Determine the angles in the air before and after the ray passes through the prism.
    (b) Trace a violet ray, with the same original angle of incidence, through the prism, determining its angle of refraction into the flint glass, its angle of incidence at the other face of the prism, and its angle of refraction back into air. The index of refraction of the flint glass for violet light is 1.70 relative to air.
    (c) What is the angle between the refracted red and violet rays as they emerge from the prism?

33. How could a small-sized source of light and a plane mirror be used to locate the focus of a convex lens? (This technique is called *auto-collimation* and is extremely accurate.)

34. In (e) of Fig. 15-18 it can be seen that $d = s + f$ as long as d and s have the same subscript. Use this relation to substitute for s_o and s_i in the relation $s_o s_i = f^2$. Express the relation between d_o, d_i and f in the simplest possible form. This is known as the *Gaussian lens formula*.

35. Prove the *Gaussian magnification formula*: $h_i/h_o = d_i/d_o$.

36. Using the labelling in Fig. 15-20, show that $s_o s_i = f^2$ can be applied to concave lenses.

CHAPTER 16

Optical Instruments

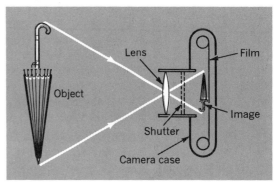

FIG. 16-1

Lenses are used in a wide variety of instruments to assist and extend human vision. In this chapter we shall see how principles from preceding chapters are applied in the construction of camera and eye, microscope and telescope.

RECORDING OPTICAL IMAGES

THE CAMERA

A camera is a device by which a permanent record of a scene can be made. It consists essentially of a light-tight case that holds a film at the back and has a lens and shutter at the front (Fig. 16-1). A real image of the object being photographed is formed by the lens on the film. The shutter can be opened for a specified length of time to admit enough light to expose the film. Such accessories as a viewfinder, a rangefinder, and an exposure meter may be added to make the operation more efficient.

The success of photography depends on materials that can be changed by exposure to light; these changes are permanent and depend on the intensity of the light. A photosensitive material such as silver bromide suspended in gelatin is called an **emulsion**. In roll films the emulsion is coated on a flexible, transparent base of cellulose acetate. The silver bromide consists of minute grains spread evenly throughout the emulsion as shown in Fig. 16-2(a). When a sil-

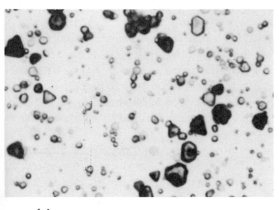

(a)

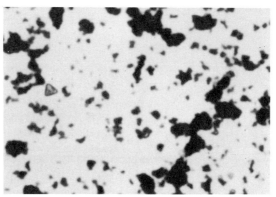

(b)

FIG. 16-2

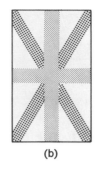
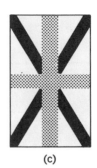
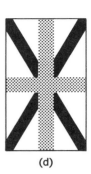

(a)	(b)	(c)	(d)	(e)

FIG. 16-3. Steps in the production of a photograph: (a) the original object, (b) the latent image on the film, (c) the developed film, (d) the fixed negative, (e) the positive print.

ver bromide grain is exposed to light some of the silver ions capture electrons to form silver atoms. These form the specks illustrated in Fig. 16-2(b). When the film is placed in a developer solution, grains that have been exposed to enough light are converted completely to silver which, in tiny amounts, is black. Unexposed grains are not affected. As shown in Fig. 16-3(c), regions where the light was intense become all black; lesser amounts of light will not have affected all the grains in a given area, and a grey tone is produced. The conversion of silver bromide to silver is stopped by placing the film in a fixing solution, often of sodium hyposulfite (hypo). The fixer dissolves all unconverted silver bromide. After being washed and dried, the negative is complete—clear where no light struck, black where there was strong light, and grey where there were medium intensities of light. These different parts may be distinguished in Fig. 16-3(d). To make a positive print, light is shone through the negative onto another piece of photosensitive paper, and after the exposure, this paper is developed and fixed. In the final result, as shown in Fig. 16-3(e), the tones of light and dark are the reverse of what they are in the negative.

The optical parts of a camera must be arranged to expose the film correctly; too much light, or overexposure, will give the final print a washed-out appearance. An underexposed negative will produce a print that is too dark.

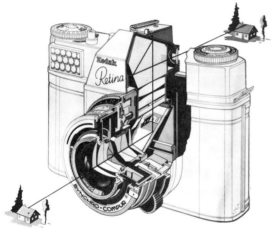

FIG. 16-4

To take pictures in different illuminations, the shutter of some cameras can be opened for different lengths of time. For example, in a bright sun one might use an exposure of 1/100 s. When the sky is cloudy an exposure of 1/25 s might be necessary. Medium-priced cameras using 35 mm roll film (illustrated in Fig. 16-4) have as many as nine shutter speeds for exposures from 1 s to 1/500 s. To photograph objects in motion a rather short exposure is needed to reduce blurring, probably 1/200 s or less. If motion makes a fast shutter speed necessary, some other device must be used to adjust for different illuminations.

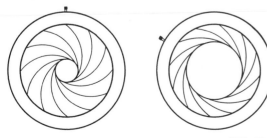

FIG. 16-5

Such a device is found in most cameras and is called a **diaphragm**. It can be adjusted to control the size of the opening (or aperture) through which light enters the camera as illustrated in Fig. 16-5. The amount of light that can enter the camera varies directly as the area

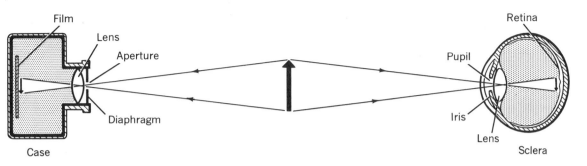

FIG. 16-6. Illustration of the main similarities between parts of camera and eye.

of the aperture (as the square of the radius or diameter). Aperture sizes are universally designated by a system known as $f/$ numbers. An aperture of $f/4$ has a diameter that is ¼ of the focal length of the lens. This system provides a measure of the light-gathering power available. When the aperture of a typical 35 mm camera lens (whose focal length $f = 5.2$ cm) is $f/4$, its diameter is 5.2 cm/4 = 1.3 cm. The largest aperture obtainable depends on the diameter of the lens —but larger lenses are more expensive. The range of a camera's apertures is listed in Table 16-1. Each aperture admits half as much light as the one on its left. The set of shutter speeds below the apertures gives examples of the choice available to a photographer—each combination admits the same amount of light to the film.

The film itself is a factor in selecting the correct exposure for a given illumination. A wide range of sensitivities or film speeds is available, colour films being, in general, slower than black and white films.

The focus of inexpensive fixed-focus cameras cannot be adjusted. All objects beyond a certain minimum distance from the camera are focused clearly on the film. In cameras that can be focused, the distance between the lens and the film can be changed. A 35 mm camera usually has its lens mounted in a tube that can be screwed into or out of the body of the camera. For distant objects the lens is located so that its focus is at the film. Then if $f = 5.0$ cm the lens needs to be moved away from the film only an extra distance of 0.50 cm to focus clearly on an object that is just 55 cm from the lens.

THE EYE

The eyes of vertebrates have a structure that is very similar to that of a camera. The parts of a human eye are illustrated in Fig. 16-6 in comparison with a camera. The principal parts of the eye are the retina, the pupil, the iris, the lens and the sclera. These correspond respectively to the film, the aperture, the diaphragm, the lens and the case of a camera.

An accurate scale drawing of a section of a human eye is shown in Fig. 16-7. The transparent **cornea** is the forward portion of the **sclera**, the outermost layer of the eyeball. The next layer, the **choroid**, becomes the **iris** at the front of the eye. Since the indices of refraction

Table 16-1

COMBINATIONS OF APERTURES AND SHUTTER SPEEDS THAT PRODUCE THE SAME EXPOSURE OF FILM FOR IDENTICAL ILLUMINATION

Aperture ($f/$)	2.8	4	5.6	8	11	16	22
Shutter speed (s)	$\frac{1}{1600}$	$\frac{1}{800}$	$\frac{1}{400}$	$\frac{1}{200}$	$\frac{1}{100}$	$\frac{1}{50}$	$\frac{1}{25}$

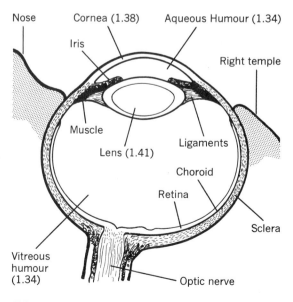

FIG. 16-7.

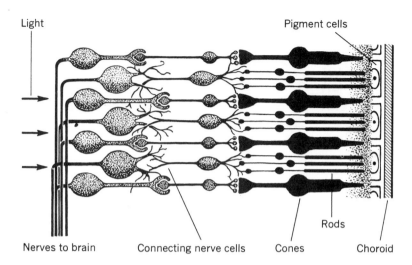

FIG. 16-8

Light

Pigment cells

Rods

Nerves to brain Connecting nerve cells Cones Choroid

of the various sections of the eye are between 1.3 and 1.4, the first re-fraction of light, from air into the cornea, is the most pronounced and it is here that most focusing is done. The major function of the **lens** is to alter the focal length of the system for fine adjustment of the focusing.

In the **retina**, which lines the back of the eye, are the photosensitive elements that are responsible for light perception. The photosensitive elements in the retina are the **rods** and **cones** illustrated in Fig. 16-8. Only the cones are sensitive to colour, but the rods are more sensitive to dimmer illumination than the cones. In the central part of the retina there are only cones, but towards the edge of the retina rods occur in greater number than do the cones. From the diagram it is evident that light must pass through the network of connecting nerves to reach the rods and cones. The nerve fibres are assembled into a bundle in the optic nerve so that when light striking a rod or cone produces an electrochemical reaction, a nerve impulse is transmitted to the brain. From all the impulses it receives, the brain constructs its visual impression of what is seen.

Since the eye is more like a television camera than a still film camera, it does not employ a shutter. The size of the **pupil** (the opening into the eye) is controlled by the **iris reflex**. Under low illumination the iris is drawn back from the centre of the eye and the pupil is large, about 8 mm in diameter. If the illumination is increased, nerve signals from the retina are transmitted to the muscles controlling the iris. They move to reduce the diameter of the pupil to protect the retina from overexposure. In full daylight the diameter of the pupil is about 2 mm.

The movements of the iris are not consciously controlled—the nerve signals that control the iris reflex bypass the conscious part of the brain. Of course, under intense illumination, such as sunlit snow, the iris control is not sufficient, and we squint, often with conscious effort.

The distance from the cornea to the retina (on the axis) is about 2.4 cm. By itself the cornea has a focal length of about 3.1 cm. The additional refraction of the lens brings an image forward to be formed sharply on the retina. The lens is a compressible ovoid composed of a great number of layers, like an onion, enclosed in an elastic membrane. It is held in position by a number of delicate ligaments around its circumference, connecting it to muscles on the inner wall of the eyeball.

For normal distant vision the muscles are relaxed, and the ligaments are relatively taut. Focusing on a nearby object involves a reflex called **accommodation**. The muscles are controlled by nerve signals from the retina. For a sharp image the lens thickness is changed to minimize the region occupied on the retina by the image of each point on the object. The action of the muscles permits the ligaments to slacken. Then the lens sags making its front surface more curved and thus reducing its focal length.

The lens of an unaccommodated eye is about 4 mm thick. In accommodation its thickness may be increased to about 5.5 mm. For humans in their teens the focus of the eye is thereby moved about 5 mm forward from the retina, permitting the focusing of objects as close as 9 cm to the eye.

We should distinguish between an image located by geometry and what is actually seen. Geometrical construction describes accurately the location from which light diverges (real image) or seems to diverge (virtual image). But the brain's reconstruction of signals from the retina does not always locate what is seen at the point determined by geometry. Things are located in space by means of a number of clues provided by the light that affects the retina. We depend, for example, on signals from the muscles that move the two eyeballs so that they both point towards the object being viewed (binocular vision), and on our familiarity with the sizes of things. Judgment of the size of an object often depends on its surroundings, but as shown in Fig. 16-9 sometimes our judgment is not sound. An adequate un-

FIG. 16-9: Which central circle appears to be the larger? Is it?

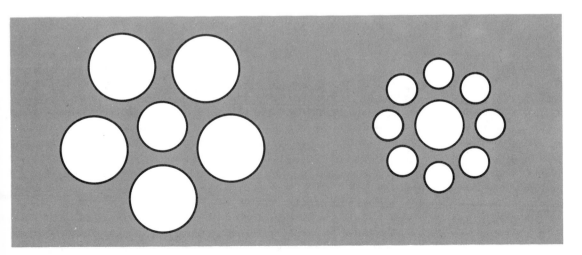

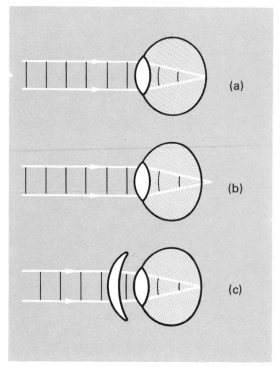

FIG. 16-10

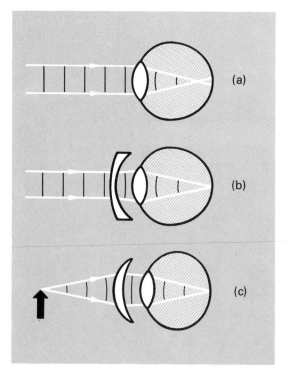

FIG. 16-11

derstanding of vision, and of how we learn to see, involves a complicated mixture of physics, physiology, and psychology.

A normal unaccommodated eye refracts plane waves to a point on the retina as shown in Fig. 16-10(a). However, some people's eyeballs are either longer or shorter than normal, so that the same optical arrangements cause plane waves to come to a point either in front of or behind the retina. We might say that the lenses of some people's eyes are too strong or too weak. A concave or convex lens placed in front of the cornea can be made to change the curvature of the waves before they reach the eye so that proper focusing can be obtained.

In far-sightedness, **hypermetropia**, plane waves are focused at a point beyond the retina (Fig. 16-10(b)). Without correcting lenses a far-sighted person can accommodate for distant vision, but he is unable to view nearby objects clearly, and his muscles of accommodation are subject to continual strain. Since the eye does not provide sufficient curvature of the waves, a convex lens is used to make up the lack as shown in Fig. 16-10(c).

In short-sightedness, **myopia**, plane waves tend to be focused at a point in front of the retina as in Fig. 16-11(a). A short-sighted person cannot see distant objects clearly. Since the eye provides too much curvature of the waves, a concave lens is used to offset it, as shown in Fig. 16-11(b).

The elasticity of the lens decreases with age. This reduces the amount of accommodation that is possible; this defect is known as **presbyopia**. The eyes cannot focus nearby objects clearly. A convex lens is used to produce the needed curvature of waves that the eye's own lens can no longer provide, as in Fig. 16-11(c). Because distant vision may not be impaired, opticians produce bifocal or trifocal lenses. Since most close work is done with the eyes lowered, the most strongly convex part of a bifocal lens is toward the bottom.

MAKING SMALL OBJECTS APPEAR LARGER
THE PROJECTOR

In a projector for slides or motion pictures, a convex projection lens forms an enlarged real image on a screen. The film or slide that contains the semi-transparent object is placed a little farther from the lens than the focus. The slide is illuminated strongly by a 500 W electric lamp. The function of the condensing-lens system is to make as much light as possible pass through the projection lens after leaving the slide. The parts and ray paths of a projector are illustrated in Fig. 16-12.

THE MAGNIFIER

A single convex lens can be used to produce an enlarged virtual image of an object located at a distance from the lens somewhat less than the focal length. When used in this way the lens is called a mag-

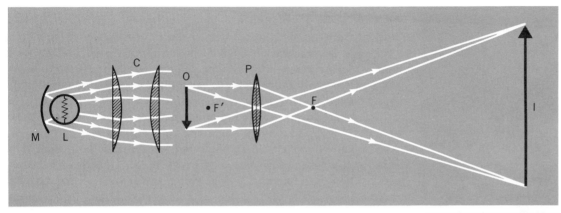

FIG. 16-12

nifying glass, or reading glass, or a simple microscope. As shown in Fig. 16-13, the apparent size of an object depends on the angle α that it subtends at the eye. With a magnifier this angle is increased, resulting in magnification of the image. In optical practice it is assumed that the image is located 25 cm from the lens for most accurate vision. The effect of the focal length of the lens on magnification is illustrated in Fig. 16-14 where equal images, each 25 cm from the lens, are used to locate the object that produced them, (a) with a lens of f = 5 cm, and (b) with a lens of f = 2 cm. It is evident that the smaller object in (b) indicates greater magnification. In fact, the magnification varies inversely as the focal length.

Single lenses of rather short focal length were used by van Leeuwenhoek for his microscopic discoveries in the seventeenth century. At that time attempts were made to increase magnification by using a second lens, but defects in the lenses prevented any significant improvement. There is no shape for a single lens that can eliminate all defects. One serious defect is that the dispersive effect of the glass lens causes the violet part of the incident white light to be focused at a different point than the red part (Fig. 16-15). This is called **chromatic aberration**. During the eighteenth century methods were devised for combining lenses to reduce chromatic and other aberrations. It was this development that led to the production of compound microscopes that were used for discoveries in biology during the nineteenth century. The multiple lenses shown in photographs in this chapter are designed to correct a variety of defects.

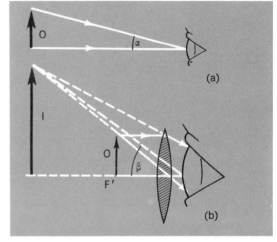

FIG. 16-13: A magnifier makes it possible to focus an object closer to the eye, so that it can subtend a larger angle (β) than it would without the magnifier (α).

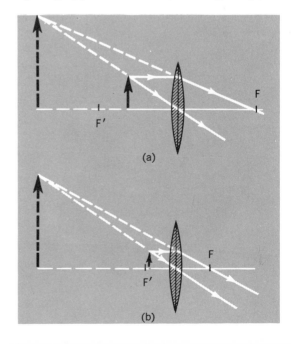

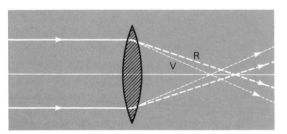

FIG. 16-15

FIG. 16-14

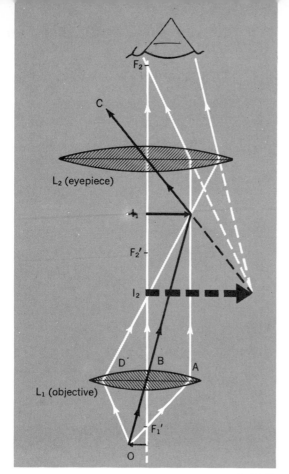

FIG. 16-16

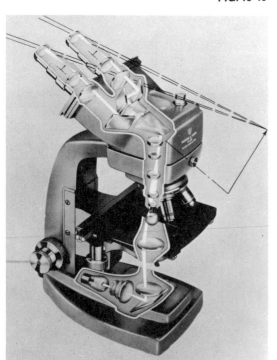

FIG. 16-17

THE COMPOUND MICROSCOPE

With achromatic (colour corrected) lenses, magnification due to a compound microscope can greatly exceed the magnification due to a simple microscope. Magnifications up to about 1000 are quite possible. The basic ray diagram for a compound microscope is a combination of the ray diagrams of the projector and the magnifier. The real image produced by an objective lens (used like a projector) is examined by the eyepiece lens (used like a magnifier).

In Fig. 16-16 the object, O, is located just outside the focus, F_1', of the objective lens, L_1. The enlarged real image, I_1, serves as the object for the eyepiece lens, L_2. The eyepiece is placed so that I_1 is between its focus, F_2', and the lens, L_2. The lens L_2 then forms an enlarged virtual image, I_2. Ray A from the top of the object through F_1' is refracted by lens L_1 parallel to the axis, and then refracted by lens L_2 to pass through F_2. Then ray B from the top of the object through the centre of the lens L_1 intersects with ray A at the top of image I_1. From that point ray C is drawn through the centre of the lens L_2. The virtual image I_2 is located at the point from which ray C intersects with ray A. Once the images have been located in this way, any other ray may be traced through both lenses from the top of the object. Ray D, through the upper part of lens L_1 is refracted to pass through the top of I_1 and then refracted by lens L_2 to appear to have come from the top of I_2. All rays from the top of O will be refracted by L_1 to pass through the top of I_1; and all rays from the top of I_1 will be refracted by L_2 to appear to have come from the top of I_2. Ray paths in a commercial microscope are illustrated in the photograph of Fig. 16-17.

MAKING DISTANT OBJECTS APPEAR CLOSER

A telescope is an optical device by which a nearby image is produced of distant objects. For this purpose a convex objective lens of large focal length is used to form a real image. The effect of focal length can be seen from Fig. 16-18. A star is so far away that light waves from it are plane (the rays are parallel). If a star A is located on the axis of the lens its image, A', is located at the focus of the lens. A telescope is effective if it increases the apparent separation between two stars. Parallel rays from star B converge on the focal plane of the lens at B'. It is evident that the apparent separation d is greater for the lens of greater focal length.

A single convex lens of long focal length f could be used as a telescope if you placed your eye at a distance a little greater than f from the lens. However, it is usual to employ an eyepiece lens as a magnifier for examining the real image. Since the objective lens inverts the image, and a convex magnifier does not, the final image is inverted. For astronomical purposes this is not a disadvantage. However, for sighting ships at sea or for birdwatching, an inverted image would be inconvenient. The following sections include several methods for producing an erect final image.

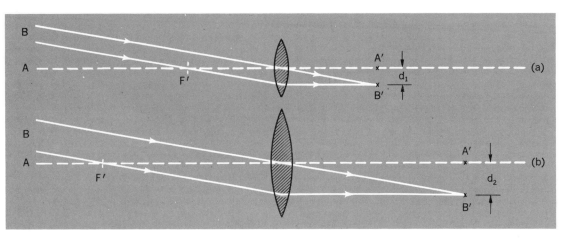

FIG. 16-18

OPERA GLASSES

The telescope that Galileo used when he discovered the moons of Jupiter had a concave eyepiece. In the ray diagram of Fig. 16-19 it can be seen that the final image is erect. The eyepiece is located so that its right-hand focus practically coincides with F_1, the right-hand focus of the objective. This diagram illustrates the basic idea of a telescope: parallel rays from a distant object are refracted so that they appear to diverge from a nearer point, I_2. This type of telescope has a limited magnification, usually about 3, and it is used mainly for opera glasses.

Galileo built his first telescope in the summer of 1609. His telescopic discoveries in the night sky were made during the following winter and reported in March 1610.

ASTRONOMICAL REFRACTOR

The most powerful astronomical telescopes are reflectors, mentioned in Chapter 14. However, refracting telescopes are useful for solar observations and for auxiliary purposes in astronomical observatories.

One advantage of reflecting telescopes is that only one surface needs to be polished.

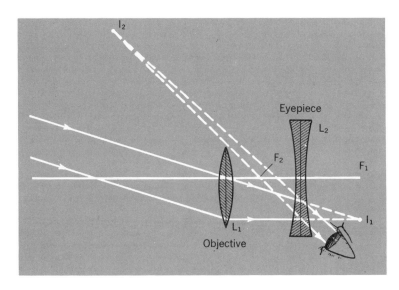

FIG. 16-19

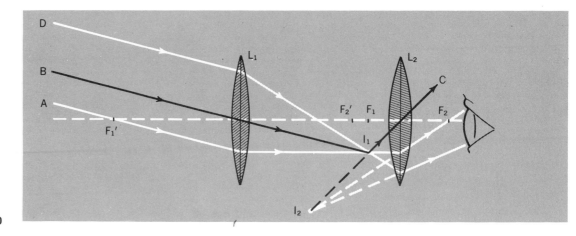

FIG. 16-20

As shown in Fig. 16-20 the convex eyepiece, L_2, is located so its left-hand focus, F_2', almost coincides with the right-hand focus, F_1, of the objective lens, L_1. If the object being observed is a star at a great distance the image of the objective is located on the focal plane, at I_1. This real image then becomes the object for the eyepiece used as a magnifier.

In Fig. 16-20, the ray A through the focus F_1' of lens L_1 is refracted parallel to the axis. At L_2 it is refracted through F_2, the focus of the eyepiece. Image I_1 is located at the intersection of ray A with ray B through the centre of L_1. Image I_2 is located at the (virtual) intersection of ray C from the image I_1 through the centre of L_2. Once the images have been located any other ray may be traced through

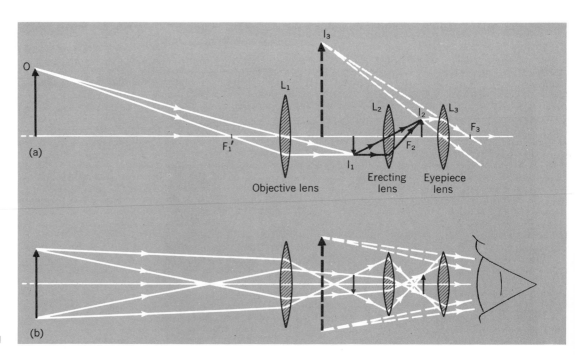

FIG. 16-21

both lenses. Ray D, parallel to rays A and B, is refracted by L_1 to pass through I_1, and then by L_2 to seem to come from I_2.

One of the largest astronomical refractors is located at the Yerkes Observatory of the University of Chicago. Its objective lens has a diameter of about 1 m and a focal length of about 20 m. The magnification of a telescope with an objective of focal length f_1, and an eyepiece of focal length f_2, is f_1/f_2. With an eyepiece of focal length 2 cm, the magnification of the Yerkes telescope is about 2000 cm/2 cm = 1000.

FIG. 16-22

TERRESTRIAL TELESCOPE

Spy glasses of the type used by Captain Kidd contain a convex erecting lens, located between the objective and the eyepiece. Ray diagrams for such a terrestrial telescope are shown in Fig. 16-21. In (a) locating rays have been drawn from the top of the object to locate the image in each successive lens. Once the images have been located using standard rays it is possible to trace any ray through all lenses as shown in (b). To produce symmetry the object and images in (b) have been shifted so that they are bisected by the axis. That changes nothing as long as image locations and relative sizes are preserved. Magnification is provided by the objective, L_1, and eyepiece, L_2, as in the astronomical refractor. The intermediate erecting lens L_3 does not contribute to the magnification, but makes the final image erect by inverting the image formed by the objective.

BINOCULARS

The term "binocular" implies having one telescopic tube for each eye. In that sense opera glasses are binoculars. However, the term is usually reserved for the instrument using prisms that is illustrated in Fig. 16-22. One such tube is called a monocular. Total internal reflection in the two prisms provides two advantages: the final image is erect, and the tube length is reduced without loss of magnification. The prisms are placed so that the tube of the telescope is "folded". In a typical small binocular the eyepiece is about 10 cm from the objective; without the prisms the distance would have to be about 18 cm.

The reflecting faces of the prisms in a binocular are the arms of the right angle rather than the hypotenuse as in the periscope. The inversion produced by one prism used this way is illustrated in Fig. 16-23(a). The two prisms in a binocular are crossed as shown in Fig. 16-23(b) to produce a vertical and a lateral inversion. In one tube of a binocular the objective lens would produce an inverted image, but the prism arrangement makes it erect. Then the eyepiece produces an erect virtual image. Such an arrangement of prisms can be used in the eyepiece assembly of telescopes used for spotting, to produce an erect final image.

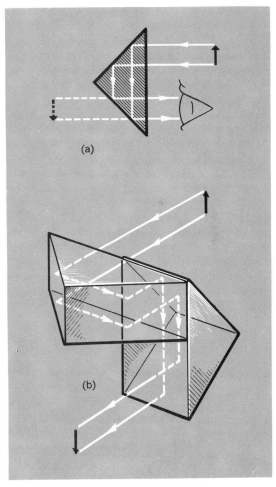

FIG. 16-23

FIG. 16-24. ELECTROMAGNETIC WAVES

When an electric charge moves it generates a magnetic field around it. If the charge accelerates, the magnetic field increases in intensity. A changing magnetic field produces an electric field (electromagnetic induction). When a charge oscillates, its acceleration changes continuously. That produces a changing magnetic field, which produces a changing electric field, which produces a changing magnetic field, which. . . . These changing fields radiate out into space as waves travelling at a speed of 3.0×10^8 m/s, in a way that is crudely illustrated in (a).

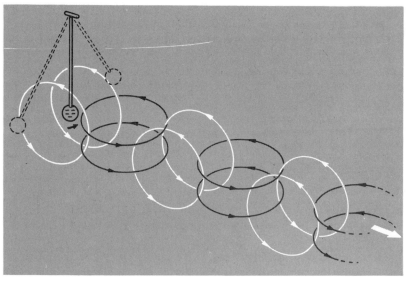

a

These are **electromagnetic waves**, predicted by James C. Maxwell in 1865 and produced by Heinrich Hertz is 1888. The known frequencies in the electromagnetic wave spectrum range from almost zero to more than 10^{23} Hz. Although frequency and wavelength provide the major distinguishing characteristics of electromagnetic waves, there is a tremendous variety in the devices by which electromagnetic waves are produced and detected in different regions of the spectrum. The whole range is illustrated in (b), where the horizontal bars define the ranges of particular portions of the spectrum. The two white bands indicate ranges of frequencies to which the earth's atmosphere is transparent. Astronomers can view the heavens through these "windows" using 60 m diameter radio telescopes and 5 m optical telescopes.

The whole range of electromagnetic radiations share the common features of being produced by accelerating charges, and of travelling at the speed of light. Power frequencies of 50 Hz to 60 Hz transmit electrical energy along wires. Unless the power lines are very long (10^3 km or more), only small fractions of the electrical energy are lost by 60 Hz radiation. The range of frequencies for radio communication extend from 10 kHz for marine use to as much as 100 GHz for microwave transmissions. In between are the bands used for standard AM broadcasting, short wave, and television and FM broadcasting.

Extremely high frequency microwaves are indistinguishable in nature from the radiations from warm objects—the infrared radiations produced by molecular vibrations. As temperature rises, the frequency increases from 1 THz to 100 THz, and infrared blends into the range of frequencies visible to humans, 0.4 PHz to 0.8 PHz. Beyond that are the ultraviolet region (1 PHz to 100 PHz), x-rays (10 PHz to 100 EHz), and gamma rays (1 EHz to 10^5 EHz). The distinctions among these overlapping bands are based mainly on the differences in the sources that produce them. In Unit IV you will learn about the modes of production of such radiations by x-ray tubes and nuclear reactions.

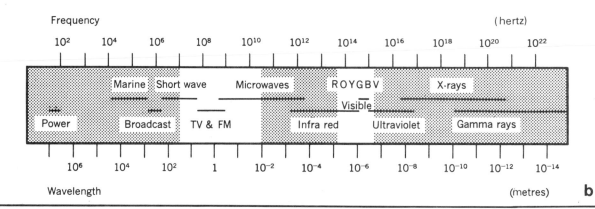

b

Exercises

A

1. Make a table of three columns to compare the parts of a camera and an eye. In one column list the various functions to be performed, and in the other two columns identify the parts of camera and eye respectively that perform each function.

2. What change occurs in the appearance of the image of an object when the aperture of a camera (or the pupil of an eye) is made smaller?

3. (a) What is the limitation in the structure of an eye that determines the nearest distance for which the eye can form a clear image?
   (b) How does this limitation change with age?

4. Most of the surface of the body can take a fair amount of misuse without serious harm. Why does any damage to the surface of the eye have such a major effect on sight?

5. A photograph is taken of a person lying on the ground with the person's feet toward the camera. Why do the feet appear unduly large in the picture?

6. Why are slides inserted upside down into a projector?

7. Why must the object being studied under a compound microscope be slightly further from the objective lens than the focal length of the lens?

8. Explain why the distance between the eyepiece and objective lenses in an astronomical telescope must be slightly less than the sum of their focal lengths if the instrument is to function correctly.

9. Referring to the terrestrial telescope in Fig. 16-21, how far from image I_1 should lens L_2 be placed? Why?

10. Popular binoculars for daytime use are often 7 × 35, where the first number refers to the magnification of the instrument, and the second number is the diameter of the objective lens in millimetres. When such binoculars are focused on a distant object it is an experimental fact that the diameter of the circle of light leaving the eyepiece is given by

$$\frac{\text{diameter of objective}}{\text{magnification}} = \frac{35 \text{ mm}}{7} = 5 \text{ mm.}$$

(If a pair of binoculars are available you can easily check this by moving your head back from the eyepiece about 30 cm, and using a transparent ruler.)
   (a) Popular binoculars for night use are often 7 × 50. Calculate the size of the exit pupil for this type of binocular. Suggest a reason why this type would be unsuitable for daytime use.
   (b) Suggest a reason for the fact that powers higher than 7 are rarely used for binoculars.

B

11. The magnification of a single lens used as a magnifying glass varies inversely as the focal length of the lens.
    (a) If a magnifying glass of focal length 10 cm has a magnification of 2.5, what is the value of the constant k in the formula $M = k/f$?
    (b) What magnification would a lens of $f = 3.1$ cm have?
    (c) According to the formula what range of focal lengths would never produce an enlarged virtual image? (Test this prediction if you have a suitable selection of lenses available.)

12. The objective lens of a compound microscope produces a real image with a magnification $h_i/h_o = 40$. The eyepiece lens has a focal length of 2.5 cm.
    (a) What magnification will the eyepiece produce? (Hint: see question 11.)
    (b) What will be the total magnification of the instrument?

13. In a certain astronomical telescope the objective lens has a focal length of 1.0 m. Calculate the magnification of the telescope if it has an eyepiece lens with a focal length of 5.0 cm.

C

14. A certain camera has a lens with a focal length of 8.0 cm. It is being used with a film rated at a speed of 50. Under a certain illumination the camera is set to an aperture of diameter 0.50 cm and a shutter speed of 1/50 s.
    (a) Calculate the $f/$ number for that aperture.
    (b) With the same film and illumination, what $f/$ number would be required for an action shot that required a shutter speed of 1/200 s?
    (c) With a film that is eight times as fast (rated at a speed of 400), what shutter speed should be used with the same aperture as in (a) and the same illumination?
    (d) What should be done if the fastest shutter speed available is 1/200 s?

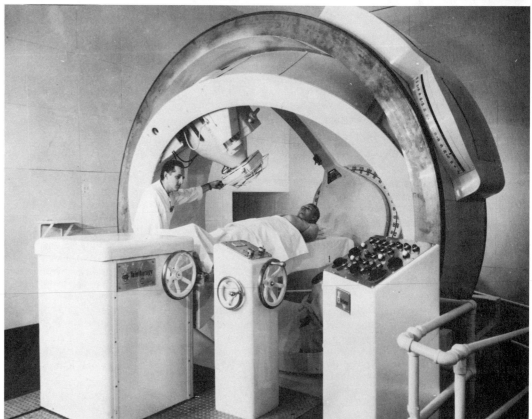

A light patch on an x-ray film reveals that a patient has a tumour in the abdomen. Tests show that the tumour is malignant. The patient's doctor consults a radiologist who recommends treating the tumour with radiation. He proposes cobalt therapy, using the high-energy radiation from cobalt that has been activated by neutrons in a nuclear reactor. The doctor authorizes the radiologist to proceed with the case. Then he goes along to observe on closed-circuit television a new surgical procedure using a laser as the cutting tool.

Modern medical practice, like many other aspects of life today, depends greatly on devices that are the fruits of the physicists' investigations of atoms and nuclei. In this unit you will learn about the basic experimental and theoretical developments in physics during the twentieth century that have so enlarged human knowledge of the fundamental structure of matter.

Atoms consist of nuclei surrounded by electrons. Your study in this unit will proceed from an analysis of the arrangements of electrons in atoms to an examination of the electronic and solid-state devices that lie at the heart of television, radios, and stereos. Then you will go on to study nuclear structures and reactions, from which originate the radiations used in medical treatment and in the generation of electrical energy.

IV

Energy in Atoms

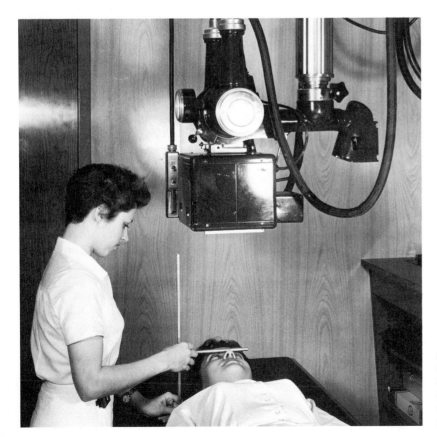

(Upper left) Equipment used to monitor the activity of the heart of a cardiac patient.
(Lower left) Gamma rays from radioactive cobalt in this therapy unit can be concentrated on the patient's cancerous tumour.
(Right) Preparing to take a skull x-ray.

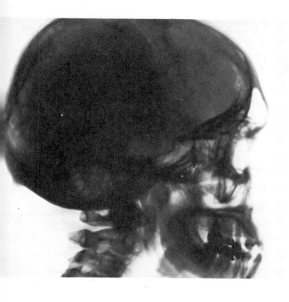

CHAPTER 17

The Discovery of New Rays

For physics, the twentieth century began in the last decade of the 1800s. The new ideas in physics did not appear overnight, nor did the new experiments take place simultaneously. Yet in fact the time span between the landmark experiments was surprisingly short. In 1895 the German physicist Roentgen observed x-rays. In the same year the French scientist Henri Becquerel discovered radioactivity, a process by which unstable atoms emit alpha (α), beta (β), or gamma (γ) rays (subsequently shown to be cores of helium atoms, electrons, and high-energy x-rays respectively—see Chapter 22). In 1897 the British physicist J. J. Thomson's experiments established electrons as constituents of all matter. In this chapter, x-rays and electrons will be discussed. Both are closely connected with the conduction of electricity in gases, and therefore this phenomenon will be dealt with first.

THE CONDUCTION OF ELECTRICITY THROUGH GASES

The most familiar example of electrical conduction in a gas is the neon lamp, and the most awe-inspiring, the lightning flash. In the latter, about 20 C of negative charge may pass in 10^{-2} s from a cloud to the earth, perhaps 3 km below.

In the laboratory the extent to which a spark can jump between two surfaces can be used as a measure of the potential difference between the surfaces. For example, a spark 4 cm in length will occur between two 2.5-cm diameter spheres if the potential difference between them is 7×10^4 V. With flat surfaces a potential difference of about 3×10^4 V is required for each centimetre that the surfaces are apart.

In the apparatus shown in Fig. 17-1 a high-voltage source is connected to a pair of spheres in parallel with two metal electrodes. These electrodes are sealed into the ends of a glass tube about 40 cm long which may be evacuated by a pump. The gap between the spheres is adjusted so that at atmospheric pressure sparks pass between them. The pressure is then reduced in the tube. Interesting effects are quickly seen. When the pressure in the discharge tube is down to one-tenth of atmospheric pressure (10 kPa) thin violet

A typical thundercloud may have a potential of 10^8 V with respect to the earth.

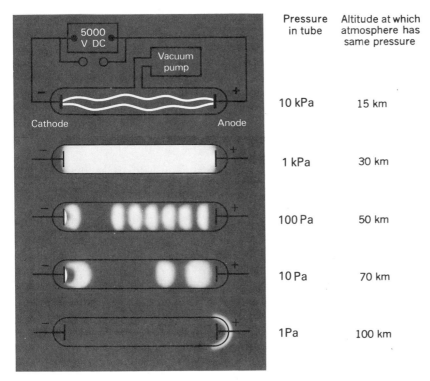

Pressure in tube	Altitude at which atmosphere has same pressure
10 kPa	15 km
1 kPa	30 km
100 Pa	50 km
10 Pa	70 km
1 Pa	100 km

FIG. 17-1

strands join the electrodes, and sparks no longer pass between the spheres because the gas in the tube is now a better conductor than the outside air. At 1 kPa a glow almost fills the tube and at 0.1 kPa one or more dark spaces appear within the tube; these expand as the pressure decreases. At 0.1 Pa (or one millionth of atmospheric pressure) the glow disappears completely, but a strong green light emanates from the glass at one end of the tube.

This kind of observation of the effects that occur when an electric current passes through a discharge tube was first made about the middle of the nineteenth century, when sources of high voltage (induction coils based on the principle of the transformer) and efficient vacuum pumps became available. For the remainder of the century a number of workers studied gaseous conduction, although many people thought that while the effects were very pretty, they were pretty useless. Nevertheless, persistence was rewarded, and, as so often happens, these investigations led to fundamental discoveries about the nature of matter and electricity.

CATHODE RAYS

In 1859, Geissler and Pluecker in Germany attributed the glow of fluorescence at the end of a highly evacuated conducting tube to rays traversing the length of the tube from the negative electrode or cathode. Confirmation of this came from later work, and by 1880 Sir

FIG. 17-2. The Maltese-cross obstacle casts a sharp shadow in the beam of cathode rays.

FIG. 17-3. When the magnet is removed the electron beam will be horizontal.

William Crookes in England summarized the properties of these rays (which are called **cathode rays**) as follows:

1. Cathode rays are emitted from the negative electrode of a highly evacuated tube.
2. They travel in straight lines past solid obstacles (Fig. 17-2).
3. On striking a solid, the cathode rays transfer energy to it. This is shown by a rise in temperature, and by the fluorescence of some materials.
4. The deflection of the rays in a magnetic field shows that they are negatively charged (Fig. 17-3).

By this time it was abundantly clear to scientists that negatively charged particles were emitted from the cathode of a highly evacuated tube. However, there were some who thought that there were two distinct effects, and that the cathode rays were different from the charged particles. These scientists considered that the cathode rays were, in fact, a form of electromagnetic radiation. This point of view was shown to be incorrect by the researches of J. J. Thomson during the last five years of the nineteenth century. By observing carefully what happened when electric and magnetic fields were applied to the tube, he showed that the behaviour of the cathode rays was exactly the same as that which could be attributed to negatively charged particles. There was thus no reason left to distinguish between them.

DISCOVERY OF ELECTRONS

In 1897, Thomson applied electric and magnetic fields of measurable size to a beam of cathode rays as shown in Fig. 17-4. The speed of the charged particles, their mass, and the charge on them would all affect the degree to which they were deflected by (a) the electric field and (b) the magnetic field. Thus by measuring the deflection of the beam of particles, Thomson was able to establish two equations containing three unknown quantities: the velocity v, the charge e, and the mass m. From his calculations he found that v was about one-

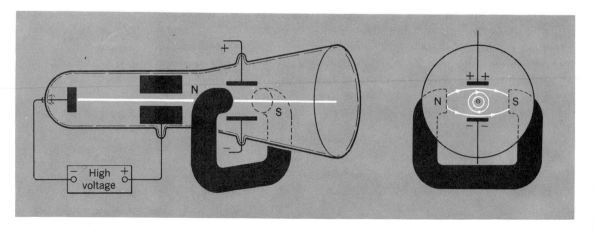

FIG. 17-4

tenth of the speed of light, but he could not obtain separate values for m and e. He could only get values for m/e. This quotient was about 6×10^{-12} kg/C. Whatever the material of the cathode, and whatever the nature of the residual unevacuated gas in the tube, Thomson found approximately the same value for m/e.

Although he was not able to calculate m or e separately, Thomson had shown clearly that the cathode rays must consist of material particles with mass and negative charge. These particles were labelled **electrons**. Thomson was convinced that these electrons must be part of all atoms of matter, and devised a model of the atom based on his ideas (see Chapter 18).

The magnitude of m/e was much smaller than had ever been measured for any particle. The smallest value of a particle's mass per unit charge previously measured was that for the hydrogen ion, about 10^{-8} kg/C. If electrons and hydrogen ions have charges of the same magnitude (though the electron charge is negative and the charge of the hydrogen ion is positive) then electrons must have about 1/2000 of the mass of hydrogen ions.

It can thus be concluded that cathode rays consist of material particles carrying a negative charge. These particles, electrons, have less than a thousandth of the mass of the lightest atoms. In a cathode-ray beam they travel at speeds greater than 10^7 m/s, with the actual value depending on the voltage producing the rays.

EXPLANATION OF GASEOUS CONDUCTION

An electric current is a movement of charge. A gas consists of moving particles, but for there to be a current these particles must be charged. In a discharge tube such as the one described at the beginning of this chapter, a free electron is accelerated by the electric field across the tube, thus gaining energy. When it collides with a gas atom it may be able to knock an electron out of the atom. This means that there are now three charged particles — the original electron, the new electron which has been knocked out of the atom, and the positively charged ion which is an atom with an electron missing. All of these particles tend to move in the electric field and thus contribute to the current as shown in Fig. 17-5. The frequent repetition of this process results in a plentiful supply of moving charged particles.

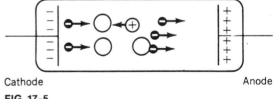

Cathode   Anode

FIG. 17-5

Consider what may happen to one electron starting off near the negative electrode. The electron is accelerated away from the electrode, picking up energy, and after it has travelled a certain distance the electron will have so much energy that if it collides with a gas molecule it will be able to transfer all this energy to the molecule. The molecule may subsequently emit this energy in the form of light, giving rise to a glow. Because the electron has lost its energy, it will not be able to excite another molecule until it has gone a sufficient distance down the tube again, once more picking up energy from the electric field. Thus, the electron will excite molecules (causing them to glow) at intervals down the tube. These striations, or alternating bright and dark patches, are actually found in the tube (Fig. 17-1). This explains what is seen at a pressure of 0.1 kPa. Similar explanations can be given for the effects seen at other pressures.

THE ELECTRONIC CHARGE

In 1897, reporting his investigations of cathode rays, J. J. Thomson wrote: "The smallness of m/e may be due to the smallness of m or the largeness of e, or to a combination of these two." Subsequent research made it apparent that the difference in m/e for electrons and hydrogen ions was entirely due to the greater mass of the hydrogen ion. To be able to describe electrons fully, scientists were anxious to know the values of m and e separately. This could be done only if one of them could be calculated independently, but early attempts to measure e were not very successful.

In 1911, R. A. Millikan in the United States devised a technique for measuring the charge on one individual droplet of oil. A droplet of oil with a radius of about 10^{-6} m will fall through air at a constant speed of about 10^{-4} m/s. If the drop picks up a charge by contact with an ion in the air, it can be acted on by an electric force. In Millikan's apparatus (Fig. 17-6) such a droplet is admitted into the space between two large brass plates. A battery can be connected to the plates through a switch so that the upper plate is given an opposite charge to that on the droplet. The electric force will then cause the droplet to move upwards. If the time is measured for the droplet to move a known distance, its speed can be calculated.

The battery is then switched off, permitting the droplet to fall. The time for it to fall the same known distance is also measured. This operation can be repeated indefinitely. From time to time the drop picks up another ion, or loses one, changing its charge and its speed of rise. From the calculated speeds, the voltage of the battery, and

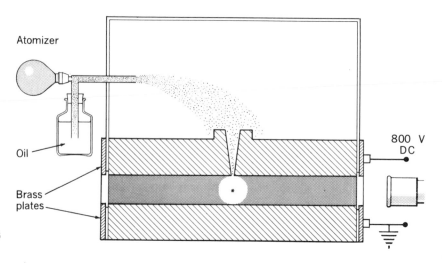

Atomizer

Oil

Brass
plates

800 V
DC

FIG. 17-6

the physical properties of the oil and air, it is possible to calculate the charge on the droplet at various times.

Every value of charge calculated in experiments of this kind is found to be very closely an integral multiple of a smallest charge (the **elementary electric charge**). The currently accepted value of the elementary electric charge is $e = 1.6022 \times 10^{-19}$ C. The charge on an electron is $-e$; the charge on a positive hydrogen ion, or proton, is $+e$.

THE RADIATION CALLED X

In 1895 Wilhelm Roentgen in Germany was experimenting with the glow of light produced in certain materials by cathode rays. He was following up some work by Philipp Lenard who had constructed a discharge tube with a thin aluminum window at the end opposite to the cathode. Cathode rays from within the tube passed through the aluminum and caused a fluorescent screen, just beyond the window, to glow. Roentgen decided to investigate the conditions necessary for the production of this glow outside the tube. He prepared a screen of paper covered with a phosphorescent salt (a material which glows when struck with light or elementary particles). Leaving the screen on a bench he completely covered an evacuated tube with a close-fitting sheath of black cardboard. He took this precaution to prevent any glow within the tube itself from confusing the effect on the screen. With the room darkened he connected a high-voltage supply to the tube's electrodes to test the tube before setting up the screen in front of the tube. As he moved to disconnect the apparatus his eye was caught by a faint shimmer of light. The light remained for as long as the tube was connected, although the covering of the tube was perfectly opaque. When he lit a match, Roentgen discovered that the light had come from his phosphor screen lying on the bench near the apparatus. He immediately surmised that he had observed a new phenomenon since cathode rays could not penetrate more than a few centimetres into air at normal atmospheric pressure.

This discovery was made on 8 November 1895. Roentgen immediately set out to determine the circumstances of this new occurrence, and published a report at the end of December of that year. In a footnote he wrote: "For brevity's sake I shall use the expression 'rays'; and to distinguish them from others of this name I shall call them 'x-rays'." In his report Roentgen described his conclusions about the properties of **x-rays**:

1. They are produced by the impact of cathode rays on the glass wall of the discharge tube.
2. Many materials are quite transparent to x-rays. Denser materials are generally less transparent. The greater the thickness of a material the more absorbent it is.
3. A number of materials such as glass, rock salt and calcium compounds emit light when exposed to x-rays.
4. X-rays can expose photographic film.
5. Pinhole images can be formed, and sharp shadows cast.

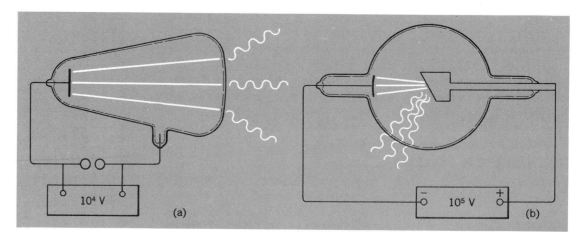

FIG. 17-7. Early x-ray tubes used cold cathodes. (a) Originally the x-rays were produced by the collision of electrons with the glass tube. (b) Later, a heavy-metal anode was introduced to increase the output of x-rays.

A slight refraction of x-rays was later observed. Eventually, diffraction and interference effects were also observed.

6. X-rays cannot be reflected or refracted or produce interference effects.

7. The x-rays can be distinguished from cathode rays since x-rays are not deflected by even very intense magnetic fields.

Several months later Roentgen reported observations that x-rays could cause the discharge of either positively or negatively charged objects, and that they were produced most effectively from the impact of cathode rays on targets of high density. This led to the design of tubes specifically for the production of x-rays (Fig. 17-7).

The penetrating effects of x-rays were soon being widely applied in medical diagnoses. However, physicists could not agree about the nature of x-rays. Some thought they were streams of particles, others that they were very high-frequency wave radiations. By 1912, von Laue in Germany and Bragg in England had demonstrated the interference of x-rays in crystals. The rows of atoms in a crystal provide the "slits" that cause incident x-rays to produce the patterns that are characteristic of waves interfering.

The evidence of these experiments was that x-rays have wavelengths of the order of 10^{-10} m. The corresponding frequency is thus

Recall that $c = f\lambda$, where c is the speed of light.

$$f = \frac{c}{\lambda} = \frac{3 \times 10^8 \text{ m/s}}{1 \times 10^{-10} \text{ m}} = 3 \times 10^{18} \text{ Hz}.$$

In contrast to the results of these experiments showing that x-rays were wave-like, during the first two decades of the twentieth century other theoretical and experimental evidence accumulated that radiation had a particle-like nature.

PARTICLE-LIKE WAVES

We will consider first the **photoelectric effect**. This was first seen by Hertz in 1887 during experiments with radio waves. He observed that his receiver worked better when it was illuminated by sparks from the transmitter; subsequently it was shown that ultraviolet light from the sparks was causing electrons to be ejected from the metal of the receiver, a process called **photoemission**. Since it takes energy to remove an electron from the metal (the amount is called the **work function**) it was reasonable to conjecture that shining light energy on the metal caused electrons to come out. Such photoemission can be made to take place from all materials and, as expected, the greater the intensity of the ultraviolet light, the greater the number of electrons emitted. However, and this was totally unexpected, there was found to be a frequency threshold below which no electrons were ejected. The value of this cut-off frequency was found to depend on the material under investigation (Fig. 17-8). If the *quality* of the radiation wasn't good enough, no increase in quantity could release an electron.

In 1905 Einstein produced an explanation of these phenomena based on the quantum theory which had just been introduced by the German physicist Max Planck (1900). To explain the energy distribution of radiation emitted by a hot body, Planck had introduced the idea that energy came in packets, or **quanta**. The energy associated with each quantum is given by multiplying the frequency (*f*) of the radiation by a universal constant *(h)*. The universal constant, known as Planck's constant, is $h = 6.63 \times 10^{-34}$ J·s. Thus, the relation between energy (*E*) and frequency (*f*) used by Planck and Einstein is

$$E = hf.$$

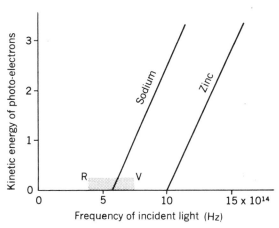

FIG. 17-8

Shorter wavelength light, which has higher frequency, therefore comes in higher energy packets than does light of longer wavelength.

Einstein proposed that each individual packet of energy, or **photon** as it is generally called, can transfer its energy to one electron in the surface of the material illuminated. If the photon's energy is less than the work function (*W*) of the material, no electron can escape from the surface. If the photon's energy is greater than *W* an electron may be emitted, the difference between *hf* and *W* being supplied to the electron as kinetic energy. Einstein's work explained all the known details of the photoelectric effect. His proposal ascribed to radiation a packet or particle-like nature. However, while many physicists accepted the mathematics of Einstein's explanation, they rejected the idea that radiation was particle-like.

Then in 1922 the American physicist Arthur Compton performed experiments with x-rays which unexpectedly confirmed Einstein's theory. It seemed as if single x-rays were colliding with single electrons, just as if each were a particle (Fig. 17-9). Again the numbers worked out correctly for the Compton effect if the photons of frequency (*f*) were regarded as packets of energy *hf*. Thus radiation must be regarded as having both wave-like and particle-like properties.

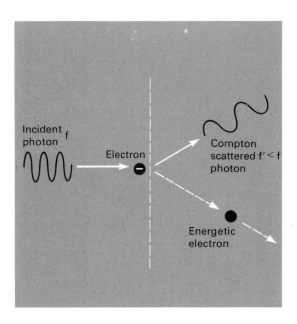

FIG. 17-9. The incident photon gives up some energy to move the electron. As a result, the energy (and frequency) of the x-ray photon is reduced by the amount of the kinetic energy transferred to the electron.

ENERGY OF RAYS

The energy of an x-ray photon of frequency 3.0×10^{18} Hz is

$$E = hf = (6.63 \times 10^{-34} \text{ J·s}) (3.0 \times 10^{18} \text{ s}^{-1})$$

$$= 2.0 \times 10^{-15} \text{ J}.$$

This energy is supplied in an x-ray tube by an electron accelerated through a potential difference V. That potential difference can be calculated from

$$V = \frac{E}{Q} = \frac{2.0 \times 10^{-15} \text{ J}}{1.6 \times 10^{-19} \text{ C}} = 1.2 \times 10^4 \text{ V}.$$

Thus, if an electron is accelerated through 12 kV and loses all its energy in one collision, it can produce a photon of 3.0×10^{18} Hz.

In atomic physics, it is convenient to have an energy unit much smaller than the joule. The one that is widely used is the **electronvolt** (eV), which is the energy acquired by one electron in moving through a potential difference of one volt. The number of joules equivalent to one electronvolt can be found as follows:

$$E = QV = 1 \text{ eV} = (1.6 \times 10^{-19} \text{ C})(1.0 \text{ V}) = 1.6 \times 10^{-19} \text{ J}.$$

Thus the conversion factor between joules and electronvolts is 1.6 $\times 10^{-19}$ J/eV. For the electron accelerated through a potential difference of 1.2×10^4 V, the energy is

$$E = QV = \frac{(1.6 \times 10^{-19} \text{ C})(1.2 \times 10^4 \text{ J/C})}{1.6 \times 10^{-19} \text{ J/eV}} = 1.2 \times 10^4 \text{ eV}.$$

The energy of the 3.0×10^{18} Hz photon is also 1.2×10^4 eV.

Planck's constant expressed with the energy units in electronvolts is

$$h = \frac{6.63 \times 10^{-34} \text{ J·s}}{1.60 \times 10^{-19} \text{ J/eV}} = 4.14 \times 10^{-15} \text{ eV·s}.$$

Example: Calculate the energy in electronvolts of a visible light photon of wavelength equal to 5.3×10^{-7} m (middle green).

First, find the frequency of the light,

$$f = \frac{c}{\lambda} = \frac{3.0 \times 10^8 \text{ m/s}}{5.3 \times 10^{-7} \text{ m}} = 5.7 \times 10^{14} \text{ Hz}.$$

Then, find the energy,

$$E = hf = (4.14 \times 10^{-15} \text{ eV·s})(5.7 \times 10^{14} \text{ s}^{-1}) = 2.4 \text{ eV}.$$

Thus a "green photon" has an energy of 2.4 eV. Under the right conditions, green light can be produced when an electron is accelerated across a potential difference of 2.4 V.

Energies of photons in the visible range extend approximately from 1.7 eV to 3.1 eV. In the x-ray region, 1000 to 1 000 000 eV, the kilo-electronvolt, keV, is used, and in nuclear physics the mega-electronvolt, or MeV, is the common unit of energy.

Exercises

A

1. Use the material of this chapter to tell in a sentence or two what each of the following scientists discovered or proved:
   (a) Roentgen
   (b) Becquerel
   (c) J. J. Thomson
   (d) Crookes
   (e) Millikan
   (f) Von Laüe and Bragg
   (g) Hertz
   (h) Einstein
   (i) Planck

2. What are cathode rays?

3. (a) What is an anode? A cathode?
   (b) A long glass tube with an electrode sealed into each end contains oxygen gas at low pressure (about 10 Pa). Within the tube there are neutral atoms and molecules of oxygen, free electrons, positive oxygen ions (atoms lacking one or more electrons), and negative oxygen ions (atoms to which one or more electrons have become attached). Draw a sketch to show which of the particles mentioned would move toward the anode and which toward the cathode, if the tube were connected to a high-voltage direct-current source.

4. What causes striations in a low pressure discharge tube?

5. Draw an end-on view of a cathode-ray tube like the one used by J. J. Thomson (see Fig. 17-4). Include the deflecting plates, and show the charge on them necessary to move the electron beam down.

6. Repeat question 5, but now use electromagnets as the deflection system, and show the magnetic polarity necessary to move the electron beam down.

7. (a) What are x-rays?
   (b) How are they produced?

8. List four differences between cathode rays and x-rays.

9. Explain the meaning of each term in the formula $E = hf$.

10. State the value of the quantum by which the score can increase in (a) a basketball game in which no foul shots are permitted, (b) a football game in which only touchdowns are counted, (c) a hockey game.

11. (a) What is the quantum of money by which the contents of the collection box in a soft-drink dispenser increases in value?
    (b) What is the quantum of money by which the value of your bank account can change?

12. What is meant by the *work function* of a material?

13. What are photons?

14. The photoelectric effect showed that light is quantized. What experiment showed that electric charge is quantized?

15. Define electronvolt.

B

For Planck's constant use $h = 6.6 \times 10^{-34}$ J·s,
$= 4.1 \times 10^{-15}$ eV·s.

16. If about 20 000 V/cm are required to produce a spark in air at atmospheric pressure, calculate
    (a) the potential difference required to produce a spark 6 cm long,
    (b) the length of the spark that could be produced by a potential difference of 300 000 V.

17. The quotient of mass divided by charge for an electron is approximately 6×10^{-12} kg/C, and for a hydrogen ion, approximately 1×10^{-8} kg/C. Calculate the ratio of the mass of a hydrogen ion to that of an electron. What assumption is made in this calculation?

18. The quotient of mass divided by charge for an electron is 5.7×10^{-12} kg/C. The charge of the electron is 1.6×10^{-19} C. Calculate the mass of the electron.

19. The quotient of mass divided by charge for a hydrogen ion is 1.04×10^{-8} kg/C. The charge of the ion is 1.60×10^{-19} C. Calculate the mass of the hydrogen ion.

20. A clean zinc plate is attached to the top of a charged electroscope (see Fig. 7-13). A carbon arc lamp, which produces both visible and ultraviolet radiation, shines through a transparent block onto the zinc plate. Make a table to show the action of the vane of the electroscope (a) when the electroscope is initially positively charged and (b) when the electroscope is initially negatively charged, in the following circumstances:
    (i) when the transparent block is made of glass, which does not transmit ultraviolet radiation,
    (ii) when the transparent block is made of quartz, which does transmit ultraviolet radiation.

21. Calculate the energy in electronvolts of the quantum of radiation of each of the following electromagnetic radiations, having the frequencies indicated:
    (a) a broadcast radio wave, $f = 1.0 \times 10^6$ Hz,
    (b) a radio microwave, $f = 1.0 \times 10^{10}$ Hz,
    (c) infrared light, $f = 3.0 \times 10^{14}$ Hz,
    (d) ultraviolet light, $f = 1.0 \times 10^{15}$ Hz,
    (e) x-ray, $f = 3.0 \times 10^{17}$ Hz.

22. The wavelength of a blue-green electromagnetic radiation is 5.0×10^{-7} m.
    (a) Calculate the frequency of the radiation.
    (b) Calculate the energy, in electronvolts, of a quantum of the radiation.

23. The frequency of a blue-violet radiation is 7.0×10^{14} Hz. Calculate the energy, in electronvolts, of a quantum of this radiation.

24. Calculate the frequency and wavelength of the radiation having a quantum of energy 1.0 eV. Where is this in the electromagnetic spectrum?

25. (a) What is the frequency of x-rays of wavelength 2.4×10^{-11} m?
    (b) What is the minimum operating voltage required in an x-ray tube to produce x-rays of this wavelength?

C

26. The aurorae borealis (northern lights) are the result of electrical discharges in the upper atmosphere. Can you explain their appearance in terms of the discussion in this chapter on conduction in gases?

27. A frequently used unit of energy in nuclear physics is the megaelectronvolt: 1 MeV $= 10^6$ eV. The frequency of a certain gamma-ray photon is 1.0×10^{21} Hz. Calculate the energy of this photon in (a) joules, (b) electronvolts, (c) MeV.

28. (a) Calculate the energy, in joules, of an electron (elementary charge, $e = 1.6 \times 10^{-19}$ C) as it strikes the face of a television picture tube after travelling through a potential difference of 1.5×10^3 V.

(b) If the electron were to give up all of its energy in one collision to produce an x-ray photon, calculate the frequency of the radiation.
(c) Calculate the wavelength of the radiation (the speed of light $c = 3.0 \times 10^8$ m/s).

29. In a 100 000 V x-ray tube the energy of electrons striking the target is 10^5 eV. Planck's constant is $h = 4 \times 10^{-15}$ eV·s. Calculate the maximum frequency and minimum wavelength of the most energetic x-ray that can be produced.

30. From research in an encyclopedia or other book, write a note of one or two paragraphs on some of the applications of x-rays in modern medicine or industry.

31. The electronvolt is an energy unit that has an appropriate size for describing events at the atomic level: 1 eV $= 1.6 \times 10^{-19}$ J. The amount of energy that must be supplied to release an electron from the surface of a metal is 1.9 eV for cesium, 2.3 eV for sodium, 3.2 eV for calcium, and 3.8 eV for zinc. Only photons with energy in excess of these respective values can liberate electrons from the metals' surfaces. Several approximate photon energies are 2.1 eV for red light, 2.7 eV for green light, and 3.4 eV for violet light. State which colours of light will be able to liberate electrons from the surface of each metal in the list.

32. In his work on the photoelectric effect Einstein established that the energy of a photon of light had to be sufficient to supply the work function of the metal in order for an electron to be emitted. Any excess of the photon's energy over the work function was supplied to the electron as kinetic energy. Suppose that photons of blue light of energy 2.9 eV illuminate the surface of cesium which has a work function of 1.9 eV.
    (a) What is the kinetic energy, in electronvolts, of each emitted electron?
    (b) Express the kinetic energy of each emitted electron in joules.
    (c) Calculate the speed of each emitted electron, given that the mass of an electron is 9×10^{-31} kg.

33. The Einstein photoelectric equation states that the kinetic energy of an emitted electron is equal to the energy of the incident photon minus the work function (W) of the metal, or

$$\tfrac{1}{2} mv^2 = hf - W.$$

If the frequency of a certain ultraviolet radiation is 1.5×10^{15} Hz, and the work function of sodium is 3.5×10^{-19} J, calculate the speed of electrons emitted from sodium by the radiation. Use $h = 6.6 \times 10^{-34}$ J·s, and $m = 9.1 \times 10^{-31}$ kg.

34. Use an encyclopedia or other books to find out about the following methods by which electrons can be liberated from the surface of a metal: (a) thermionic emission, (b) field ion emission, (c) secondary emission.

CHAPTER 18

The Structure of Atoms

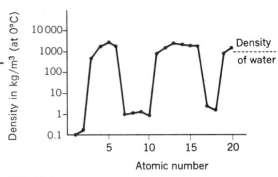

FIG. 18-1

As the twentieth century dawned, the experiments with electrons led physicists to become more involved with chemistry than they had been. During the preceding century atoms had been primarily of interest to chemists working out the structure of matter, but now physicists began to work out the structure of atoms themselves.

By the nineteenth century, chemists had identified most of the elements of which matter is composed—hydrogen, carbon, oxygen, iron, copper, etc. The atomic theory of John Dalton of England (about 1805) proposed that there existed indivisible chemical **atoms** characteristic of each element, that for any element all the atoms are identical in mass and size, and that chemical compounds are made by the joining together of the individual atoms of different elements in pairs, triplets or larger combinations. This theory was the basis for establishing molecular formulae such as H_2O for water and Fe_3O_4 for magnetic iron oxide. A notable feature is that the atomic masses of many elements are nearly whole number multiples of the atomic mass of hydrogen.

Later in the century (1868), the Russian chemist Mendeleev arranged the known elements by putting them in order of increasing atomic mass. He then placed elements in rows and columns, with all the elements in the same column having similar properties, including density (see Fig. 18-1) and valency. Because Mendeleev's table underlines the fact that chemical properties are repeated at fairly regular intervals as the masses of the atoms increase, it is called the **Periodic Table**.

For your study of atomic structure there are several terms to be noted. The first is that the numerical place of an element in the Periodic Table is called its **atomic number**, symbol Z (Table 18-1). The second is that the masses of atoms are expressed in **unified atomic mass units** (u), where

$$1 \text{ u} = 1.660 \times 10^{-27} \text{ kg}.$$

The mass of one hydrogen atom is 1.0078 u, and of one aluminum atom 26.98 u. Finally, for descriptive purposes, we use the **atomic**

Table 18-1

Element	Z
hydrogen	1
carbon	6
oxygen	8
aluminum	13
iron	26
copper	29
uranium	92

mass number, symbol A, which is the whole number nearest to an atom's atomic mass expressed in the unit u. Thus for hydrogen, A is 1 and for aluminum $A = 27$.

ATOMIC MODELS

You saw in Chapter 17 that the electrons that come out of atoms have a negative charge and a r ıss which is a tiny fraction of the mass of the whole atom. What remains behind is much more massive and is positively charged. What arrangement of the parts of an atom can include these features, as well as accounting for the stability that permits atoms to continue in existence for long periods of time?

Two possible pictures for holding together the parts of the atom achieved prominence, though others were suggested in the early years of this century. One of these two is the concentration of the heavy positively charged particles into a core or **nucleus** at the centre of the atom, with the electrons in orbit around this nucleus, like planets around the sun. This picture has the advantage that some of the electrons will be less tightly bound than others and so it will be possible to remove one electron with comparative ease, two with more difficulty, and so on, in agreement with the observed facts. To keep the atom stable it is necessary for the electrons to rotate round the nucleus, the electric attraction between the positive and negative parts taking the place of the gravitational attraction that exists for example between the sun and the planets.

This **nuclear atom model**, as this theory is called, suffers from the important defect that by the very nature of rotation the electric charges keep changing their direction. In Fig. 18-2 at point A they are going downwards and at point B upwards; this change of direction, which is an acceleration, causes the charges to radiate energy. It may help you to understand this if you remember that if you decelerate your hand by hitting it on a desk, you get a sound, which is a radiation of mechanical energy; when electric charges change their direction, they radiate electrical energy. It is easy to calculate the rate of loss of energy, and it would appear that the electrons should lose all their energy and spiral into the nucleus in a matter of 10^{-8} s. This is clearly absurd, for the atoms are normally stable.

For this and other reasons J. J. Thomson favoured a model of the atom in which the positive charge was spread over the whole volume of the atom, and the electrons distributed throughout the positive charge. This "Thomson atom" is drawn in Fig. 18-3. As it is known that atoms do radiate energy if excited (an electric light is a simple example of such a radiation process), Thomson had to assume that the electrons could oscillate about their mean positions if disturbed in some way.

FIG. 18-2

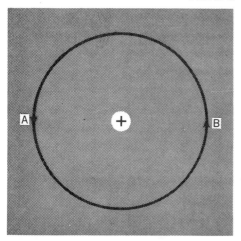

FIG. 18-3

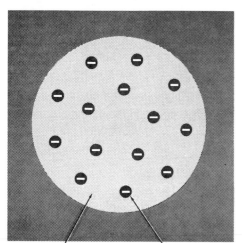

Uniformly distributed positive charge
Negative electrons

DISCOVERY OF THE NUCLEUS

A test to find which picture was right was made in the years about 1910 by the New Zealand physicist Ernest Rutherford and his colleagues. As a probe to see what was inside the atom he used alpha (α) particles that were shot out of radioactive nuclei. First of all he found that α-particles could pass through atoms, which would suggest that as seen from a microscopic point of view the atom is not a continuous thing, but is porous. In these experiments he used thin foils of gold 9×10^{-8} m thick. In such a thickness of gold foil there are 160 layers of atoms, all closely packed together, and yet most of the α-particles passed through the foil undeflected. Some alpha particles were, however, deflected by making collisions with the electric charges in the atom. If the Thomson model were correct, with a uniform positive charge and light negative charges distributed throughout the volume of the atom, it would be expected that the heavy alpha particles would make relatively small-angle collisions with the atoms as in Fig. 18-4(a), in the same way that a big football player could charge through a line of small boys without much effect on his direction of motion. But if the nuclear model were right, there would be a small chance that the α-particle would collide with a body as heavy as or heavier than itself, and in this case it might be deflected from its path by a large angle as in Fig. 18-4(b). The test then was to see if the α-particles were deflected through large angles or not.

The apparatus available in Rutherford's laboratory at that time was relatively primitive—the only way of "seeing" the α-particles was by the flash of light they gave when they hit a zinc sulfide screen. Two of Rutherford's students sat for hours at a time in a darkened room counting the scintillations on a screen (Fig. 18-5) and they

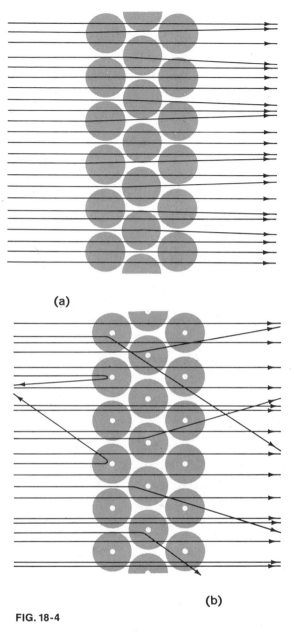

(a)

(b)

FIG. 18-4

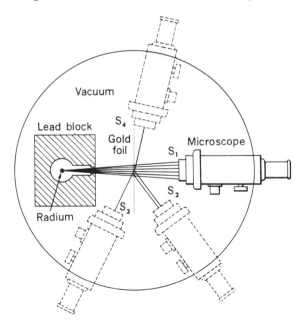

FIG. 18-5: The "S's" show four locations of zinc sulphide screens.

In 1936 Rutherford said of this experiment, "It was quite the most incredible event that has ever happened to me in my life. It was almost as incredible as if you fired a 15-inch shell at a piece of tissue paper and it came back and hit you."

See Fig. 24-13 for *The construction of a cloud chamber.*

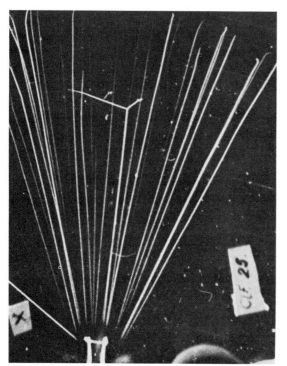

FIG. 18-6

found that from a piece of gold about 1 in 8000 of the incident alpha particles were scattered by angles of more than 90°.

This result made the Thomson atom untenable, and the nuclear atom was accepted as a more correct picture. Actually the Rutherford scattering experiment does not tell whether the nucleus is positive or negative in charge, simply that it is charged and heavy. Combining this with Thomson's results that the electrons were much lighter than the positive particles tells us that indeed the nucleus contains all the positive charge and most of the mass of the atoms. The electrons are then thought of as rotating round this positive core.

Using an instrument called a cloud chamber, it is possible to see the track of an alpha particle going through a gas. The photograph in Fig. 18-6 shows an α-ray deflected by a chlorine nucleus.

Another piece of information that is obtained from the scattering experiments described above is an idea of the size of the nucleus. This depends upon the particular atom measured, but for a typical element the nucleus has a radius of about 5×10^{-15} m and a volume of about 5×10^{-43} m³. This is very small compared with the size of the atom, the radius of which is usually of the order 10^{-10} m.

The reason that most of the alpha particles in Rutherford's experiments went right through the foil is now clear; as the cross-sectional area, πr^2, of the nucleus is only 25×10^{-10} times that of the atom $[\pi(5 \times 10^{-15})^2/\pi(10^{-10})^2]$, it is unlikely that an alpha particle will come anywhere near the nucleus and be deflected by it. The relation between the sizes of the atom and the nucleus can be illustrated by considering what would happen if the atom were magnified so that the nucleus had the size of a pea. An alpha particle would also be the size of a pea but the atom itself would be about 300 m across. The chance of hitting a pea in a large football stadium by throwing another one at random is very small.

The density of the nucleus is extremely high, as almost all the mass of the atom (over 99.9%) is concentrated in the very small nuclear volume. The density of nuclear matter in fact is of the order of 10^{17} kg/m³ as we see above from the relative sizes of the atom and the nucleus. Gross material with this density is found in some parts of the universe—in *neutron stars* matter is so condensed that the whole star can be thought of as one big nucleus.

From the alpha-scattering experiments we can also find the charge on the nucleus—the probability that a large-angle scattering will occur varies directly as the square of the charge on the nucleus. The experiments showed that the nuclear charge varies directly as the atomic number of the elements. In fact, it has been found that the charge on a nucleus is Ze, where Z is the atomic number of the element and e is the elementary electric charge. Thus the nuclear charge is $1e$ for hydrogen, $2e$ for helium, $8e$ for oxygen, $92e$ for uranium and so on.

ELECTRONS IN ORBIT

Despite the necessity for accepting the nuclear model of the atom because of the results of the alpha-scattering experiments, the problem mentioned on page 240 about the radiation of electrical energy expected from the orbiting electrons still existed. In order to get around this difficulty, Niels Bohr (1885-1962) postulated in 1913 that certain **allowed orbits** exist in which electrons would not radiate, in which they could circle forever without losing energy. This postulate was based on the quantum ideas of Planck discussed in Chapter 17.

The trouble was that Bohr's postulate restricted things too much. Atoms do radiate, they do lose energy if they have been excited (if they didn't, it wouldn't be much use switching on a lamp to get light). Moreover, the radiation emitted by atoms of a particular element is very characteristic, peculiar to that element. The light emitted by a heated gas or vapour is of a very definite colour, or, more frequently, a mixture of a few very distinct colours. You can tell with the unaided eye that the yellow colour of the sodium flame is different from the red colour of a neon lamp; instruments which will analyze light more carefully, called spectroscopes, show that the light intensity is concentrated into narrow wavelength or frequency lines, the *spectrum* produced being characteristic of the element (Fig. 18-7).

Even more surprising to scientists was the fact that the different frequencies emitted by, say, hydrogen atoms were numerically related to one another—physicists began to speculate that the atom was like some miniature violin, which could emit notes related to one another by the tension in the strings and the fingering applied to them. Any acceptable model of an atom must be able to explain these connected series of distinct frequencies or, using the relation between frequency and photon energy, to explain these inter-related energies.

To cover the fact that atoms do radiate, Bohr further postulated that an electron can jump from one of the allowed orbits to another with the absorption or emission of energy. In the solar system, an equivalent postulate would say that the only allowed transitions are those from the orbit of one planet to the orbit of another. Neglecting air resistance and so on, the trip from one planet to another nearer the sun results in the release of (gravitational) energy, and the reverse trip requires the using up or absorption of energy.

Working out the radii of the allowed orbits for the single orbiting electron of a hydrogen atom, it is found that they are given by the formula

$$r_n = n^2 \times 0.53 \times 10^{-10} \text{ m}$$

in which n can take the values 1, 2, 3, 4, etc. Corresponding to each of these integers n there is an allowed orbit of radius r_n. The smallest allowed value of n, $n = 1$, gives a value of r which you will see is the same order of magnitude as the radius of the atom which we quoted before. Drawings of the Bohr orbits for hydrogen are given in Fig.

That only certain orbits for electrons are allowed means that the energy of electrons in atoms is quantized (see *Standing waves* in Chapter 12).

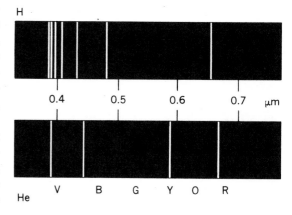

FIG. 18-7

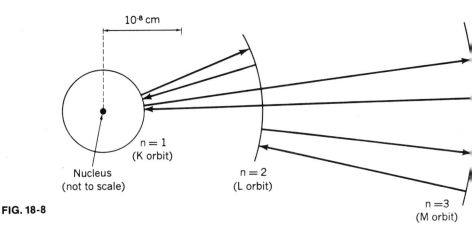

FIG. 18-8

18-8. From the formula for r_n it is clear that the radii must bear to each other the ratios of the squares of the natural numbers, 1, 4, 9, 16 and so on, and this is shown on the diagram. Radiative transitions between different levels are shown by the arrows, and correspond to the jumping of an electron from one level to another.

To each of these orbits corresponds a particular energy, the lowest energy orbit being that with $n = 1$, the one nearest the nucleus. It is found that the energies E_n of the various orbits are given by $E_n = -\text{constant}/n^2$. Thus the energies of the succeeding orbits are in inverse proportion to the square of the natural numbers. As the energy difference between different orbits are of the greatest importance, it is common to draw energy level diagrams as shown in Fig. 18-9. Each level represents the energy associated with an electron in a particular orbit, and from the diagram we can read off the energy of any transition by measuring the length of the arrow joining the two levels under consideration. It will be seen that the levels get closer and closer together as n becomes larger. Finally the separate levels are indistinguishable and merge into a continuum of levels. For conven-

FIG. 18-9

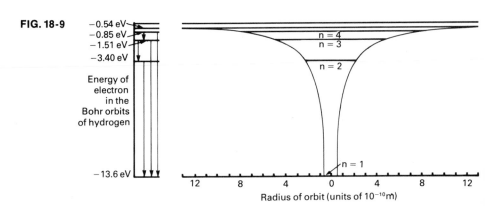

ience, we take the energy of the electron as zero when it is a long way from the nucleus, that is when $n = $ infinity.

You will see that the difference in energy between a level with $n = 1$ and one with $n = 2$ is

$$-\text{constant} \times \left(\frac{1}{1^2} - \frac{1}{2^2} \right),$$

and that the difference in energy between levels 1 and 3 is

$$-\text{constant} \times \left(\frac{1}{1^2} - \frac{1}{3^2} \right).$$

There are, in fact, a whole series of energy level differences which are proportional to $(1 - \frac{1}{4})$, $(1 - \frac{1}{9})$, $(1 - \frac{1}{16})$, and so on. These differences in energy mean that if an electron falls from the second, third or fourth energy levels to the first level, photons of energies proportional to $(1 - \frac{1}{4})$, $(1 - \frac{1}{9})$, and $(1 - \frac{1}{16})$, respectively, will be emitted by the atom. This is just the relationship found experimentally between the energies of different lines in the spectrum of light emitted by hydrogen; the miniature violins are explained!

We have spoken only of electrons falling towards the lowest energy level with the emission of energy, but the reverse process is also possible. In this case, an electron absorbs energy and rises up the energy level diagram to a higher orbit. Such a process is called **excitation** of the atom, and normally it is followed after a very short interval by emission of energy as the electron falls back. If the electron in one of the levels is given energy greater than that necessary to raise it to the continuum (the levels with high values of n), then it escapes entirely from the atom and becomes a free electron. The atom has now a net positive charge and is in fact an ion. The process is therefore called **ionization**, and the least energy required to cause this is the **ionization energy**. In the case of hydrogen, for example (Fig. 18-9), it takes at least 13.6 eV to raise an electron from the $n = 1$ shell and make it a free electron.

Modern theories of matter have caused the abandonment of the idea that, in fact, there are particles going round a nucleus in fixed orbits, though the Bohr model still has great usefulness for grasping what happens in most atomic phenomena. It is now thought that although the positive charge is concentrated in the nucleus, the negative charge is smeared throughout a volume, and the order of magnitude of the radius of this volume is given by the Bohr radius. Pictures of possible configurations of this charge are given in Fig. 18-10.

The use of a model is very common in physics. We do not believe that the atom really looks like the Bohr atom, but this picture acts as an aid to thought, and when it has served its turn it is respectfully put back on the shelf, perhaps to be brought out again in some slightly different form when a new problem arises.

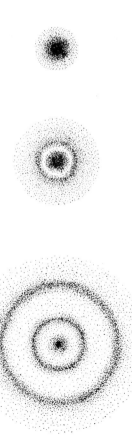

FIG. 18-10

To summarize, it is useful to picture the atom as having at its centre a dense, positively charged nucleus, of radius about 5×10^{-15} m, surrounded by negative electrons, whose distances from the nucleus are about 10^{-10} m. The electrons may be pictured as being allowed only in certain orbits, which have definite energies associated with them. Jumps between these orbits require the absorption or emission of radiation.

Exercises

A

1. Use the material of this chapter to tell in a sentence or two what each of the following scientists discovered or proved:
   (a) Mendeleev   (c) Bohr
   (b) Rutherford

2. What is meant when it is said that "density is a periodic property"?

3. (a) Distinguish between atomic number and atomic mass number.
   (b) What are the atomic numbers (Z) and atomic mass numbers (A) of the following elements:
   (i) helium   (iv) lead
   (ii) carbon   (v) uranium
   (iii) calcium   (vi) lawrencium
         (Hint: Use the Appendix.)

4. What is the mass of an atom of carbon $(Z = 6, A = 12)$ in unified atomic mass units and in kilograms?

5. You are told that there is a certain mass of glass on the top of a table, but not told if the glass is in the form of marbles randomly distributed on the surface or in the form of one large piece of glass in the centre of the table. With some marbles that you can roll along the table, suggest a means by which you can find how the glass is distributed. Assume that you can neither see nor touch the glass on the top of the table.

6. In order to probe the nucleus, Rutherford had to use a tool, the alpha particle, which was of nuclear dimensions. Give three examples taken from everyday life of cases in which this use of the correct size of probe is illustrated (for example, the size of a dentist's drill compared with a cavity in a tooth).

7. What are the essential differences between the Thomson model of the atom and the Rutherford model?

8. (a) How many times larger than the diameter of a typical atom is a person whose height is 2 m? (Hint: Use the atomic radius given on page 243).
   (b) How many times smaller than the diameter of the sun $(14 \times 10^8$ m$)$ is a man whose height is 2 m?

(c) How many times smaller than the diameter of an atom is the diameter of a nucleus?

9. (a) What was a major defect of Rutherford's nuclear atomic model?
   (b) What postulate did Bohr make to modify the Rutherford model to overcome this defect?

10. What is an emission spectrum?

11. What happens to the electron of the hydrogen atom, according to the Bohr theory, when (a) the atom absorbs a certain amount of energy, and (b) it emits a certain amount of energy?

12. What is meant by the terms (a) energy level, (b) the continuum?

13. How can the energy of the light in one of the lines of an emission spectrum be determined from the energy-level diagram (Fig. 18-9) for the emitting atoms?

B

14. On the Rutherford-Bohr model of the hydrogen atom, what are the radii of the orbits with $n = 1, 2, 3, 4$ respectively?

15. In Fig. 18-9 the energy levels of the hydrogen atom are given for $n = 1$ to 5. What are the energies of the levels for (a) $n = 6$, (b) $n = 7$.

16. The lowest energy level of the hydrogen atom has $n = 1$ and an energy of -13.6 eV. Calculate the energy emitted when an electron jumps (a) from level $n = 3$ to level $n = 2$, and (b) from level $n = 4$ to $n = 2$ (the colours of the light emitted in these jumps are red and blue-green respectively).

17. Calculate the frequency of the light emitted when an electron jumps (a) from level $n = 3$ to level $n = 2$, and (b) from $n = 4$ to $n = 2$ in the hydrogen atom.

18. Calculate the frequency of the light emitted when an electron jumps from level $n = 3$ to $n = 1$ in the hydrogen atom. (This jump results in the emission of ultraviolet light.)

19. Calculate the energy required to raise an electron from level $n = 1$ to $n = 4$ in the hydrogen atom.

C

20. (a) The spectrum obtained from singly ionized helium (that is, He which has lost one of its electrons) is very similar to that obtained from hydrogen. However, the ionization energy is much higher, so that the $n = 1$ orbit is at -54.4 eV. Calculate the energies of the $n = 2$ and $n = 3$ orbits for singly ionized He.

    (b) The value -54.4 eV is 4 times that of the ionization potential for the hydrogen atom. What is the reason for this?

21. It is found that the radii of most atomic nuclei are given by the formula $r = (1.2 \times 10^{-15}$ m$)\ \sqrt[3]{A},$ where $\sqrt[3]{A}$ is the cube root of the atomic mass number A. Thus for copper, $A = 64$ and $\sqrt[3]{A} = 4$, and thus $r = 4.8 \times 10^{-15}$ m. Calculate the radii of the nuclei with A equal to (a) 27, (b) 125, (c) 216.

22. Since the volume of a sphere of radius r is given by $V = \frac{4}{3}\pi r^3$, the volume of a spherical nucleus is $\frac{4}{3}\pi(1.2 \times 10^{-15}$ m$)^3\ A$. Calculate the density of nuclei with A equal to (a) 27, (b) 125, and (c) 216, in atomic mass units per cubic metre and kilograms per cubic metre. One atomic mass unit $= 1.66 \times 10^{-27}$ kg.

23. What is the radius of a neutron star whose mass equals that of our sun (10^{30} kg)?

24. (a) Hydrogen can be frozen solid if it is cooled sufficiently. Assuming that in solid hydrogen the atoms are very closely packed, estimate the distance between atoms which are in their lowest energy state, that is, with $n = 1$.

    (b) How thick must a layer of solid hydrogen be which is composed of one million atoms piled on top of each other?

25. Use a library to learn something of the life of Niels Bohr, and write a summary in a few paragraphs.

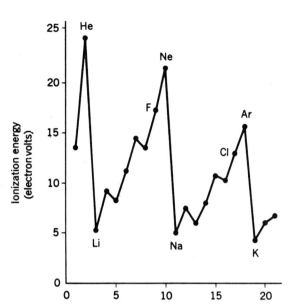

CHAPTER 19

Electrons in Atoms

FIG. 19-1

The Bohr theory of the atom assigns allowed orbits to an electron moving around the positively charged central nucleus. Atoms having a nuclear charge Ze (where Z is the atomic number) must be orbited by Z electrons in order to be neutral. The Bohr theory seemed to provide an attractive basis for describing the structure of all atoms. But in atoms having a large nuclear charge, how are the electrons arranged around the nucleus? This chapter considers the evidence on this subject, and its consequences.

IONIZATION ENERGY

Since a system tends towards the lowest possible energy state, it might be supposed that all electrons in an atom would occupy the orbit closest to the nucleus (with $n = 1$). Before accepting this, we need to examine the experimental evidence. In Fig. 19-1, the ionization energy, the energy required to remove an electron from an atom, is plotted against the atomic number of the atoms. It is quite clear that there is not a smooth variation of ionization energy with atomic number. A smooth variation would be expected if every electron went into the same orbit, merely making a slight alteration to the energy of the orbit as it did so. Instead we see very marked breaks between the adjoining elements helium (He) and lithium (Li), and between neon (Ne) and sodium (Na), although between these discontinuities the ionization energies do vary relatively smoothly with the nuclear charge Z. The elements at the lowest points of the graph, lithium (Li), sodium (Na), and potassium (K), all have very similar properties, both chemically and physically; for example, they are all very reactive, light metals. Similarly all the elements that have the highest ionization energies are the inert gases—helium (He), neon (Ne) and argon (Ar). Highly active gases such as fluorine (F) and chlorine (Cl), which combine with hydrogen to form acids, all occupy places on the graph just to the left of the inert gases.

There is thus a periodic variation in the ionization energies, as shown in the pattern of the ionization energy rising with the atomic number then falling to a low value, which is clearly related to the periodic nature of the chemical and physical properties of the elements as illustrated by the few examples above.

In 1868 Mendeleev classified the known elements in his Periodic Table (Fig. 19-2). The Table showed that there was a regular family resemblance between groups of elements when listed in order of their atomic masses. The second element (helium, chemical symbol He) is similar to the 10th (neon, Ne), the 18th (argon, Ar), and the 36th (krypton, Kr). The third element (lithium, Li) is similar to the 11th (sodium, Na), the 19th (potassium, K), and the 37th (rubidium, Rb). The fourth (beryllium, Be) is similar to the 12th (magnesium, Mg), the 20th (calcium, Ca) and the 38th (strontium, Sr). This list could be greatly extended.

You will note that in the first list the differences in the numbers are 8, 8, 18, and these differences are the same in the other lists. Taking the first list (that of the inert gases) rather further, and including xenon and radon, we find that these very stable elements occupy the 2nd, 10th, 18th, 36th, 54th and 86th positions in the Periodic Table. It excited scientists' interest to note that

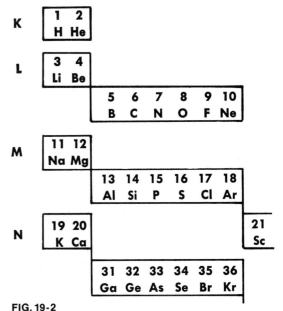

FIG. 19-2

$$2 = 2 \times 1^2$$
$$10 - 2 = 8 = 2 \times 2^2$$
$$18 - 10 = 8 = 2 \times 2^2$$
$$36 - 18 = 18 = 2 \times 3^2$$
$$54 - 36 = 18 = 2 \times 3^2$$
$$86 - 54 = 32 = 2 \times 4^2$$

Thus the position of the heaviest inert gas in the Periodic Table can be expressed by $2(1^2 + 2^2 + 2^2 + 3^2 + 3^2 + 4^2)$ and the positions of lighter elements of this series can be found by cutting off the series earlier; for instance, the position of argon is $2(1^2 + 2^2 + 2^2) = 18$.

Now simple rules or formulae like these do not occur by accident. It would seem that built into the structure of the atom is something which produces a periodicity of properties, or, putting it another way, there must be a repetition of particular characteristics of atomic structure matched to the repetition of particular characteristics of the physical and chemical properties of the elements.

ELECTRON SHELLS

In the theory of atomic structure developed from the Bohr picture of the hydrogen atom, this regularity is achieved by the principle that only a limited number of electrons can be in any one allowed orbit, and that when a full complement of electrons is in such an orbit the structure is very stable. An analogy may help in the understanding of this model. Consider a theatre with seats for the customers in rows in front of the stage. If all the seats are equally priced, the first person will occupy a lone seat in the front row so that he will get a good view of the actors, and then others will come in and fill up the front row until all the available places there are taken. Then the next person will occupy a lone position in the second row. Once again the row will fill with more people until it too is full, after which the next person will occupy a lone position in the third row. By having only limited accommodation in the various rows, and by filling up the seats one by one, a regularity in character is achieved—every so often there is a single person sitting outside a filled row, every so often there is a row with just one unfilled space, and so on. This analogy does not give the idea of stability of the filled row structure, though indeed there is no doubt that when everyone is in his place things grow much quieter!

The first row or "shell" of the atom, labelled the K shell, has places for two electrons in it (Fig. 19-3). These places are occupied by the electrons in hydrogen and helium and the "filled row" or "closed shell" structure of helium accounts for its chemical stability. We thus consider that for helium there are two electrons in the orbit of smallest radius. Lithium, the third element, has a charge of three units on its nucleus, and therefore must have three electrons in orbit round the nucleus in order that the atom as a whole will be electrically neutral. As the K shell is full, this third electron must occupy a space in the $n = 2$ orbit, called the L shell of the atom. For each step up the Periodic Table, one more electron has to be fitted in, and with neon there are eight electrons in the L shell (plus two in the K shell). Eight is the maximum that the L shell can hold, and therefore neon has a closed shell structure, giving it great chemical stability and a high ionization energy. The eleventh atom, sodium, once more has an electron by itself outside a closed shell, and thus is in a similar position to lithium in its electronic structure. This structural similarity produces the chemical similarity of sodium and lithium and indeed of potassium, rubidium and cesium, all of which have one electron outside a closed shell.

So far the build-up of the atoms has been simple—the K shell has 2×1^2 electrons in it, and the L shell has 2×2^2 electrons in it. We might expect that the next shell, the M shell, corresponding to an orbital radius with $n = 3$, would have 2×3^2 electrons in it. In that case we would expect the next inert gas after neon to have a total of $2(1^2 + 2^2 + 3^2) = 28$ electrons, and thus to occupy the 28th position in the Table. Actually the next inert gas, argon, has a charge on the nucleus of 18, and therefore 18 electrons. This can be explained by carrying our analogy of the theatre seats farther.

We had considered that all seats had the same price (in the atomic case, that all electron positions had the same energy). Let us imagine instead that the K seats are in a single row at one price, the L seats in two rows both at a lower price, the M seats in three rows all at a still lower price, and the next group, the N seats, in four rows all at one price which is, however, less than that for the M seats (Fig. 19-4). Those customers who would normally be seated in the 3rd row of the M seats may decide that they would see almost as well and pay less if they went into the first row of the N's. Therefore two rows of

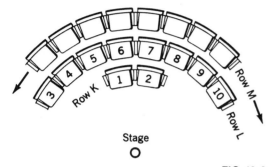

FIG. 19-3

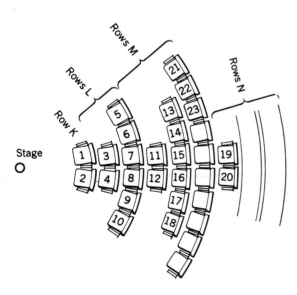

FIG. 19-4

M's will be filled up first (in the atomic case, eight positions of the Periodic Table, up to argon) and then some seats in the N's, after which the vacant seats in the M's will be filled. Therefore the stability of argon is due to the filling of two of the "sub-shells" of the M orbit. In the case of krypton, the inert gas in position 36 of the Table, the spaces in the M's have all been filled, and two rows of the N's also. The position of Kr can therefore be written as

$$36 = 2[1^2(K) + 2^2(L) + 3^2(M) + 2^2(N)]$$

$$= 2[1^2 + 2^2 + 2^2 + 3^2]$$

with still more space in the N shell left to be filled. A chart of the lower part of the Periodic Table is given in Fig. 19-2 to illustrate these points, and a full chart of the Table is given in the Appendix.

The radii of the electron shells of an atom depend on the nuclear charge (Ze). Consider one electron near an oxygen nucleus. Since the nuclear charge is eight times that for hydrogen (as oxygen has $Z = 8$), the electron is attracted by a force eight times as great and its orbit is one-eighth of that for hydrogen. In fact, the innermost shell for any atom has a radius equal to r/Z (r is the radius of the orbit of an electron in a hydrogen atom). That is,

$$\text{the radius} = \frac{0.53 \times 10^{-10} \text{ m}}{Z}.$$

Therefore for oxygen, where $Z = 8$, the radius of the innermost orbit

is $$\frac{0.53 \times 10^{-10} \text{ m}}{8} = 6.6 \times 10^{-12} \text{ m}.$$

The radii of the outer orbits are of course larger than this.

EMISSION OF RADIATION

We saw in Chapter 18 that radiation is emitted or absorbed when an electron jumps from one orbit to another, a jump to an orbit of lower n being associated with the emission of radiation. The same is true in the case of heavier atoms, with the complication that many of the lower orbits may already be filled with electrons, and so transitions to these are not possible. In most low-energy transitions therefore we are dealing with jumps of electrons between the outermost filled orbit and the unfilled orbits of higher n value. As the energy associated with any of these orbits is dependent upon the charge on the nucleus of the atom under consideration, the energy change associated with jumps from one orbit to another will also be characteristic of the particular atom. This energy is typically given up in the form of visible light, and the characteristic colour of neon or sodium or mercury lights is due to this dependence of energy on the nuclear charge, that is, to the position of the atom in the Periodic Table.

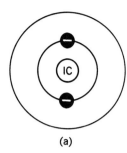

(a)

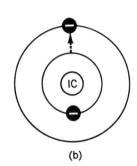

(b)

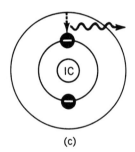

(c)

FIG. 19-5. In this diagram of a heavy atom, such as that of mercury, IC represents the *inner core*—the nucleus and inner electrons. Two outer electrons are shown separately.

To illustrate these electron jumps, we will consider what happens in a mercury lamp. In the lamp, energy is given to the mercury atoms by an electric field (Fig. 19-5). This transfer of energy means that electrons in the outer orbit of the mercury atoms are made to jump to higher orbits, leaving a vacancy in the orbit from which they came. After a short time, about 10^{-8} s, the electrons will drop back into their original orbits, filling in the vacancies, and emitting, in the jump, radiation energy in the form of light whose colour is determined by the energy difference between the orbits. This is what happens in a lamp where the radiator, mercury vapour in the example, is in a gaseous state. Where the radiator is a solid, as in the ordinary tungsten filament lamp, very many more electronic transitions become possible, and a very wide range of frequencies are emitted, giving the effect of white light; this is discussed further in Chapter 20.

ABSORPTION, FLUORESCENCE AND PHOSPHORESCENCE

In the last section we discussed a situation in which the atoms of a gas received energy from an electric field. Energy can also be taken from a beam of light. For example, if white light is shone through sodium vapour, the sodium atoms may absorb from it the photons whose energy corresponds to a jump of an electron from the lowest state of the atom to an excited state. As white light contains photons of all optical frequencies, the absorption of photons of a particular energy will mean that the light that comes through the vapour is no longer truly "white." In fact, a spectroscope shows that the otherwise uniform spectrum has gaps in it; the gaps are at just the same frequencies as the lines in an emission spectrum of sodium vapour. These *absorption* spectra are just as characteristic of an element as the emission spectra. Material in the outer layers of the sun (and in the earth's atmosphere) can for example be identified by looking at the spectrum of sunlight. This spectrum shows gaps which are caused by absorption by the material through which sunlight passes on its way to earth.

The energy absorbed from light is subsequently re-emitted in the form of characteristic photons. Usually this re-emission is immediate (in less than a microsecond), and the process is called **fluorescence**. The frequency of the radiation emitted may be the same as that absorbed, but in general it is smaller, that is, the wavelength is longer. Thus if ultraviolet radiation ("black light") is shone on some materials, it may be absorbed but visible light emitted.

For one atomic reason or another, the emission of the radiation may be delayed for times of the order of minutes or even hours. In this case the phenomenon of re-emission is called **phosphorescence**.

THE PRODUCTION OF X-RAYS

So far we have treated electrons being raised from the outermost orbits. It is also possible for electrons to be raised from the innermost orbit (the K shell) though this requires more energy. For example,

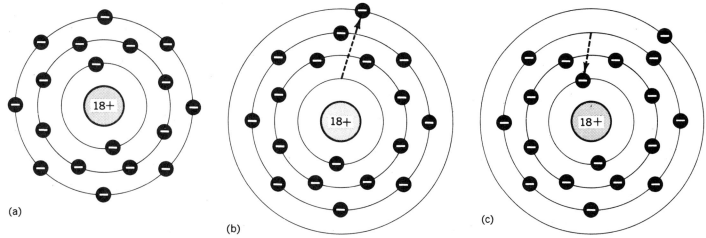

(a)

(b)

(c)

FIG. 19-6. This illustrates the production of x-rays from argon ($Z = 18$).

one of the K electrons may be excited by the transfer by collision of kinetic energy from a moving electron, and the K electron may either be raised to one of the unfilled orbits or given sufficient energy to escape from the atom altogether (Fig. 19-6). In either case a hole is left in the K shell, which may be filled by an L or M electron dropping down, or by some free electron being captured into the K shell, the inverse of the original ionization process. The radiation emitted in any one of these transitions is usually in the x-ray region for a medium-weight or heavy atom because of the great energy associated with the K shell of such an atom. Thus the excitation of atoms can give rise to characteristic x-rays as well as light of characteristic wavelengths in the visible part of the spectrum.

Recall that the greater the energy of a ray the shorter is its wavelength.

CHEMICAL BONDING

The inert gas structure of a closed shell is a most stable one, and therefore is the one which atoms will try to attain if possible, in the same way, for example, that ball bearings will roll to the bottom of a saucer or rocks to the bottom of a hill. In the case of lithium, which has one electron outside a closed shell, it can obtain a closed shell structure if it loses the lone electron. Similarly fluorine can obtain a closed shell structure (that of neon) if it gains one electron. If lithium and fluorine atoms are in proximity to one another we can think of a transference of the electron originally on the lithium atom to the fluorine atom, giving both of them closed shell structures. However, both of the atoms were originally electrically neutral, and now as a result of the transfer the lithium will be positively charged and the fluorine, which gained an electron, will be negatively charged. These oppositely charged ions will attract one another by the normal laws of electrostatic charges and will hold together as the chemical compound lithium fluoride, LiF (Fig. 19-7). The two elements are said to be chemically bound or combined.

The word **valence**, or valency, describes the power that an atom has for combining with other atoms. As both Li and F are satisfied by combining with one other atom, they are both said to have

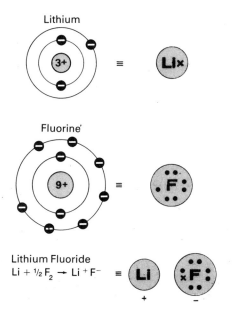

FIG. 19-7

Carbon

Hydrogen

Methane
$C + 2H_2 \rightarrow CH_4 \equiv$

FIG. 19-8

valency one, or unit valence. The relatively free electrons which can exchange and move about are called the **valence electrons**. The type of bonding described above is called **electrovalence** because the operative force can be thought of as the electric force between the charged ions.

Another type of chemical bonding is called **co-valence**. In this, the two bonding atoms share electrons between them. Again, the atoms "feel" as if they have a closed shell of electrons. In the case of methane, CH_4, for example (Fig. 19-8), four electrons originally on the carbon atom are shared equally with the four hydrogen atoms. Thus, each H atom has two electrons associated with it ("its own" and one of the "carbon's"), and so has the full complement for the K shell. Now the C atom, in addition to its 2 K electrons, has shares in 8 L electrons—the full complement for the L shell.

FIG. 19-10: LASERS

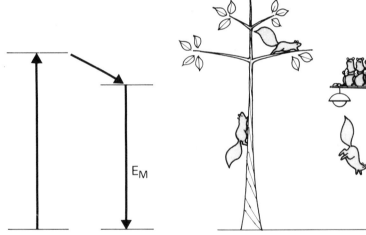

You have seen that atoms of a particular element in gaseous form have definite energy levels, and that the jumps of electrons from one level to another require the absorption or emission of light photons of a precise frequency or energy. Usually such excitations or de-excitations of the atoms are quite random and independent of one another. When light is shone on a gas, the effect is usually that electrons are stimulated to jump up from their lowest state to a higher one. In fact, the light would also stimulate a jump down of an electron which was in an excited state, but usually there are very few electrons in such an excited state at any one time.

It is possible however to increase the population of excited atoms—this is done by exciting them to a high level, and then trapping them in a lower level which does not easily de-excite, that is, in a so-called **metastable** state. An analogy would be of a squirrel which climbs an easy tree, jumps across to the neck of a lamppost and is stuck there. With a large supply of (stupid) squirrels, the number of stranded squirrels could be greatly increased; the population of excited atoms can be built up if there exist suitable ways of getting the atoms into a metastable state.

If light of energy E_M (see diagram) is now shone on the excited population, *emission* of light would

In solids this type of co-valent bonding is very common, helping to lock the atoms in place with respect to one another. In Chapter 20 we will discuss the structure of crystals of germanium (Ge), an element with valency 4. Each one of the Ge atoms in the crystals shares "its" electrons with its four nearest neighbours; each one of these neighbours in turn shares "its" electrons, so that each atom has 8 valence electrons around it, giving it a full complement and a stable structure (Fig. 19-9).

We may summarize our findings in this chapter by saying that the model of the atom in which electrons occupy a limited number of places in the various allowed orbits round the nucleus enables us to explain most of the obvious characteristics of atoms, namely the variation in ionization energies, simple chemical bonding, and the characteristic optical and x-ray spectra emitted by excited atoms.

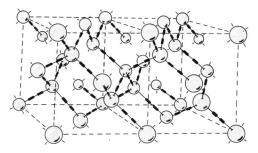

FIG. 19-9

be stimulated. In principle one photon could start the process off, and the photons produced by the *stimulated* emission would stimulate further emission of *radiation* until all the atoms were de-excited. There would thus be amplification of the number of photons (starting with one, finishing with many), or *light amplification*. Altogether then, one has Light Amplification by Stimulated Emission of Radiation. The acronym for this is **Laser**.

It is of importance in applications of the laser to realize that every photon "knows" all about the others—the emission of a photon was stimulated by one of the other photons, and so the process is not random as in normal emission. The laser light is called *coherent* light because of this property.

In an actual laser the initial excitation is done by shining white light on a gas, which picks out the radiation it likes to absorb and so becomes excited. Suitable choice of material ensures that there is a metastable state to go to. The presence of the white light ensures that there are always a few photons of the right frequency to stimulate the emission from this metastable state.

The probability of stimulating emission is small —the light is therefore constrained to reflect back and forth in a pipe to increase the total path length and thus the probability of stimulation. The restraint of having to travel a very long distance in a narrow pipe makes laser light very parallel—more so than sunlight.

Thus a laser consists of a tube of gas (e.g., he-lium-neon) with highly reflecting ends (not quite perfect reflection, otherwise no laser light would ever emerge), surrounded by an intense white light source. The colour of the laser light is governed by the atomic characteristics of the lasing gas. Some fraction of the energy of the white light is then finally emitted as a highly parallel, very intense beam of coherent light of a very definite wavelength.

The high intensity of the highly directional beam may be used to put a lot of energy into a very small spot, and thus raise its temperature very greatly. This makes possible "spot-welding" on a very tiny spot. An interesting example is welding to the back of the eye a piece of retinal tissue which has become detached—here the lens of the eye itself acts to focus the laser beam. Industry also makes use of this high-precision welding.

In research into nuclear fusion (see Chapter 23), lasers are used to raise fusion materials to very high temperatures ($10^{7°}$ C) very rapidly, so that they fuse before blowing apart.

In communications, the fact that a laser beam has a high frequency (compared with a radio signal) enables it to carry much more information, and so one beam could carry many telephone calls at one time. Because of the parallel nature of the laser beam, it can act as a highly efficient transmitter of long-distance signals, such as to the moon or to artificial satellites.

Exercises

A

1. Define ionization energy.

2. What is meant by a periodic property?

3. (a) What are the chemical properties of the elements with ionization energies on the peaks of the curve of ionization energy versus atomic number?
   (b) Which elements have the lowest ionization energies?

4. What is the maximum number of electrons that can fit into each of these shells: (a) K, (b) L, (c) M?

5. What must occur to make an electron jump from a lower orbit to a higher one?

6. (a) What usually happens very shortly after an electron has been excited to a higher orbit?
   (b) What is the usual time during which an electron is in an excited orbit?

7. Distinguish between fluorescence and phosphorescence.

8. How does an absorption spectrum differ from an emission spectrum?

9. What is the theoretical difference between the production of x-rays and the production of light, both of which occur during de-excitation of atoms?

10. What is meant by (a) electrovalent bonding, (b) covalent bonding?

11. How many electrons would a magnesium atom ($Z = 12$) have to shed before it had a closed shell structure?

12. How many electrons would an oxygen atom ($Z = 8$) have to gain before it had a closed shell structure?

13. Why are the "inert gases" chemically inactive?

14. (a) What is meant by a metastable state?
    (b) Name several ways in which laser light differs from light from an ordinary incandescent lamp.

B

15. Rubidium is a metal with chemical properties very similar to those of lithium, sodium and potassium. It has an atomic number of 37. Use Fig. 19-1 to help you estimate its ionization energy in units of electron-volts.

16. Krypton is an inert gas, like helium, neon and argon. It has an atomic number of 36. What would you expect its ionization energy to be, in units of electron-volts? (Hint: Use Fig. 19-1.)

17. Estimate the ionization energies of cesium (an alkali metal similar to lithium, sodium, and potassium, but with atomic number 55), and of xenon, an inert gas of atomic number 54.

18. Lithium and fluorine combine by the transfer of an electron from lithium to fluorine. Suggest other pairs of elements that might form compounds in a similar way.

19. You are told that a certain element of atomic number in the range of 10 to 15 has an ionization energy of 6.0 eV. Using Fig. 19-1 say what element you think this would be.

20. Sketch the characteristic electron arrangement for the outer shell of a single atom of
    (a) an alkali metal such as potassium,
    (b) an alkaline earth element such as calcium,
    (c) an inert gas such as argon,
    (d) a gas such as fluorine.

C

21. Calculate the radii of the innermost orbit of the atoms of lithium ($Z = 3$), iodine ($Z = 53$) and uranium ($Z = 92$).

22. The electrons in the L shell of an atom, those with $n = 2$, are partially screened from the nucleus by the two K electrons. As a result, the L electrons are attracted not by the full charge Z of the nucleus but, effectively, by a positive charge of $(Z - 2)$ units. On this basis, calculate the radii of the L shell orbits in the nuclei of sodium ($Z = 11$), cesium ($Z = 55$) and uranium ($Z = 92$).

23. Write a paragraph or two to describe the contributions of Mendeleev to our understanding of chemical elements. Use an encyclopedia.

24. Name some physical and chemical properties of elements that vary periodically as the atomic number increases.

25. The spectrum of nitrogen molecules, N_2, is different from that of nitrogen atoms, N. In fact, the spectrum of N_2 is called a *band spectrum*, whereas that of N is called a *line spectrum*. Find out what the difference is, and why there is a difference.

26. In the text it was stated that the heaviest known inert gas was radon, which occupies the 86th position in the Periodic Table. If the Periodic Table extended much further than it does, which position would you expect to be occupied by
    (a) the next heaviest inert gas,
    (b) the next one after that?

27. We know that lithium has two electrons in the innermost K shell, and one in the L shell. If, however, all three electrons were in the K shell, what would you estimate its ionization energy to be?

CHAPTER 20

Electrons in Solids

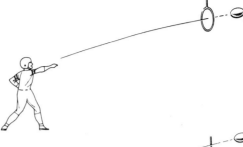

FIG. 20-1

In the Bohr model of the atom, there exist narrow energy levels. Electrons are only allowed to have these particular energies, or to make jumps between them. When many atoms are closely packed together, however, the narrow levels broaden out into energy bands. An analogy may be drawn from the football field. At practice, a good quarterback may be able to throw a ball every time through a small ring (Fig. 20-1)—the variation in angle of throw is very small. But on the field, with opposing players threatening him, his throwing becomes more erratic, the variation in angle of throw becomes much greater. Similarly when two atoms are brought close together, the allowed energy levels of each are split into two so that there are now double the number of allowed energies. Although both of these are close to the energy predicted by the Bohr model, the energy which an electron may have is no longer definite and unique. With 10^{20} atoms close together, as in a crystal, there are so many levels close together that the individual levels are smeared into a band (Fig. 20-2). Moreover, the higher energy bands become common to all the atoms in the crystal. Electrons can move relatively freely within a band; but to move from one band to another definitely requires energy.

In a metal such as aluminum, which is a conductor, the lower bands are full of electrons (Fig. 20-3). But the band in which the outermost electrons sit is not full and only very small energy changes are required to move electrons around inside it. The fact that the atoms are at a non-zero temperature means that they have some energy and so will be able to move freely around in the band of the aluminum metal. These "free electrons" are the ones whose movement in the "conduction band" constitutes an electric current. The fact that there are freely mobile electrons makes aluminum a good electrical conductor.

In a diamond crystal, however, the outermost electrons just fill completely one of the energy bands (Fig. 20-3). Between this and the next, empty, band there is a wide energy gap of about 6 eV (10^{-18} J). Since at room temperature the average thermal energy available is about 0.02 eV, very few of the electrons are able to pick up enough

FIG. 20-2 and **20-3** appear on page 258.

By "non-zero temperature" is meant a temperature greater than 0 K (= −273°C).

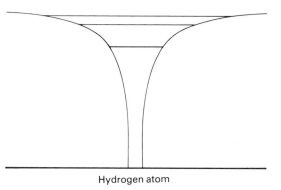

Hydrogen atom

Hydrogen molecule

FIG. 20-2

energy to jump this gap into the conduction band, and so there are only very few free electrons available to carry a current. Diamond is in fact a good insulator.

Diamond is also very transparent to light because at optical frequencies the photons only have about 3×10^{-19} J of energy. As this is not sufficient to cause a jump between bands, no energy can be absorbed from the light, and so the light is transmitted and reflected. On the other hand, aluminum is opaque to light because optical frequencies are fully sufficient to cause electrons to change energy within a band, and so the light energy can be readily absorbed by the metal.

Recall that "green photons" have energies of $2.4 \text{ eV} = 2.4 \times 1.6 \times 10^{-19} \text{ J} = 3.8 \times 10^{-19} \text{ J}$.

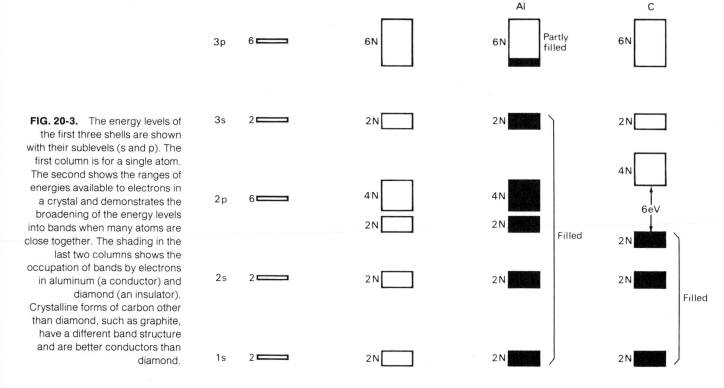

FIG. 20-3. The energy levels of the first three shells are shown with their sublevels (s and p). The first column is for a single atom. The second shows the ranges of energies available to electrons in a crystal and demonstrates the broadening of the energy levels into bands when many atoms are close together. The shading in the last two columns shows the occupation of bands by electrons in aluminum (a conductor) and diamond (an insulator). Crystalline forms of carbon other than diamond, such as graphite, have a different band structure and are better conductors than diamond.

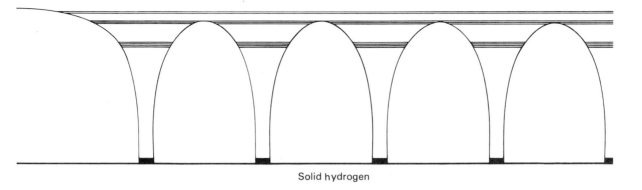

Solid hydrogen

The other side of the story regarding the opacity of aluminum is that metals at high temperatures shine with a white light. Rather than emitting light of precise wavelengths, as do gases, the spectrum of high temperature solids is very broad. This is because there are very many electron energies allowed, and therefore very many different electron "jumps" are allowed. The very many allowed frequencies blur into one, so that the spectrum is not distinct but diffuse. With a gas, the wavelengths emitted are characteristic and precise; as the density of the gas is increased, the lines become broader; in the solid state, all characteristic information is lost from the spectrum.

SEMICONDUCTORS

An important class of materials is that for which the outermost electrons are in a filled band, but the gap between this band and the empty band above it is very small (Fig. 20-4). In this case thermal agitation may allow a very significant number of electrons to be in the conduction band, and a small current may flow if a voltage is applied across the material. Such materials are called **semiconductors**.

There is no sharp distinction between conductors, semiconductors and insulators as far as resistance itself is concerned (Fig. 20-5), but with changes of temperature the resistances of conductors and semiconductors do change differently. In a semiconductor, higher temperatures push more electrons into the conduction band, and so the

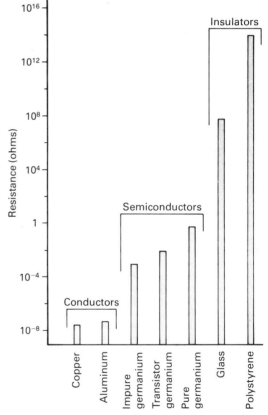

FIG. 20-5

FIG. 20-4. The seating of the outermost electrons in three crystals. In aluminum (a conductor) the outer band is half filled. In diamond (an insulator) the outer electrons just fill a band separated by a 6 eV gap from the next band. In germanium (a semiconductor) the gap between the outer bands is small and electrons can occasionally move across it to the conduction band.

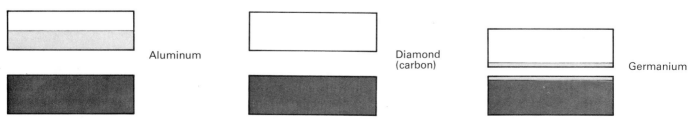

Aluminum

Diamond (carbon)

Germanium

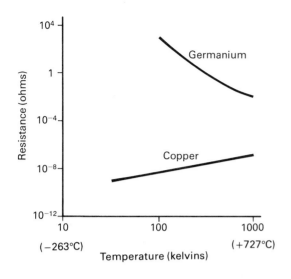

Resistance (ohms)

Germanium

Copper

Temperature (kelvins)

(−263°C) (+727°C)

FIG. 20-6

resistance decreases. On the other hand (Fig. 20-6), the effect of heat on a conductor is rather to disturb the crystal lattice to make things less ordered; as a result the flow of electrons is disturbed and the resistance increases.

DOPED SEMICONDUCTORS

Germanium, Ge, is a semiconductor now widely used in industry. In the form of a pure crystal (called "intrinsic germanium"), there is a small gap between the filled band containing the valence electrons and the (almost completely) empty conduction band above it (Fig. 20-4). Some electrons can jump the narrow gap; thus pure Ge (Fig. 20-7) is slightly conducting. If, however, impurities are introduced into the crystal, the effective gap between the bands can be made smaller. This introduction of impurities is called **doping**. Arsenic (As) has an atomic size almost equal to that of Ge, but whereas Ge has a valence of 4, As has one of 5 (Ge is in Group IV of the Periodic Table, As in Group V). If As atoms are introduced into a crystal of Ge, these new impurity atoms can fit into the Ge crystal lattice fairly well (Fig. 20-7(b)), but only 4 of the 5 valence bonds are saturated. Looking at it another way, the fifth electron is not needed for bonding and cannot sit in one of the energy bands. Instead it and its fellows occupy a new energy band in the gap between the (filled) valence band and the (empty) conduction band. This new band is very close to the conduction band, within 0.10 eV of the latter, so that there are now electrons which can very readily move into the conduction band.

The type of **doped semiconductor** in which there is apparently an excess of negative electrons is called an n-type semiconductor. It must be realized, however, that the crystal as a whole is still electrically neutral—the Ge atoms are neutral and so are the As ones; there are, however, many more free or almost free electrons in n-type material than in intrinsic Ge. These have been *"donated"* by the As, and the As is therefore called the **donor impurity**. The band where the excess electrons sit is sometimes called the **donor band**.

Conversely, if Ge is doped with aluminum, a tri-valent atom (Al is in Group III), again the impurity atom fits into the crystal, but this time there is a shortage of a valence electron (Fig. 20-7(c)). This lack of an electron can be thought of as a hole in an otherwise uniform sea of electrons. Electrons from elsewhere in the crystal can move to fill the hole, but in so doing create a new hole, which may itself be filled by the movement of another electron, which creates a new hole, and so on. From the outside, it could look as if the hole were moving; and as the hole is a shortage of negative charge, the movement of the hole looks like a movement of positive charge. For this reason, this type of material is called a p-type semiconductor.

In terms of energy bands, the introduction of the Al impurity (called an **acceptor impurity** in contrast to the donor impurity above)

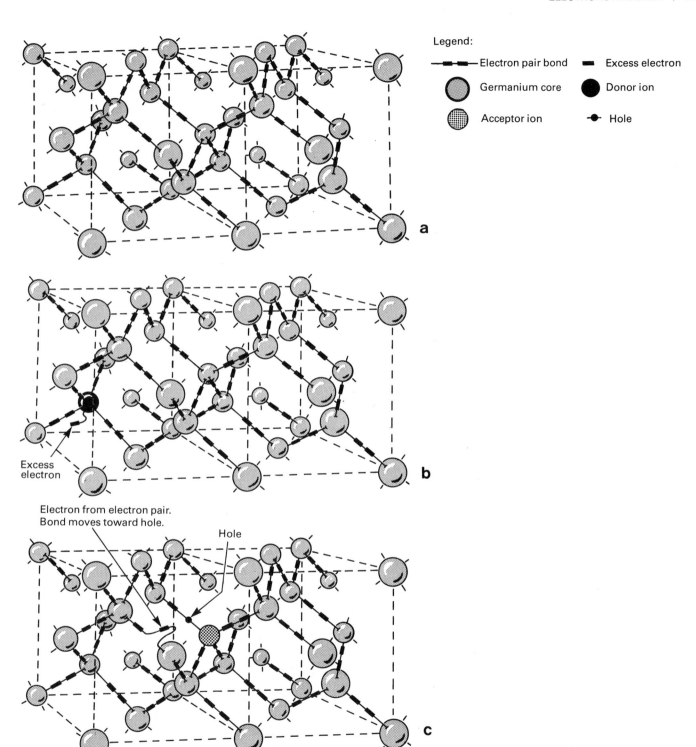

Legend:

- ▬ ▬ Electron pair bond
- ▬ Excess electron
- ⬤ Germanium core
- ⬤ Donor ion
- ⬤ Acceptor ion
- •— Hole

Excess
electron

Electron from electron pair.
Bond moves toward hole.

Hole

a

b

c

FIG. 20-7. (a) The three-dimensional structure of a germanium crystal shows the four pairs of electron bonds surrounding each atom. (b) Each arsenic donor atom makes one electron free to move about in the n-type semiconductor. (c) Each aluminum acceptor atom creates one hole in the p-type semiconductor.

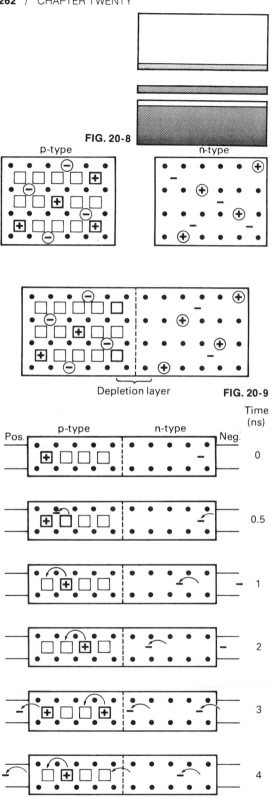

FIG. 20-8

p-type   n-type

FIG. 20-9

Depletion layer

FIG. 20-10

produces an **acceptor band** just above the valence band (Fig. 20-8). The unsatisfied electrons of the Ge, those not needed to match up with Al atoms, can readily move into this acceptor band, leaving holes in normally full valence bands. Thus again there are freed charge carriers.

SEMICONDUCTING DIODE

Now imagine that n-type material is in close (electrical) contact with p-type material (Fig. 20-9). Although both are initially electrically neutral, with as many positive charges as negative ones, the free electrons of the n-type will tend to drift around, with some of them drifting into the p-type (a similar picture holds for the "holes," but here we will only discuss the electrons). This drift of negative charge *from* the n-type *to* the p-type makes the former somewhat positive in charge and the latter somewhat negative (moving money from A to B makes A poorer and B richer, transferring debts from A to B makes A richer and B poorer!).

Thus there will be a difference of electric potential across the n-p interface, which will impede the further drift of electrons from n to p. Some electrons will, however, still be able to drift across because their kinetic energy is sufficient for them to overcome the electrical repulsion.

One way to picture what is happening is to imagine that the free electrons near the interface will fall into those holes of the p-type which are near the interface. This cancellation of charge in the region called the **depletion layer** (Fig. 20-9) will leave the p-type slightly negative and the n-type slightly positive. The charge on the p-type will repel electrons, preventing any more from crossing the interface (unless they have a lot of kinetic energy which lets them "bull" their way across). If now a voltage is applied across the n-p junction such that the p-type is made positive with respect to the n-type (Fig. 20-10), there will no longer be the electric force repelling the electrons, and they will be able to flow across the interface; that is, a current will flow. On the other hand, if the p-type is made negative, there will be an even bigger force repelling the electrons, and no current will flow (except that some few electrons will always have enough kinetic energy to cross over).

Another way to picture what is happening is to think of a gymnast's "living pyramid." At the beginning there are a lot of people at ground level, who build themselves into a pyramid by jumping onto each others' backs (Fig. 20-11). As each layer is built up, it gets harder and harder for the next person to jump up—more difficult simply because people before him have jumped up to the state of higher gravitational potential energy. After some time an equilibrium situation will be reached, with one group of people piled on top of another, and with a second group remaining at ground level. You can think of this state of equilibrium as being a dynamic one—if people at the top fall off, the ones at ground level can now jump up

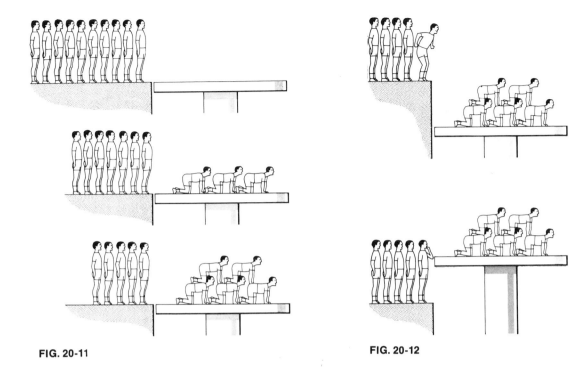

FIG. 20-11   **FIG. 20-12**

to fill the gap—but the net result is the same, with some in the pyramid and some on the ground.

By exact analogy, an electric potential (height) will be built up across the n-p interface until an equilibrium is established. At equilibrium, there is no net movement of charge, no current. In actual practice this equilibrium electric potential is about a volt.

Now imagine the pyramid to be built on a platform that can be raised or lowered (by the piston in the drawing) (Fig. 20-12). Obviously if the platform were lowered, it would be much easier for more people to pile up on top of the pyramid—a net current can flow in the electrical situation. On the other hand, if the platform were raised, it is certain that nobody would be able to jump up, that is, no current will flow. In the electrical situation, the same effect will be obtained by changing the voltage across the n-p interface; and thus by changing this voltage, a current can be switched on or off. This is the principle of the **semiconducting diode**, so-called because it has two (*di*) elect*rodes*. The conventional sign for a diode is a bar at the apex of a triangle (Fig. 20-13). Electron flow is normally from the bar to the triangle, with the conventional direction of flow of current in the direction of the symbol's arrow. Thus the diode has a low resistance to current flow from left to right in the diagram, and a high resistance to flow in the opposite direction. This property of the diode is used in *rectification*.

FIG. 20-13

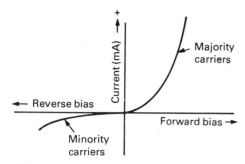

FIG. 20-14: With positive voltage (forward bias), the current is large, that is, the resistance is low; with reverse bias the resistance is high.

$$8.3 \times 10^{-3} \text{ s} = \frac{1}{120} \text{ s.}$$

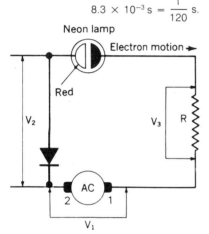

FIG. 20-15

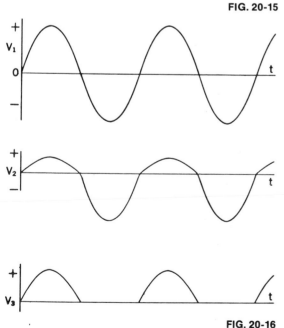

FIG. 20-16

RECTIFICATION

As described in Chapter 11, electrical energy is usually supplied in the form of alternating current, but often a supply of direct current (or, at least, non-alternating current) is required. The process of converting alternating current (AC) to direct current (DC) is called **rectification**. Since a diode has a high resistance in one direction and a low resistance in the other (Fig. 20-14), it does not conduct during both halves of an AC cycle. Fig. 20-15 illustrates a diode connected in a circuit with an AC generator and a neon tube. The neon tube contains neon at low enough pressure that only the cathode glow is visible. That is, whichever electrode is negative will produce the red glow characteristic of neon. Both electrodes glow when a neon tube is connected to alternating current, but they glow alternately. In the circuit illustrated, only one plate glows, indicating that the other plate is never negative.

When the generator produces 60 Hz alternations, Terminal 1 is positive for 8.3×10^{-3} s, while Terminal 2 is negative; then Terminal 1 is negative for 8.3×10^{-3} s while Terminal 2 is positive, and so on for each succeeding cycle. Since the diode ideally conducts only when the triangle in the symbol is positive there will be current only when Terminal 1 is positive and no current when Terminal 1 is negative. As a result electrons will move around the circuit only in the direction shown by the arrow, never in the other direction. The graphs of Fig. 20-16 illustrate the voltage relations in this rectification process. Since the voltage across the load resistance varies, the current through the resistor will also vary, but it never changes direction. For this reason, it can be called **varying** or **pulsating direct current**.

TRANSISTORS

Semiconductors can also be used as amplifiers of electrical signals. We have to have 3 doped semiconductors in combination to make an amplifying system—two pieces of n-type semiconductor separated by (but in close contact with) a piece of p-type, or two pieces of p-type separated by n-type (the first is called an n-p-n combination, the latter a p-n-p combination.

Thinking again of our human pyramid, we now have, as it were, people trying to get higher in the pyramid from both sides. Once again an equilibrium will be established when people can't jump high enough to get higher up the pyramid. Now imagine that not only the pyramid group is on a platform, but also the group on the right (Fig. 20-17(a)).

The right-hand platform (R) is now moved well down (Fig. 20-17(b)). There is no possibility of people now jumping from the R to the centre, and any people who fall off the pyramid are likely to go to the R and never be able to get back up. Their places will be taken by people on the left (L). Thus there will be a slow L→R movement of people.

Now if the centre platform is dropped slightly (Fig. 20-17(c)), it will be possible for a lot more people to jump from the L to the centre, and correspondingly more who lose their footing will fall to the R—the small decrease in the height of the centre platform causes a large change in the L→R current of people. Conversely, a small increase in the height (Fig. 20-17(d)) may make it quite impossible for any person to move from L to the centre. Essentially small changes in the potential of the centre element can produce large changes in the current flow.

In the *transistor*, it is the free electrons and holes which drift and, by crossing the interfaces between n- and p-types of semiconductors, produce electric potential differences across the interfaces (Fig. 20-9). If things are left alone, a dynamic equilibrium will be set up. If the R-hand, p-type material (collector) is deliberately put at a different potential than that of the L-hand piece (emitter), a small standing current can flow from the emitter to the collector. But small changes in the potential of the middle piece, called the base, will cause relatively large changes in the current to the collector (Fig. 20-18). These changes in current can cause relatively large changes in the voltage across a resistor connected in series with the voltage source and the collector (Fig. 20-19). Thus the small voltage change on the base has been *amplified* into a large change across the resistance attached to the collector.

FIG. 20-17

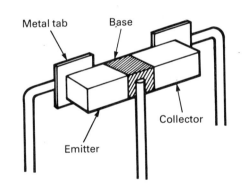

FIG. 20-18

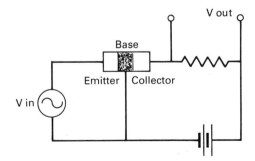

FIG. 20-19

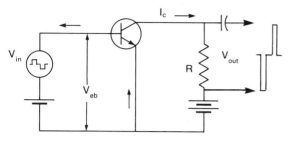

FIG. 20-20. The symbol on the left represents the input voltage; the one in the top centre is the conventional symbol for a transistor.

The amplification of transistors is often given as a current ratio. Since we have been discussing the voltage changes across the interfaces of the transistor, we give the amplification as a voltage ratio. The two ratios are equivalent.

THE TRANSISTOR AS AN AMPLIFIER

The circuit shown in Fig. 20-20 can be used to amplify small signals. The heart of the circuit is the n-p-n transistor, and its purpose is to control the flow of electric charge through the various circuit elements. As we have seen, the flow from the emitter to the collector depends on the relative voltages of the emitter and the base and, to a lesser extent, on that between the base and the collector.

Normally the emitter-base voltage V_{eb} is held at some convenient level by a battery. If now a signal V_{in} is applied across the emitter and base, the collector current I_c will alter. Imagine that V_{in} is a short duration positive voltage signal of size 0.04 V, shown by a rectangular signal in the diagram. Momentarily it will become more difficult for positive charge carriers to cross the interface between the emitter and the base, and correspondingly fewer carriers will reach the collector while the positive signal is applied. The collector current I_c will drop to 20 mA from its normal of 40 mA. The voltage across the resistor R will also change, from 40 mA $\times$ R to 20 mA $\times$ R, that is, using the value of $R = 100 \ \Omega$, from 4 V to 2 V. The signal of 0.04 V applied to the base has thus produced a voltage change of 2 V. This 2 V pulse constitutes the *output signal* from the circuit. It is $\frac{2}{0.04} = 50$ times the input signal, and the system is said to have an amplification of 50 times.

A negative input signal will cause increases in collector current, and again a voltage signal is produced across R, but now in the opposite direction from before. Then with an alternating voltage input signal, the output signal will also be an alternating voltage, but of size increased by the amplification of the system.

Despite the fact that the output signal is larger than the input signal, it should be clearly understood that one does *not* get something for nothing. The transistor controls the system in a way analogous to that in which small amounts of energy supplied to the gas pedal or accelerator of a car controls the much greater energy output of the car's engine. In the case of the automobile, the engine's energy comes from the gas tank; in the transistor amplifier, the output energy comes from the battery in the base-collector circuit.

Exercises

A

1. What is the major difference between the energy levels of gas atoms and those of atoms in a solid?

2. How does the electrical resistance of a conductor differ from that of an insulator?

3. In both conductors and insulators the lowest energy bands are full. For which class of material is the band in which the outermost electrons sit partially filled?

4. (a) What is a typical energy gap, in eV, between bands in an insulator?
   (b) What is the average thermal energy, in eV, available at room temperature?

5. How does the resistance change with increase of temperature of (a) a semiconductor such as germanium, and (b) a conductor such as copper?

6. (a) What is an intrinsic semiconductor?
   (b) What is a doped semiconductor?
   (c) What is the purpose of doping?

7. What is the difference between a donor impurity and an acceptor impurity?

8. (a) What are the charge carriers in an n-type semiconductor?
   (b) In a p-type semiconductor, what can be regarded as the charge carriers?

9. If two objects X and Y both are originally electrically neutral, and if positive charge then moves from X to Y, will X become more positive or more negative? What will happen to Y?

10. Define depletion layer.

11. What is meant by rectification of an alternating current?

12. What is meant by an amplifier?

13. Distinguish between the emitter, base, and collector of a transistor.

B

14. It is stated in the text that 6 eV are needed to make an electron jump across the gap between bands in diamond. What is the frequency and wavelength of a photon of 6 eV? Would you expect diamond to be transparent to radiation of this frequency?

15. A transistor system has a current amplification of 8 times. If the emitter-base current increases by 1.1 mA, by how much does the base-collector current increase?

16. Draw a diagram similar to Fig. 20-20 showing how to connect an n-p-n transistor in order to have it amplify.

17. A semiconductor can be made more conducting in several different ways. Name two.

C

18. Find the position of silicon in the Periodic Table. Silicon is a semiconductor. Would aluminum atoms introduced into a silicon crystal act as an acceptor impurity? Why or why not?

19. One end of an n-type doped semiconductor is heated. It is found that an electrical potential difference develops between the heated end and the cool end. Which end will be negative?

20. If one end of a piece of p-type semiconductor is heated, what potential will that end assume with respect to the cool end?

21. Two transistors, each designed as amplifiers, are put in series so that the base-collector current of one is also the emitter-base current of the other. Each has a current amplification of 8 times. If the emitter-base current of the first changes by 0.40 mA, by how much will the base-collector current of the second change?

CHAPTER 21

Electronic Communication

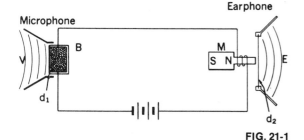

Experimenting with a laser beam as a communications channel.

During the twentieth century the development of methods for rapid, long-distance communication has gone hand-in-hand with the growing interdependence of widely separated parts of the world. For many centuries, detailed news could travel only as fast as a person could carry it, whether on horseback or by sailing ship, although warning of danger could be conveyed by beacon fires or by the ringing of church bells. Today, the transmission of news around the world is practically instantaneous. The development of radio and television communication has depended to a large extent on the discovery of scientific principles. In fact, the electronics industry represents a rapid assimilation of scientific knowledge into technology.

COMPONENTS OF A COMMUNICATIONS CHANNEL

There is a minimum number of items that must be present in any system by which information is to be conveyed from one place to another.

1. In planning such a system you must decide on the medium or **carrier** by which the information or **signal** will be transmitted. As a simple example, consider the principles of the telephone. In the simple arrangement of Fig. 21-1, copper wires provide the medium that connects the transmitter to the receiver. A steady current in the wires is the carrier on which the signal (or message) is impressed.

2. The **transmitter** in this situation is a microphone. It provides a means for **modulating** the carrier, that is, for changing the current in a way that corresponds to the sound waves from the person speaking.

3. The **receiver** is a device that converts the varying electric current into sound waves. This process is called **demodulation**, or **detection**. In more complicated systems, other items might be required.

4. If the information is to be transmitted any distance, it may be necessary to provide **amplification** of the signal.

5. In some systems one must be able to select one from a number of available messages being transmitted. This process is called **tuning**.

FIG. 21-1

Microphone

Earphone

B

M

S N

E

d_1

d_2

As we proceed to consider radio and television you will find it is necessary to provide for these processes: a carrier must be generated; the carrier must be modulated by the signal; the modulated carrier must be transmitted through a medium; the receiver must be tuned to select the desired signal from the many that are available; in the receiver the signal must be amplified, and demodulated.

VOICE COMMUNICATION BY RADIO

In radio communication the carrier is an electromagnetic wave. A signal frequency is generated in the range from 10^4 Hz to 10^9 Hz depending on the application. The radio wave is transmitted through space at a speed of 3.0×10^8 m/s from an antenna in which electrons are oscillating at the required frequency. For efficient transmission an antenna must be at least one-quarter of the wavelength of the radio wave to be transmitted.

See Fig. 16-24 for *Electromagnetic waves.*

Example: The US Navy has installed a very low-frequency transmitter for communication with ships around the world. The antenna (which is equal in length to half a wavelength) is so long that it is suspended between two mountain ridges, with the transmitter in the valley below. For a transmission frequency of 2.0×10^4 Hz, how far apart are the ends of the antenna?

Use the wave relation
$$v = f\lambda, \qquad \text{therefore} \quad \lambda = v/f.$$

The wavelength is
$$\lambda = \frac{3.0 \times 10^8 \text{ m/s}}{2.0 \times 10^4 \text{ Hz}} = 1.5 \times 10^4 \text{ m} = 15 \text{ km}.$$

Therefore, the antenna has a length of $\lambda/2 = 7.5$ km.

To transmit sound by radio requires that some property of the radio-frequency carrier must be changed at the audio-frequency rate. In ordinary radio broadcasting, the amplitude of the carrier is changed at the audio frequency. This process is called **amplitude modulation** (AM).

The carrier frequency is generated in an **oscillator**. In the early days of radio, oscillators sometimes consisted of alternating current generators, with many separate windings, operating at high speed. However, electronic systems are now used for this purpose. The frequency of the oscillations can be controlled by the choice of circuit elements.

Pressure variations in the air caused by speech or music generate in a microphone an electrical signal that has a voltage variation with the same frequency and relative amplitude as the sound waves. This electrical audio-frequency signal is supplied to a transistor and amplified. At the same time the radio-frequency voltage variations generated in the oscillator are also amplified. The audio-frequency (AF)

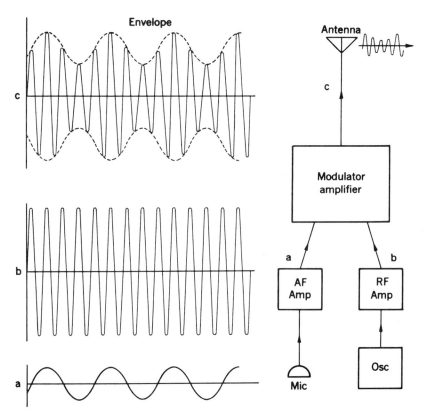

and radio-frequency (RF) voltage variations are supplied to the **modulator** as shown in Fig. 21-2; the output of this is an RF carrier wave whose amplitude varies at the audio-frequency rate. The result is an **amplitude modulated signal** that is supplied to the antenna circuit.

The wave-forms of the electric currents in the transmitter are illustrated in Fig. 21-2. (In actual practice a typical audio wave might have a frequency of 10^3 Hz and a typical radio wave might have a frequency of 10^6 Hz.) These are graphs of the currents as they vary with time:

(a) the audio-frequency signal from the microphone, amplified;

(b) the radio-frequency carrier produced in the oscillator, and then amplified;

(c) the modulated carrier with amplitude varying according to the audio signal, represented by the envelope.

Electromagnetic waves are radiated from the antenna with the electric and magnetic fields varying according to the graph of Fig. 21-2(c). Except as noted later in Fig. 21-7, radio waves can be received only a short distance beyond the horizon, about eighty kilometres, since the electromagnetic radiation, like light, travels more or less in straight lines.

The oscillation of electrons in the receiving antenna reproduces the variations of the modulated waves. The antenna is connected to a radio-frequency amplifier, which restores the amplitude of oscilla-

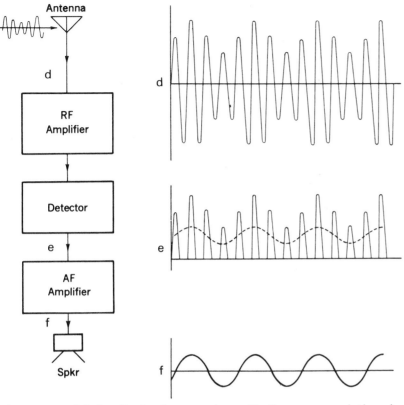

FIG. 21-2

tion to a useful size. In the detector the audio-frequency variations in amplitude are extracted from the carrier, as shown in Fig. 21-2(e), amplified, and applied to the loudspeaker. In the speaker the electrical variations cause the cone to vibrate and to reproduce sound more or less like the original at the transmitter.

The mass of the speaker cone is in fact too great to permit it to respond to the rapid variations of radio frequency. It would simply move in response to the average value of RF supplied to it. As the average value of the modulated RF shown in Fig. 21-2(d) is zero, there would be no net effect on the speaker. If, however, the detected signal is passed through a semiconducting rectifier (or through a diode), current will only flow during the positive half of the RF cycle, and now the average value of the positive halves of the RF, shown in Fig. 21-2(e), can be reproduced by the speaker. This average value to which the speaker responds is the same as the audio frequency originally generated by the microphone in the transmitter. The effective current to the speaker has the wave-form of Fig. 21-2(f).

Higher fidelity transmission can be achieved if the audio-frequency signal varies the frequency of the carrier wave rather than its amplitude. This is called **frequency modulation** (FM). The process is more difficult to describe but an analogy will help to show what goes on. At some street intersections there are blinking red lights—the amplitude of the red light is modulated, or changed with time, and this modulation carries the message "stop, then proceed with caution if the road is clear." This is rather more information than contained by an unmodulated red light, which simply says "stop." If the single light could change its colour (frequency) to green, and then to amber and then to red again, while retaining the same intensity or amplitude, information can be transmitted by *frequency modulation* even though there is no amplitude modulation. Further information on FM is given in Fig. 21-3.

Some more details of radio communications are described at the end of this chapter: tuned radio circuits in Fig. 21-5, transmission via the ionosphere in Fig. 21-7, and cathode-ray tubes in Fig. 21-8.

TELEVISION BROADCASTING

The existence of an efficient, economical television service available to almost all the peoples of Canada, the United States and Europe is a tribute to the ingenuity of radio engineers in applying scientific principles to a complex problem. Devices must be provided for supplying a video signal to a communications channel and for reconstructing it at the receiver to form an image of the original scene be-

---

FIG. 21-3: FREQUENCY MODULATION

As in amplitude modulation (AM), the first step in the transmission of information by frequency modulation (FM) is the change of sound energy, produced at audio frequencies (AF), into electrical signals of the same AF. This transformation is carried out by the microphone. Let us say that these signals have an instantaneous voltage $V(t)$. This AF wave is then mixed with a very high-frequency radio wave (VHF) of about 100 MHz. The mixing is such that if the unmodulated frequency of the VHF wave is f_c the instantaneous frequency f is given by $f = f_c + kV(t)$, where k is a constant. Thus as $V(t)$ goes alternatively positive and negative, f varies about f_c. The transmitted signal does not vary in amplitude, and therefore extraneous amplitude variations due to, for example, dirty spark plugs of passing cars, do not affect the receiver. Thus FM is much less "noisy" than AM; that is, it has higher fidelity.

STEREO FM

The variation of f will depend on k and on V. In North America f is allowed to vary by ± 75 kHz from the assigned station frequency f_c, a total of 150 kHz. To stop interference between stations, a 25 kHz guard band is assigned at each end of the 150 kHz band, which means that stations have to be separated by (more than) 200 kHz. A *monophonic* station's signal can swing the full 75 kHz on either side of f_c. If a station is *stereophonic* it has to use its 150 kHz band for transmitting signals for the "right-hand speaker," R, as well as for L signals, and also make it possible for the information to be received by a monophonic radio.

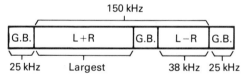

(G.B. means Guard band)

This is achieved by using most of the frequency channel to broadcast a left plus right (L + R) signal. This is the signal used by monophonic receivers, and it contains all the AF information. The rest of the channel (38 kHz) is used for an L - R signal.

In the stereo set, the L + R and the L - R signals are added to get the left-speaker signal (2L) and subtracted to get the right-speaker signal (2R).

ing televised. The video signal must contain a point-by-point representation of the brightness across the whole area of the scene. The pattern of varying brightnesses must be unravelled in some regular way so it can be put back together by a reverse process. An analogy for this process can be constructed: produce a black and white picture on a square of knitted material, pull the yarn out into a single strand, wind it on a ball, and send it by mail across the country. If the person who receives the ball of yarn knows the size of the stitches and the lengths of the rows, the yarn can be reknitted to form the picture again. The television problem is further complicated by the requirement that the motion of figures in the scene must be reproduced satisfactorily.

In summary, a television transmission system must provide:
1. an analysis of the scene into distinct elements;
2. the representation of the brightness of the elements in an electrical signal;
3. an orderly sequence of conversion from light intensity to electric current over the whole area of the scene;
4. a continuous retracing or **scanning** of the scene to represent motion.

The video signal so formed can be used to modulate a radio wave carrier that can be detected at the receiver. In the receiver, provisions must be made for reconstructing the visual field from the video signal.

The amount of picture detail that needs to be produced is limited by the extent to which human eyes can be fooled. Two black rectangles separated by a white space 2 mm wide seem to be touching when viewed from a distance of 7 m. For this reason it has been determined that 525 horizontal lines are sufficient to reproduce an acceptable picture. A complete television picture consists effectively of about one hundred thousand individual elements, each about 1 mm^2. In the same way a newspaper photograph viewed through a magnifying glass can be seen to consist entirely of black dots on a white background. The distance between dots determines the darkness of any portion of the picture.

To create the illusion of motion it is sufficient to present still pictures each differing slightly from the preceding one, at a rate of about twenty per second. Standard motion pictures operate at the rate of 24 frames (individual pictures) per second. In television the repetition rate is 30 frames per second. If an object is alternately seen and not seen, vision will appear to flicker if the rate is slow enough. However, an image will persist on the retina for a certain length of time, between 0.033 and 0.025 s. So a flicker frequency of 40 Hz is not noticeable. In a motion-picture theatre each frame is on the screen for 0.021 s. After 0.021 s of darkness the next frame appears, and blends in with the image of the preceding one. In television, flicker is avoided by presenting each frame twice, for 0.0167 s each time; each presentation contains only half of the 525 lines, selected alternately. This process is called **interlaced scanning**, and the rate was chosen to coincide with the 60 Hz line frequency of the electrical supply.

In a television-camera tube the scene is focused by lenses onto a photo-electrode, a rectangular element that is capable of producing an electric charge that varies directly with the intensity of the light on it. In this way a distribution of electric charge over the area of the photo-electrode provides an electrical image of the scene. An **electron gun** in the tube emits a narrow beam of electrons that is made to scan the surface of the photo-electrode. That is, the beam is deflected in such a way as to sweep across the photo-electrode in a series of almost horizontal lines (Fig. 21-4), at the rate that would produce 525 lines in each 0.033 s. As the electron beam strikes each point on the photo-electrode it restores the charge there to zero. This action produces an electric current in the output of the tube that varies with the charge (and therefore the light intensity) at each point. Where bright light is focused on the photo-electrode the negative charge is great, the change in charge produced by the electron beam is great, and the electric current in the output is great. So an electric current that reproduces the variations in light intensity is available to be amplified and used to modulate the radio carrier wave. The picture has been unravelled in time the way the knitted picture was unravelled in space.

The scanning of the photo-electrode is accomplished by magnetic deflection coils that cause the electron beam to sweep the surface horizontally and vertically. The deflection coils are arranged on the outside of the tube to produce a magnetic field that exerts a force on the electrons in the beam. By this magnetic deflection the beam is made to move in a straight line across the photo-electrode at a constant speed. It is then returned to the opposite side at about five times the speed. During this retrace period, the control grid of the electron gun is made negative to stop the electron beam. The motion of the beam is caused by a varying current in the deflection coils (greater current causes greater deflection).

The radio carrier wave for television is modulated by several distinct signals:

1. the video signal from the camera tube;
2. pulses of synchronization that are necessary to control the sweep oscillators in the receiver;
3. the FM audio signal from the microphone.

When the radio wave has been received, amplified and detected, special circuits in the receiver permit the various components of the modulation to supply energy to the appropriate circuits.

Television reception is based on the cathode-ray tube. A description of this is given in Fig. 21-8. Each television receiver contains oscillators to supply current to the horizontal and vertical deflection coils of the cathode-ray picture tube. The pulses of synchronization from the transmitter ensure that these oscillators will begin the

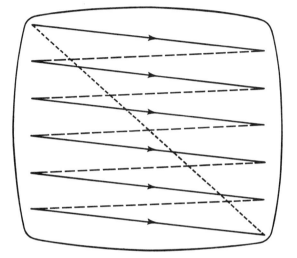

FIG. 21-4

FIG. 21-5: THE RESONANCE OF TUNED CIRCUITS

The diagram illustrates a simple circuit that can be tuned to the frequency of a broadcasting station. Incident electromagnetic waves induce a small alternating current in the coil. The current produces opposite charges on the plates of the capacitor. (In its simplest form a capacitor consists of two large parallel metal plates close together, insulated from each other.) When the charge reaches a maximum it flows back through the coil in the opposite direction. When the charge on the capacitor is a maximum the energy is potential. When the current in the coil is a maximum the energy is kinetic. Electrons oscillate back and forth through the circuit, with their energy being alternately potential in the capacitor and kinetic in the coil. The physical dimensions of the coil and capacitor determine the natural frequency of vibration of electrons in the circuit. The natural frequency can be changed by altering the distance between the plates of the capacitor. That is what happens when you turn the tuning knob on a radio. The radio responds to the broadcast wave that has the same frequency as the natural frequency of the tuned circuit.

This description of a tuned circuit has many similarities with the description of the action of a simple pendulum. A pendulum has a natural frequency that depends on a physical dimension (its length). When a pendulum is at the highest point of its swing, its energy is all in the form of gravitational potential energy. As it starts to swing down, this energy is transformed to kinetic energy of motion until, at the bottom of the swing, all the energy is in the kinetic form; then the transformation starts to go the other way. Because of friction, there is also a continual loss of energy which goes to heat, and to keep the oscillation going, energy has to be fed in—in the case of a clock, from a spring or from falling weights; in the case of a tuned circuit, energy loss in resistances has to be made up from an electric source.

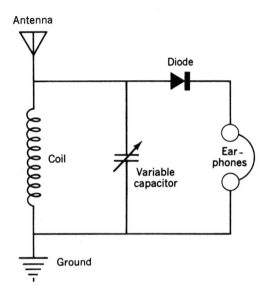

The operation of tuning can be described by reference to a tuning fork with sliders on its arms for changing its natural frequency. Suppose that a number of sound frequencies are directed at the tuning fork. If one of them has the same frequency as the natural frequency of the fork, the fork will resonate with the energy in the wave. The fork will not be affected appreciably by waves of other frequencies. If the sliders are now moved, the natural frequency of the fork is changed, and it will no longer respond to the same frequency as before. In the same way a tuned radio circuit resonates with the energy of radio waves having the same frequency as its own natural frequency, and its natural frequency can be altered to respond to any one of many broadcast frequencies.

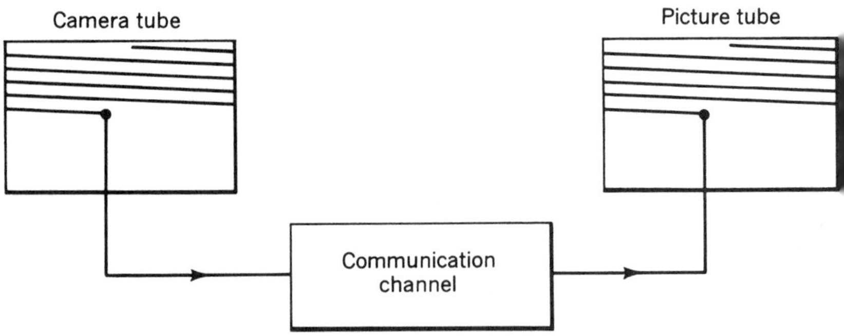

Camera tube

Picture tube

Communication channel

FIG. 21-6

deflection sweeps at the instants that correspond correctly to the video signal. This is needed so that the top left corner of the picture will be at the top left of the cathode-ray tube, as illustrated in Fig. 21-6. The pattern of varying brightness is displayed on the face of the cathode-ray tube by the scanning of the electron beam from the tube's electron gun. The video signal is supplied to the control grid of the cathode-ray tube. The variations in the video signal control the intensity of the electron beam. Where more electrons strike the face of the tube, it is brighter.

The energy transformations through a television system may be summarized as follows:

1. Light energy from the scene being televised falls on the photosensitive element of the camera tube. In the camera tube the light energy controls the electrical energy of electrons flowing in the output circuit.

2. Through amplifiers this electrical energy is able to control larger amounts of electrical energy, eventually reaching the modulator. The modulated carrier oscillations in the antenna produce electromagnetic energy in oscillating electric and magnetic fields.

3. The fields in the electromagnetic wave induce electric currents in the receiving antenna—electrical energy. After amplification and detection the electrical energy of the video signal is applied to the grid of the cathode-ray tube to control the number of electrons in the beam.

4. The impact of electrons on the phosphorescent material of the face of the tube causes them to emit light in proportion to the number of electrons that strike the face. The tube then glows with a light pattern that reproduces the original changing scene.

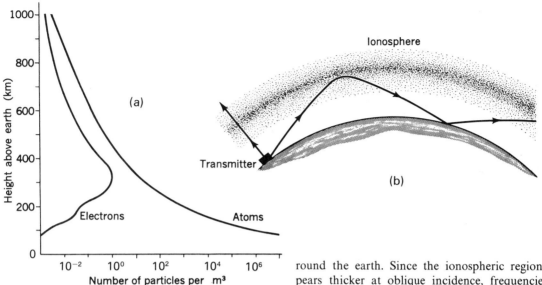

FIG. 21-7: RADIO WAVES AND THE IONO-SPHERE

The long-distance transmission of radio waves is made possible by the action of free electrons in the upper atmosphere. Concentrated in a region called the **ionosphere** extending from about 100 to 1000 km above the earth's surface, the electrons oscillate at the frequency of incident radio waves. This action results in the absorption of energy from the electromagnetic wave. The energy is then radiated at the same frequency in all directions by the electrons. At frequencies in the range from 1 to 10 MHz (the AM broadcasting band) the absorption is so great that no electromagnetic energy can escape through the ionosphere. The re-radiation by electrons constitutes a "reflection" or return of the energy to the surface of the earth. Most of the energy that is not transferred to ions by collision is returned in a direction that conforms to the normal laws of reflection.

Electrons are less able to absorb energy from waves of higher frequency; the density of electrons in the ionosphere (a) is determined from measurements of the frequencies of radio waves that are just able to penetrate the ionosphere. Ordinary communication paths strike the ionosphere at large angles of incidence (b), may be reflected, and are then able to be received at distances up to 5000 km from the transmitter. Several reflections back and forth between the earth and the ionosphere enable radio signals to be transmitted more than half way

round the earth. Since the ionospheric region appears thicker at oblique incidence, frequencies as high as 35 MHz may be reflected.

The ionosphere is produced by the impact of radiation from the sun on atoms of nitrogen and oxygen in the upper atmosphere. The collision of ultraviolet photons with the atoms ionizes them. There is a region of maximum ionization (a) because at heights above 500 km the atmosphere is too rare for the production of a great many ions, and below 100 km it is so dense that most of the ultraviolet radiation has already been absorbed at greater heights.

The density of ionization above a particular place depends on the local time of day, since it depends on solar radiation. It rises to a maximum just after local sunset. At that time the atmosphere very high above is being irradiated obliquely so that the light travels through the greatest amount of atmosphere. Nightfall is then the time at which absorption and reflection are greatest and one starts to get "interference" from distant stations. As the signal received depends on ionospheric conditions, and these vary, the interference fades and then gets stronger irregularly.

The vivid colours of the aurorae (northern and southern lights) are produced in polar latitudes at ionospheric heights. Ions emitted from the sun and trapped in the earth's magnetic field excite atoms of nitrogen and oxygen to emit light. These solar ions also influence the structure of the ionosphere and produce variations in the earth's magnetic field. They are emitted from solar flares and from the regions of sunspots.

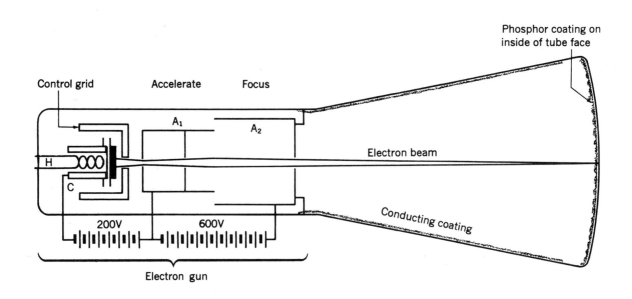

Electron gun

FIG. 21-8: CATHODE-RAY TUBES

In the cathode-ray tubes used in television receivers it is necessary to have a narrow beam of electrons which can be moved back and forth across the screen to "paint" the picture. This electron beam is provided by a system of electrodes called an **electron gun**. The **heater, H**, raises the temperature of the cathode to about 1000°C. At this temperature the **cathode, C**, can send out, by thermionic emission, a large supply of electrons into the space in front of it. The voltage between the **control grid** and the cathode determines the rate at which electrons can pass out of the gun through the aperture in the grid, in a way analogous to that in which the emitter-base voltage in a transistor controls the passage of electrons to the collector.

The voltages between the cathode and the two anodes provide electric fields that accelerate and focus the electrons. The "rays" in the diagram indicate the edges of the electron beam; and it can be seen that in the picture they are converging to a point at the face of the cathode-ray tube. The inner surface of the tube face is coated with a phosphorescent material, which radiates light when struck by electrons. The brightness of the spot on the screen varies with the rate at which electrons are hitting it. In a television picture tube the phosphor

is a mixture of the sulfide and silicate of zinc with metallic manganese and silver. The inside of the tube between the gun and the screen has a conducting coating connected to the final anode. The electric circuit is completed through this coating.

The provision of a method for deflecting the electron beam from its normal path enables patterns to be produced on the face of the cathode-ray tube. The two methods of electron deflection are magnetic and electrostatic, such as employed by J. J. Thomson in his studies of cathode rays (Chapter 17). In television receivers the electron beam is swept back and forth and up and down across the face of the picture tube by the changing magnetic fields of coils mounted on the outside of the neck of the tube. On the other hand, it is usual for the cathode-ray tube in an oscilloscope to employ electrostatic deflection. Potential differences are applied across a pair of plates situated so that the electron beam passes between them on its way from the electron gun to the face of the tube. Voltages are applied across plates that can move the beam up and down. A second pair of plates, arranged to move the beam sideways, is supplied from a circuit within the oscilloscope in order to spread a voltage-time graph across the face of the tube.

Exercises

A

1. What is the "carrier" in (a) telephone communication, (b) radio communication, (c) television communication?

2. (a) What device enables the carrier in the telephone system to be modulated?
   (b) What is the receiver in the telephone electrical system?
   (c) What is the significance of the term "broadcasting" as used in radio or television by contrast with, say, a telephone circuit?

3. What is the speed of transmission of radio signals?

4. (a) What is a typical (AM) radio frequency?
   (b) What is a typical audio frequency?

5. What are the two uses of antennas in radio communication?

6. What is meant by rectification? Why is it necessary in radio reception?

7. (a) Suppose that you have lost a ten dollar bill in a large field. Draw a sketch of the path along which you might walk to scan the field if it were rectangular in shape.
   (b) What is meant by interlaced scanning?
   (c) At what rate does one picture follow another on a TV screen?

8. What is meant by the "natural frequency" of an electric circuit? How can it be changed?

9. (a) How high in the atmosphere is the ionosphere?
   (b) What produces the ionization in the ionosphere?
   (c) How does the density of ionization in the ionosphere change with day and night?

10. "In an AM broadcast, a loud sound has a large amplitude signal." Write a corresponding statement for a loud sound in an FM broadcast.

11. Why does a stereo FM station not merely broadcast left (L) and right (R) signals?

12. What does the electron gun of a cathode-ray oscilloscope do?

13. How is the electron beam in a TV receiver deflected?

B

14. The half-wave antenna of a certain broadcasting station has a length of 100 m. Calculate the frequency of the station.

15. A certain radio station has a frequency of 1010 kHz. What should be the length of a half-wave antenna for this frequency?

16. If the 60 Hz domestic power supply were to be transmitted by radio rather than by wires, what would be the length of the corresponding half-wave antenna?

17. What is the length of a half-wave antenna for receiving TV channel 35, at a frequency of about 600 MHz?

18. The moon is 3.8×10^5 km from the earth. How long does it take a radio signal to get from the earth to the moon?

19. The sun sometimes puts out sudden bursts of "radio noise." How long does it take these signals to reach the earth? The sun is 1.5×10^8 km from the earth. Would we see the solar eruption which caused the radio noise before the radio signal reached us?

20. What must be the frequency of the oscillator that provides the energy to move the electron beam in a TV picture tube back and forth horizontally, if 525 trips across the face of the tube occur in each thirtieth of a second?

21. What is the frequency of the oscillator which causes the electron beam of a TV receiver to move down the screen in a sixtieth of a second?

22. When viewed end on, the electrostatic deflection plates of a cathode-ray tube have the appearance of the four sides of a rectangle with the corners missing. Draw diagrams to show how the plates should be charged so that the spot on the face of the tube produced by the electron beam is seen
   (a) near the centre of the right side,
   (b) near the centre of the bottom side,
   (c) near the upper left corner.

23. If an alternating potential difference is applied between the upper and lower deflection plates of a cathode-ray tube what will appear on the face of the tube?

24. As you look at the face of a certain cathode-ray tube, the left-hand deflection plate is positive with respect to the right-hand plate, and the lower plate is positive with respect to the upper plate. The voltages in the left-hand and lower plates are then uniformly decreased through zero to an equal negative value. Describe the motion of the spot across the face of the tube.

C

25. List four differences between sound waves and radio (electromagnetic) waves.

26. Just as each FM station occupies a band of frequency, so each AM station occupies a section of the total AM band. The width of frequency required by an AM station is roughly given by twice the upper limit of audible frequencies. This upper limit is about 20 kHz. Calculate how many AM stations there may be in the AM band from 500 to 1500 kHz.

27. Television band widths are about 6 MHz wide. How many TV channels can be carried in the VHF band which extends from 174 MHz to 216 MHz. (The lowest frequency corresponds to channel 7.)

28. Use an encyclopedia or other books to find out about the work of:
   (a) Hertz (radio)
   (b) Baird (television)
   (c) Marconi (radio)
   (d) Bell (telephone)
   (e) Appleton (ionosphere)
   (f) Armstrong (radio).

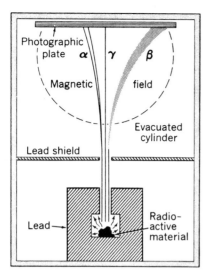

Photographic plate
α γ β
Magnetic
field
Evacuated cylinder
Lead shield
Lead → Radioactive material

FIG. 22-1

CHAPTER **22**

Radioactivity and Nuclear Structure

RADIOACTIVE RAYS

The experiments of J. J. Thomson in 1897, discussed in Chapter 17, showed that atoms are not indivisible. Other experiments carried out at about the same time also pointed the same way. In 1896 Henri Becquerel found that uranium salts emitted radiations of high energy which could penetrate paper and cause fogging of photographic plates. The name **radioactivity** was given to this phenomenon. Becquerel had in fact been studying the fluorescence of various minerals (that is, the glow or radiation that the minerals emit when illuminated by sunlight or other strong lights) and had been using photographic plates as detectors of the radiation. At a time of little sunshine he had stored the uranium mineral with the plates, and unexpectedly found the effect described.

Many elements at the top end of the Periodic Table were found to have this property. Mme and Pierre Curie of France in a long series of experiments (1898) separated the most active elements. It then became possible to look at the particular types of radiation emitted by different elements. Three main types are distinguishable, the alpha (α), beta (β) and gamma (γ) rays. Gamma rays can penetrate matter readily and are undeflected by magnetic fields; they are in fact just very energetic x-rays. Beta rays are fast-moving electrons. They were the penetrating rays observed by Becquerel. Alpha rays are easily stopped by matter and are positively charged particles, as shown by the fact that they are deflected by a magnetic field in the direction opposite to that in which electrons are deflected (Fig. 22-1). The m/e ratio for the α-rays was found to be the same as that of doubly charged helium ions. Rutherford collected in a discharge tube large numbers of these α-rays (Fig. 22-2); when an electrical discharge was passed through the tube the spectrum of light emitted was identical with that given by helium gas. The α-particles are the nuclei of helium atoms.

Now helium is known to be a chemical element, and a very inactive one chemically; it is the lightest member of the series of "inert gases," the series starting helium, neon, argon, and krypton. There can be no question of the helium being part of a chemical compound with the radon, itself indeed being a member of this series of inactive gases. The only explanation for the phenomenon is that the radon atom had exploded into two parts, one of these being helium. This

The three kinds of rays were first distinguished by their penetrating power. Alpha rays are stopped by thin paper or any material of mass/area greater than about 50 g/m². Beta rays are stopped by plates of light metals where the mass/area ratio is 10 kg/m² or more. To stop gamma rays takes several centimetres of lead or other dense metal.

explosion is not a chemical process, and in fact the energy involved in this explosion is about a million times that normally met in chemical reactions.

TRANSMUTATION OF ELEMENTS

These discoveries stimulated research to find out if similar transformations take place in other radioactive materials. Rutherford, a physicist, and Frederick Soddy, a chemist, worked together at McGill University in Montreal on this problem in the years 1900 to 1902 and found that this **transmutation of elements**, as it was called, was characteristic of radioactivity. Uranium, for instance, changes to thorium with the emission of an alpha particle. This is called alpha decay. Reference to the chart of the Periodic Table in the Appendix shows that helium is in place 2 of the Table, and that thorium is just 2 places below uranium. In fact, every alpha decay is accompanied by a transmutation of two places down the Table.

Those elements which are transmuted by the emission of β-rays are said to undergo beta decay. Every decay of this type is accompanied by a change of one place up the Periodic Table; one type of bismuth (place 83 in the Table) emits a beta particle and becomes polonium (place 84). These changes are illustrated by the diagram which shows the series of radioactive decays which starts with uranium (Fig. 22-3). The emission of gamma radiation does not involve a

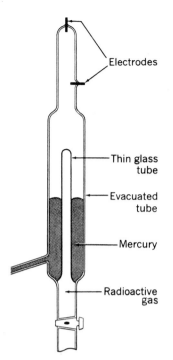

Electrodes

Thin glass tube

Evacuated tube

Mercury

Radioactive gas

FIG. 22-2

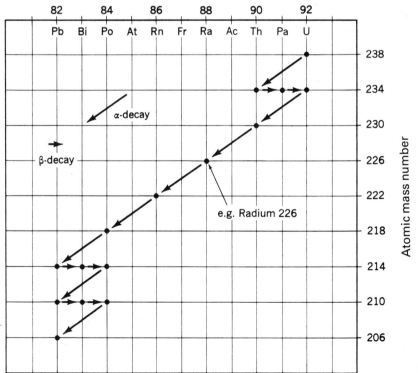

Atomic number and chemical symbol

Atomic mass number

α-decay

β-decay

e.g. Radium 226

FIG. 22-3

transmutation; it is simply a way by which a nucleus gets rid of excess energy.

THE BUILDING BLOCKS OF THE NUCLEUS

The fact that alpha, beta and gamma radiations come out of (some) nuclei makes one think that perhaps nuclei are made up of helium nuclei and electrons, held together in some energetic state. Such speculation about sub-atomic structure is not new. As early as 1815 the English chemist William Prout had suggested that all atoms were made up of hydrogen atoms bound together in some way. With the discovery of the nucleus (Chapter 18) this idea was modified, and it was suggested that the nuclei of all atoms were built up of hydrogen nuclei, that is, of the particles we call **protons**. There is a very serious objection to this idea, however. On a convenient scale, with the charge and the mass of the hydrogen nucleus both equal to unity, it would be expected that if nuclei were simply composed of many protons they would all have masses (A) equal to their charge (Z). For many nuclei the mass is approximately equal to twice the charge.

Alpha particles have a mass equal to twice their charge. Moreover they are ejected by nuclei in one type of radioactive decay. An α-particle model of the nucleus was therefore suggested, in which all nuclei are built of these helium nuclei. Although there is undoubtedly some truth in this, it cannot be the whole truth—for example, it is not possible to make hydrogen out of α-particles, and the only nuclei that should exist on this picture are those with masses 1, 2, 3, 4, 5 . . . times the mass of the helium atom.

Then in 1932 the **neutron** was discovered. This is a particle with a mass almost the same as that of the proton (actually it is just slightly heavier), but it has no electrical charge. Using the proton (the hydrogen nucleus) and the neutron as building blocks, it is possible to construct any nucleus. Nuclei are characterized by their atomic number Z, which is just the charge on the nucleus in units of the elementary electric charge, and their atomic mass number A. The typical nucleus can be written as ^AZ, although commonly the chemical symbol for the element is written as well as, or instead of, the nuclear charge. In order that it may have a charge Z, the nucleus must have Z protons in it. To make up the remaining mass, ($A - Z$) units, requires N neutrons where $N = (A - Z)$.

Thus uranium 238 may be written $^{238}92$ or $^{238}_{92}U$ or ^{238}U since uranium occupies position 92 in the Periodic Table. This nucleus has 92 protons and (238 - 92) = 146 neutrons. The alpha particle, the nucleus of helium 4, can be written ^4_2He or ^4He, and has two protons and two neutrons (Fig. 22-4). The oxygen 15 nucleus can be written $^{15}_8O$ or ^{15}O and has eight protons and seven neutrons. There are 328 combinations of protons and neutrons found in nature, although others have since been made. Of these 328, only 272 are stable, the others all being radioactive to some degree. More than 1200 other combinations have been made in laboratories, and all these artifi-

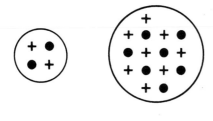

(a)   (b)

FIG. 22-4

cially produced combinations are radioactive.

The nucleus found naturally with the largest number of protons is uranium, with 92. All values of Z from 0 (the neutron) to 92 are found naturally with the exceptions of 43 (technetium, found in stars) and 61 (promethium). Each value of Z corresponds to a particular chemical element.

ISOTOPES

Every atom of any one chemical element has the same number of protons in its nucleus and therefore the same atomic number, Z. However, quite commonly nuclei of the same element will have different numbers of neutrons in them and therefore will have different atomic mass numbers. For example, oxygen nuclei all have 8 protons in them ($Z = 8$), but oxygen nuclei are found in nature which have either 8, 9 or 10 neutrons in them. All these nuclei fit in the same place in the Periodic Table, and are therefore called **isotopes** of oxygen (from two Greek words meaning "same" and "place"). To repeat, these isotopes all have the same chemistry but differ from each other first of all in mass, and sometimes in other physical properties such as their relative stability against radioactive decay, or their mode of decay if they are radioactive.

Soddy was the first to show the existence of such different forms. He found that three samples of the element thorium, formed by three different radioactive decay processes, had the same chemical properties, yet had different radioactive characteristics. He gave the name isotope to such nuclei in 1910. A few years later the English physicist F.W. Aston, measuring the mass of the neon nucleus, found that ordinary neon was a mixture of two isotopes with atomic masses 20 and 22. These isotopes are called neon 20 and neon 22, written $^{20}_{10}$Ne and $^{22}_{10}$Ne. These each have 10 protons but have 10 and 12 neutrons respectively (Fig. 22-5). The relative abundance of the two nuclear species is approximately 91:9, so that neon has an average atomic mass of

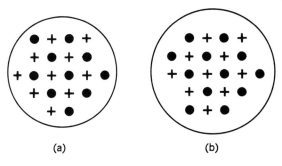

FIG. 22-5

Abundance refers to the proportions of the isotopes found in nature—of every 100 atoms of neon, 91 are neon 20 and 9 are neon 22.

$$\frac{91 \times 20 + 9 \times 22}{100} = 20.18.$$

Chlorine, with an atomic mass of 35.45, is approximately a 75:25 mixture of $^{35}_{17}$Cl and $^{37}_{17}$Cl.

The lightest chemical element, hydrogen, has three known isotopes, of masses 1, 2, and 3 units. Because of their importance, the two heavier isotopes have their own names. They are illustrated in Fig 22-6. Hydrogen 2 is called deuterium, symbol D. It is not radioactive, and is found with a natural abundance of 0.015%. It combines with oxygen to form water, but whereas ordinary water, H_2O, has a molecular mass of 18 units ($2 \times 1 + 16$), this water has a molecular

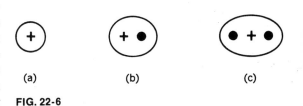

FIG. 22-6

mass of 20 units (2 × 2 + 16). D_2O is therefore called heavy water. It is of great importance in the development of nuclear power, and its use in nuclear reactors will be discussed in Chapter 23.

D_2O has a freezing point of 3.82°C and a boiling point of 101.42°C. Because of this slightly higher boiling point, it is possible to make a separation of the heavy water from ordinary water by distillation. The small difference in mass also leads to the fact that the residual solution in electrolytic cells which have been bubbling off hydrogen and oxygen for many years has a slightly higher concentration of heavy water than does ordinary water.

Hydrogen 3 is called tritium, symbol T. It is radioactive, slowly turning into helium 3. Tritium is one of the materials that can be used in hydrogen bombs or fusion reactors.

The heaviest naturally occurring element, uranium, has isotopes of mass numbers 234, 235, and 238. All have 92 protons in their nuclei. All three are in fact radioactive, but are so long lived that significant amounts occur naturally. The least abundant is $^{234}_{92}$U (0.006%); there is more $^{235}_{92}$U (0.72%), but most of natural uranium is $^{238}_{92}$U (99.27%).

THE STABILITY OF NUCLEI

You will see from the graph of the naturally occurring nuclei, Fig. 22-7, that they lie about a broad line which has a slight curve. The nuclei which lie on the straight dotted line have equal numbers of protons and neutrons and you will see that many nuclei do in fact have $Z = N$. Towards the heavier end of the Periodic Table, the nuclei tend to have more neutrons than protons. Any nucleus, such as $^{14}_{6}$C, that would be placed below the band of stable nuclei would have an excess of neutrons. In the course of time one of these would change into a proton with the emission of an electron, that is, with the ejection of a (negative) beta particle. The emission of a negative electron will result in the nucleus having one extra positive charge, and so it will be changed into a different element, one place up the Periodic Table. Any nucleus to the left of the band would have an excess of protons, and one of the protons would change sooner or later into a neutron. This change results in the creation and emission of a positive electron or **positron**. The ejection of a positron will send the nucleus one place down the Table.

Alpha decay, in which a nucleus emits a helium nucleus, occurs mainly in the heaviest nuclei. It results in a transmutation to two places down the Periodic Table.

NUCLEAR BINDING

Another question which arises is how the protons and neutrons hold together in the nucleus. In the atomic case this is easy since the nucleus and electrons have opposite charges, and so attract one another —in fact the trouble is to find why they keep apart! But in the nucleus the only electrostatic effect is the mutual repulsion of the posi-

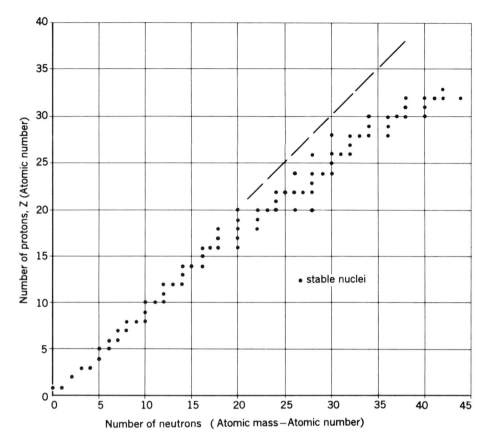

FIG. 22-7

tively charged protons which should tend to blow the nucleus apart. There must be some attractive "nuclear force" between all the particles in the nucleus which will more than compensate for the electrostatic repulsion. Much of the work being done in modern physics is the search for information about this force so that we can more readily understand how and why it operates. We know that there are 272 nuclei in which the mutual attraction between the protons and neutrons in the nucleus is sufficient to overcome the repulsion between the protons. As the number of protons increases, the number of neutrons must increase also, otherwise the nucleus is unstable, and in fact in all the heavier nuclei the number of neutrons exceeds the number of protons. However, as we go up the Periodic Table the electrostatic repulsion finally becomes so great that the nuclei are unable to hold together for any great length of time. Although elements heavier than uranium once existed in nature, they were so unstable that they are no longer found on earth.

In 1932 Hideki Yukawa, a Japanese theoretical physicist, suggested that there exists a particle which holds the protons and neutrons together, as mortar holds together the bricks of a house. This particle he predicted should have a mass about 200 times the mass of the electron. Because this mass is between that of the electron and the proton, the predicted particle was called a *meson* (meso means middle, as in mezzo-soprano, one in the middle voice range). In 1938 such a particle was found in cosmic radiation, and since then a number of types of these particles in the middle range have been discovered. For many years the high energy cosmic rays coming in from outer space were the only source of mesons, but since 1948 mesons have been produced artificially in the large nuclear machines now built in many countries, and this has made research into their properties much easier.

It is now believed that stable nuclei consist of protons and neutrons held together by mesonic forces; in unstable nuclei the forces are just not quite strong enough to keep the particles together.

THE RATE OF RADIOACTIVE DECAY

We have spoken of the fact of radioactivity—the fact that some atoms are in such a state that they spontaneously disintegrate into smaller parts with the emission of energy—but no mention has been made of the rate at which this emission takes place. All chemical reactions are readily affected by such things as heat or pressure—the hotter the materials are, the quicker the reaction proceeds—but this was found not to be the case with radioactivity. Nothing that could be done to a lump of uranium would alter the rate at which it emitted alpha particles. In fact the number of particles shot off in unit time is purely dependent on the amount of the uranium that is there. If you have only a tenth of the weight of uranium, you have only a tenth of the activity, and nothing you can do in the way of heating, cooling, melting or pressurizing the uranium alters this rate of decay. Naturally if you start with 1 g of uranium, and some of it is turning into thorium, the amount of uranium will be decreasing with time, and therefore the activity of the lump will decrease with time, because it is not all pure uranium any more. In fact at all times it is found that: *The rate of decay is proportional to the amount of the radioactive material present.*

To see what this can mean, imagine a situation where initially you have $100 in the bank and you are told that you can take out 20% of what is in the bank at the end of each week. At the end of the first week, you would take out $20 leaving $80 in the bank. At the end of the second week, you would remove 20% of $80 or $16, leaving $64 in the bank, and so on. The figures for several weeks are shown in Table 22-1.

A graph of these results is drawn in Fig. 22-8. Several conclusions can be drawn from the table and graph. First of all, the balance fell to half the initial $100 in just over 3 weeks, to half of this again in just over 6 weeks, and to half of this again, that is to $12.50, in just over 9 weeks. Thus a time of the order of three weeks can be taken as the **half-life** of the balance, the time in which any balance is reduced by a factor of two. In a period of 6 weeks the balance is reduced to ½ × ½ of its original value, in 3 half-lives to ½ × ½ × ½

The unit of radioactivity is the becquerel (Bq), where 1 Bq is a rate of one disintegration per second. The activity of uranium 238 is 1.25×10^4 Bq/g.

Table 22-1

HALF-LIVES IN BANK
WITHDRAWALS

Week	Withdrawn (Dollars)	Balance (Dollars)
0	—	100.00
1	20.00	80.00
2	16.00	64.00
3	12.80	51.20
4	10.24	40.96
5	8.19	32.77
6	6.55	26.22
7	5.24	20.98
8	4.19	16.79
9	3.36	13.43
10	2.69	10.74
20	0.29	1.16
21	0.23	0.93
22	0.18	0.75
30	0.03	0.13

or $(\frac{1}{2})^3$. After slightly more than 21 weeks, that is 7 half-lives, we would expect it to be reduced to $(\frac{1}{2})^7$ or $1/128 = 0.0078$ of the original, and in fact we see that after 21 weeks there is just a little more than 78¢ left in the bank. Secondly, the rate of withdrawal goes down with time in just exactly the same ratio as does the balance. Twenty-one weeks after the first withdrawal (of $20) the withdrawal is only 18¢, just slightly more than $20 \times (\frac{1}{2})^7$, or 16¢.

In general, the rate of withdrawal is proportional to the amount of money left in the bank. As this is the same type of law as was found to be true for radioactive materials, we should expect that a radioactive substance would exhibit the same type of decay, characterized by a half-life, and could be represented by a graph of the same shape. This is indeed the case, except for the slight difference that the radioactive decay of a large number of atoms is a continuous process, whereas we had assumed that money was only taken out at the end of each week. In the radioactive series headed by uranium for example (Fig. 22-3), the first member of the series, uranium, has a half-life of 4.5 billion years. Radium (Ra) has a half-life of 1620 a and radon (Rn) one of 3.8 days. Fig. 22-9 shows the decay of radium as it varies with time.

We arbitrarily stated a constant of proportionality in the money case—20% is removed each week. This could be called the *decay constant* of the money. Similarly there is a **radioactive decay constant** which for each radioactive substance is predetermined; it is a unique characteristic of the particular material. The larger this constant, the shorter is the half-life of the material.

Since radium (^{226}Ra) has a half-life of 1620 a, its decay constant is 1.36×10^{-11} s^{-1}. That is, in each second 1.36×10^{-11} of all the nuclei present break up. Since a lump of 1 g of ^{226}Ra contains $\frac{1}{226} \times 6.02 \times 10^{23}$ nuclei, its activity will be 3.7×10^{10} Bq. This amount of activity used to be the unit of radioactivity and was called one curie (1 Ci).

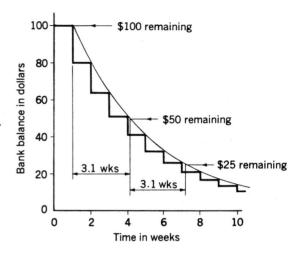

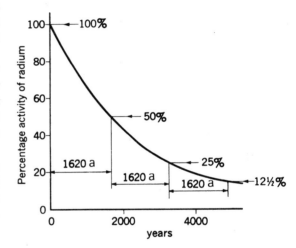

FIG. 22-9

FIG. 22-10 RADIOACTIVE DATING

CARBON DATING

Carbon 14 is a type of carbon atom (or an isotope of carbon) which is continuously produced by the action of cosmic radiation on the nitrogen of the air, and which is radioactive with a half-life of 5600 years. Living plants absorb carbon 14 in the form of carbon dioxide from the air, along with the more ordinary carbon 12, both being used in the process of photosynthesis. As a result all living material is slightly radioactive, and 1 g of carbon from living organic material has an activity of 0.26 Bq. After a plant dies no more carbon 14 is absorbed, and the amount in the plant gradually decreases with the characteristic half-life of this isotope. Thus 1 g of carbon produced 5600 years ago has now an activity of 0.13 Bq, and so on. The activity of such a specimen when the weight of carbon in it is measured can therefore be used to date the sample. Examples of specimens whose history is known and whose activities have been measured are shown on the graph.

As described above, carbon dating depends on the assumption that cosmic radiation has always had the same intensity. This assumption has been regarded with suspicion, and recently comparison has been made of the age of wood from very old trees (bristle-cone pines in California) by both carbon dating and by tree-ring counting. This has shown that over tens of thousands of years the cosmic-ray intensity must have changed quite often, probably as a result of changes in the magnetic field of the earth. Calibration by the tree-ring method has now enabled the carbon method to be used with much greater confidence in archeological studies.

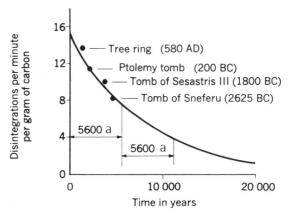

GEOLOGICAL DATING

As many rocks contain uranium, which decays to lead after a series of disintegrations, it is possible to date the time of formation of rocks by comparing the amounts of uranium and lead of radioactive origin in them. In particular, one form of uranium (^{238}U) has a half-life of 4500 million years and decays finally to a form of lead (^{206}Pb). In some granite rocks of the Canadian Shield from the vicinity of Tory Hill, Ontario, for instance, the ratio of the number of atoms of lead 206 to the number of atoms of uranium 238 is 1:5.9; that is, about one-sixth of the uranium has decayed since the formation of the granite. Clearly this rock has been in place much less than a time equal to one half-life. Doing the necessary calculation gives the answer that the rock was formed 1020×10^6 years ago, that is, over a thousand million years ago. Such measurements have been of the greatest value in telling us about the history of our earth, and recently have told us about the history of the moon.

Exercises

A

1. Use the material of the text to tell in a sentence or two what each of the following scientists discovered, proved, or, in two cases, suggested.
   (a) J. J. Thomson   (e) Aston
   (b) Becquerel   (f) Prout
   (c) Marie and Pierre Curie   (g) Yukawa
   (d) Rutherford and Soddy

2. What is meant by the term radioactivity?

3. Make a table to compare alpha, beta, and gamma rays under the headings (a) what each is, (b) sign and magnitude of the charge on each, (c) behaviour in a strong magnetic field, (d) mass, (e) penetrating ability.

4. (a) What is meant by transmutation of elements?
   (b) What happens to the atomic mass number of an atom that undergoes (i) alpha decay, (ii) beta decay, (iii) gamma decay?
   (c) What happens to the atomic number in each case in (b)?

5. One part of the uranium series of radioactive decays is
   $$^{238}_{92}U \rightarrow ^{234}_{90}Th \rightarrow ^{234}_{91}Pa \rightarrow ^{234}_{92}U.$$
   What particle or particles are emitted in each of these three decays respectively?

6. In your body, naturally occurring radioactive potassium is decaying. Part of this decay can be represented by
   $$^{40}_{19}K \rightarrow ^{40}_{20}Ca + ?.$$
   What particle is emitted in this process?

7. (a) What are the "basic building blocks of the universe"?
   (b) If you know the shorthand symbol, $^A_Z X$, for an atom of an element, how can you determine (i) the number of neutrons in the atom's nucleus, (ii) the number of electrons normally orbiting the nucleus of the atom?

8. How many protons and neutrons are there in nuclei of
   (a) ^1_1H,   (d) $^{16}_8O$,   (g) $^{238}_{92}U$,
   (b) ^4_2He,   (e) $^{40}_{19}K$,   (h) $^{249}_{98}Cf$.
   (c) $^{12}_6C$,   (f) $^{208}_{82}Pb$,

9. What are isotopes?

10. What property of the nucleus of an atom determines the basic chemical properties of the atom?

11. What is (a) deuterium, (b) tritium, (c) heavy water? Which of these three is radioactive?

12. (a) What is a positron?
    (b) What is the difference between nuclei that emit electrons and those that emit positrons?

13. What is a meson?

14. All living or formerly living substances contain radioactive carbon 14. How does this come about?

15. On what does the rate of decay of any specific radioactive material depend?

16. What is meant by the half-life of a radioactive substance?

17. Compared with the original rate of disintegration, what will be the rate of disintegration of a radioactive substance after (a) one half-life, (b) two half-lives, (c) three half-lives?

18. Define the unit of activity, the becquerel.

B

19. Certain isotopes of the following elements are radioactive and emit alpha particles. Use the Periodic Table in the Appendix to determine into which elements they are transmuted:
    (a) uranium, (c) samarium (atomic number = 62),
    (b) radium, (d) thorium.

20. Certain isotopes of the following elements are beta-active, emitting negative electrons. Determine into which elements they are transmuted:
    (a) potassium,   (c) strontium,
    (b) lead,   (d) carbon.

21. Calculate the density of heavy water, D_2O, assuming that the volume occupied by the D_2O molecule is the same as that occupied by an H_2O molecule.

22. Calculate the density of "super-heavy water," T_2O, making an assumption similar to that in question 21.

23. The only isotope of sodium which is not radioactive is ^{23}Na. (a) If you made some ^{24}Na, would it decay by the emission of a positive electron or by the emission of a negative electron? (b) What would happen in the case of ^{22}Na?

24. Silver consists of two isotopes, of approximately equal abundance, whose atomic mass numbers are 107 and 109. What is the atomic mass number of natural silver?

25. Copper consists of two isotopes, ^{63}Cu, of 70% abundance, and ^{65}Cu, of 30% abundance. What is the atomic mass number of natural copper?

26. It has been found that 3.7×10^{10} radium nuclei disintegrate each second in a piece of radium of mass 1 g. How many disintegrations will occur per second in a piece of mass 0.2 g? What is the activity of this smaller piece in becquerels?

27. Using the analogy discussed in the text of the withdrawal of money from a bank, find approximate values for the half-life of the bank balance when at the end of each week the following percentages of the remaining balance are removed: (a) 10%, (b) 15%, (c) 30%, (d) 50%.

28. Using the analogy of the withdrawal of money from a bank, find approximate values of the half-life of the bank balance when (a) 10%, (b) 20%, (c) 30%, (d) 50% of the remaining balance is removed at the end of each 2 weeks.

29. The natural radioactivity of air, due to radon gas normally present, is about 10 disintegrations per second per cubic metre of air. Express this in (a) disintegrations/second per litre, (b) disintegrations per minute per cubic metre.

30. The half-life of radium is 1620 years. (a) Using the data from question 26, in 1620 years what will be the activity in becquerels of the radium in a piece which currently has a mass of 0.2 g? (b) In 3240 years? (c) In 6480 years? (d) What will be the mass of radium in the piece after 6480 years?

31. A certain specimen of charcoal found in the buried remains of a wood fire was found to have a radioactivity due to carbon 14 of 13 disintegrations per minute per gram of carbon. How old is the charcoal? (You may find it helpful to use Fig. 22-10.)

32. A sample of wood from an ancient tomb is thought to be 8000 years old. (a) What carbon 14 activity would you expect it to have? (b) What activity would you expect if the age was thought to be 13 000 years old?

33. Samples of charcoal from the remains of a fire made beside a grave in L'anse Amour in Labrador give carbon 14 activities of 6.4 disintegrations per minute per gram of carbon. What is the age of the grave?

C

34. Use an encyclopedia or other books to learn more about the lives of (a) Marie Curie, (b) Ernest Rutherford, (c) Frederick Soddy, and write a few sentences on each.

35. Use the chart of the stable nuclei (Fig. 22-7), and the Periodic Table in the Appendix to determine whether the following nuclei are radioactive or not. If you decide that a nucleus is radioactive, state whether it is more likely to decay by emitting a negative electron or a positive electron.

^{30}S ^{32}S ^{34}S ^{38}S ^{24}Mg ^{26}Mg ^{28}Mg

^{11}C ^{12}C ^{13}C ^{14}C ^{5}Li ^{6}Li ^{7}Li ^{8}Li

^{43}Sc ^{45}Sc ^{47}Sc

36. The nuclei ^{8}Be and ^{12}C can be considered to be aggregates of 2 and 3 alpha particles respectively. Make a list of a few more stable nuclei that could be made simply by the coalition of alpha particles.

37. Boron, which has an atomic mass of 10.8 u, is a mixture of two isotopes whose relative abundances are 20% and 80%. One of the isotopes has an atomic mass number of 11. What is the atomic mass number of the other isotope?

38. The element thallium, which has an atomic mass of 204.4 u, consists of a mixture of two isotopes whose relative abundances are 30.0% and 70.0%. The atomic mass number of the more abundant isotope is 205. What is the atomic mass number of the other isotope?

39. Using the bank balance analogy noted in the text, find the approximate percentages of the remaining balance removed each week if the half-life of the balance is (a) 1 week, (b) 2 weeks, (c) 4 weeks.

CHAPTER 23

Nuclear Reactions and Energy

This chapter is about the interactions between nuclei—what happens when they collide or break up. The earliest discovered type of nuclear reaction was discussed in the previous chapter. You will remember that in the alpha decay of nuclei, the nucleus breaks up into a helium nucleus and a residual or daughter nucleus. We write this, for example,

A nuclear blast at the Nevada test site.

$$^{238}_{92}\text{U} \rightarrow {}^{234}_{90}\text{Th} + {}^{4}_{2}\text{He}$$

where in each case the subscript is the charge on the nucleus, and the superscript the atomic mass of the nucleus. In nuclear physics it is customary to ignore the electrons round the nucleus, and so in the equation we make no mention of whether the helium is ionized or not.

NUCLEAR REACTIONS

The reverse process to α-decay is also possible—in this case an alpha particle is *absorbed* by a nucleus. In 1919 Rutherford bombarded nitrogen with alpha particles and found that particles that had all the characteristics of protons were ejected from the nitrogen. What happens in this experiment can be represented by the diagram in Fig. 23-1, or more conveniently by the nuclear equation

Recall the discussion of protons in Chapter 22, *The building blocks of the nucleus*.

$$^{4}_{2}\text{He} + {}^{14}_{7}\text{N} \rightarrow {}^{17}_{8}\text{O} + {}^{1}_{1}\text{H}.$$

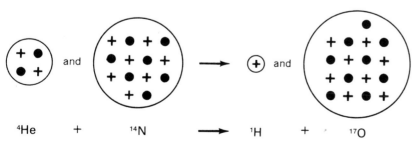

| ^{4}He | + | ^{14}N | $\longrightarrow$ | ^{1}H | + | ^{17}O | **FIG. 23-1** |

Recall that the atomic number tells how many protons, each of unit charge, are in the nucleus.

This shows that the nucleus of helium 4 (symbol He, atomic number $Z = 2$, atomic mass $A = 4$) combines with a nitrogen nucleus (symbol N, $Z = 7$, $A = 14$) to give oxygen 17 (symbol O, $Z = 8$, $A = 17$) and a proton (the nucleus of hydrogen 1, symbol H, $Z = 1$, $A = 1$).

Since 1919 large numbers of nuclear reactions have been investigated. All these reactions have some things in common. If we consider the simple nuclear reaction

$$\,^2_1H + \,^2_1H \longrightarrow \,^3_2H + \,^1_0n$$

representing what happens when two nuclei of hydrogen 2 react giving a nucleus of helium 3 and a neutron, we see that the sum of the nuclear charges on the left-hand side of the equation ($1 + 1 = 2$) equals the sum of the nuclear charges on the right-hand side ($2 + 0 = 2$). Similarly the sums of the atomic masses on both sides of the equation are the same ($2 + 2 = 4 = 3 + 1$), at least to two figure accuracy. To a higher order of accuracy however, the masses do not quite add up properly. In fact, the total mass on the left-hand side is 3.5×10^{-3} u more than that on the right-hand side of the equation.

The symbol u is the atomic mass unit, 1 u = 1.66×10^{-27} kg.

The difference in mass is associated with a term which so far we have left out of the equation, though for completeness it should be there. This is the **reaction energy**. By carrying out the nuclear experiment and measuring the energy released in the process, we find that the reaction can be more fully represented by

$$\,^2_1H + \,^2_1H \longrightarrow \,^3_2He + \,^1_0n + 5.2 \times 10^{-13}\ J$$

that is, 5.2×10^{-13} J is the energy released when two nuclei of hydrogen 2 react to form helium 3 and a neutron. This may be compared with the 9×10^{-19} J that is released when two molecules of hydrogen react with one molecule of oxygen to form two molecules of water. You will see that there is about a million times more energy released in the nuclear reaction than in the chemical reaction. In both cases, however, the energy is in the form of kinetic energy of the reaction products.

In all nuclear reactions we find that the ratio of the energy released to the mass difference is a constant. We can find the value of the constant from the figures for the above experiment, and from the fact that one nuclear mass unit is equal to 1.66×10^{-27} kg. Then the value of the constant is

$$\frac{5.2 \times 10^{-13}\ J}{3.5 \times 10^{-3} \times 1.66 \times 10^{-27}\ kg} = 9.0 \times 10^{16}\ \frac{kg \cdot m^2/s^2}{kg}$$

$$= (3.0 \times 10^8\ m/s)^2.$$

Now it may readily be appreciated that the value of this constant is the square of the speed of light—in fact we have illustrated the Einstein relationship between mass and energy $E/m = c^2$, or $E = mc^2$, which is of such great importance in the world today. What has happened in the course of the nuclear reaction is that some of the **mass-energy** of the system has been converted into energy of motion of the reaction products, the helium nucleus and the neutron. The same thing actually happens in a chemical reaction, but here the decrease in mass-energy is so small (10^{-35} kg) that it is completely undetectable.

Three of the characteristics of nuclear reactions are therefore
1. the total charge remains constant;
2. the total energy (mass-energy and kinetic energy) remains constant;
3. the total number of protons plus neutrons remains constant.

You have seen that many nuclear reactions result in a "transmutation of the elements"—for example, Rutherford started with nitrogen and converted it into oxygen. In ancient days it was believed that elements could be converted into others by alchemy. In particular, alchemists were interested in making gold because of its great value. Such transmutations cannot be carried out by chemical means, but by physical methods they are possible—but at a much greater price that it would cost to buy ordinary gold! Very often, however, the product of a nuclear reaction is not "ordinary." Quite commonly a radioactive isotope of an element is formed, and this isotope can be extremely valuable for many purposes that will be discussed in Chapter 24.

So far we have spoken only of the use of alpha particles as the nuclear projectiles which are shot at nuclei to break them up. Originally alpha particles were used because they were available from natural sources, but once nuclear accelerators were built, other high-energy particles such as protons and deuterons (ions of heavy hydrogen) could be used as well. The simplest type of accelerator consists of a positive high voltage supply and a tube down which positive ions are accelerated due to the electrostatic repulsion between the positive charges on the ions and the high voltage terminal. It is usual to measure the energy which the ions gain in the acceleration in units of electronvolts (eV). One electronvolt is the energy acquired by a particle with a charge equal to the electronic charge falling through an electric voltage of 1 V. The energy of 1 eV $= 1.6 \times 10^{-19}$ J, and one million electronvolts, written 1 MeV, is equal to 1.6×10^{-13} J. The MeV is a very convenient unit of energy in nuclear physics.

In 1932 Cockcroft and Walton in Cambridge, England, made an accelerator of this simple type and were able to obtain protons with an energy of 150 000 eV, that is, 150 keV. With these they carried out the first transmutation using artificially accelerated ions. This was the nuclear reaction

$$^{7}_{3}\text{Li} + ^{1}_{1}\text{H} \longrightarrow ^{4}_{2}\text{He} + ^{4}_{2}\text{He} + \text{energy.}$$

FUSION

Also in 1932 **deuterium**, $_1^2H$, was discovered, and soon deuterium ions or **deuterons** were commonly used as projectiles. Deuterium is sometimes denoted by the symbol D, but in this chapter we will write it $_1^2H$. One of the simplest possible nuclear reactions is that obtained when accelerated deuterons hit a deuterium target. In this case there are two possible end products. These reactions are illustrated in Fig. 23-2 and are represented by the two equations

and

$$_1^2H + _1^2H \rightarrow _1^3H + _1^1H + 4.0 \text{ MeV}$$

$$_1^2H + _1^2H \rightarrow _2^3He + _0^1n + 3.3 \text{ MeV.}$$

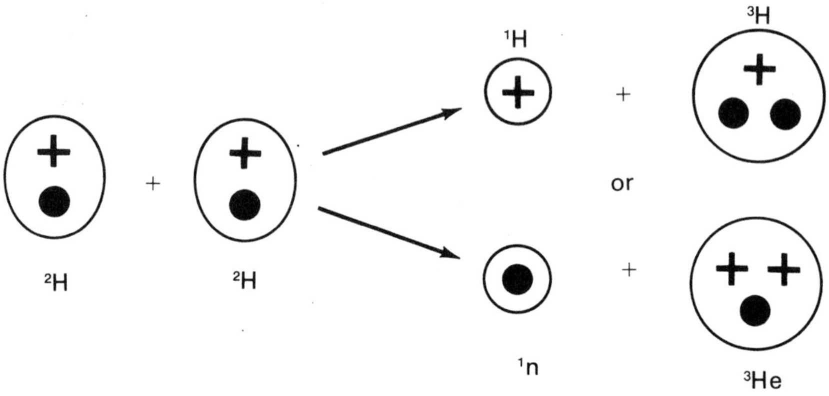

FIG. 23-2

$_2^3He$ is a stable isotope of helium, $_0^1n$ is the neutron; $_1^3H$ is tritium and $_1^1H$ is the proton, the nucleus of ordinary hydrogen. Both these reactions result in **fusion** of two light nuclei to make a heavier one plus a particle of unit mass. Both also result in the release of energy.

Fusion reactions are of the utmost importance because our whole life depends upon them; the energy of all the stars, including our own sun, is obtained from reactions such as these going on in the interior of the star. In effect what happens is that four hydrogen nuclei fuse together to make helium 4. In order to keep the total electric charge the same on both sides of the equation, two positive electrons, or positrons, have to be emitted with the helium. The whole process can therefore be represented by the nuclear reaction equation

$$4\,_1^1H \rightarrow _2^4He + 2\,_1^0e + \text{energy}$$

where we have written $_1^0e$ for the positron, which has unit positive charge and very small mass.

In practice it is improbable that just a single reaction takes place, as represented above, but rather several consecutive reactions must take place. This is because it is highly improbable that the necessary four protons will all be together in one place at the same time. (Although it is quite common for two cars to collide at an intersection, it is very uncommon for four cars to hit each other simultaneously at the intersection. At a later time another car may hit the first two cars that collided, but that is a separate reaction.) It is considered that there are two main ways by which the $^4_2$He is produced. In one of these, the hydrogen cycle, beryllium and lithium are formed as intermediate steps, whereas in the carbon-nitrogen cycle, carbon and nitrogen nuclei act as catalysts to speed up the conversion process, but are not themselves used up. The carbon-nitrogen cycle is illustrated in Fig. 23-3. Although the cycle looks complicated it is clearly seen that four hydrogen nuclei go into the cycle and that a helium nucleus and two positrons come out.

Looking at the mass-energy balance in this fusion reaction, we find that the four protons have a mass 2.650×10^{-2} u greater than the

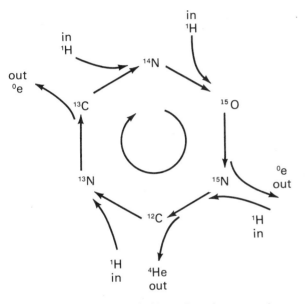

FIG. 23-3

sum of the masses of helium 4 and two positrons. This mass difference is equivalent to the energy released in the fusion, a total of about 25 MeV being released for every helium nucleus created.

It is interesting to consider the case of our own sun to get an idea of the magnitudes involved in nuclear reactions on a stellar scale. Knowing the total energy radiated from the sun, we can calculate how fast the sun's mass is decreasing. We find that each day the sun radiates away 4×10^{14} kg in the form of heat and light. As the sun's total mass is about 2×10^{30} kg, it can fortunately continue to radiate at this rate for a long time yet!

If we could learn how to make a power station work using nuclear fusion as the primary source of energy, we would be a long way towards relieving the world's energy shortages, for hydrogen is a very common substance, at least when it is chemically compounded with oxygen to form water. Even if deuterium had to be used for technical reasons, there would still be an ample supply. Lake Ontario alone has enough deuterium in it to supply the whole of Canada with energy for 10 million years at the present rate of use. The difficulty is that although we can easily make these reactions work in the laboratory, the cost of running the laboratory equipment is far greater than the value of any energy produced. To make energy economically seems to require operating temperatures equal to those in the sun, and by this temperature all normal equipment has vaporized. A current trend is to try to use a magnetic field to hold in the hot gases—to use what is called a "magnetic bottle"–another is to use lasers (see Chapter 19).

Energy has been produced from fusion in the form of hydrogen bombs or H-bombs. In these a high temperature, of the order of $10^7°C$, is first attained by the explosion of an atomic, or nuclear fission, bomb (see Fig. 23-10). This temperature is just about that found in the interior of stars, and so the light nuclei, with which the atomic bomb is surrounded, fuse with the liberation of immense amounts of energy in a very short time. The rate of energy production here is too great for most peaceful applications. Some means must be found for allowing the energy to be released more slowly. There seems little doubt that fusion energy will eventually become available for domestic and industrial purposes, but it is taking a long time to achieve.

This is like using a paper fire to start a wood fire.

FIG. 23-10 appears on page 303.

FISSION

Fusion is a reaction in which light nuclei come together to form more complex nuclei with the release of energy. At the other end of the Periodic Table **fission** can take place in which the most complex nuclei such as uranium or thorium split up into lighter components with the release of energy. In many ways the nuclear processes of fusion and fission are analogous to the composition of or the splitting up of chemical compounds. Taking two chemical reactions to illustrate the two phenomena, we would say that the combining of hydrogen and oxygen to form water,

$$2H_2 + O_2 \rightarrow 2H_2O,$$

is an example of chemical *fusion*, whereas the break up of the explosive tri-nitrotoluene (TNT) into water and carbon dioxide, etc., is an example of a chemical *fission* process. Both of these chemical reactions result in the release of energy. This energy from the chemical reaction is, however, a million times less than that released in the analogous nuclear reactions.

The TNT fission process is not spontaneous, for the TNT has to be triggered off by an electrical spark or by some other means before it will explode. Similarly the fission of uranium will not take place to any great extent unless some energy is pumped into the nucleus. This energy can be provided by the capture of a neutron by the nucleus. Neutron capture experiments became possible in 1932 after the neutron was identified, but in fact fission was not discovered until 1939.

When a nucleus fissions, it may break up in a large number of dif-

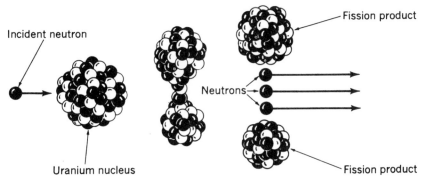

FIG. 23-4

ferent ways. Usually it breaks up into two nuclei which both have about half the weight of the original nucleus, and in addition two or three neutrons are emitted. Thus we might have

$$^{235}_{92} U + ^1_0 n \rightarrow ^{236}_{92} U \text{ (excited)},$$

followed by

$$^{236}_{92} U \text{ (excited)} \rightarrow ^{90}_{38} Sr + ^{143}_{54} Xe + 3 ^1_0 n,$$

where Sr is the symbol for strontium and Xe the symbol for xenon (Fig. 23-4). The three neutrons are now available for interacting with more uranium to cause more fissions, with the release of even more neutrons and so on with an avalanche effect. Such a process which uses some of the products of a reaction to cause more reactions is called a **chain reaction** (Fig. 23-5). However, if the fission has taken place in a small lump of uranium 235, the neutrons may escape before they are able to interact with other uranium nuclei. The bigger we make the lump, the less chance there is of escape, and there will come a time, as the lump or pile of uranium is made bigger, when at least one of the neutrons emitted must be captured by another ura-

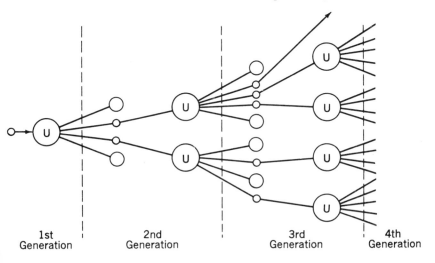

FIG. 23-5

FIG. 23-6. The NRX research reactor at Chalk River, Ontario. The fuel rods are inserted from above. In the foreground are the ports for experimenting with the neutron bombardment of materials.

Table 23-1

THE TRANSURANIC ELEMENTS

Atomic Number	Name	Chemical Symbol
93	Neptunium	Np
94	Plutonium	Pu
95	Americium	Am
96	Curium	Cm
97	Berkelium	Bk
98	Californium	Cf
99	Einsteinium	Es
100	Fermium	Fm
101	Mendeleevium	Md
102	Nobelium	No
103	Lawrencium	Lw

nium nucleus. At this **critical size**, the number of fissions in unit time will keep steady; with greater than a critical size, the number of fissions will increase with time, and therefore the amount of energy released will greatly increase also.

Each fission results in the production of about 200 MeV of energy. In other terms, the complete fissioning of about 20 kg of uranium—a handful or two—is sufficient to provide the total energy used in Canada in one day. However, as even under perfect conditions only one isotope of the uranium, ^{235}U, is primarily useful, at least 3000 kg of natural uranium would be required per day. In order to use this fission energy, it must be released slowly. This controlled, slow, release of energy is carried out in the **nuclear reactors** of nuclear power stations. They have more than a critical amount of uranium in them, but also have **control rods** made of material such as cadmium which can absorb neutrons very readily. By inserting the control rods into the reactor the number of neutrons left to cause fission in uranium can be easily kept at any desired steady level.

The most abundant isotope of uranium, ^{238}U, captures high energy neutrons to form radioactive ^{239}U without fission resulting. To slow the neutrons down rapidly, so that they react with the fissionable ^{235}U rather than with the ^{238}U, a **moderator** is used in most power reactors. Under these circumstances more of the neutrons cause fission in the less abundant ^{235}U. The reactors must also have **coolants** in them to remove the heat energy produced in the fission process so that the heat energy can be converted in turbines to useful electrical energy. In most Canadian reactors (Fig. 23-6) heavy water (deuterium oxide) is used both as the moderator and as the coolant. In British power reactors graphite (pure carbon) was used as moderator and carbon dioxide as the coolant, while in the USA, uranium enriched in the isotope ^{235}U is used as fuel and ordinary water as moderator.

The high intensity of neutrons in a reactor makes the reactor an ideal source for neutron capture reactions. One of these we have just mentioned,

$$^{238}_{92}\text{U} + ^{1}_{0}\text{n} \longrightarrow ^{239}_{92}\text{U}.$$

This isotope, uranium 239, has a half-life of 23 min. It decays to neptunium by the emission of an electron. Neptunium is the first of the **transuranic elements** (that is, those with a higher atomic number than that of uranium),

$$^{239}_{92}\text{U} \longrightarrow ^{239}_{93}\text{Np} + ^{0}_{-1}\text{e}.$$

The neptunium then itself decays radioactively to form element 94, plutonium, $^{239}_{94}\text{Pu}$. The $^{239}_{94}\text{Pu}$ is very similar to $^{235}_{92}\text{U}$ in its fissioning properties, and may itself be used in reactors. Other transuranic elements can be made by further neutron capture or by other means. A list of those known (up to 1977) is given in Table 23-1. All isotopes of these elements are radioactive. It is thought that many of them may have existed on earth at one time, but their half-lives are so short that they have all decayed away long ago.

One of the reasons for believing that transuranic elements once existed naturally is the recent discovery of the remains of a natural fission reactor in Gabon, West Africa. At an early time in the earth's history (1.8 billion years ago) there was a higher percentage of ^{235}U in natural uranium than there is now; at a few places in the earth where uranium was sufficiently concentrated and when moisture conditions were such that just the right amount of moderator was present, a chain reaction took place. This was controlled naturally by the fact that the fissions created heat which evaporated the moderating water and stopped the reaction until the water recondensed—a procedure which is a safety feature in man-made water moderated reactors. Such a reactor would have produced power at a rate of 20 kW for half a million years, creating 6000 kg of fission products and 1000 kg of the transuranic element plutonium. These products have now all decayed, but the remaining uranium is slightly deficient in ^{235}U because of the ancient fission process. It is of interest to note that these quantities of fission products are roughly those which would be produced in Canada each year if all power production was by nuclear means.

This natural reactor could be described as an enriched uranium, light (i.e., ordinary) water moderated and cooled system. This is similar to the present-day US system, but dissimilar to the Canadian one.

Reactors are also used as sources of radioactive isotopes for use in industry and research. For example, if cobalt is put in a reactor, the nuclear reaction

$$^{59}\text{Co} + {}^{1}\text{n} \rightarrow {}^{60}\text{Co}$$

will proceed. The new isotope is radioactive with a half-life of 5 years and emits negative electrons. Some of the uses of these isotopes in industry and research will be discussed in Chapter 24. Such radioisotopes are now common commercial products in North America and Europe.

ELECTRICITY FROM NUCLEAR ENERGY

The Canadian nuclear electric generating system is based on a heavy water, natural uranium reactor system in which D_2O, heavy water, is used both as the neutron moderator and the heat removal system. Such reactors are called CANDU, for the **Can**adian **d**euterium oxide, natural **u**ranium method of producing energy (Fig. 23-7). Both the Canadian and US systems require the production of a separated isotope, in the Canadian case the separation of heavy water from ordinary water, in the US case that of ^{235}U from natural uranium.

At the time of writing, the largest nuclear generating stations in Canada are the Pickering station, east of Toronto, Ontario (Fig. 23-8), and Bruce, near Kincardine, Ontario. The power rating of the

The normal abundance of uranium 235 is 0.72%. At Gabon the abundance is found to be 0.63%.

FIG. 23-7 and 23-8 appear on page 300.

FIG. 23-7

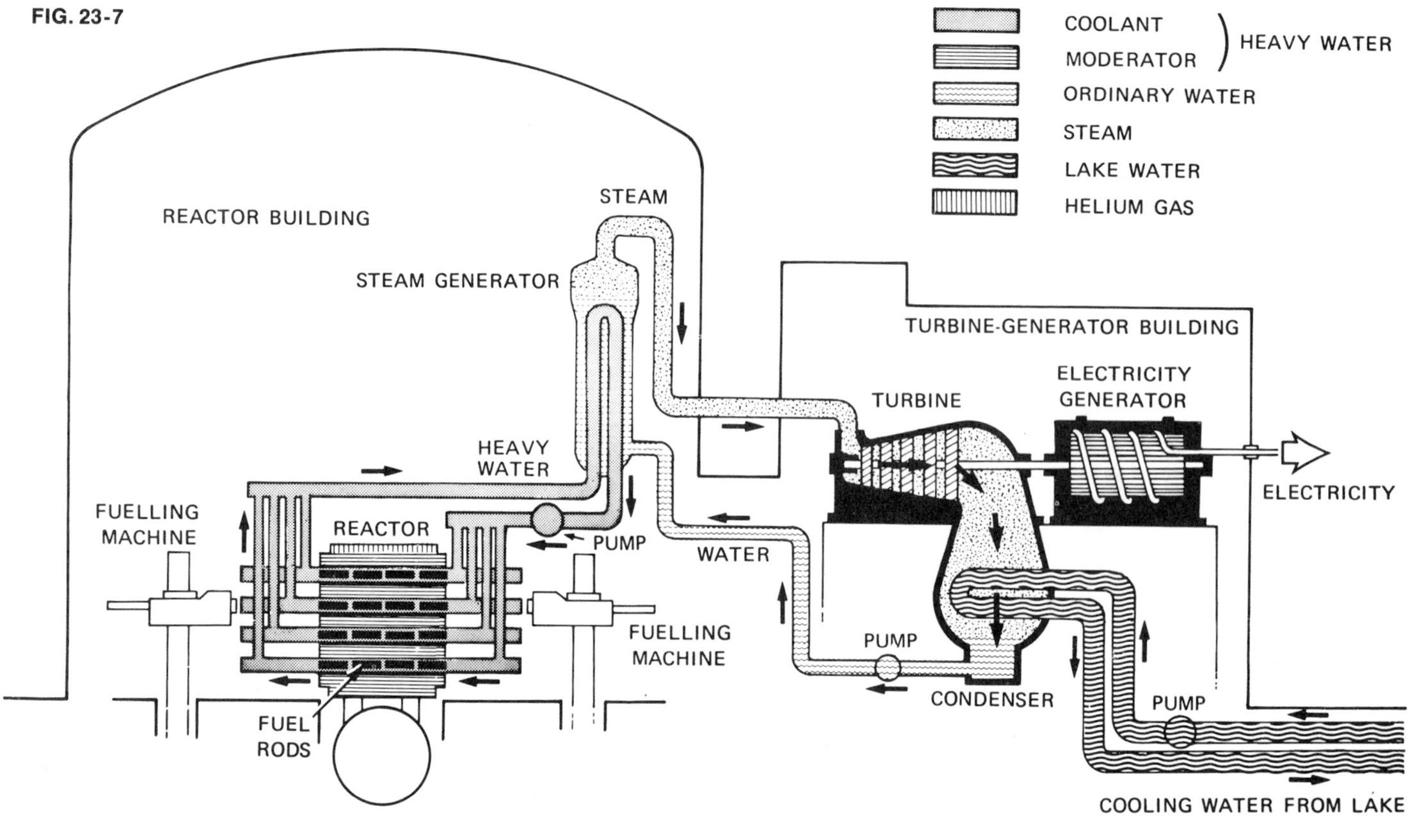

COOLANT ⎫
MODERATOR ⎬ HEAVY WATER
ORDINARY WATER
STEAM
LAKE WATER
HELIUM GAS

REACTOR BUILDING

STEAM

STEAM GENERATOR

TURBINE-GENERATOR BUILDING

TURBINE

ELECTRICITY GENERATOR

HEAVY WATER

ELECTRICITY

FUELLING MACHINE

REACTOR

PUMP

WATER

FUELLING MACHINE

PUMP

CONDENSER

PUMP

FUEL RODS

COOLING WATER FROM LAKE

CANDU-PHW (PRESSURIZED HEAVY WATER) SYSTEM

FIG. 23-8

Pickering station, with its four reactors, is 2000 MW(*e*). To put this into context, this production rate is just about equal to that of Ontario Hydro's electricity production from Niagara Falls, and is approximately the rate at which energy is used by Metropolitan Toronto. Electricity produced at nuclear power stations is exactly the same as any other electricity, and is fed into the electric grid system. Currently about 17% of all Ontario's usage of electricity is nuclear in origin; it is planned that the percentage will be increased with time so that nuclear power will supply about half of all Canada's needs by the turn of the century.

The reasons for the increasing dependence of Canada and other countries on nuclear power are the decreasing availability of cheap fossil fuels (oil, natural gas, coal) and the lack of development of other cheap sources of energy. Although more effort is now being put into renewable sources, such as solar energy and geothermal power, there can be no doubt that the demand for nuclear power will continue for the next few decades.

Nuclear power brings with it its own problems, brought about by the facts that the fuel is radioactive, that the "ash" or fission products are highly radioactive, and that radioactive materials are produced as by-products of the nuclear reactions. Although radioactivity has been studied for almost a hundred years, large concentrations of radioactivity have only been around for a decade or two, and people are still working out how to live with the new problems associated with nuclear disintegration.

These new problems are encountered at almost all the steps in the production of power. Uranium miners are exposed to an atmosphere which contains radioactive decay products of uranium and the workers in the ore refineries may inhale radioactive dust. Workers at the nuclear generating stations have to be protected from the radioactivity of the reactors and the fission products, and the spent fuel rods have to be so dealt with that their radioactivity does not constitute a hazard. By-products of the processes include low level uranium wastes from refining, tritium gas produced by neutron irradiation of heavy water, and the plutonium produced from uranium.

It must be realized that any concentration of energy is dangerous, whether it be the kinetic energy of a moving automobile, or the potential energy of a natural gas tank or of a loaded rifle or a concentration of radioactivity. In all cases society, largely through government, steps in to try to control the danger. These controls are generally in the form of government acts or regulations. One does not have to look far to realize that controls are not always effective, and to realize that society is prepared to put up with certain risks in order to gain certain advantages (for example, in transportation and home heating). Normally people's acceptances of risk come gradually, as new standards of living develop, but in the case of nuclear power the new problems have been thrust rather quickly onto society.

Many regulations have been designed to safeguard workers and

The (*e*) means *electricity;* that is, the electrical output is 2000 MW—the *heat* generated (input to the steam turbines) is 6000 MW or more.

Examples of geothermal sources are the hot water springs at Banff or the geysers at Yellowstone Park.

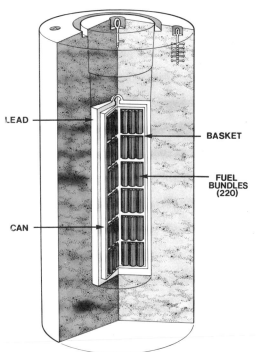

CONCRETE CANISTER FOR DRY STORAGE OF SPENT FUEL

LEAD

BASKET

FUEL BUNDLES (220)

CAN

FIG. 23-9

the public from potential dangers of nuclear energy. They are by necessity based on existing knowledge and within that framework are designed to bring risks below that which society accepts in other situations. For instance, there are regulations with respect to concentrations of radioactivity in the air of mines and factories to limit the radiation doses received by the workers. Others are designed to limit doses received by the general public. One issue that will be of continuing concern is what to do with the fission products. While being kept in well-shielded tanks at the generating station (Fig. 23-9), the shorter-lived isotopes die away; the present Canadian philosophy is that after this the "ashes" with their long-lived radioactivity are put into heavily shielded "management areas" where they will be kept under continual surveillance for essentially all time. In the future the possibility exists that the "ashes" will be sealed in solid rock as was done by nature in the case of the Gabon reactor.

RADIATION DOSES

To put into context the "government regulations" noted above, it is worthwhile to speak first of the *background* radiation to which humans (and every other living organism) have always been exposed. This background radiation comes from cosmic rays and from naturally occurring radioactive materials like radium and potassium (radioactive ^{40}K occurs naturally with an abundance of 0.0119% in all potassium). These elements exist around us and to some extent in our bodies. All these sources of radiation, cosmic and "internal" and "external" terrestrial sources, give rise to some dose of radiation to the body.

The unit in which radiation doses are measured is the gray (Gy). Each year we receive about one milligray (1 mGy) from natural sources. Only a rough figure can be given, as the amount varies greatly depending on circumstances.

People who live in brick houses receive slightly more than those who live in wooden ones, and those who live on granite, such as on the Canadian Shield, get a little more than those who live on sedimentary soils. The shielding effect of the atmosphere is reduced with height, and people who live in Banff, Alberta, or Denver, Colorado, receive about 0.5 mGy extra per year because of the higher cosmic-ray intensity there. At 10 000 m the shielding is even less, and taking a return jet flight across Canada, or over the Atlantic, results in an extra dose of about 0.05 mGy.

These "natural" doses do not, of course, include radiation received for medical purposes; the average dose received from this source is some 0.5 mGy per person per year. Nor do the natural doses include what persons receive because of their work or other people's work. Doctors have attempted to set standards or limits within which people should work so that no one receives an excessive amount of radiation. These limits are based on the natural background radiation mentioned above, and on experience gained during the last 80 years of the effects of radiation on people.

At present it is laid down that those relatively few people actually working with radiation should not receive more than 50 mGy per year, but that the general population should not receive a dose over their whole body of more than 2 mGy per year, in addition to the natural background dose and to medical exposure. From the extensive bomb testing around 1960 the average dose received by people was less than 0.1 mGy per year. Up to 1977 the general radiation exposure from nuclear power plants has been less than 5×10^{-8} Gy per year.

Very obvious effects of radiation do not start until the safety limits have been far exceeded. A person who receives about 1 Gy over his whole body will become ill, and with about 3 to 5 Gy his death from the effects of the radiation is very likely. It should be noted, however, that people can tolerate these doses over small parts of their bodies —in medical treatments, doses far in excess of these figures are often given to one small part of the body in order to kill the cells there.

FIG. 23-10 THE ATOMIC BOMB

In a nuclear power reactor, the rate of fissioning is kept at a low, constant, level by control rods. If an amount of ^{235}U greater than the critical mass is uncontrolled, the rate of fissioning may build up rapidly, and a large amount of energy may be released in a very short time, causing an explosion. The atomic (or fission) bomb is designed to cause such a sudden release of energy. Two or more pieces of ^{235}U, each less than the critical size, are **super-critical** when all are brought together very quickly. In a nuclear bomb, once the critical size is exceeded, the uranium starts to fission extremely rapidly. The tamping and heavy casing prevent the bomb blowing itself apart before the chain reaction has built up to a high level. The release of energy by the reaction produces a very high temperature, and there is a rapid expansion of the vaporized bomb components and the surrounding air. The out-rushing of this gas causes the blast damage of an atomic bomb explosion.

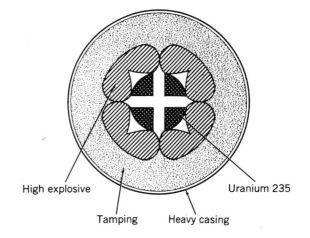

High explosive

Uranium 235

Tamping

Heavy casing

FIG. 23-11 RADIATION PROTECTION

APPROXIMATE THICKNESSES OF
MATERIALS WHICH WILL REDUCE THE
INTENSITY OF FISSION PRODUCT GAMMA
RAYS TO A TENTH

Lead	6 cm	Earth	46 cm
Steel	10 cm	Water	66 cm
Concrete	30 cm	Wood	130 cm

It is of great importance that workers in the nuclear industries should be protected against radiation to as great a degree as possible, and this is usually done by putting **shielding material** between any strong sources and the workers. Thus, in the case of nuclear reactors, there is usually at least two metres of concrete all around the reactors, and gamma rays, neutrons, and so on are absorbed in the concrete. In other cases, where radio-isotopes have to be manipulated, complicated devices have to be built so that the worker can "handle" the isotopes by remote control. The workers are separated from the radioactivity by a thick wall with possibly a window of lead glass in it. The thickness of various materials required to cut down by a certain amount the gamma radiation from fission products is given in the table. The thicknesses of materials which will reduce the intensity to one-tenth of the original are given in centimetres. Two such thicknesses will reduce the intensity by a factor of 10^2, three such by a factor of 10^3, and so on.

FIG. 23-12 BREEDER REACTORS

In the standard nuclear reactor, the primary fuel is ^{235}U, only a minor constituent of natural uranium. This is because the major constituent, ^{238}U, is not *fissile*, that is, it cannot be fissioned by low-energy neutrons. However, by neutron bombardment and subsequent radioactive decay ^{238}U can be converted to ^{239}Pu (plutonium) which is fissile;

$$^{238}U + n \rightarrow ^{239}U \rightarrow ^{239}Np \rightarrow ^{239}Pu.$$

In a CANDU reactor this *breeding* of fissile material from the *fertile* ^{238}U automatically takes place to some extent and the plutonium then becomes part of the nuclear fuel in the reactor.

As the fission process results in the emission of 2 or 3 neutrons per fission, and as only one of these is required to keep the chain reaction going at a constant rate (zero population growth), 1 or 2 are available for breeding new nuclear fuel. Thus, 1 or 2 new fissile nuclei may be bred for each one used up! Each of these newly bred nuclei could breed more, so that in principle all the ^{238}U could be bred to fissile ^{239}Pu. Thorium 232, the 100% abundant isotope of the relatively common element thorium, may also be bred to fissile ^{233}U.

Despite the fact that there are inevitable snags, such as the need for chemical processing of spent fuel rods, breeding can open up the abundant fertile isotopes as energy sources.

FIG. 23-13 FALLOUT

In the bursting of an atomic bomb, fission products are spread over large areas. If a bomb bursts near the ground, the fission products become bound to dust particles sucked up from the ground, and quickly fall back to the ground, giving an intense activity spread over perhaps hundreds or thousands of square kilometres. This is called **local fallout** of the radioactivity. In the case of larger bombs, much of the activity is carried up to the upper part of the atmosphere and may not return to earth for many months or years. By this time most of the isotopes with short radioactive half-lives will have decayed, and the **long-range fallout** therefore consists mainly of long-lived isotopes such as zirconium 95 (half-life 75 days), strontium 90 (half-life 28 years), and cesium 137 (half-life 30 years). The last two can be incorporated into the body as they are chemically similar to calcium (used to make bone tissue) and potassium (in muscle) respectively.

FIG. 23-14 NUCLEAR PROLIFERATION

Since the explosion of the first nuclear weapon in 1945, nations have been concerned about atomic bombs getting into the "wrong" hands. To make a bomb requires either isotopically separated ^{235}U or plutonium separated chemically from the other nuclei produced when uranium is irradiated with neutrons in a reactor. The cost of setting up ^{235}U separation plants is huge; the major powers have therefore concentrated on trying to prevent other countries getting plutonium. However, any reactor which produces nuclear power for peaceful purposes also produces plutonium which can (with knowledge and equipment) be chemically extracted from the used fuel rods. In India, plutonium produced in a Canadian-built reactor has in fact been used for making an atomic bomb. There is considerable concern as to whether Canada and other countries should be providing potential plutonium supplies to countries which might use them for making bombs.

Exercises

A

1. What are three characteristics of all nuclear reactions?

2. Write down the missing products in the following nuclear reaction equations involving deuterium:
   - (a) $^{2}_{1}H + ^{6}_{3}Li \rightarrow ^{4}_{2}He + ?$
   - (b) $^{2}_{1}H + ^{12}_{4}C \rightarrow ^{1}_{1}H + ?$
   - (c) $^{2}_{1}H + ^{9}_{4}Be \rightarrow ^{1}_{0}n + ?$
   - (d) $^{2}_{1}H + ^{9}_{4}Be \rightarrow ^{1}_{1}H + ?$

3. Write completed equations for the following nuclear reactions:
   - (a) $^{1}_{0}n + ^{109}_{47}Ag \rightarrow ?$
   - (b) $^{1}_{0}n + ^{235}_{92}U \rightarrow ^{137}_{55}Cs + ? + 3 ^{1}_{0}n$
   - (c) $^{1}_{0}n + ^{14}_{7}N \rightarrow ^{14}_{6}C + ?$
   - (d) $^{1}_{0}n + ^{1}_{1}H \rightarrow ?$

   (Note: It is because of the reaction in (c) that carbon dating is possible.)

4. Which of the following nuclear reactions are possible? For those that are not possible, tell why not.
   - (a) $^{1}_{0}n + ^{107}_{47}Ag \rightarrow ^{108}_{47}Ag$
   - (b) $^{1}_{1}H + ^{16}_{8}O \rightarrow ^{23}_{11}Na$
   - (c) $^{12}_{6}C + ^{12}_{6}C \rightarrow ^{20}_{10}Ne + ^{4}_{2}He$
   - (d) $^{4}_{2}He + ^{27}_{13}Al \rightarrow ^{30}_{15}P$
   - (e) $^{23}_{11}Na + ^{2}_{1}H \rightarrow ^{25}_{11}Na + ^{1}_{0}n$
   - (f) $^{4}_{2}He + ^{14}_{7}N \rightarrow ^{17}_{8}O + ^{1}_{1}H$

5. Explain the meaning of each symbol in the equation $E = mc^2$, as the equation relates to nuclear reactions.

6. (a) What was the original use of nuclear accelerators?
   (b) What is the value of (i) 1 MeV in joules, (ii) 1 keV in joules?

7. (a) What is meant by nuclear fusion?
   (b) In what sense does all life on earth depend on nuclear fusion?

8. At its present rate of radiation, for how many days can the sun continue to shine before its mass is exhausted? How many years is that?

9. (a) What is meant by (i) nuclear fission, (ii) a chain reaction, (iii) critical size?
   (b) Give 2 examples of chain reactions that are not connected with nuclear physics.

10. In a nuclear reactor, what is the function of (a) a neutron moderator, (b) control rods, (c) a coolant?

11. (a) What is meant by a transuranic element?
    (b) Name four transuranic elements.

12. What are the distinguishing features of the CANDU generating system, as compared to the USA nuclear power system?

13. What are the (a) major potential advantages and (b) disadvantages of generation of electrical power by nuclear means?

14. (a) What is the normal background radiation in Canada, expressed in greys?
    (b) What natural factors affect the background radiation at a location?

15. (a) Define critical size, in the context of nuclear explosives.
    (b) Distinguish between atom bombs and hydrogen bombs.
    (c) Aside from immediate blast damage in the vicinity, what is another major hazard of nuclear bomb explosions?

16. What thickness of concrete is needed to reduce the intensity of typical gamma rays to (a) one hundredth? (b) one thousandth?

17. What is meant by the breeding of nuclear fuel?

B

18. Using the masses given below for the various nuclei, calculate the mass excess which is available in each of the following reactions.
    (a) $^2_1H + ^2_1H \rightarrow ^3_2He + ^1_0n$
    (b) $^2_1H + ^2_1H \rightarrow ^3_1H + ^1_1H$

    Masses: ^1_1H ———— 1.0078 u
    ^1_0n ———— 1.0087 u
    ^2_1H ———— 2.0141 u
    ^3_1H ———— 3.0160 u
    ^3_2He ———— 3.0160 u
    1 u = one (unified) atomic mass unit = 1.66×10^{-27} kg.

    Express each answer in atomic mass units and in kilograms.

19. Using the Einstein relation $E = mc^2$, express the answers to question 18 in joules.

20. The simplest nuclear reaction is the capture of a neutron by the nucleus of a hydrogen atom to form a deuteron, $^1_0n + ^1_1H \rightarrow ^2_1H + $ energy. Using the mass values given in question 18, calculate the energy which is available due to the mass excess when this reaction takes place.

21. The fission of $^{235}_{92}U$ may be triggered by the capture of a neutron. Four of the possible modes of break-up of the resultant nucleus $^{236}_{92}U$ result in the formation of $^{95}_{40}Zr$, $^{90}_{38}Sr$, $^{131}_{35}I$, and $^{137}_{55}Cs$. For the last, the nuclear reaction may be written $^1_0n + ^{235}_{92}U \rightarrow ^{137}_{55}Cs + ^{96}_{37}Rb + 3\ ^1_0n$. On the assumption that each of the other modes of fission also results in the emission of 3 neutrons, write down the nuclear reaction equation for each of the other three cases.

C

22. The names of the first two transuranic elements (listed in Table 23-1) are derived from the names of the two planets farther out than Uranus. The names of most of the heavier transuranic elements are connected with people or places important in nuclear physics. Find out about these connections and write brief notes on four of them.

23. In the text it is stated that the complete fissioning of about 20 kg of uranium 235 would provide the total energy generated in Canada in one day. Calculate how much energy this is, and give the answer in joules. (Atomic mass number of uranium = 235; energy per fission = 200 MeV; 1 MeV = 1.6×10^{-13} J; Avogadro's number = 6.0×10^{23} atoms per mole.)

24. The production of one helium nucleus by the fusion of 4 hydrogen atoms ($A = 1$) results in the release of about 25 MeV of energy. Calculate the energy release if 20 kg of hydrogen were converted to helium. Compare this with the result of question 23. (Use 1 MeV = 1.6×10^{-13} J and Avogadro's number = 6.0×10^{23} atoms per mole.)

25. The fusion of 4 hydrogen nuclei gives 25 MeV of energy. Calculate the energy radiated by the sun each day, assuming that 6×10^{16} kg of hydrogen per day fuse to form helium. Calculate the energy received by each square metre of the earth each day, knowing that all the energy passes through the surface of the sphere containing the earth's orbit, that the earth-sun distance is 1.5×10^{11} m, and that the surface area of a sphere is πr^2.

26. The earth receives energy from the sun at the rate of 3×10^{22} J/d. Considering this effect alone and that this energy may be measured in terms of mass, calculate the rate of increase of the mass of the earth per day in kilograms. What percentage of the total mass of the earth is this daily increase? (Mass of the earth is 6×10^{24} kg.)

27. The kinetic energy of a particle increases linearly with its temperature expressed in kelvins (K). At room temperature (about 300 K) the kinetic energy is about 0.025 eV. What is the corresponding energy at the centre of an atomic explosion, at roughly 10^7 K?

28. Thirty centimetres of concrete will reduce gamma ray intensity to one tenth. How much is needed to reduce it to one half?

29. The power rating of a certain automobile is 100 kW. Assuming that the car is used on an average of 1 hour per day, and that the engine is only able to convert 20% of all available energy to useful work, calculate the mass of ^{235}U which could keep the car going for 4 years. (235 grams of ^{235}U contain 6×10^{23} nuclei; the fission of each one of these produces about 200 MeV.)

CHAPTER 24

Applications
of
Nuclear
Radiations

FIG. 24-1. Numerous cloud-chamber tracks of alpha particles and protons (the finest lines). The prominent oblique line shows the paths (up to the right and down to the left) of the two fragments of a fissioned uranium atom caused by the impact of a neutron with the target located near the centre.

We have discussed in some detail the production of electric power from nuclear fission and some of the problems associated with it. In this chapter we will consider other uses of nuclear physics. Very often these applications depend on the properties of a radioactive isotope of an element; usually these isotopes are produced in a reactor. In some cases (e.g., ^{131}I used in medicine) the isotopes are fission products; in other cases they are produced by neutron capture (e.g., stable sodium, ^{23}Na, can be converted to radio-sodium, ^{24}Na, by irradiation by neutrons in a reactor).

In almost every case use is made of the facts that nuclear radiation penetrates materials and is easy to detect. When, in medical practice for instance, radioactive isotopes are taken into the body, these two facts enable the radiation to be observed outside the body; as a result we can find out what goes on in the body without surgical invasion of the body. As a preliminary to considering uses of nuclear physics, we will first discuss how nuclear radiation may be detected.

Iodine 131 is a radioactive isotope used for examining and treating the thyroid gland, which takes up iodine readily.

Sodium 24 is used to trace the activity of sodium chloride in the body.

THE DETECTION OF NUCLEAR RADIATION

Alpha, beta and gamma rays are all energetic, the energy being either the kinetic energy of charged particles or the energy of electromagnetic waves. None of the rays is directly detectable by human senses, but in all cases their energy can be converted to other forms of energy which we can detect.

The **cloud chamber** makes charged particle tracks visible to the eye. It makes use of the facts that the charged particles will ionize matter through which they pass, and that vapours condense more easily on charged ions than on uncharged particles. In the chamber, which contains dust-free air and a vapour such as that of alcohol, it is arranged that the alcohol vapour becomes supersaturated, and therefore in a condition to allow condensation to occur. In Fig. 24-13 instructions are given for building your own cloud chamber. If an ionizing radiation goes through the chamber, it will leave a trail of ions on which droplets of alcohol will form. These droplets are easily visible in a strong light, and thus we can see and photograph the tracks of the rays. The photograph Fig. 24-1 is, of course, not a pic-

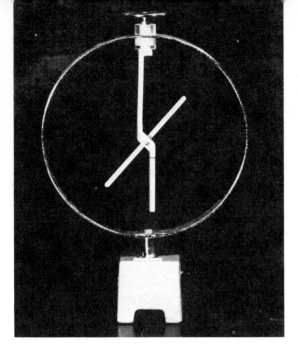

FIG. 24-2

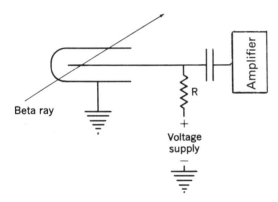

Beta ray

R

Amplifier

Voltage
supply

FIG. 24-3

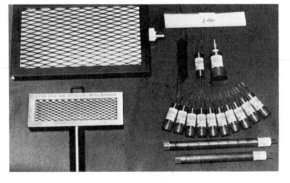

FIG. 24-4. A variety of Geiger tubes.

ture of the particles, but only of the tracks they make. They are, in a sense, footprints of the particles themselves. The heaviness of the track, that is the number of droplets per centimetre, tells something of the nature of the ionizing radiation in the same way as the depth and frequency of footprints can tell a lot about the person or animal making them.

Other detection systems make more direct use of the ionization produced by energetic charged particles. When beta rays, for example, travel through a gas such as air, they split up some of the atoms of the gas into electrons and positive ions. This makes the gas a conductor of electricity, and if there is an electric field across the gas, a current will flow. In the metal-vane electroscope shown in Fig. 24-2, a thin metal vane attached to a metal support is given a charge by means of the method of induction discussed in Chapter 7, or by some other means. The ends of the vane will be repelled away from the support because both have the same charge. When a radioactive source is brought near, the charge will leak away because of the increased conductivity of the air, and the vane will return to its original position.

Such a system is suitable for measuring radioactivity if the source is strong enough, but it is not sufficiently sensitive for most applications. In order to magnify the effects of the radiation, amplification is often produced by electronic devices similar to those in radio and television sets. In one form of counter, such as that shown in Fig. 24-3, an electric field is applied across the gas through which, for example, the beta rays to be detected are travelling; the ionized particles produced are attracted to the charged electrodes. This flow of ionized particles constitutes an electric current which passes through the resistance R, giving rise to a voltage drop across the resistance proportional to the current and thus to the number of beta particles per second. This voltage is then measured by an electronic circuit. In the case of a single beta particle, a single pulse of ionization will be produced and therefore a pulse of electricity will be received by the electrodes. Once again, this will give rise to a voltage across the resistance, and the voltage pulse may be amplified by standard electronic circuits. The output signal from the amplifier may then be used to drive a mechanical counter or other such device. Thus the number of beta particles striking the counter can be measured.

If the electric field across the gas is high enough, the number of ionizations will be vastly increased by an avalanche process: the electrons that split away from the gas atoms will acquire energy in the electric field, which will enable them to ionize other gas atoms, which will give rise to more electrons, which are capable of causing further ionization, and so on, and so on. This is the principle of the **Geiger counter** (Fig. 24-4) which is widely used in applied nuclear physics.

The **scintillation counter**, which is used even more widely in research than the Geiger counter, works on a somewhat different principle. The counter consists primarily of a crystal of, for example, so-

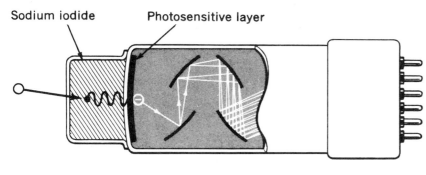

Sodium iodide   Photosensitive layer

FIG. 24-5

dium iodide. When radiation goes through the crystal, ionization takes place as before. A short time later the atoms will de-ionize, that is, an electron will rejoin the ion to form a neutral atom again, and energy is then given out in the form of a pulse of light. This light gets out of the crystal and is detected by an amplifying photo-cell or photo-multiplier (Fig. 24-5), which converts the light scintillation into an electrical pulse. This pulse can then be amplified by electronic circuits.

Solid-state detectors are also available. If radiation hits the depletion layer of a semiconducting diode (see Chapter 20), particle-hole pairs will be produced. The electric field across the diode will cause the charges to separate, and the resulting electrical signal can be used to actuate some electronic measurement system after suitable amplification. Compared with scintillation counters these detectors have the advantage of being better able to differentiate among radiations of different energies, but, being smaller, are less efficient.

TRACER TECHNIQUES

All isotopes of an element, stable or radioactive, have the same chemical properties. Therefore if a radio-isotope is mixed with the stable element it will behave in all chemical and biological processes exactly as does the stable element, but it will in addition emit radiation which will betray its presence and therefore that of the stable element. For example, if a chemical engineer wishes to find out what happens to the sodium introduced in the form of sodium hydroxide at a particular place in a chemical operation, all he needs to do is to mix with the stable sodium hydroxide some hydroxide made with radioactive ^{24}Na, which emits beta rays. With a Geiger counter, he can follow the hydroxide through all stages of the system, finding out how long the hydroxide takes to flow from one part to another, how much of the sodium reacts with one chemical and how much with another, how much is wasted, and so forth. This information can usually be obtained by quantitative chemical analysis, but at much greater expense of time and labour.

The radioactive method above is an example of what is known as a **tracer technique** (Fig. 24-6). In the biological sciences these techni-

FIG. 24-6. Injecting a liquid containing a radioactive tracer into a tree trunk. A Geiger counter can then be used to track the motion of the liquid through the living system.

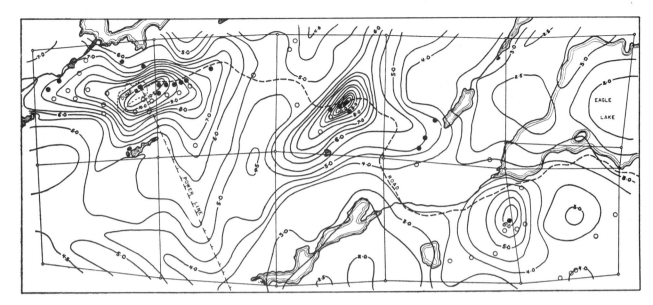

FIG. 24-7. Contours of gamma radiation intensity in the Eagle Mine area of Saskatchewan.

ques are widely used to study the uptake by plants of elements from soil. For example, a radio-isotope may be incorporated into fertilizer which is spread over the land, and then subsequently the activity of the plants can be measured. By this means the efficiency of different fertilizers can be tested.

INDUSTRIAL USES

Beta and gamma rays can penetrate a considerable thickness of material, and can be used not only like x-rays in the examination of things which are opaque to ordinary light, but also to measure the thickness of, for example, paper which is being made in a factory. This use depends on the fact that the thicker a material is, the fewer beta rays can pass through it. By putting a beta source on one side of the paper and a Geiger counter on the other, an immediate and continuous measurement of thickness can be made. If there is any variation in thickness as the paper rolls through the gauge, the gauge will indicate this and the fault can be corrected immediately.

The penetrating power of gamma rays makes them ideal for examining heavy metal castings for faults. In this work the casting is placed between a gamma source and an x-ray film which is very sensitive to the gamma rays. If, for example, there is an air hole in the casting, the developed film will show a black spot, as the air allows the gamma rays to pass more freely than would the metal that should have been in the hole.

Neutrons are also used in industrial applications of nuclear physics. Neutrons have the same mass as hydrogen atoms and are reflected very easily by them. Oil drillers want to know the nature of the rock through which they are drilling since certain types are more likely to hold oil than others. By putting a neutron source and recorder down bore holes, an idea can be obtained of the different types of rock, for when the rig is passing strata with a higher than normal hydrogen content, more neutrons will be reflected back from the rock and therefore the detector will count more neutrons. This is called *neutron oil-well logging*.

The scintillation detector is also used in the mining industry, for prospecting possible uranium-bearing rock. Such rock has a higher than normal radioactivity, and thus the atmosphere in a region over it has more radiation than it has over ordinary strata. By flying an aeroplane carrying a large scintillation detector over the country, likely places for drilling may be found (Fig. 24-7).

MEDICAL USES

In both the diagnosis and the treatment of some diseases, radio-isotopes are extremely valuable. In diagnosis, radio-isotopes may be used as tracers to find if the body is not absorbing, or not using, certain chemicals that it needs for proper health. They may also be used to obtain a "photograph" of a diseased organ by injecting the patient with an isotope which collects in the organ under examination (Fig. 24-8). A detector called a *scintillation camera* is placed over the organ. This scintillation camera will measure the rays given off by the isotope and thus give a picture of the parts of the organ which are biologically active; any portion which is not functioning properly will not have collected any isotope and thus will not affect the detector.

The use of the scintillation counter may be combined with the use of neutrons to perform quantitative analysis in **neutron activation analysis**. In this, the material to be analyzed is exposed to neutrons, which convert some nuclei to radioactive forms. A scintillation detector measures the activity and is able to differentiate between the rays from different elements. If a person is exposed to a small dose of neutrons and subsequently counted by a scintillation detector, the activity of the rays characteristic of, say, calcium, will give a measure of the mass of calcium in the body, and therefore a measure of bone mass—a value which currently cannot be obtained in any other way.

In therapy, or treatment, the ionizing properties of the rays are used. If the ionization is sufficiently intense, the cells in which the ionization takes place may be totally destroyed, and if these cells are bad for the body their destruction may result in a cure. The gamma rays from cobalt 60 are much used in this **radiation therapy**, as is the radiation produced by nuclear machines such as betatrons and clinical linear accelerators ("clinacs"). Gamma rays have an advantage over x-rays because as well as being ionizing they are more highly penetrating, and thus can attack tumors which are deep inside the body. In order that healthy tissue not also be destroyed, it can be arranged that the source giving a beam of rays rotates around the patient in a circle of which the unhealthy tissue is the centre. Then these cells always receive a radiation dose, whereas healthy tissue is only irradiated for part of the time.

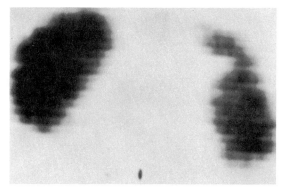

FIG. 24-8. The patient's right kidney does not appear to be fully functional.

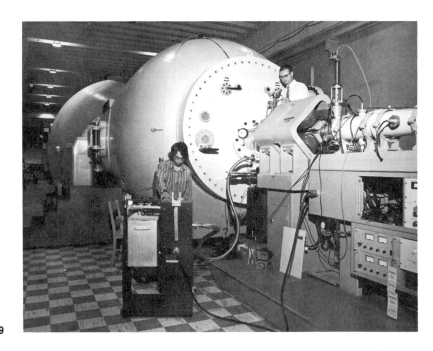

FIG. 24-9

NUCLEAR MACHINES

In these last chapters there has often been mention of nuclear reactors as sources of electrical energy and sources of neutrons for making radio-isotopes. For other purposes we must have sources of fast charged particles, and different types of machines are used to give the particles the necessary energies.

The **Van de Graaff generator** (Fig. 24-9) produces voltages of up to tens of millions of volts between its high voltage terminal and ground. In this generator, charges are sprayed onto a moving belt made of insulating material which then carries the charges to the high voltage terminal where they are removed. An evacuated *accelerating column* is also connected between the terminal and ground, and down this electric field charged particles such as protons can be accelerated.

The **cyclotron** uses a different principle entirely. Fig. 24-10 shows that there are two D-shaped electrodes across which a radio-frequency (RF) electric field can be developed. The whole system is in a magnetic field which is perpendicular to the Ds. Protons are accelerated across the gap between the Ds, and are then curved round by the magnetic field. As a result they come to the gap between the Ds again. The frequency of the RF field is such that if the left-hand D were negative with respect to the right-hand one at the first crossing of the gap, it is now positive, so that once more the protons are accelerated. Now they have a higher energy, and will describe a larger circle under the influence of the magnetic field. Once again they come to the gap, again to be accelerated, and so on. Each acceleration results in a larger radius of circle, so that they spiral out-

The charging of a Van de Graaff generator is described in Exercise 23 of Chapter 7.

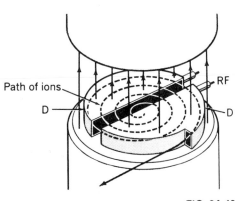

Path of ions
RF
D
D

FIG. 24-10

wards and finally will emerge from the Ds as shown. During the acceleration they may travel many kilometres, and if there were many atoms in their path they would lose their energy by collision. As a consequence, all nuclear machines have to be evacuated of as much air as possible.

The **betatron** is similar to a transformer except that the secondary is a single turn of electrons rather than a wire. The electrons naturally have to be contained in an evacuated vessel, called a doughnut because of its shape, but just as the electrons in the wire of a transformer gain energy when the magnetic field in the primary of the transformer changes (and so give rise to a current in the secondary), so the electrons in the doughnut gain energy. As they do not lose their energy by collision, they can keep on gaining energy until they attain as much as 20 MeV. These machines are widely used for the production of high energy x-rays for cancer therapy. These x-rays are produced when the electrons hit a tungsten target.

Another machine used in cancer therapy is the **linear accelerator**, or linac (Fig. 24-11). Here the energy needed to accelerate electrons comes from a radio-frequency wave. The electrons as it were, "surf-ride" on the RF waves, gaining energy as they do so. The longer the joy ride, the higher the energy. Most clinical linear accelerators are a few metres in length, and the electrons are accelerated up to 10 or 20 MeV. However, one "linac" at Stanford in California, which is used for high energy nuclear research, is 3 km long, and produces electrons with energies up to 40 GeV (Fig. 24-12).

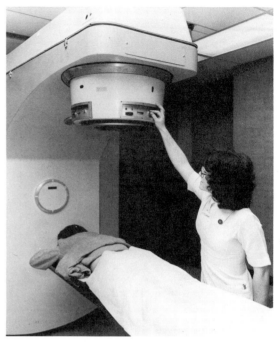

FIG. 24-11

FIG. 24-12

FIG. 24-13 THE CONSTRUCTION OF A CLOUD CHAMBER

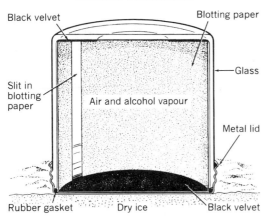

1. For the successful construction of a diffusion cloud chamber, it is important to have an air-tight vessel. A glass jar with a screw-on metal lid, such as a peanut butter jar, is suitable. A rubber gasket should be cut to make an airtight seal.
2. Onto the inside of the lid there should be glued a piece of black velvet using preferably a rubber-based glue. The chamber cannot be used until the glue is thoroughly set. To the inside of the bottom of the jar a circle of velvet is glued (leave a hole in the centre of the circle big enough that you can easily see what is going on in the chamber). Then a strip of dark coloured blotting paper, of width equal to the depth of the jar, should be inserted into the jar to form a collar round its inside. The paper should be in contact with the two pieces of velvet when the jar is closed. The length of the strip has to be such that a gap is left between the ends of the paper. Now some alcohol can be poured into the jar to soak the velvet and blotting paper thoroughly, and to leave a reserve of alcohol liquid in the jar. Screw the lid of the jar on firmly, and then invert the jar, placing its metal lid on a block of "dry ice" (solid CO_2). An intense beam of light should now be sent into the jar through the gap left in the blotting-paper collar.
3. Soon after the jar is set on the dry ice, a mist should be seen to fall in the chamber. This is due to the condensation of alcohol vapour on dust particles.
4. After the dust particles are "rained-out," tracks should appear due to the condensation of vapour on the ionization left in the path of ionizing particles such as beta rays, alpha rays, and cosmic-ray mesons. Probably the sensitive region where the tracks form will be near the bottom of the chamber.
5. The chamber will not work if there is not enough alcohol (make sure there is some liquid visible) or if the bottom is not cold enough (ensure that the lid makes good contact with the dry ice). The "rain" will not cease if air is continually leaking in (and bringing dust with it) or if the solvent of the glue is contaminating the chamber.
6. Most of the tracks you will see will be due to electrons (beta rays) produced by cosmic radiation. Some will be due to the slight radioactivity of the walls of the chamber. Once a minute or so you may see a thicker track due to an alpha particle from radon, the natural radioactive gas.

Exercises

A

1. (a) Name four methods of detecting nuclear radiation.
   (b) What effect does nuclear radiation have on the matter through which it passes? (Hint: Most radiation detectors rely on this effect in order to function.)
2. What do cloud chamber tracks represent? What are the tracks composed of?
3. Describe the (a) structure and (b) operation of a Geiger counter.
4. What does a scintillation counter system consist of?
5. What properties of radio-isotopes allow them to be

used as tracers?

6. What property of nuclear radiation do thickness gauges rely on for an accurate determination of thickness?

7. Briefly explain what is meant by neutron activation analysis.

8. What properties of high-energy gamma rays make them useful in radiation therapy?

9. (a) Name four machines used to produce high energy charged particles.
   (b) Why must the charge on the electrodes in a cyclotron be periodically reversed rather than be left constant?

B

10. (a) In the text it is stated that radioactive ^{24}Na is made by the irradiation of stable sodium, ^{23}Na, by neutrons. Write down the nuclear reaction equation representing this process.
    (b) Cobalt 60 is used in radiation therapy. Write down the nuclear reaction equation representing its formation from stable ^{59}Co by neutron irradiation.

11. ^{131}I is stated in the text to be a fission product. Assume that in the fission process ^{235}U absorbs a neutron and then fissions to ^{131}I, three neutrons and one other nucleus. What is the Z, chemical symbol and A of this other nucleus?

12. The intensity of gamma rays falls off with distance according to an "inverse square law" — that is, doubling the distance from the source reduces the intensity by a factor of four. If a counting ratemeter connected to a Geiger counter reads 1200 counts per second when a source is 50 cm from the Geiger tube, what will it read when the distance is (a) increased to 100 cm, (b) decreased to 25 cm?

13. In a Geiger counter tube, an ionizing particle may give an energy of 1 MeV to the gas in the tube. An "avalanche" process may then take place, by which the number of original ionizations is greatly increased, and which therefore results in the production of large numbers of electrons. These are attracted to the positive electrode and flow through the resistance R of Fig. 24-3. This flow of charge through the resistance gives rise to a voltage across the resistance which will persist while the charge flows. A voltage of 1 V exists across the resistance, whose value is 10^2 Ω, for 3×10^{-6} s.

   (a) Calculate the energy in joules associated with the current in the resistance.
   (b) Convert the original energy of 1 MeV to joules.
   (c) Calculate the energy amplification that has taken place due to the "avalanche."
   (d) Where has the extra energy come from?

14. The strength of the radio frequency field applied to the D's of a certain cyclotron is such that a proton gains an energy of 11 000 eV each time it crosses from one D to the other.
    (a) How many revolutions must a proton make to gain a total energy of 4.4 MeV?
    (b) If the average radius of the spiral path followed by the proton is 12 cm, what is the total distance travelled by the proton during the acceleration?

C

15. The Stanford 3 km Linac accelerates electrons to 40 GeV. What is the minimum wavelength of x-rays which would be produced by these electrons when they are stopped by colliding with matter? Compare this length with the size of atomic nuclei as discussed in Chapter 18.

16. In cloud chambers associated with nuclear accelerators, it is sometimes possible to observe the results of the annihilation of positive electrons and negative electrons. Using $E = mc^2$, calculate the energy, in MeV, released when such an annihilation takes place — the masses of the positive and the negative electrons are identical.

17. In a certain nuclear accelerator (called Nimrod, the "mighty hunter"), protons make a million orbits and travel about 1.3×10^5 km in just less than one second. In the process they each gain an energy of 7 GeV (7×10^9 eV). The machine accelerates 10^{11} protons each second.
    (a) What is the power of the beam (in watts)?
    (b) What is the average speed of the protons during the acceleration period, the average acceleration and the force required to give this acceleration to each proton? (Charge on the proton is 1.6×10^{-19} C; mass of the proton is 1.7×10^{-27} kg.)

18. In a certain cyclotron protons are travelling in a flat spiral. When the radius of the curved path is 15 cm, the speed of the protons is 3.0×10^7 m/s. What is the frequency of the applied radio-frequency field? Remember that the protons are accelerated twice in each revolution.

Afterword

Every action or process in the universe involves some kind of energy transformation. Throughout the four units of this book you have had an opportunity to study a variety of such energy transformations—many of them connected with collections of matter that you can see and handle. Now that you are able to look back over your year's study of physics, it is appropriate to put energy transformations into a different perspective.

This can be done by considering a collection of what can be called unit reactions. Let us get right down to various single particles of matter in different forms. At this basic level it can be shown that the vast majority of energy transformations fall into a range of about twelve orders of magnitude. The table in the margin illustrates a variety of these energies for a range of phenomena that embraces virtually the whole range of science—not only physics (the fundamental science), but also chemistry and biology.

Even when all the energy you can imagine has been removed from matter, reducing it to a very low temperature, there still remains what is called the zero-point energy, given here for helium. In the air you breathe, the amount of energy per particle is roughly ten times greater than the zero-point energy of helium. Another step of about ten brings you to the magnitude of the energy transformations that run the complexities of living organisms—the breaking and uniting of organic chemical bonds, largely in processes that are mediated by enzymes. In the body, enzymes are able to make do with energies that are about a tenth of those required in inorganic test-tube reactions, as in the bond energies shown for water and carbon dioxide. These latter are of course also involved in the essential biochemical processes of photosynthesis and respiration. Photosynthesis is the process by which carbon is released by the action of light, in order to make it available for building up (with water and other materials) the complex molecules of living organisms. You can see from the table that no single visible-light photon has enough energy to do that. Three or four red photons are needed to supply the energy to break away one carbon atom.

The processes involving the fundamental particles of which matter is composed have energies per particle that are about five orders of magnitude more energetic than those just mentioned. Notice that the annihilation of matter (in which very energetic photons are produced) always leads to c^2 J/(m^2/s^2) of energy per kilogram. Throughout the table, of course, the energies per kilogram depend on the masses of the particles—the less massive particles result in relatively larger numbers in the final column.

We hope that this small taste of general energetics will whet your appetite for the richer fare of scientific investigation that still lies before you.

THE ENERGIES OF SOME BASIC PROCESSES

Particle	Energy in joules Per particle	Per kilogram
Zero-point energy of helium atom at 0 K	4×10^{-22}	6×10^4
Kinetic energy of nitrogen molecule at 0°C	6×10^{-21}	1×10^5
Typical biochemical bond	4×10^{-20}	–
Red photon	3×10^{-19}	–
Violet photon	5×10^{-19}	–
Bond energy in water molecule	5×10^{-19}	2×10^7
Bond between atoms in hydrogen molecule	7×10^{-19}	2×10^8
Energy to release carbon from carbon dioxide molecule	8×10^{-19}	1×10^7
Kinetic energy of electron in solid silver	9×10^{-19}	1×10^{12}
Ultraviolet photon	1×10^{-18}	
Annihilation of electron-positron pair	8×10^{-14}	9×10^{16}
Fusion reaction to produce helium nucleus	4×10^{-12}	6×10^{14}
Fission reaction of uranium nucleus	3×10^{-11}	8×10^{13}
Annihilation of proton-antiproton pair	2×10^{-10}	9×10^{16}

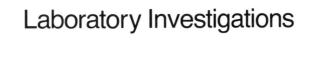

Laboratory Investigations

List of Laboratory Investigations

*Recommend doing before studying related text material

Introducing Investigations

In the laboratory part of your course you will have a chance to work with stopwatches, roller-skate dynamics carts, the cork-in-a-bottle accelerometer, an electric model train, slinkies, tuning forks, curved mirrors, prisms, lenses, batteries, semiconductors, magnets, electromagnets, generators, transformers, photocells, and transistors, among other things. It can be fascinating and a lot of fun, and we hope that you will enjoy it. Here are a few practical suggestions.

Most of these investigations are designed to be done by an average pair of students in forty minutes or fewer. If class size makes larger groups necessary, spread the work around. Don't just sit and watch while one person does everything.

An axiom: "Never expect apparatus to work. That way you may sometimes be pleasantly surprised." This may sound negative, but it is a realistic statement. There are bound to be sets of defective or touchy apparatus in any large batch. Often only minor adjustments are necessary. Since your teacher cannot be everywhere at once, it will save time, frustration, and aggravation if you try to fix simple things yourself first rather than always calling immediately for help.

If you are not able to complete an investigation in class time, you may be able to arrange with your teacher to finish it after school. This is likely to happen a few times during the year. Besides, scientists sometimes have to work overtime, too.

Regarding records of observations, what would you think of a bank that didn't record transactions but just promised to "remember" them? Or one that recorded transactions on scraps of waste paper or even paper towels? Probably not much. It may be more painful in the short run, but habits of recording complete observations do pay off in learning in the long run. Also, it is wise to have the telephone number of your lab partner for the occasions when you get home and find you are missing some crucial observation.

Finally, a word about mathematics in investigations. Like learning to use a knife and fork for eating, learning to think in numbers is not automatic. But it does make things so much easier that it really is worth trying to learn. For example, suppose you are asked to compare two things. Which sounds more sophisticated: "A is longer than B" or "A is 7.2% longer than B?" There is a world of difference between the mental processes of the person who automatically gives the first answer and of the person who automatically responds by taking measurements and calculating the second answer.

Some of the investigations are *qualitative* — that is, few numbers are involved. You merely have a good look at a phenomenon so that you, your classmates, and your teacher have something in common to talk about. Others, like some of the electromagnetism investigations, are *semiquantitative* — you take measurements, but stop short of making full use of them. Other investigations are *fully quantitative* — you record data and use techniques of graphic analysis to develop equations and laws.

Preparing Graphs

A graph is a precise mathematical tool for presenting and analyzing data. These are some of the guidelines that are usually followed in preparing scientific graphs.

AXES
The coordinate axes should be drawn on the graph paper in ink, leaving

space for the labels and numbers, which are placed outside these axes. If you are to draw a graph of *a* versus *b*, the first named, *a*, goes vertically and the second named, *b*, goes horizontally.

CHOICE OF SCALES

The choice of scale along each axis must be such that the coordinates of any point on the plot may be read instantly, without the need of any computation. Ease of visual interpolation of values should not be sacrificed just to make a graph fill the sheet of paper. In some cases the scales need not start from zero, but when the origin is a point on the curve it should be on the graph. The scales should be chosen so that the graph will cover a reasonably large portion of the sheet. The best choice of scales will give a curve or straight line at about 45° to the axes. In this case any deviations of points will be most noticeable, and a smoothed line can be drawn most precisely.

LABELLING THE AXES

The major intervals of the graph paper should be numbered, ideally with multiples of 10. In any case the intervals should be marked so that the coordinates of any point on the graph sheet can be interpolated instantly, without counting or computation. The numbers must be uniformly spaced and frequent enough to make interpolation easy, but not so close as to cause loss of clarity. All numbers, on both axes, should read horizontally. The name of the quantity represented by the *x*-coordinate, with the units in which it is measured, is printed horizontally below the numbers and parallel to the *x*-axis. For the *y*-axis, the corresponding label reads up, parallel to the *y*-axis.

Could you locate 1.7 on either of these axes without performing a calculation? The axes lack "ease of visual interpolation."

MARKING THE PLOTTED POINTS

Each plotted point should be carefully shown by a small circle around it. If two curves are drawn on the same graph, the points for the second one may be marked by using small crosses. For a graph drawn to show an equation rather than data, the curve passes exactly through each point and the point symbols may be omitted.

DRAWING THE CURVE

The line is drawn as a smooth curve passing through the average positions of the plotted points. It may pass exactly through some but not all of the points or it may not pass through any of them. The true average curve will have approximately the same number of points on each side.

The average curve may first be sketched in lightly in pencil, examined for discontinuities in slope by looking along it at an oblique angle, smoothed out with pencil and eraser, and finally drawn in. Drafting curves or a ruler may be useful for the final drawing, but do not use them until the position and shape of the curve have already been decided by freehand sketching. *Never* join the points with a series of straight lines.

If it is known definitely that the relationship between the variables is linear, a transparent ruler may be used to place the straight line in the best average position. But if the graph is to provide a test of linearity the best average curve must be drawn. It is quite possible that it may be nearly, but not quite, a straight line.

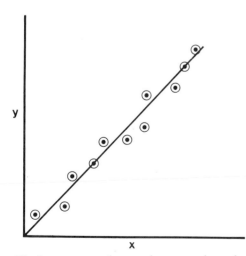

The best average line need not pass through all the points, but it should have about as many points above it as below it.

THE TITLE

The title of a graph should give concise but full information as to what the graph shows. The labels on the axes show what quantities are plotted, for example, **Distance Travelled (in metres) versus Time Taken (in seconds)**, but this graph would tell little if its title did not give the further information that it is a **Distance versus Time Graph for a Styrofoam Ball Falling in Air**.

Below the title and in somewhat smaller print should be the name of the investigation and the date on which the investigation was performed. If two or three curves are plotted on the same sheet the distinguishing label for each curve should be printed along the curve. If there are several curves it may be necessary to collect the labels in a table or legend, using numbers or letters for identification.

GENERAL APPEARANCE

The graph as a whole must be clear and neat. The test as to whether the number, labels, and titles are large enough and clear enough is to imagine the graph reduced to a half or third of its size. Would all parts still be easily readable?

Do styrofoam balls fall any differently than other types of balls? Try dropping a styrofoam ball and a golf ball through a vertical distance of about 3 m. Can you detect any difference?

PART ONE
Mechanics

APPARATUS
helical steel spring kit (PSSC-style)
metre stick
spring support
tape
spring-type force gauge, 0 to 40 N (one
per class)

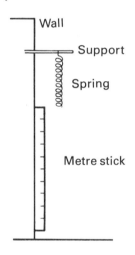

See page 54 for a brief discussion of
Hooke's law.

INVESTIGATION 1-1

Direct Variation: Hooke's law

One of the most difficult tasks for students beginning the study of physics is to get used to thinking quantitatively. This investigation is designed to familiarize you with the idea of direct variation, one of the most basic quantitative ideas. You will also discover Hooke's law, an apparently simple fact that has wide use in many branches of physics.

PRE-LAB
Before doing this investigation you should be able to draw a graph correctly and take its slope. You should also be familiar with the various ways of defining direct variation.

PROCEDURE
Suspend a spring from the kit vertically so that the spring does not bind against the wall or the side of the lab bench. If the spring is new, you may have to stretch it gently so that the coils do not touch when the spring has nothing hung on it. Tape the metre stick to the wall or desk so that its zero is level with the bottom end of the spring.

The force of gravity on the smaller mass in the kit is about 5 N and on the larger one, 10 N. You can verify this by hanging the masses on the force gauge on display.

Hang the smaller mass from the free end of the spring and record the change in length of the spring. Use a data table with the headings **Stretching Force (in newtons)** and **Change in Length of Spring (in metres)**. Then use forces of 10 N, 15 N, and, if they do not stretch the spring more than 1 m, 20 N, 25 N, and so on by borrowing masses from other groups. Be sure to record the result for a force of zero newtons. Draw a graph of the data.

CONCLUSIONS
1. Show that your data obey the various definitions of direct variation. Calculate the slope of your graph, with units, and use it to state the actual equation obeyed by your data.
2. In what sense does the slope of your graph represent the "stiffness" of your spring?
3. In one sentence, state what the data from this investigation illustrates. This is known as Hooke's law.

INVESTIGATION 1-2

Inverse Variation: The Simple Balance

In this investigation you will study an example of the idea of inverse variation. Inverse variation is another basic quantitative idea in physics. You will also learn about the concept of torque.

PRE-LAB
Before doing this investigation, you should be familiar with the various definitions of inverse variation. You should also be able to simplify expressions like

$$\frac{N}{1/m}$$

APPARATUS
metre stick
metre stick fulcrum and support
box of masses
spring-type force gauge, 0 to 20 N (one
per class)
string

PROCEDURE

Attach a fulcrum to a metre stick and balance the stick on a support. It may help if the support is on a totebox to give it some height.

Hang a 500 g mass by a string from the 20 cm mark on the metre stick. This mass will stay at the same position throughout the rest of the investigation. The force of gravity on it provides a constant force of about 5 N, as you can check with a force gauge.

Balance the metre stick by hanging a 1500 g mass on the other side of the stick. Measure the distance of this mass from the fulcrum. Record your observations in a data table with the headings **Force to Achieve Balance (in newtons)**, and **Distance of Force from Fulcrum (in metres)**. You can get the force of gravity on the mass by using the spring-type force gauge on display.

Repeat the procedure by using masses of 1000 g, 800 g, 600 g, 400 g, and just to break the pattern, 320 g, one at a time. In each case record the force of gravity on these balancing masses and their distances from the fulcrum.

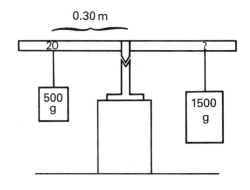

CONCLUSIONS

1. Show that your data obey the various definitions of inverse variation. From the graph of force versus inverse distances, calculate the slope, with units, and use it to state the actual equation obeyed by your data.

2. The twisting effect of a force on an object is called the *torque* applied by the force. The torque depends on the size of the force and its perpendicular distance from the fulcrum. Using the formula shown, calculate the torque provided by the 500 g mass that was kept fixed on one side of the balance. If you answered the first conclusion correctly, you should recognize this number, complete with units. What is it?

3. State in one sentence what this investigation shows about the relationship between forces and their distances from the fulcrum in order to get equilibrium.

4. For an object to be in balance, what must be true about the clockwise torque and the counterclockwise torque acting on it?

$$T = F \times d_{\perp},$$
where, T = torque in newton metres
F = force in newtons
$d_{\perp}$ = perpendicular distance of the force from the fulcrum in metres.

INVESTIGATION 1-3

Measuring Speeds

How fast can you go, and how slow is slow? In this investigation, you will measure typical human speeds from slow to fast. You will also become familiar with the speed formula.

PRE-LAB

Before doing this investigation, you should know how to calculate average speed given the distance covered and the time taken. You should also know what a conversion factor is and how to use one to convert from one set of units to another, such as from seconds to minutes.

PROCEDURE

Set up a measured distance. Have your partner use a stopclock to determine your times over the measured distance for a slow walk, a normal walk, a fast walk, a trot, and a run. Calculate your speed in each case. Record your results in a data table with the headings **Type of Motion, Distance Travelled, Time Taken,** and **Speed**.

How fast can you move your hand? Use the photocell-operated millisecond timer on display and a table tennis paddle to get the speed of the paddle as

APPARATUS

tape measure or metre sticks
stopclock or stopwatch
photocell-operated millisecond timer
  (one per class)
table tennis paddle (one per class)

you pass it through the light beam. The distance covered in this case is the width of the table tennis paddle, since that is the distance it moves while the light is interrupted and the timer is on. Again, record your results in your data table.

CONCLUSIONS

What is the typical range of human speeds in metres per second and kilometres per hour? Show how you converted from metres per second to kilometres per hour.

QUESTIONS

1. What is the speed of your normal walk? How long does it take you to walk to school? How long is that in seconds? Use the formula for speed to *calculate* how far the school is from your home. Show your work.
2. What is your running speed? What is the distance from school to your home, as calculated in question 1? If you ran to school instead of walking, how long would it take? What would that be in minutes? Show your work.
3. In some schools, students are allowed five minutes to go from class to class. If you moved at your slow walking speed, how far would you go in that time? Show your work.

INVESTIGATION 1-4

Graphic Analysis of Uniform Motion I

In this investigation, you will use an electric model locomotive to get data for uniform motion. When you analyze that data, you will discover an interesting property of *v-t* graphs of motion. You will also review the properties of *d-t* graphs.

PRE-LAB

Before doing this investigation, you should know how to calculate speed from a *d-t* graph of uniform motion.

APPARATUS

electric model train with track the length of the room (nickel-silver track is recommended as it does not need frequent sanding to maintain electrical contact)
train power supply
8 to 15 stopclocks

There should be 8 to 15 equally spaced places marked off along the length of the track. Tape should be placed on one of the rails so that the train stops with its nose even with the last marker when it travels down the track.

This investigation is designed to be done with large groups of 8 to 15 or more. While half of the class is taking data, the other half can be preparing or doing something else useful.

PROCEDURE

One student is needed to act as "engineer" to operate the train controls, and one is needed as a "starter" to call out when the train passes the starting-point. The rest are timers and need a stopclock or stopwatch each.

Measure the total distance of each place from the first marker. There should be a person with a stopclock at each of the marked positions.

The engineer operates the train at a constant power supply setting. The starter calls out loudly 'three-two-one-go' in such a way that the nose of the train reaches the starting marker at the word "go". At the word "go" from the starter, all timers start their clocks. As the front of the train reaches each position on the track, the timer for that position stops his or her clock. In order to get accurate results, repeat twice more and average the times. Record the results in a data table with the headings **Distance**, **Time 1**, **Time 2**, **Time 3**, and **Average Time**.

Repeat the entire procedure, but use a different power supply setting so that the train has a different constant speed. Again set up a data table.

CONCLUSIONS

1. Use your data to draw a distance versus average time graph for each speed table. What feature of each graph indicates uniform motion?
2. Use the graphs to draw speed-time graphs for each speed. Be sure your speed-time line in each case extends to, but not beyond, the last recorded time. Calculate the area under each of the speed-time graphs, taking proper account of units. If you have done it correctly, each area should be about the same and should correspond to a recognizable quantity. What is that quantity?
3. Comment on what you have learned by doing this investigation.

INVESTIGATION 1-5

Graphic Analysis of Uniform Motion II

This investigation is a repeat of Investigation 1-4 with the following change. Two extra "timers" are added midway along the track. When the train reaches them, the engineer stops the train. The first extra timer records the time at which the train stops. After about 5 s, the engineer starts the train again. The second extra timer records the time at which it started again.

Note that all timers downtrack are to leave their stopclocks running during this stop-start routine. They stop their clocks *only when the train reaches their position*. Do this timing only once.

Record your results in a data table with the headings **Distance** and **Time Taken**. The distance column will have two extra entries this time, for the midway stop position and the midway start position. Of course, these two distances will be the same, but the times for them will not.

CONCLUSIONS

1. Use the data to draw a distance versus time graph for the entire trip. Use the *d-t* points for STOP and START as part of the regular data. Indicate on your graph the portion of the journey during which the train was stopped.
2. Find the slope of each of the three portions of your graph, and use these to draw a speed-time graph for the journey. Make sure that your speed-time line extends to, but not beyond, the last recorded time.
3. Calculate the total area under the speed-time graph. What does it represent, within experimental uncertainty?
4. Comment on what you have learned by doing this investigation.

INVESTIGATION 1-6

Accelerations

In this investigation you will use a cork accelerometer to investigate a number of properties of acceleration.

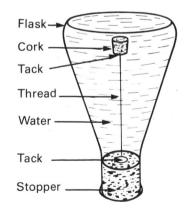

Flask
Cork
Tack
Thread
Water
Tack
Stopper

PROCEDURE

Assemble the accelerometer so that when the stopper is put into the mouth of the flask, the cork can hang freely just above the bottom of the flask. Then fill the flask with water, insert cork and stopper, make sure the stopper is tight, and invert the flask. The assembly is now a cork accelerometer.

Hold the cork accelerometer firmly in both hands and investigate what happens when you accelerate. Take this to be a positive acceleration. Whenever

APPARATUS

large Erlenmeyer flask with solid rubber stopper to fit
cork or fishing float
length of thread
2 tacks

the cork moves in the same direction in the remainder of the investigation, that will be a positive acceleration also. What happens when you decelerate the accelerometer? Take the direction of motion of the cork for this as indicating a negative acceleration in the remainder of the investigation. What happens when you move the accelerometer in a straight line at constant speed?

Is there a difference in response between going forward, but decelerating, and accelerating backward? Between going backward, but slowing down, and accelerating forward?

Is there a difference between moving in a straight line at constant speed and rotating in a circle at the same constant speed?

CONCLUSIONS

Summarize your findings in a table with the headings **Type of Acceleration** and **When It Occurs**. Under Type of Acceleration, list positive acceleration, negative acceleration, zero acceleration, and constant (non-zero) acceleration. For example, under positive acceleration, you would list under When It Occurs "when going forward and speeding up" and "when going backward and slowing down".

A liquid-surface accelerometer can be used to measure accelerations, rather than merely indicate them. If the length of the accelerometer is 19.6 cm, the height of the liquid above or below normal will give the acceleration in m/s².

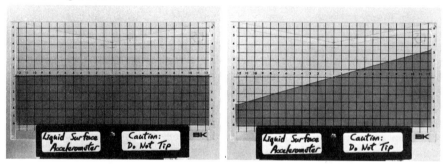

INVESTIGATION 1-7

Acceleration Due to Gravity

In this investigation you will measure what is perhaps the most famous acceleration of all, the acceleration due to gravity.

The acceleration due to gravity, like many practical accelerations, is so large that objects literally whiz by. One must measure very short time intervals in order to calculate the acceleration. Thus, accurate timing becomes a major experimental problem.

There are many ways of getting around the problem. Two methods are presented here, chosen for their conceptual and mathematical simplicity, but not necessarily for their cleverness or their accuracy. The second method can be quite accurate, however, and the first uses some rather sophisticated apparatus.

Wooden block

To timer

Photocells

Light sources

To power supply

APPARATUS

1 m or longer retort stand
chunk of wood
2 photogates (that is, photocell and light pairs)
photocell-switched millisecond timer

METHOD 1: PHOTOCELL-SWITCHED MILLISECOND TIMER

PROCEDURE

Connect the photocells in series so that when the upper light beam is interrupted the timer is started and when the lower light beam is interrupted the timer is stopped.

Hold the chalkbrush or piece of wood so that it is above the upper photogate and so low that it almost turns the timer on. Drop the brush several times and record the average time to fall from rest through the photogates.

Now disconnect the top photocell and use only the bottom one. Connect it so that the timer operates only while its light beam is interrupted. Drop the brush from the same position as before. Record the average time for the brush to fall through the lower photocell. From the length of the brush, *d*, calculate the instantaneous speed

$$v_2 = \frac{\Delta d}{\Delta t}$$

at the end of the drop.

Then use the formula

$$a = \frac{v_2 - v_1}{\Delta t}$$

and the fact that the brush started from rest to calculate the acceleration due to gravity, *g*.

CONCLUSIONS

What value of *g* do you get? How does your value of *g* compare with the accepted value of 9.8 m/s²? (Be quantitative, that is, calculate the percentage difference.)

QUESTIONS

1. Calculate the percentage difference between the largest and smallest values of the total time of fall.
2. Calculate the percentage difference between the largest and smallest values of the time for the brush to fall through the second photogate.
3. Do the percentage uncertainties calculated in questions 1 and 2 above account for the percentage difference between your value of *g* and the accepted value of *g*?
4. What orientation of the brush as it passes the second photogate is needed to minimize errors?

When is an experimental result acceptable? If the total uncertainty in an experiment is greater than the final error, the error is accounted for.

Suppose, however, the error is larger than the total uncertainty. In this case, there is either a hidden source of error not accounted for in the uncertainties *or* the experiment proves that the previously accepted value used to get the final error is incorrect.

An analogy might be a contractor who estimates that a building will cost $500 000, give or take $100 000. If the final price turns out to be $550 000, his final error is less than his uncertainty and all is well. However, should the final price turn out to be $700 000, his final error is more than his uncertainty and he had better have a good explanation. Either he doesn't know how to estimate prices and uncertainties, or, if he does, there was a hidden source of cost that he failed to take into account.

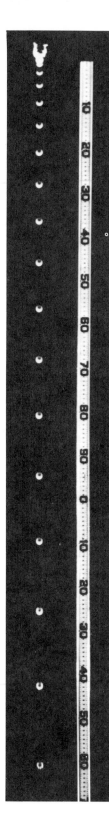

METHOD 2: MULTIPLE-IMAGE PHOTOGRAPHY

Look at the multiple flash photograph of a steel ball bearing dropped from rest. Since the strobe light illuminated the bearing for only a small fraction of a second each time the light flashed, the bearing looks still in each image. The strobe rate was 30 flashes per second.

PROCEDURE

Use the strobe rate to calculate the time interval between flashes.

Use the 1 m long scale in the photograph to calculate the scale factor. That is, calculate how many centimetres on the page equal 1 m in the original setup.

Measure successive displacements of the ball on the photograph. Estimate to the nearest hundredth of a centimetre on the photo. (An eye loupe, which is basically a fixed-focus compound microscope with a reticle graduated in hundredths of a centimetre, may be of help.) Then, calculate the average speed of the ball through each time interval, using your displacement measurements, the scale factor, and the period between flashes. Show the measurements and calculated results in a data table. Then draw a graph of speed versus time.

QUESTIONS

1. Is the acceleration of the ball constant? Does your graph line pass through the origin? Explain your answers to both questions.
2. Determine the acceleration of the ball from your speed-time graph.
3. Calculate the percentage difference between your value for g and the accepted value of $9.8 \ m/s^2$.

INVESTIGATION 1-8

Graphic Analysis of Uniform Acceleration

The apparatus and procedure for this investigation are similar to those for Investigation 1-4. The only differences are that this time the train is started from rest at the zero mark and the engineer speeds up the train by increasing the voltage at a uniform rate.

This investigation is designed to follow your class study of graphic analysis of accelerated motion.

PROCEDURE

It is wise to do a few practice runs so that the engineer gets some idea of how fast to turn the power pack or variac in order to have acceleration all the way down the track.

QUESTIONS

1. Use your distance and average time data to draw a distance-time graph for this motion.
2. Use the distance-time graph to develop a speed-time graph.
3. Use the speed-time graph to develop an acceleration-time graph.
4. Should the d-t graph for uniformly accelerated motion be linear? What about the v-t graph? The a-t graph?
5. What does this investigation show about uniformly accelerated motion? Comment on sources of error.

INVESTIGATION 1-9

Inertia and Motion

How does an object move if there are no forces acting on it? That is, what is the unforced, "natural" motion of an object? This investigation will lead you to the answer by means of what might seem to be a series of trivial steps. Write down answers to each step before you proceed to the next.

This investigation is designed to precede your study of this topic in the text.

PROCEDURE

1. Tape the ruler to the cart and place the ball bearing in the groove of the ruler so that it can roll freely. Roll the cart forward to accelerate it. Observe the ball very carefully when you first accelerate the cart. Describe the ball's motion relative to the cart. Describe the ball's motion relative to the table.
2. Suppose the ball had been taped to the cart. How would it have moved relative to the table? Why does the tape make this difference?
3. Use your answers to 1 and 2 to state whether you think rest is a natural state of an object.
4. Now pull the cart and ball (without tape) to get them moving together at a constant speed in a straight line (so-called *uniform motion*). Then observe the ball carefully as you pull backward on the cart to decelerate it. Describe the ball's motion relative to the table when you decelerate the cart. Was a force necessary to keep the ball moving in this uniform motion when you decelerated the cart? If so, what was the force?
5. Use your results from 4 to state what you think is natural for an object that is already in motion.
6. What practical difference do you think it would have made if you had used a much larger ball bearing and repeated 1 or 4? Why?
7. Suppose you had a flat plate on top of the dynamics cart so that the ball was free to move in two dimensions. Imagine that the cart and ball were moving in uniform motion and then the cart made a right turn. Describe how the ball would move relative to the table. Explain.

APPARATUS
dynamics cart
grooved ruler
tape
large steel ball bearing

CONCLUSIONS
Summarize in one or two sentences what you have discovered by doing this investigation.

QUESTIONS
1. State Newton's first law of motion.

INVESTIGATION 1-10

Factors that Affect Acceleration

Suppose you are trying to accelerate a stalled car by pushing it. What factors affect the acceleration? List a few before proceeding — you will need the list to proceed.

Now suppose you have the same car upside down on level, smooth ice and are again going to accelerate it by pushing it. Which of the factors you listed before would still affect the car's acceleration? That is, which factors are so basic that they apply to acceleration under any circumstances?

This investigation may be made quantitative (and much more time-consuming) by using ticker-tape recording timers.

APPARATUS
about 5 m of grit-free level surface
dynamics cart with grit-free wheels
supply of additional carts or of masses
    equivalent to a cart
0 to 3 N force gauge
50 to 100 cm of string
stopwatch (optional)

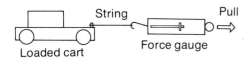
Loaded cart — String — Force gauge — Pull

F_1

F_2

Part of this force F_2, is trying to lift the cart off the table, and hence is not contributing to the acceleration of the cart in the direction the cart is moving.

In this investigation you will study the two basic factors that affect all accelerations and how they do so. The investigation is qualitative. Once you know what the two factors are, you may even be able to predict the results without doing the investigation. What will probably startle you, however, is the actual feel of what a constant acceleration is like. If you get nothing out of the investigation other than this physical sensation, you will have been at least modestly successful.

PRE-LAB
Before doing this investigation you should be able to state in words qualitative definitions of direct variation and of indirect variation.

PROCEDURE
1. *Force* is one of the two basic factors that affect acceleration. The object of this part of the investigation is to discover how the acceleration of an object is related to the force applied to the object. To apply a constant force to the loaded dynamics cart that you will accelerate, you will pull the cart with a force gauge stretched a constant amount. To keep the force constant is very difficult, especially for the larger forces, and you may have to make several practice runs. It may also help to have a long piece of string between the cart and the spring balance so that the puller and the catcher at the end of the run can be two different people.

Keeping these hints in mind, use a two-cart mass and accelerate it with a constant force of 1 N. Remember to keep the force constant for the whole length of the surface you are using. Also, try to pull only in the same direction as the cart moves, rather than at an angle — you want all the force to be accelerating the cart (F_1) rather than part of the force trying to lift the cart up (F_2). You are not going to measure the acceleration directly in metres per second squared, as that would be very time-consuming. Instead, merely try to get a feel for the size of acceleration produced so that you can compare it with the other accelerations that follow. If you wish and time permits or if your teacher tells you to, you can get a rough set of numbers by timing the cart from rest with a stopclock over a set distance. If you do this, you must use the formula $a = 2 d/t^2$ to get the acceleration.

Repeat the procedure, using twice the force.

Try other forces (half, triple, etc.) on the same mass until you think you can state at least qualitatively the relationship between acceleration and force when the accelerating mass is constant. Record what you think the relationship is.

2. *Mass* is the other basic factor that affects acceleration. The object of this

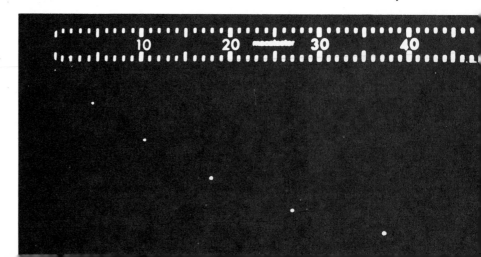

part of the investigation is to discover how the acceleration of an object subject to a constant applied force is related to the mass of the object. You will use the same general technique you used in part 1.

Accelerate a two-cart mass with a constant force of 1 N. As in part 1, try to remember the physical feel of the resulting acceleration so that you can compare it with the other accelerations that follow.

Repeat with a three-cart mass and the same force.

Repeat with a one-cart mass and the same force.

Try other masses and the same force, time permitting, until you think you can state at least qualitatively the relationship between acceleration and mass when the force is constant. Record what you think the relationship is.

3. This part of the investigation deals with *constant velocity* (no acceleration).

Pull a cart at a constant velocity (constant speed *and* direction). When the cart is moving at constant velocity, record the force required to keep it moving at that velocity. Comment on your result.

CONCLUSIONS
Summarize what you have learned by doing this investigation.

INVESTIGATION 1-11

Kinetic Energy and Potential Energy

In this investigation you will use a multiple-flash photograph of a swinging pendulum to measure kinetic energy and potential energy. You will find a very important relationship between them, one that took famous scientists decades to discover and that has been enormously useful in various forms ever since.

PRE-LAB
Before doing this investigation you should be able to calculate kinetic energies and gravitational potential energies.

PROCEDURE
The photograph shown is a multiple-exposure photograph of a pendulum bob in motion. The strobe light was flashing at a steady rate of 20 flashes per second. The mass of the bob was 67.5 g.

Use the strobe rate to calculate the time interval between flashes. Use this and the distance the bob travelled between flashes at the bottom of its swing to calculate the speed of the bob at the bottom of its swing. Then calculate the kinetic energy of the bob at the bottom of its swing.

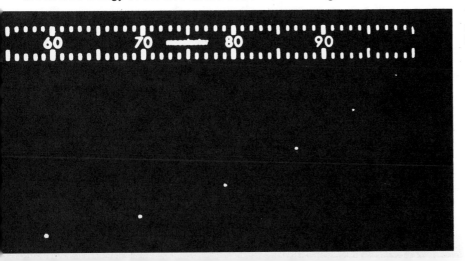

The shiny surface of the ball acts as a convex mirror to focus the light to a point image, which is what is seen in the photograph.

What was the speed of the bob at the very top of its swing? Thus, what was its kinetic energy there?

How much did the kinetic energy of the bob increase in going from the top to the bottom of its swing (ΔE_k)?

Measure the height of the bob at the top of its swing, using the metre stick in the photograph. Use this to calculate the gravitational potential energy of the bob at the top of its swing.

How much gravitational potential energy did the bob lose in going from the top to the bottom of its swing (ΔE_p)?

Allowing for experimental errors, how do your results for ΔE_k and ΔE_p compare?

CONCLUSIONS

Summarize in a sentence what you have learned from this investigation about the relationship between kinetic energy and potential energy.

QUESTIONS

1. Suppose a ball of mass 250 g is thrown straight up with a kinetic energy of 10 J. How high will it rise before it starts to come down again?

INVESTIGATION 1-12

Student Power

In this investigation you will measure your power twice, once for running up a flight of stairs and once for lifting a pile of books at a steady rate.

Running up a flight of stairs at top speed develops a power that is usually close to the human maximum for short periods. You will get a more reasonable estimate of the power that you can develop and maintain over a lengthy period of time by doing the second part of the investigation.

PRE-LAB

Before doing this investigation you should be able to solve problems such as the following, using correct units and formulas:

If a person of mass 60 kg runs up a flight of stairs 10 m long to a vertical height of 4 m in 3.0 s, what power does the person develop?

APPARATUS

tape measure or metre sticks

stopwatch or watch with sweep second hand

several-kilogram mass or pile of books of known mass

PROCEDURE

1. Time each person in your group as they run up a flight of stairs. It may help to have a running start before you reach the first stair, if that is possible. The more steps you take at a time, the better your time is likely to be.

Measure the vertical height of the stairs.

Find your mass on a set of kilogram scales or the force of gravity on you on a set of newton scales. Record.

Calculate your power in watts for running up the stairs. What is that in kilowatts?

2. Time each person in your group as they lift a several-kilogram mass through a known height repeatedly. About 20 repetitions should be adequate.

Calculate your power in watts for this type of task. Don't forget to take 20 times the height into your calculations. What is your power in kilowatts?

CONCLUSIONS

1. How do your powers for the two types of task compare?

2. Compare the lowest and highest powers in your class for the stair climbing.

It may be helpful to post each group's results on the chalkboard as they become available.

3. Does there seem to be any similarity among those people who can develop the larger powers in climbing? What is the similarity among those who develop larger powers in repeated liftings?

INVESTIGATION 2-1

Electrified Objects

In this investigation you will electrify objects and study their qualitative behaviour. The conclusions you reach will provide a major first step in building a model of electric charge.

PRE-LAB
No preparation is required but after you do the procedure and *before* you try to answer the questions, you should see or read about the thermionic emission effect so that you know which type of charge is free to move in a conductor and which is not.

APPARATUS
Almost any solid can be charged if it is rubbed on some other appropriate substance. This investigation uses acetate and vinylite strips rubbed with paper because they are inexpensive and work well.

PROCEDURE
Set up vinylite and acetate strips on a ring stand as shown. Make sure the plastic strips are free to swing. Rub the acetate strip with a paper towel, then rub another acetate strip with a paper towel and bring them close together with long side facing long side. Record what happens.

Try various other charged strips. Bring a charged vinylite near another charged vinylite, a charged vinylite near a charged acetate, and a charged acetate near a charged vinylite. Record your observations. In each case how does what you observe seem to depend on distance between the two strips?

Tear off several very tiny pieces of paper. What happens when you bring a charged strip near them? Also, try bringing a charged strip near a very fine stream of water from a tap. What happens? Can you see why, when one wants to prove that an object is charged, the crucial test is whether it *repels* a charged object and not whether it attracts a charged object? Why?

Vinylite rubbed with paper develops a charge that corresponds to what Benjamin Franklin first called "negative" electricity. Similarly, rubbed acetate develops "positive" electricity. Now rub together substances other than acetate and paper and vinylite and paper until you find a pair that charges easily. Bring one of the pair up to the suspended charged strips. What kind of charge does it have? (Keep in mind your answer to the last two questions in the previous paragraph.) What about the other member of the pair?

PART TWO
Electricity and Magnetism

APPARATUS
acetate strips
vinylite strips
retort stand
masking tape
paper towel
styrofoam ball painted with conducting graphite and suspended by a good insulator, such as nylon

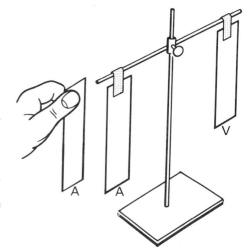

How to make a suspended conducting ball
1. Push a pin through the card and impale the ball on it.
2. Coat the ball with graphite in alcohol to make it conductive.
3. When the graphite dries, make a hole all the way through the ball with the pin. Insert a nylon thread or monofilament through the hole, and put a dab of glue on the end. Try not to get the nylon dirty with graphite.
4. Pull dab of glue into the ball and let it set. You now have a suspended conducting ball.

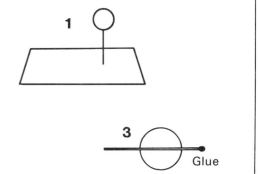

Use a suspended styrofoam ball coated with graphite and bring up a charged vinylite strip. Record all that you observe. You may have to discharge the ball and recharge the strip several times in order to avoid missing anything.

CONCLUSIONS
1. What do you conclude from the first two paragraphs of the procedure? These conclusions are often known as the *laws of electrostatics*.
2. Make a general statement that covers both results from the third paragraph of the procedure. This can be thought of as a third law of electrostatics, although it can be explained in terms of the others, as you will see in the following questions.

QUESTIONS
1. Use a diagram or diagrams to account for conclusion 2 in terms of the idea of "induced charge separation."
2. Use a diagram or diagrams to account for all you observed in the fifth paragraph of the procedure.
3. What evidence is there that the effects you observed in this investigation are not due to magnetism?
4. When you comb your hair on a dry day, why does it sometimes stick out all over?

INVESTIGATION 2-2

Electrification by Contact and Induction

Investigation 2-1 showed that substances can be charged by friction, that is, by rubbing them on other appropriate substances. In this investigation you will use an extremely sensitive detector of charge, the moving-vane electroscope, to study the electrification of conductors by the processes of conduction and induction.

See **Fig. 24-2** for an illustration of a moving-vane electroscope.

PRE-LAB
Before doing this investigation you should know the difference between conductors and insulators and have seen or studied the thermionic emission effect so that you know which type of charge is free to move in a conductor and which is not.

APPARATUS
vinylite and acetate strips
paper towel
moving-vane electroscope

PROCEDURE
Charge a vinylite strip by rubbing it on a piece of paper. Touch the charged vinylite to the top of the electroscope and then remove it. Record what happens.

Discharge the electroscope by touching it with your hand. Then bring up a charged vinylite strip as before, but this time rub the strip along the top of the electroscope as though you were rubbing soft butter off a knife. Record what happens. This is known as charging by *contact*, or charging by *conduction*.

Bring a charged vinylite strip close to but not touching the top of an electroscope that has been charged by conduction with vinylite as previously. What happens? Bring up a charged acetate strip, again not touching, to the same electroscope. What happens this time? What do these observations tell you about the charge on the electroscope?

To charge an electroscope by *induction*, bring a charged vinylite strip close to the top of an electroscope, but not so close that the strip touches the electroscope or that a spark jumps between them. While the strip is held close to the electroscope, touch the top with a finger and then remove the finger. Last, remove the charged strip. Record what you see in each of these three steps.

Test the charge on the electroscope with charged vinylite and acetate strips as you did before. What do you find this time?

CONCLUSIONS
What practical difference is there between charging an electroscope, or any conductor, by conduction or by induction?

QUESTIONS
1. Draw a diagram or a series of diagrams to show what is going on when you charge an electroscope or a conductor by contact (a) negatively and (b) positively.

2. Draw a diagram or a series of diagrams to show what is going on when you charge an electroscope or conductor by induction (a) negatively and (b) positively.

INVESTIGATION 2-3

Measuring Potential Differences

In this and the following two investigations, you will gain experience in setting up electric circuits, in measuring potential difference and current, and in interpreting the physical significance of your readings. You will also learn how to protect electric meters from possible damage.

The investigations have been designed so that if you follow the instructions no harm will come to you or to the expensive meters that you will be using.

PRE-LAB
Before doing this investigation, you should have had some practice in reading a multi-range meter, either with an overhead projector diagram of the type of meter your school has or with a series of diagrams on the chalkboard. You should also know the meaning of potential difference and a definition of the volt.

PROCEDURE
Set a voltmeter scale at some high value, say 100 V full-scale deflection (FSD), that is, a scale for which, when the potential difference across the voltmeter is 100 V, the pointer is all the way across the meter face. Connect a lead to each of the terminals of the meter. The terminals will either be marked plus and minus or colour coded—black for negative, red for positive. Connect the voltmeter across the terminals of a dry cell so that the positive on the meter is connected to the positive on the cell. *If the needle of the meter goes off the scale, disconnect the meter instantly!* It is wise to connect one terminal of the meter, and then merely touch the wire to the second terminal before actually connecting it. Once you are sure the meter is properly connected, you can turn it to more and more sensitive scales until you get a sizable deflection of the pointer. Set up a data table with the column headings **Number of Cells in Series**, **Measured Potential Difference (in volts)**, and **Measured Potential Difference (in joules per coulomb)**.

Repeat the investigation with two cells connected in series to form a battery. See the diagram for wiring details.

Repeat with three cells connected in series.

APPARATUS
multi-range voltmeter
three 1.5 V dry cells
3 connecting leads (always use relatively short leads if you have a choice in order to avoid having a confusing maze of wire all over your work area)

The 4 mm banana plug leads are recommended as they fit most modern lab apparatus. For other apparatus, *Mueller 60* alligator clips slip easily over the banana plug to make an excellent connector.

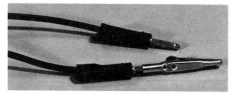

Also handy is the number 28 stranded PVC-coated wire, which can be snapped like thread and stripped by using a ruler on a hard surface.

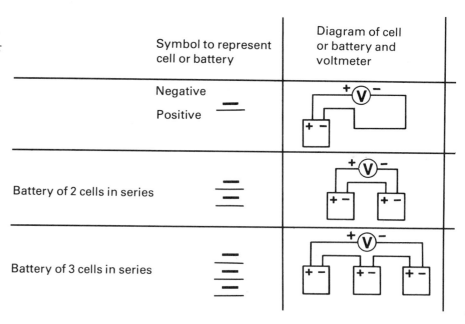

Symbol to represent cell or battery		Diagram of cell or battery and voltmeter
Negative Positive	—	
Battery of 2 cells in series		
Battery of 3 cells in series		

CONCLUSIONS
1. What general conclusion can you draw about the total potential difference across a battery of several cells connected in series?
2. How are cells connected in series? Draw a diagram showing four cells in series.

INVESTIGATION 2-4

Measuring Potential Difference in a Series Circuit

In this investigation you will study the voltage properties of a circuit with two light bulbs in series.

PRE-LAB
See the previous investigation. Also review the precautions to follow in using a multi-range voltmeter.

PROCEDURE
Set up a circuit consisting of a battery of three cells in series, two light bulbs in series, and three connecting wires AB, CD, and EF. Do not connect the voltmeter. If the bulbs do not light up even faintly, check your connections or replace the bulbs, batteries, or connecting wires as necessary.

Once you have both light bulbs lit, connect two wires to the voltmeter as in Investigation 2-3 and measure the potential differences: (a) across light bulb #1 by connecting the meter at B and at C (use the technique you used in Investigation 2-3 to set the scales on the voltmeter); (b) across light bulb #2; (c) across the wire AB; (d) across the wire CD; (e) across the wire EF; (f) across the battery AF. Record your readings in a data table with the headings **Connection Points**, **Device**, **Meter Reading (in volts)**, and **Meter Reading (in joules per coulomb)**.

If time and interest permit, the instructions in this investigation may easily be used as the basis for an investigation to measure potential difference in a *parallel* circuit as well.

APPARATUS
three 1.5 V dry cells
two 6 V light bulbs and sockets
multi-range voltmeter
short connecting leads

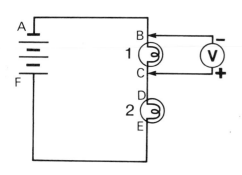

CONCLUSIONS

1. Add up all of the potential difference readings in parts (a) to (e) and compare the sum with the potential difference of the battery of three cells which you determined in part (f). What do you conclude? Interpret this conclusion in terms of energy and charge.

2. Can you use your results to see why wires are used as connectors in electrical circuits? Explain in terms of energy and charge.

3. In order for a voltmeter to function correctly in a circuit, how must it be connected?

Bare copper wires attached to the miniature socket make it easy to connect the socket in a circuit.

INVESTIGATION 2-5

Measuring Current in a Series Circuit

The comments introducing Investigation 2-3 also apply here. Current has been left to the last of these three investigations because multi-range ammeters are often much easier to damage than multi-range voltmeters. In Investigations 2-3 and 2-4 you gained some familiarity with multi-range instruments. Don't let familiarity lead you to abandon caution in this investigation.

If time and interest permit, the instructions in this investigation may easily be used as the basis for an investigation to measure current in a *parallel* circuit as well.

PRE-LAB
Review Investigation 2-3. You should also know the meaning of current and a definition of the ampere.

PROCEDURE
Connect two light bulbs in series with a battery of three cells in series. *Do not connect the ammeter yet.* If the bulbs do not light up even dimly, check your connections or replace the bulbs, batteries, or connecting wires as necessary.

To measure the current in the wire AB, the ammeter must be inserted as shown. This may be done by cutting the wire. Instead of actually cutting the connecting wire, you should be able to figure out how to insert the ammeter with the aid of an additional lead. However, *do not connect the ammeter until you have read the next paragraph.* Note particularly that ammeters are not connected like voltmeters. Indeed, if you do connect them that way, you will likely destroy the meter. Ammeters are connected in *series*, whereas the voltmeters you used previously were connected in parallel.

Typical multi-range ammeters have as many as six different scales. Start with the largest scale (say 10 A) and work down to one that will give a large deflection of the needle. Milliamperes are much smaller than amperes, so *never* start with one of the milliampere scales, no matter how sure you are that you know what you are doing. The proper order is 10 A, then 5 A, then 1 A, then 500 mA, then 100 mA, and last, 10 mA if necessary.

Now measure the current in the circuit: (a) in the wire AB; (b) in the wire CD; (c) in the wire EF; (d) in the battery AF, if possible. Record your results in a data table with the headings **Connection Points**, **Meter Reading (in amperes)**, and **Meter Reading (in coulombs per second)**.

CONCLUSIONS
1. What general conclusion can you draw about the current at any point in a series circuit?

2. In order for an ammeter to function correctly in a circuit, how must it be connected?

APPARATUS
three 1.5 V dry cells
two 6 V light bulbs and sockets
multi-range ammeter
short connecting leads

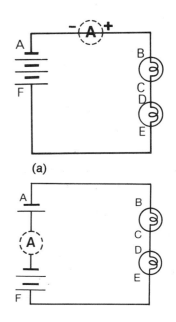

(a)

Part (d): To measure the current in the battery AF, you must insert the meter *between* two of its cells.

INVESTIGATION 2-6

Resistance of Conductors and Semiconductors

In this investigation you will measure the resistance of a conductor and see how it depends on temperature. Then you will measure the resistance of a semiconductor in order to discover one of the basic differences between these two types of material.

PRE-LAB
Before doing this investigation you should know the definition of resistance and be able to calculate resistance with the correct units. You should also have learned how to wire simple circuits and measure current and voltage.

APPARATUS
conductor (3 V electric lamp)
semiconductor (thermistor—about 470 Ω, 1.5 W. Philips 213BD/P470R or equivalent works well.)
two 1.5 V dry cells
ammeter
voltmeter
short connecting leads

PROCEDURE
Connect a light bulb to one dry cell so that the bulb lights, then insert an ammeter and voltmeter to measure simultaneously the current through the bulb and the potential drop across it. Calculate its resistance.

Next connect the light bulb to two cells in series. Remeasure, simultaneously, the current and voltage. Calculate the bulb's resistance now. Also, look at the bulb's filament. How does the filament temperature now compare with its temperature when it was connected to only one dry cell? Why do you say so?

Now connect a thermistor across a 1.5 V dry cell. It will not light up or do anything noticeable. Simultaneously measure the current through it and the potential difference across it. Calculate the resistance of this semiconductor.

Keep the semiconductor connected as described in the previous paragraph, but heat it by holding it firmly between two fingers. Remeasure its resistance when it is at body temperature (about 37°C) rather than at room temperature (about 20°C).

CONCLUSIONS
1. How did the resistance of the conductor change with temperature?
2. How did the resistance of the semiconductor change with temperature?
3. Use the first two conclusions to state a basic difference between conductors and semiconductors.

QUESTIONS
1. Use the text (see page 90) to describe an atomic model of a conductor that explains its ability to conduct electricity easily. Use this model to account for the effect of temperature on a conductor's resistance. Do not try to explain the semiconductor's behaviour at this time.

INVESTIGATION 2-7

Resistances in Parallel

In this investigation you will study how the total resistance of three resistors in parallel is related to the individual resistances. The basic idea has application in every type of parallel circuit, from house wiring to the most minute integrated circuit. If time permits or your teacher instructs you to, you could also investigate total series resistances merely by substituting "series" for "parallel" throughout the following.

PRE-LAB
Draw a circuit diagram showing how you will connect the apparatus in order

to measure the total resistance of three resistors in parallel. Do not proceed until your diagram has been checked by your teacher.

PROCEDURE

Connect the apparatus in accordance with the schematic diagram you prepared. Measure and record V, the total potential drop across the parallel combination of resistors. Measure and record I, the total current to the parallel combination of resistors. Be sure to include units with your observations.

Calculate the total resistance from your V and I observations.

CONCLUSIONS

How does the total resistance of resistors in parallel compare with any of the individual resistances?

QUESTIONS

1. Use the definition of a parallel circuit to explain your conclusion.
2. Use the formula

$$\frac{1}{R_T} = \frac{1}{R_1} + \frac{1}{R_2} + \frac{1}{R_3}$$

to calculate the total resistance R_T. How does the calculated R_T compare with your measured value of the total parallel resistance? That is, calculate the percentage difference.

APPARATUS
3 resistors of known resistance
ammeter
voltmeter
1.5 V. dry cell
short connecting leads

INVESTIGATION 2-8

Properties of Magnets

Everyone, from child to adult, is fascinated by the apparent magic of magnets. This investigation is intended to introduce you to some of the fundamental properties of magnets. Feel free to consult the relevant section of the text as you do each part.

PROCEDURE

1. *Poles.* Obtain a bar magnet and some iron filings. If the magnet cannot lift another magnet its own size, it will have to be remagnetized using the magnet rejuvenator.

Dip the entire bar magnet into a pile of iron filings. What do you observe? (Draw a diagram.) What are the regions of most iron filings called? What did this part of the investigation establish?

The iron filings can be cleaned off the magnet with a cloth or a paper towel.

2. *Names for the Poles.* Put a bar magnet in a stirrup or brass test tube holder, and suspend the holder with string from a retort stand that is not made of iron. Let the magnet swing freely until it comes to rest. When it comes to rest, note to which direction each pole of the magnet points.

Twist the magnet through 180° and let go. What happens this time?

The common abbreviations for the poles of a magnet are N and S. What three-word phrases are these short for? Why are the poles so named?

If you think of the earth's magnetism as being due to a giant bar magnet, what type of pole must be at the north part of the globe? Why?

3. *Laws of Magnetic Forces.* Suspend one bar magnet as in part 2. Bring up another magnet in your hand and approach the ends of the suspended mag-

APPARATUS
bar magnet
magnet rejuvenator (one per class)
iron filings
brass test tube holder or stirrup
various substances, such as copper, iron, aluminum, nickel, zinc, cobalt, wood, paper, pieces of recording tape, porcelain ceramic, ferrite ceramic, etc.

Ferrites are substances that are ferromagnetic (see part 4 of this investigation) but that are electrical insulators as well. Because of this unique combination of properties, ferrites have been used in everything from computer memories to transformer cores.

Best results with a magnet rejuvenator are obtained if the object to be magnetized is the smallest diameter part of the magnetic circuit, so that the lines of force are most concentrated.

The Stansi magnet rejuvenator has wing nuts on one of the coils. These allow the distance between the coils to be adjusted so U-shaped magnets can be inserted.

APPARATUS
2 bar magnets
iron filings
blank paper
1 cm (or smaller) plotting compass
U-shaped magnet
soft iron (or transformer steel) bar
soft iron ring or large washer
*dipping needle
*compass
*plumb bob
magnet rejuvenator (one per class)
* Optional

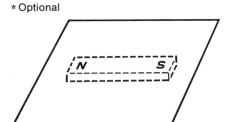

net, one at a time. Record your observations. Then try the effects on the other pole of the magnet you are holding. Use your observations to state two qualitative laws of magnetic forces.

4. *Classification of Substances.* Test with a magnet pellets or small pieces of various substances listed in the apparatus section. Which are magnetic (more precisely, ferromagnetic) and which nonmagnetic (non-ferromagnetic)? This classification gives a crude distinction, but it might miss finer differences between various substances.

5. *Optional.* Look up paramagnetism and diamagnetism and tell how substances of each type would behave in an extremely strong magnetic field. To which of these classes are ferromagnetic substances most similar? If it is available, you might enjoy viewing the filmloop *Paramagnetism of Liquid Oxygen* for a spectacular demonstration of paramagnetism.

CONCLUSIONS
In a sentence or two for each part of the investigation, summarize what you think are the most important things you learned.

QUESTIONS
1. Suppose you have a bar of metal and a compass. What could you do to test whether the metal is (a) nonmagnetic, or (b) magnetic but not magnetized, or (c) magnetic and magnetized? (This is a fairly important test. You will need to know how to do it in later investigations.)

INVESTIGATION 2-9

Properties of Magnetic Fields

In this investigation you will continue your study of magnetism, this time concentrating on what happens near magnets rather than on the magnets themselves. What you learn here will be of use in later investigations when you study electromagnetic effects, where an actual magnet is not present, but a magnetic field is.

PROCEDURE
1. Place a bar magnet on the table, cover it with a piece of blank paper, and support the edges of the paper with books so that it is flat. Sprinkle iron filings on the paper and tap it gently. Magnetic field lines should be visible. The *direction of magnetic field lines* is defined as that direction in which a tiny N pole would point.

Draw a sketch of the magnetic field pattern of a bar magnet and use a small plotting compass (a compass is just a magnet pivoted so that it can swing freely) to get the directions of representative lines of the field pattern. Use arrows to show the directions on your sketch. Where do magnetic field lines seem to begin? Where do they end? What property of magnetic field lines could be used to predict where the magnetic force is strongest?
2. Plot the magnetic field patterns for a pair of bar magnets arranged first with opposite poles adjacent and then with like poles adjacent. Don't forget to put directional arrows on the field lines. What evidence is there that individual field lines seem to repel each other?
3. Plot the magnetic field patterns and directions for a pair of bar magnets arranged parallel to each other with like poles adjacent and then parallel to each other with opposite poles adjacent. What can you say about the mag-

netic force between two magnetic fields with lines that are parallel?; between two magnetic fields with lines that are anti-parallel?

4. Plot the magnetic field pattern of a U-shaped or a horseshoe magnet (U-shaped magnets are preferred because they can be put into most remagnetizers). Can you see from your diagram what advantage there is to bending a magnet into this shape?

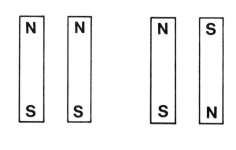

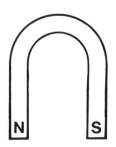

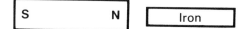

5. Plot the magnetic field pattern of a bar magnet near a soft iron bar. Compare this with the pattern of a single bar magnet found in part 1. What effect does the iron bar have?

6. Plot the magnetic field pattern near an iron ring (large washer) in a magnetic field. Can you see an application for what you have found?

Magnetically soft iron is iron that loses its magnetism easily and, conversely, is very easy to magnetize.

*7. *Angle of Dip.* In part 2 of Investigation 2-8 you may have noticed that a suspended magnet not only came to rest in a north-south orientation, but also that the north-seeking pole pointed downward. A *dipping needle* is a magnet pivoted so that it is free to move in the vertical plane. A *magnetic compass*, on the other hand, is a magnet pivoted so that it is free to move in the horizontal plane.

Obtain a compass and a dipping needle, and line up the dipping needle so that its plane is parallel to the compass needle. What is the angle of dip? What does this tell you about the earth's magnetic field lines?

*8. *Angle of Declination.* Mark a true north-south line on the floor by holding up a string to which is tied a mass (that is, by holding up a plumb-bob) exactly at noon standard time on a sunny day and marking the position of the string's shadow. (Your teacher or another member of the class may have already done this for you.) Put a compass on this line and let it come to rest. The angle between the N-pole of the compass and the true north-south direction is called the *angle of declination*. Record its value. Interpret this, using a diagram if necessary.

* Optional

CONCLUSIONS

Summarize what you have learned about magnetic fields by doing this investigation.

A magnetic compass (left) and a dipping needle (right)

INVESTIGATION 2-10

The Theory of Ferromagnetism

What is going on inside a magnet? How does magnetized iron differ internally from unmagnetized iron? When magnets lose their strength does the magnetism seep out to the surroundings like heat or is something else happening? In this investigation you will make a number of observations that are designed to illustrate the domain theory of ferromagnetism and to increase your understanding of it.

APPARATUS
2 unmagnetized knitting needles or 20
  cm lengths coat-hanger wire
bar magnet
magnet rejuvenator (one per class)
compass
unmagnetized wire cutters
Bunsen burner
test tube and stopper
iron filings
*Barkhausen solenoid and amplifier
*nail and heavy-gauge copper wire
*optional

Every ferromagnetic substance has a characteristic temperature called the *Curie point.*
Above this, the substance ceases to be ferromagnetic.

Element	Curie point (°C)
Cobalt	1131
Iron	770
Nickel	358
Gadolinium	16

APPARATUS
long nail
bar magnet
small nails or tacks
compass
two thin nails 7 or 8 cm long
magnet rejuvenator (one per class)
dipping needle (shared)
iron or steel rod of 10 cm length (or a
  longer nail)
mallet or piece of scrap wood
rectangular plate of soft iron from the
  core of a large transformer

PRE-LAB
Before you do this investigation read the appropriate section of the text so
that you are familiar with some of the basic ideas of the domain theory of
magnetism. On a practical level, you should know how to use a compass to
distinguish among a piece of nonmagnetic substance such as brass, a piece
of unmagnetized iron, and a piece of magnetized iron.

PROCEDURE
1. Use a compass needle to test the magnetic polarity of each end of a 20
cm length of steel wire. Next, use a bar magnet to stroke the length of wire
repeatedly in the circular fashion shown. Then retest the magnetic polarity of
each end of the steel needle. Record your observations.

In your report, explain your observations in terms of a simple domain theory. What would happen if you had not lifted the magnet well away on the return stroke?
2. Use the needle you magnetized during part 1. Cut it in half and test each
half with a compass. Have you isolated the north and south poles? Cut each
half in half again and retest. Repeat as often as you can, cutting each half in
half again, and record your observations.

In your report, make a hypothesis about what would have happened if you
could have continued subdividing the needle further. Try to explain your results in terms of a model of the needle.
3. Use a needle magnetized as in part 1. Heat it strongly with a Bunsen burner. Then test it with a compass and record your observations.

In your report, interpret your results in terms of the domain model. What
would have happened had you reached the needle's Curie point?
4. Lay a stoppered test tube full of iron filings on the table. Test each end for
magnetic polarity. Keep the test tube stationary and stroke it as described in
part 1. Without moving it, again test each end. Then shake the tube and test
again. Record your observations.

Explain your results. If you could have used a bar magnet of any strength
you wished, do you think there would have been a limit to how much you
could magnetize the tube of filings? For your report, look up and define magnetic saturation.
*5. A Barkhausen solenoid is a coil of many (400 or more) turns of wire with
a core just large enough to hold a large nail. Connect a Barkhausen solenoid
to the low impedance input of a sensitive amplifier (for example, a tape recorder or a cassette recorder amplifier input designed to take a 200 to 500 Ω
dynamic microphone) and loudspeaker. Insert a nail in the coil. Bring a magnet near one end of the nail repeatedly. If the hiss you hear is millions of domains lining up, why does it decrease with repetition? Try the experiment
again without a nail and then with a piece of heavy gauge copper or aluminum wire. Try reversing the nail or the magnet and repeating. In your report,
try to interpret your observations in terms of the domain theory.
*optional

CONCLUSIONS
In a sentence or two for each part, summarize what you have learned by doing this investigation.

INVESTIGATION 2-11

Induced Magnetism

In this investigation you will study induced magnetism in terms of practical
results and in terms of the domain theory of magnetism.

PRE-LAB

Before doing this investigation you should be familiar with the basic ideas of the domain theory and be able to use a compass to distinguish between an unmagnetized piece of iron and a magnetized piece of iron.

PROCEDURE

1. Arrange a long nail, a bar magnet, and a pile of books as shown. Test the end of the nail farthest from the magnet for magnetic polarity. Then, holding the nail to the end of the magnet, try to pick up tacks with the free end of the nail. Remove the nail and, holding the magnet the same distance from the tacks, see if it alone will pick up any tacks.

  In your report, explain your observations.

2. Loosely hold the heads of two 7 or 8 cm nails to one pole of a strong bar magnet. What happens to their tips? Why?

3. Test a long (10 cm or more) nail for magnetism to make sure it is not magnetized. Use a compass to set up a dipping needle so that it indicates the direction of the earth's lines of magnetic force in your area (see Investigation 2-9). Hold the long nail pointing in the direction of the dipping needle and hammer the nail with a wooden mallet ten or fifteen times. Retest each end of the nail for magnetic polarity. Explain why it is now magnetized. Explain why it has the polarity it now has.

4. The idea behind part 3 may be illustrated without hammering if you use a piece of very soft iron, such as a strip of metal from the laminated core of a large transformer. Hold the strip horizontally and test each end with a sensitive compass to make sure the strip is not magnetized. Then turn the strip so that it hangs vertically, and retest each end. Explain why the strip was magnetized the second time.

CONCLUSIONS

Summarize what you have learned by doing this investigation.

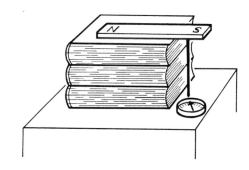

Ships, bridges, buildings, etc., that are riveted (that is, involve hammering) may be slightly magnetized during construction. For ships, this can be dangerous as many mines are designed to be triggered by the magnetic field of the ship. As a result, the Canadian Armed Forces have been known to spend large sums to demagnetize the hulls of some of their craft. To minesweep, wooden-hulled vessels or aircraft can be used to tow magnetized iron sleds.

INVESTIGATION 2-12

The Magnetic Field about a Straight Wire

In this investigation you will study the magnetic field about a straight wire that is carrying an electric current. The fact that there is a magnetic field at all was a major discovery in itself. This investigation is designed to lead you to a thorough understanding of the working of this most basic electromagnetic phenomenon. It is probably best done before you study this topic in the text.

PRE-LAB

Before doing this investigation you should be able to use a small plotting compass to determine the direction of the lines of force of a magnetic field.

PROCEDURE

1. Connect the switch, conductor, and dry cell in series. This investigation is very hard on the dry cell, thus do not operate the switch for more than a few seconds at a time.

2. With the conductor flat on the table in a north-south direction and the leads well away from it, use a plotting compass to test the magnetic field at various locations around the conductor, close to it, under it, and over it, when a current is flowing through it. Summarize your results.

3. Reverse the connections to the dry cell and repeat part 2.

APPARATUS

piece of straight, fairly stiff conductor
piece of stiff cardboard
push-button switch
1.5 V dry cell (types 4FH or #6 work well)
3 long electrical leads
1 cm plotting compasses (5 or 6)
iron filings

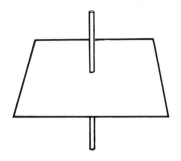

The wire should be long enough that the wires connected to its ends are far from the plane of the cardboard.

○ wire, as seen from above
⊙ wire, with electrons flowing upward
⊗ wire, with electrons flowing downward

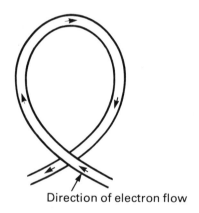

Direction of electron flow

APPARATUS
1 cm plotting compasses (5 or 6)
helix of wire, mounted in a stiff card
1.5 V dry cell
push-button switch
3 electrical leads
iron filings

These helices are wound in different ways.

4. Now push the conductor through a hole in the centre of a piece of stiff cardboard and support the conductor vertically by any convenient method. The cardboard should be horizontal and you should make sure the leads to the ends of the conductor are kept well away from the plane of the cardboard.

Place five or six small plotting compasses on the cardboard in various locations about the conductor. When the current is flowing you should be able to see the shape of the magnetic field. Draw a diagram showing a view of the card from above. On the diagram indicate whether the electron flow is out of the card or into it and show the direction each N pole is pointing.

5. Reverse the connections to the conductor and repeat part 4.

6. Sprinkle iron filings lightly over the card while holding the switch closed and tapping the card lightly. Record the pattern seen. Since this part of the investigation requires a strong current (8 to 10 A) to work well, you may get disappointing results unless your dry cell is fresh or unless you use two or more dry cells in series.

CONCLUSIONS

1. You can use your diagrams from parts 4 and 5 to develop a rule that neatly summarizes the results of this investigation. For each diagram, curl the fingers of your left hand in the direction of the magnetic field arrows, with your thumb pointing along the direction of the wire. When you do this for either diagram, how does the direction in which your thumb is pointing compare with the direction of the electron flow in the wire?

2. Use what you have learned to predict what effects coiling the conductor into a loop (as in the diagram) would have. *Hint.* There are two effects—one concerning the direction of the resulting magnetic field and one concerning the magnitude of the net magnetic field.

3. State the left-hand rule for conductors.

INVESTIGATION 2-13

The Magnetic Field about a Helix

In this investigation you will study the magnetic fields about current-carrying helices and develop a convenient rule that can be used to describe these magnetic fields.

This investigation is probably best done before you study this topic in the text.

PRE-LAB
Before doing this investigation you should be able to describe how to use a compass to determine the directions of magnetic field lines.

PROCEDURE
1. Connect the helix, dry cell, and push-button switch in series. Since this investigation is very hard on dry cells, do not operate the switch for more than a few seconds at a time in any of the parts that follow.

Place five or six small plotting compasses in and around the helix. Record on a diagram the way in which the helix is wound, the general shape of the

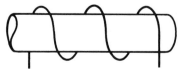

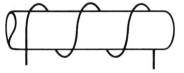

magnetic field that results when you momentarily operate the switch, and the direction in which the electrons are flowing in the coils of the helix.

2. Reverse the connections to the dry cell and repeat part 1.

3. If you have a relatively fresh dry cell (or two or more dry cells to connect in series), try sprinkling iron filings lightly all over the card while holding the switch closed and tapping the card gently. Make a diagram to show the additional fine detail that you can now see.

CONCLUSIONS

1. In what ways are the magnetic fields of a bar magnet and a current-carrying helix similar?

2. You can use your diagrams from parts 1 and 2 to develop a rule that neatly summarizes your observations. Curl the fingers of your left hand around the helix so they point in the direction of the electron flow. Extend your thumb along the axis of the helix. What is the relationship between the direction in which your thumb is now pointing and the magnetic field of the helix? For your report, make up a one-sentence rule that summarizes your observations.

3. Now apply the rule you have just developed. The helices shown have the magnetic polarity indicated. Copy each and use the helix rule to determine the direction that electrons must have been flowing through each. Indicate this direction on each diagram.

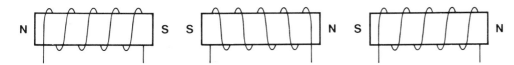

INVESTIGATION 2-14

The Strength of an Electromagnet

In previous investigations you have seen that a current-carrying conductor has an associated magnetic field. In the Conclusions part of Investigation 2-12, you probably predicted that looping such a conductor would produce a stronger magnetic field in the centre of the loop. This would have been verified in Investigation 2-13. What other factors affect the strength of an electromagnet?

APPARATUS
about 1.5 m of fine wire (e.g., #28)
two 1.5 V dry cells
soft iron core
aluminum core (two of the common
  density cylinders taped together)
test tube of about the same diameter
  as the iron core
tape
compass
pile of small iron masses, such as 1 cm
  nails, tacks, etc.
push-button switch
3 connecting leads

PROCEDURE

Wind all of the wire on to the test tube, using a small piece of tape at each end to hold the wire in place if necessary. Connect this coil in series with a push-button switch and a dry cell. Test the coil for magnetism with a compass. How many small iron masses will it pick up?

Wind the coil on an aluminum core and repeat. Then repeat with an iron core.

Remove half of the windings from the iron core and repeat. Do *not* cut off half the wire; just remove it from the iron core but leave it in the circuit. Be sure to record the number of turns remaining on the core.

Finally, connect the half-coiled wire in the iron core to *two* dry cells in series. What effect will this have on the current in the coil? How many small masses does it pick up this time?

What effect does reversing the connections to the dry cell have in any of the above parts?

Other cores that may prove interesting in comparison are cobalt, ferrite, nickel, laminated transformer steel, and permalloy.

CONCLUSIONS
1. What factors affect the strength of an electromagnet?
2. Do your results for the iron masses show any signs of a non-linear effect?; a saturation effect?
3. Define magnetic permeability. Use the table of permeabilities in the Appendix to find which substance would make the best core for an electromagnet.
4. Suppose that you had cut out half the wire rather than simply removing it from the iron core. What effect would this have had on (a) resistance, (b) current, and (c) strength of the electromagnet?

INVESTIGATION 2-15

The Motor Principle

In this investigation you will see a dramatic demonstration of how an electric current experiences a force when placed in an external magnetic field. You will also discover a simple way of predicting in which direction this force will act, given the directions of the electron flow and of the external magnetic field. The ideas developed in this investigation form the basis of all electric motors and of most electric meters.

PRE-LAB
Before doing this investigation, you should be able to state which of the pairs of magnetic fields shown will experience a repulsive force and which an attractive force.

APPARATUS
U-shaped magnet with about 5 cm between poles
magnet rejuvenator (one per class)
strip of aluminum foil less than 1 cm in width and about 70 cm long, or several pieces of Christmas-tree tinsel taped together
1.5 V dry cell
2 long connecting leads
metre stick or ruler
tape
retort rod and clamp

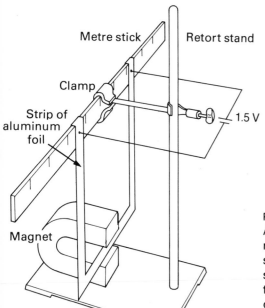

In practice, the aluminum foil is unlikely to hang with such neat right-angled bends. However, what really matters is that the foil between the poles of the magnet swings freely.

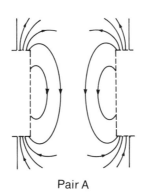

Pair A

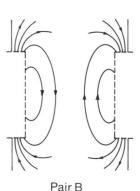

Pair B

PROCEDURE
Arrange the apparatus as shown, but do not connect the dry cell. The aluminum foil is taped to the metre stick and arranged so that it hangs in a U shape. The retort clamp is set at a height that allows the bottom of the foil to swing freely between the poles of the magnet. The magnet need not be extremely strong or expensive, but it should be able to pick up another magnet of the same size. If it won't, use the magnet rejuvenator to remagnetize it.

Since this setup involves a short circuit across the dry cell, it is very rough on the cell. You may connect one wire solidly to the dry cell, but merely *touch* the second wire to the cell momentarily when you want current to flow.

Connect the cell momentarily and note what happens. Record your observations by means of a diagram similar to the one shown, indicating the magnetic polarity of the external field, the direction of electron flow and the direction of the force on the conductor.

Reverse the connections to the dry cell and repeat the procedure. Then repeat with the original connections but with the magnet reversed. Finally, repeat with both the external magnetic field and the electron flow reversed.

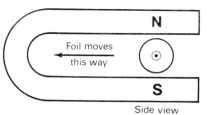

Side view

Use $\odot$ to indicate electron flow out of the page, and $\otimes$ for electron flow into the page.

CONCLUSIONS

1. Use the left-hand rule to draw the magnetic field about the conductor in each of your four diagrams.
2. Draw a few field lines of the U magnet's field on each of your diagrams. Indicate their directions, as on the diagram shown.
3. Determine which side of the conductor will experience an attractive force and which a repulsive force (see the Pre-Lab part) and, thus, which way the conductor will move in each diagram. This should agree with your observations. (For example, the force will be to the left in the diagram shown.)
4. Write a one-sentence statement that summarizes your observations and conclusions.

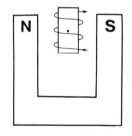

Magnetic field of the current

Magnetic field of U-magnet

QUESTIONS

1. Suppose you had a tightly wound helix pivoted as indicated between the poles of a U magnet. What would happen if an electron current were passed through the helix as indicated?
2. If you wanted the helix to rotate more than 90°, what would you have to do at about the time it reached 90°?
3. What is a split-ring commutator? What is the purpose of a split-ring commutator attached to such a pivoted helix?

INVESTIGATION 2-16

Operation of a Simple DC Motor

In this investigation you will study the simple electric motor and the factors that affect its speed and direction of rotation.

PRE-LAB
Before doing this investigation, you should know the correct name for the automatic reversing switch in an electric DC motor, why it is necessary, and what it looks like.

PROCEDURE
The first part of the investigation is to get the motor to work when connected to 6 V DC. Check for these problems: the stationary magnets may need remagnetizing; the brushes may not be making good contact with the armature; the brushes may be binding against the armature and stopping it from rotating; the battery may have one or more dead cells; the brushes may need turning until they are arranged so that the commutator reverses the armature's current at the proper place.

Once you have it working, investigate what effect each of the following has on the motor: reversing the connections to the battery; reversing the external magnets; removing just one of the external magnets; reducing the current by using less voltage; turning the brushes to various locations; pulling the stationary magnets apart.

APPARATUS
simple DC motor (St. Louis type)
dry cells to make a 6 V battery
3-pole DC motor (one per class)
magnet rejuvenator (one per class)
2 electrical leads
2 commercial DC motors per class, one assembled and one dissected and labelled (Sargent-Welch dissectible motor recommended)

A commercial DC motor that has been taken apart. Can you identify the stator, rotor, commutator, and brushes?

When you have found the position of the brushes that gives the greatest speed of rotation, draw a view from above, showing the stationary magnets, the brushes, and two views of the armature—just before its current is reversed and just after its current is reversed.

Examine the commercial DC motor on display and tell how it differs from the simple motor you used. Use the headings **Stationary Magnets (Stator), Armature (Rotor), Commutator,** and **Brushes.**

Compare the starting and running characteristics of the three-pole St. Louis motor with those of the two-pole one you used. How do their characteristics differ?

CONCLUSIONS

Summarize what you have learned about electric motors by doing this investigation.

QUESTIONS

1. Explain why each of the factors that you listed in your summary as affecting the speed of rotation should do so.

INVESTIGATION 2-17

The Cause and Size of an Induced Current

Just as electricity can cause magnetism, magnetism can be used to cause electricity. In this investigation you will study how this can be done and what factors influence the magnitude of the effect.

Caution: Galvanometers are extremely sensitive meters and should *never* be connected in the same circuit as a dry cell, battery, or power pack. If as you do this investigation you think that any of the following instructions tell you to do such a thing, *stop immediately and reread*—they do not.

APPARATUS
2 coils of wire that fit into one another, the inner one having many times fewer turns than the outer one (for example, the Griffin and George L88-541 set)
iron core that fits down the centre of the smaller coil
cylindrical magnet that fits down the centre of the small coil (that is, of diameter not exceeding 13 mm)
galvanometer
4 connecting leads
1.5 V dry cell

PROCEDURE

1. *Cause of an Induced Current.* Connect a galvanometer to the large coil and insert a magnet into the centre of the coil. Keep the magnet stationary for a few seconds and then remove it. Try keeping the magnet in the centre of the large coil and twirling it without pulling it out.

Connect the smaller coil to a 1.5 V dry cell and repeat the procedure, using the smaller coil instead of the magnet.

Leave the smaller coil inside the large coil and then connect and disconnect the dry cell to the small coil to see what happens.

Finally, put the iron core in the centre of the large coil, then bring up a bar magnet and touch it to one end of the iron core.

2. *Size of the Induced Current.* Connect a galvanometer to the large coil and insert a magnet first slowly and then rapidly into the coil.

Repeat, but use the small coil instead of the large one.

Reconnect the large coil to the galvanometer and insert an electromagnet made by connecting the small coil to a 1.5 V dry cell. Then use the same speed of insertion, but have the iron core in the small coil.

Finally, leave the small coil and iron core stationary in the centre of the large coil and merely connect and disconnect the dry cell to the small coil.

CONCLUSIONS FOR PART 1

1. What four methods can be used to cause an induced current?
2. How is the third method of causing an induced current equivalent to the first two?

3. An electric current (that is, moving electric charges) causes a magnetic field. Try to make a similarly general statement about the cause of an induced current. It should cover all the possibilities you investigated.

CONCLUSIONS FOR PART 2

1. What three factors affect the magnitude of the induced potential difference? (We use "induced potential difference" here instead of "induced current" in order to avoid having to include "the resistance of the circuit" as one answer.)

2. Why was the induced current at the make and break of the current in the small coil so large? (You may have to review your final conclusion to part 1 before answering this question.)

QUESTIONS

1. Without the galvanometer connected to the coil there would be an open circuit. Would there still be an induced current? Would there be an induced potential difference?

2. What application or applications can you see for induced currents?

INVESTIGATION 2-18

The Direction of an Induced Current

In this investigation you will study the directions of induced currents and develop a simple rule, sometimes known as the "law of pure cussedness", that can be used to predict them. You will also see a fascinating example of the working of this law in a magnetic levitation device.

PRE-LAB

Before doing this investigation you should be able to use the helix rule to find the magnetic polarity of a helix, given the direction of the current in the helix. You should also know the basic laws of magnetic force.

> **Caution:** Review the cautionary note in Investigation 2-17. It applies to this investigation as well.

PROCEDURE

The terminals of the galvanometer are marked with a + or a − (or are red and black respectively) to indicate that when electrons enter via the − terminal and leave via the + terminal, the needle will deflect to the right. If the electron current is in the opposite direction, the needle will deflect to the left.

You must also know the sense in which your coil has been wound. If the sense cannot be determined by inspection, your teacher will be able to tell you.

Connect the coil to the galvanometer and insert the N pole of a magnet in the coil. Note the direction of deflection of the galvanometer. Then draw a diagram showing the magnet and its poles, the direction of motion of the magnet, the direction in which the coil is wound, the terminals of the galvanometer, and the direction of deflection of the galvanometer. (Refer to the diagram shown.) Deduce the direction of the electron flow and indicate it on the diagram. Then deduce the polarity of the coil from the helix rule, and mark that on the diagram.

Repeat, this time withdrawing an N pole from the coil.
Repeat, this time inserting an S pole into the coil.
Repeat, this time withdrawing an S pole from the coil.
The floating-ring apparatus on display in your classroom consists of a coil

APPARATUS
coil of many turns (the large coil used in Investigation 2-17 works well)
galvanometer with marked terminals
magnet
2 connecting leads
floating-ring apparatus (one per class)

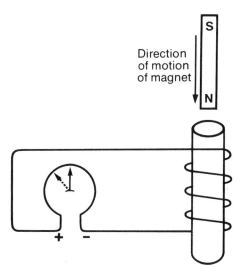

As seen from above, the coil is wound anticlockwise. For this apparatus and setup, the galvanometer deflects to the left.

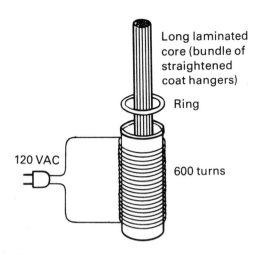

Long laminated core (bundle of straightened coat hangers)

Ring

120 VAC

600 turns

For best results, the long laminated core should *completely fill* the core of the coil of wire.

of 600 or more turns with a laminated iron core (dissectible transformer core or a bundle of straightened coat hangers). The coil is connected directly to 120 V AC. The ring is made of copper or aluminum and so is nonmagnetic. What happens when the coil is plugged in?

CONCLUSIONS
1. Inspect the magnetic polarities of the coils in your diagrams. How does the coil polarity compare with the polarity of magnetic poles being inserted into the coil? As a result, would you say that the coil polarity caused by the induced current is trying to help or to hinder the insertion of the magnet?
2. How does the coil polarity compare with the polarity of magnetic poles that are being withdrawn from the coil? As a result, would you say that the coil polarity caused by the induced current is trying to help or to hinder the withdrawal of the magnet?
3. Make a general statement about the direction of induced currents that will include both of these results. (This statement was originally discovered by Heinrich Lenz and is now known as *Lenz's law*.)

INVESTIGATION 2-19

AC and DC Generators

In previous investigations you studied the cause, the size, and the direction of induced currents. In this investigation you will study what is probably the most important application of these effects, the electric generator. Its importance is emphasized by the fact that electricity from dry cells costs upward of $100/kW·h, while energy from typical commercial generators is currently in the range of $0.02 to $0.06/kW·h.

PRE-LAB
Before doing this investigation you should be able to use Lenz's law to predict the direction of current in the coil shown when an S pole is inserted in one end and an N pole in the other end, as indicated.

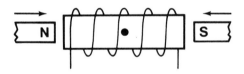

APPARATUS
St. Louis generator with AC armature
St. Louis generator with DC armature
(The Sargent-Welch type of generator has both AC and DC connections on one device.)
galvanometer
2 connecting leads

An *earth inductor* is a device that uses the magnetic field of the earth to generate an AC current. You can make one by slitting the outer circumference of a hula hoop and winding many turns of wire into it. When connected to a sensitive galvanometer, it should register a deflection when rotated in the earth's magnetic field. You will also find that it is quite sensitive to a large, powerful magnet moving in its vicinity.

PROCEDURE
Connect a galvanometer to the terminals of an AC generator and turn the armature slowly, a half or a quarter turn at a time if necessary. How does the galvanometer needle deflect? Can you see why this is called an alternating current generator?

Now, mark one end of the armature with chalk and observe the position of the armature relative to the stationary magnets when the current is maximum and positive, zero, maximum and negative, and then zero again. Record your observations with the aid of diagrams from above, showing the armature and the stationary magnets.

Note the method by which the armature is connected to the external terminals. Are the connections to the external terminals reversed during the rotation of the armature?

Repeat all of the above, this time with a DC generator.

CONCLUSIONS
1. In both AC and DC generators an alternating current is generated in the armature. Illustrate the essential parts of each that allow them to deliver such different currents to the external terminals.
2. Sketch a voltage-time graph to illustrate what is meant by an AC voltage.
3. Sketch a voltage-time graph to illustrate the DC that a DC generator devel-

ops. On the same graph, illustrate the type of DC that a dry cell would deliver.

QUESTIONS
1. How fast would the AC generator you used have to be rotated to generate 60 Hz AC? What physical modifications could be made to the generator to reduce this rate of rotation but still obtain 60 Hz AC?
2. Explain your observations of the positions of the armature relative to the stationary magnets for maximum, zero, and minimum currents. Use diagrams to help.

PART THREE

Waves, Sound and Light

INVESTIGATION 3-1

Transverse Vibrations

In this investigation you will use a pendulum to study transverse vibrations. In addition to becoming familiar with the terms and quantities associated with transverse vibrations, you will learn about several useful, and perhaps surprising, properties of pendulums.

PRE-LAB
Before doing this investigation you should know the meanings of transverse, frequency, period, and amplitude. You should also know the SI units for frequency and period.

PROCEDURE
Attach the bob to the string and the string to the support. Set the bob swinging freely. Measure and record the starting amplitude.

Set the bob swinging with about the same starting amplitude and then time 30 or more complete vibrations. Record the number of vibrations and the total time taken. Calculate the number of vibrations per second (the *frequency*) and the time for one vibration (the *period*). Then use a different starting amplitude and repeat the measurements and calculations. Record the new starting amplitude and the length of the pendulum.

Change the length of the pendulum and remeasure the period and frequency. Record the new length.

APPARATUS
pendulum bob
string
pendulum support
watch with sweep second
 hand, or stopclock
metre stick

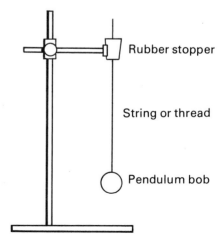

Rubber stopper

String or thread

Pendulum bob

A solid rubber stopper with a slit cut in it and held by a retort rod test tube clamp can be used as a pendulum support. This arrangement allows one to change the length of the pendulum easily.

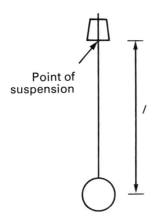

Point of suspension

l

The length of a pendulum is the distance from the point of suspension to the centre of mass of the bob.

APPARATUS
2 springs of different stiffnesses
2 different-sized masses to hang on springs (the PSSC-type helical steel springs kits come with two masses and two springs)
rigid support
stopclock or watch with sweep second hand
metre stick

Using the same length and amplitude but a different mass for the pendulum bob, repeat the measurements and calculations. Is the new mass greater or smaller than the first mass you used?

CONCLUSIONS
1. What effect does a change in amplitude have on the frequency and period of a pendulum?
2. How does a change in length affect the frequency and period of a pendulum?
3. How does a change in the mass of the bob affect the frequency and period of a pendulum?

QUESTIONS
1. Why is a pendulum's motion called a transverse vibration?
2. You have probably seen large, expensive clocks that have pendulums. What purpose do you think is served by these pendulums?

INVESTIGATION 3-2

Longitudinal Vibrations

In this investigation you will use a spring to study longitudinal vibrations. In addition to becoming familiar with the terms and quantities associated with longitudinal vibrations, you will learn about several useful, and perhaps surprising, properties of oscillating springs.

PRE-LAB
Before doing this investigation, you should know the meanings of longitudinal, frequency, period, and amplitude. You should also know the SI units for frequency and period.

PROCEDURE
First, find which spring is stiffer. You can do this by hanging the same mass on each spring and seeing which spring stretches less.

Use the stiffer spring first. Suspend the spring from a rigid support and attach a mass to the spring's lowest end. For the remainder of the investigation, the amplitude of the vibrations must *never* be so great that the spring's coils come together and touch on the upswing.

Pull the mass down and let it go. Does the amplitude on the downward part of the vibration equal the amplitude on the upward part?

Set the mass oscillating with about the same starting amplitude as before, and then time 30 or more complete vibrations. Record the number of vibrations and the total time taken. Calculate the number of vibrations per second (the frequency) and the time for one vibration (the period).

Repeat the measurements and calculations but use a different starting amplitude.

Repeat the measurements and calculations but use a different mass on the spring.

Repeat the measurements and calculations but use a spring that is less stiff. For the mass use a value that you used with the other spring so that you can compare results without the mass affecting them.

CONCLUSIONS
1. What effect does a change in amplitude have on the frequency and period of a vibrating spring?
2. How does a change in mass affect the frequency and period of spring?
3. How does a change in stiffness affect the frequency and period?

QUESTIONS
1. Why is the spring's motion called a longitudinal vibration?

INVESTIGATION 3-3

Transverse Waves in Slinkies

In this investigation you will study what happens when two waves meet each other on a slinky — the idea of interference. The investigation is intended to be done before you study interference in class.

PROCEDURE
A long slinky tends to twist and tangle as it is stretched out. In order to avoid this, place the slinky on the floor, tie a one metre piece of string to one end, and stretch the slinky out by pulling on the string. Once the slinky is stretched to about 6 to 8 m, someone should hold on firmly to each end of the slinky itself so that it cannot snap closed and become tangled. (If your slinky does become tangled, it is your responsibility to untangle it. When you have finished the investigation, the slinky should be closed by reversing the string procedure.)

To make a transverse wave pulse in the slinky, hold one end and quickly snap your hand sideways 50 cm or so and all the way back. Practise sending pulses from each end.

First, tie a small piece of string to one coil somewhere along the slinky. Send a pulse down the slinky and carefully observe the string's motion. Compare it with the pulse's motion. Can you see why these pulses are called transverse?

Now send identical pulses down the same side of the spring from both ends. What happens when the two pulses meet? Try to be quantitative, that is, measure amplitudes before the pulses meet and at the instant they meet. What happens after the pulses meet?

Try two pulses that do not have the same amplitude but are on the same side of the slinky. What happens when these pulses meet? Try to be quantitative.

Repeat the instructions in the last two paragraphs, but use pulses that are on opposite sides of the slinky. Again, try to be quantitative.

What happens when a pulse reflects from a fixed end? Hold one end still and try it. Predict what would happen if a series of these reflected pulses met with a series of incident pulses. Try it by keeping one end fixed and vibrating the other end repeatedly. The waves produced by this are called *standing waves*. Can you see why? The regions of almost no motion are called *nodes*; the regions of maximum movement are called *antinodes*, or *loops*. Measure the amplitude at a loop and compare it with the amplitude of a single pulse generated in the same manner.

APPARATUS
large diameter coil spring (slinky)
about 1 m or more of string
metre stick

CONCLUSIONS
1. What happens when two wave pulses meet? Try to make the most quantitative and general statement possible.
2. What happens to two wave pulses after they interfere?

QUESTIONS
1. What is the principle of superposition?
2. Distinguish between constructive interference and destructive interference.

APPARATUS

ripple tank with light and screen
straight barrier to use as plane mirror
wood dowel
medicine dropper
curved barrier for use as a concave
    mirror
2 coins (supplied by students)

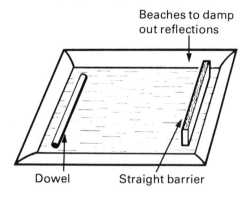

Beaches to damp
out reflections

Dowel   Straight barrier

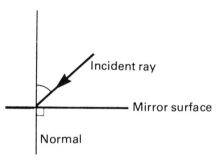

Incident ray

Mirror surface

Normal

The incident angle is the angle between the
incident ray and the *normal*.

A *wave front* is what you see actually moving
in the tank. All the points on a wave front
are in phase. A *ray* is a straight line that
points in the direction of travel of a wave
front. A *normal* is a line at 90° to a surface.

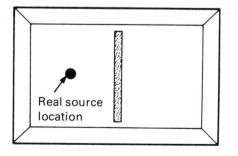

Real source
location

INVESTIGATION 3-4

Reflection of Water Waves

In this investigation you will study the reflection of waves using a ripple tank.

If you do this and the other ripple tank investigations before you study light, you are likely to wonder "What's the use of all this?", and if you do them after you study light, you are likely to say "Why didn't we do this before; it would have made light so much easier?" Also, since most ripple tanks are bulky and time-consuming to set up, it is likely that your teacher will want you to do all ripple tank investigations together, rather than have you set up and take down ripple tanks several times over a period of weeks. Since these investigations had to be put somewhere, we chose to put them before the investigations on light, although they fit in just as well after light and your teacher may, in fact, wish you to postpone doing them until then.

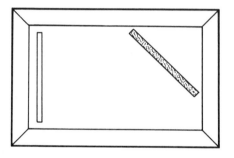

PROCEDURE

1. *Reflection from a Plane Mirror.* Put a straight barrier at one end of the tank. Use a dowel at the other end of the tank to make a straight pulse—roll the dowel a quarter turn or so forward and back. Practise until you can get a good pulse as seen on the screen. The pulse should stay straight (if it started straight) all the way down the tank and all the way back, except for a small amount of bending at the edges. If it doesn't, the tank may need levelling or other adjustments. This is intended as a check that everything is set up and working properly. Do not proceed until it is.

Next, put the straight barrier at an angle. Generate a straight pulse at the other end of the tank. Put a piece of paper on the screen below and trace (a) the reflecting barrier, (b) an incident wave front, and (c) a reflected wave front. Then construct (d) an incident ray hitting the surface, (e) the normal to the surface where the incident ray hits, and (f) the reflected ray from the same point. Label each. Measure and label (g) the angle of incidence and (h) the reflected angle. How do the two angles compare? How should they compare? Calculate your percentage difference.

Place the straight barrier in the middle of the tank parallel to the ends of the tank. Generate a circular pulse on one side of the mirror by means of a drop of water from a medicine dropper. Mark the place by means of a coin placed in the tank. This is a *real source*. Mark where the centre of the reflected pulse seems to be with a second coin. This is a *virtual image*, as the reflected pulse just *seems* to be coming from there. Measure the perpendicular distance from each source to the mirror line. How do these distances compare? How should they compare? What is the percentage difference? Illustrate your observations in this section with a labelled diagram.

2. *Reflection from a Concave Mirror.* Put a curved barrier at one end of the tank to act as a concave mirror. Generate a straight pulse at the other end with a dowel. Illustrate what happens with a diagram or diagrams. The point where the reflected waves converge before spreading out again is called the *focal point.* Place a coin at the exact focal point in the tank and leave it there for the next step of the investigation.

Generate a circular pulse at the focal point. The reflected wave front should be straight if you have the exact focal point. Illustrate what happens with a diagram or diagrams. The analogy here is a searchlight or headlamps. Sketch what happens when a pulse is generated to either side of the focal point (analogy: high beams and low beams on a car). What happens when the pulse is made at a point closer than F? Further from the mirror than F?

CONCLUSIONS
Summarize what you have learned about waves by doing this investigation.

INVESTIGATION 3-5

Refraction of Water Waves

In this investigation you will study some properties of waves as they bend in passing from one medium to another, that is, as they are refracted. The comments made at the beginning of Investigation 3-4 apply here also.

APPARATUS
Refraction with most ripple tanks can be tricky and frustrating if one has to set up the tank from scratch. If this investigation is to be kept to a single class period, we recommend setting up the three situations in advance. Then student groups can move from one to the next in rotation.

PROCEDURE
1. *Refraction at Zero Angle of Incidence.* Set up a section of a ripple tank so that it is much shallower than the rest of the tank. Generate straight waves in the deep section of the tank. Arrange the front surface of the shallow part so that it is parallel to the incident waves from the deep part. Is the wavelength greater in shallow water or in deep water?

The frequency of the waves is the same in both parts of the tank since the frequency is determined only by the wave generator's voltage. Use this fact, your observations from the first part of the investigation, and the universal

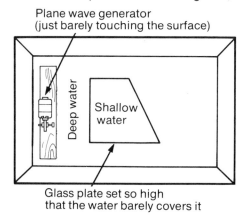

Plane wave generator
(just barely touching the surface)

Deep water

Shallow water

Glass plate set so high
that the water barely covers it

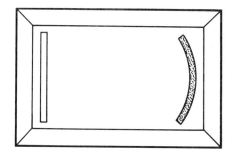

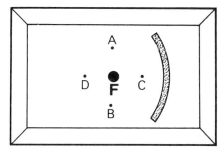

A and B are on either side of F. C is closer to the mirror than F; D is further away than F.

APPARATUS
tank set up for refraction at normal incidence, with a motor-driven plane wave generator

tank set up for refraction at oblique incidence, with a motor-driven plane wave generator

tank set up with a convex refractor, with a motor-driven plane wave generator

Some makes of ripple tanks are designed to give the best refraction when the glass plate is set directly on the bottom of the tank, and the water drained until it barely covers the plate.

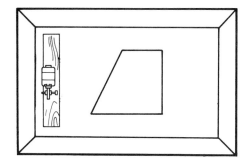

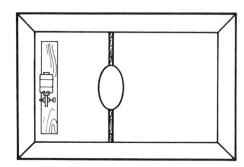

A *hand-stroboscope* is a circular disc with slits around its rim, mounted on a handle so that it can be rotated. If you hold the strobe up to your eye and view a repetitive motion through the slits as the disc rotates, at certain frequencies of rotation the periodic motion will appear to be stopped. For periodic waves, for example, if each wave moves exactly one wavelength between glimpses, a person viewing the waves will see crests at exactly the same places each time he or she gets a glimpse, and thus the waves will seem to be stopped.

wave equation to deduce whether the speed of water waves is greater in shallow water or in deep water.

2. *Refraction from a Fast to a Slow Medium.* Now arrange the shallow section so that its front interface is at an angle to the incident waves. Use the hand stroboscopes provided to ''stop the waves''. Illustrate what you see, and label the incident and refracted wave fronts and the interface. Construct the incident ray, the normal to the interface, the refracted ray, the angle of incidence, and the angle of refraction.

Compare the angle of incidence and the angle of refraction. Do the waves bend towards or away from the normal when they go from a fast to a slow medium?

Observe the front interface again. Can you see any reflection taking place?

3. *Convex Refractor (Lens).* Send plane waves towards a convex refractor in a ripple tank. Observe the wave fronts very carefully as they pass over the lens. What happens after they converge at the focal point? Draw a page-size illustration of your observations in this section.

CONCLUSIONS

Summarize what you have learned about waves by doing this investigation.

INVESTIGATION 3-6

Interference and Diffraction of Water Waves

In this investigation you will take a look at interference in waves moving in two dimensions, rather than in one dimension as on a slinky, and you will see some fascinating new patterns. In addition, you will learn about a phenomenon called diffraction.

APPARATUS

tank with a straight wave generator, for use in parts 1 and 2 and the end of part 3

tank with a two-point-source generator, for use in part 3

APPARATUS

As for Investigation 3-5, it is probably most efficient of class time if the ripple tanks have been set up previously and groups rotate from one tank to another.

PROCEDURE

1. *Standing Waves.* The purpose of this section is to show you standing waves in a ripple tank that are similar to the standing waves that you observed in Investigation 3-3.

Set up a straight wave generator at one end of a ripple tank. Halfway down the tank, set up a straight barrier that blocks the plane waves from one-quarter of the tank. Observe the waves when the generator is set in motion. Compare the wavelength of the travelling waves in the unblocked side of the tank with the distance between the flashing bright bars in the other side. Illustrate your observations of these standing waves and travelling waves.

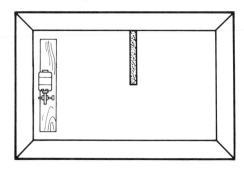

Do the flashing bright bars in the standing waves represent nodes or loops?

2. *Diffraction.* Use straight barriers near the straight wave generator to block the entire width of the tank except for a narrow aperture in the centre. Start with an aperture that is narrow compared with the wavelength of the incident waves, and widen it progressively. Illustrate several cases. How does the aperture width compare with the wavelength for the greatest diffraction?

3. *Interference of Circular Waves.* Instead of a straight wave generator, use a wave generator with a single point source attached to it. What pattern does it generate? If it is not a series of concentric circles, something is wrong and needs adjustment.

Now, lower the second point source and operate the generator. Observe the pattern produced. Draw a diagram of what you see. Label regions of constructive interference (supercrests and supertroughs) and regions of total continuous destructive interference (nodal regions, or lines). You should be able to tell the constructive regions from the destructive ones by the brightness and darkness of the regions on the screen, compared with the brightness when there are no waves at all in the tank.

Increase the frequency of the dippers. What happens to the spacing between the nodal lines when you have higher frequency waves?

Now use a straight wave generator again and a series of barriers arranged to give two apertures. There is only one generator now. Why do you still get interference?

CONCLUSIONS
Summarize what you have learned about waves by doing this investigation.

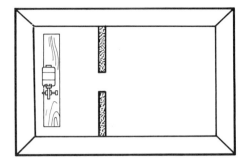

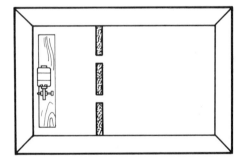

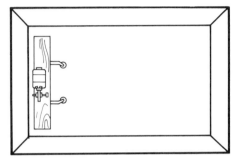

INVESTIGATION 3-7

Interference of Sound Waves

In this investigation you will study the conditions necessary for interference in sound. You will study two types of sound interference — interference that varies with location but is constant with time, and beats, which is interference that does not vary with location but does change with time.

PRE-LAB
Before doing this investigation, you should know the meanings of constructive interference, destructive interference, rarefaction, and compression.

PROCEDURE
Strike the tines of an unmounted tuning fork against the fleshy part of your hand or some other soft surface. As the tuning fork is sounding, hold it vertical and rotate it slowly about its axis, holding it near your ear. Make sure it is not touching your hair. You should hear regions of different loudness. Your partner can tell you the orientation of the fork for different loudnesses. Make a sketch looking from above, such as the one shown, and label each region A to H as relatively loud or relatively quiet.

In a 30 cm or larger piece of card, cut a slot about the width and length of a tine of the tuning fork. Sound the fork and hold it with one tine close to the slot and parallel to it. Describe the change in loudness when the fork is near the slot. Bring the different regions A to H around the fork close to the slot.

A different type of interference, beats, can be studied with the use of two otherwise identical tuning forks, one of which has an elastic band wound around one of its tines. The elastic band slightly lowers the frequency of that

APPARATUS
2 identical unmounted tuning forks
30 cm × 30 cm or larger piece of card
scissors
elastic band

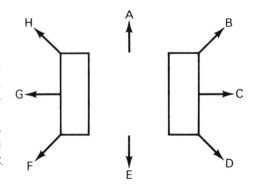

The tines of a tuning fork vibrate as indicated in the diagram, as you can easily verify by touching a vibrating tine to the surface of a beaker of water. Further, the tines vibrate in opposite phase. When they come together as in A a compression (or condensation) is formed between them, and rarefactions are formed in positions I and II. Can you see what will happen when they move apart, as in B?

If you can hear an unmounted tuning fork at a distance of 1 m, you have probably struck it incorrectly and are hearing harmonics.

APPARATUS
tall graduated or ungraduated cylinder
glass or plastic tube about 4 cm in diameter and 40 cm long
2 different tuning forks, frequency 1024 Hz or more
thermometer (one per class)

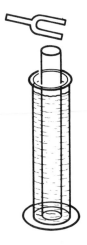

fork. Sound the two forks at the same time and have your partner hold them parallel about 1 or 2 cm apart and close to your ear. Describe what you hear.

CONCLUSIONS
1. Account for your observations in the first paragraph of the procedure.
2. How can you account for the effect of the slotted card on the loudness of the tuning fork tone?
3. In a length of 10 cm, draw a diagram of 10 compressions and 10 rarefactions. Below it, in the same length, draw a diagram of 8 compressions and 8 rarefactions. Below that, use the principle of superposition to add the two wave trains, and thus account for the observations you made in following the instructions of the last paragraph of the procedure.
4. Summarize what you have learned by doing this investigation.

QUESTIONS
1. How are beats useful in tuning musical instruments?

INVESTIGATION 3-8

Measuring the Speed of Sound

In this investigation you will apply your knowledge of resonance in air columns to calculate the speed of sound in air.

PRE-LAB
Before doing this investigation, you should know what is meant by resonance, two factors that affect the resonant frequency of an air column, where nodes and loops occur in a closed air column, and how to use the temperature coefficient of the speed of sound.

PROCEDURE
Put the glass or plastic tube in the tall ungraduated cylinder. Fill the cylinder almost to the top with water.

Sound a tuning fork on your hand or something soft and hold it momentarily to your ear so that you have clearly in mind its first harmonic. Then hold the vibrating fork near the top of the tube. Gradually raise the tube until you find a length of air column that resonates loudly with the tuning fork's first harmonic. Measure the length of the air column and record it. Then raise the tube further until a second resonant length is reached. Measure and record it.

Repeat this procedure several times, using the same fork or a fork of a different frequency. Be sure to record the frequency stamped on each fork.

Finally, use a thermometer to get the temperature of the air in the room.

CONCLUSIONS
1. Draw a diagram to illustrate the relationship between the first resonant length of an air column and the wavelength of the sound in resonance with it. Repeat for the second resonant length. What relationship exists between the *difference* of these lengths and the wavelength of the sound? Use this last relationship and your measurements to calculate the wavelength of the sound produced by each tuning fork.
2. Use the universal wave equation, the wavelength from Conclusion 1, and the known frequency of each fork to calculate the speed of sound in air for each set of results. Show all calculations. Average the final results to get a more accurate value for the speed of sound.
3. In order to see how accurate you were, calculate the expected value of

the speed of sound in air by using the measured air temperature and the temperature coefficient of the speed of sound. How does the expected value compare with your final result from Conclusion 2? That is, what is the percentage difference?

4. Summarize what you have learned by doing this investigation.

QUESTIONS

1. At the open end of a resonant air column, a small length of air outside the tube is also set in vibration. Therefore, the effective length of the vibrating air column is greater than the length of the pipe by an end correction. (The correction is about 0.6 times the tube radius.) How do Conclusions 1, 2, and 3 avoid the use of this end correction?

INVESTIGATION 3-9

Interference and Diffraction of Light

In this investigation you will study two phenomena that were decisive in the history of physics. Both were and are put to important practical uses and both give beautiful effects.

PRE-LAB

Before doing this investigation, you should have done the ripple tank investigation in Investigation 3-6 or at least have seen equivalent filmloops. Review your notes before doing this investigation.

APPARATUS

The procedure that follows makes use of commercially prepared devices called Slitfilms usually available in schools. If, however, your school does not have them or if your teacher wishes you to make your own slits, the procedure will have to be modified accordingly.

PROCEDURE

Examine the showcase bulb before you plug it in so that you are aware of just how narrow its filament is.

Use elastic bands to cover the bulb with red cellophane, plug the bulb in, and examine it at a distance of about 2 m with the unaided eye. Make a mental note of how wide the incandescent filament seems to be.

Now, standing at the same 2 m distance, view the bulb through a single slit (use the slit at the bottom left of the slitfilm when the long side of the film is vertical and the CAL monogram is in the upper-right-hand side) and note how wide the filament seems to be. Ignore the sidebands and merely note how wide the *filament* seems to be. What is the name of this effect?

Try single slits of various widths down the left-hand side of the slitfilm. How does the effect depend on slit width? Does this agree with what you saw with water waves in a ripple tank?

View a bulb covered with a red filter, from a distance of about 2 m, through a double slit (use the second slit from the top in the second column from the right). The two slits act as point sources of waves, much as two dippers do in a ripple tank. In ripple tank interference you saw nodal regions and regions of travelling supercrests and supertroughs. What do you see through the double slits that might correspond to nodal regions? If you are not sure, compare this pattern with that of the single slit directly above it.

Optional. What effect does increasing the number of slits have on the interference pattern for red light? To find out, view the bulb through the finely

APPARATUS

light bulb with a narrow straight filament (showcase bulb)

red cellophane filter for light bulb

Slitfilm—a commercially prepared set of single and double slits of various widths and spacings photographically reproduced and protected by two glass plates.

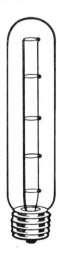

spaced multiple slit (grating, for short) in the centre column of the slitfilm. In order from the top down, the gratings have 15, 30, 80, 40, and 20 slits. Try it also without the red filter on the bulb. How many colours are visible? Can you see why gratings with as many as 5000 slits per centimetre are used in spectroscopes, instruments used to analyze light?

CONCLUSIONS
Summarize what you have learned by doing this investigation.

INVESTIGATION 3-10

Plane Mirrors

When you look in a regular flat mirror, such as a washroom mirror, where is the image: in the glass? in front of the glass? behind the glass? or somewhere else? Is the image the same as you?

In this investigation you will use a ray box to find the rather surprising answer to the first set of questions. You will then use this information to discover the answer to the last question.

APPARATUS
ray box with mask
plane mirror for ray box
pinboard
large corner mirror (2 plane mirrors at right angles—one per class)

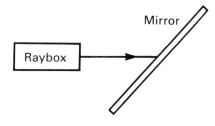

A ray of light incident at an oblique angle

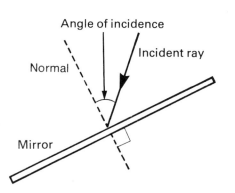

Angles of incidence and reflection are always measured from the normal, not from the mirror line. A *normal* is an imaginary line at right angles to the mirror.

PROCEDURE
Adjust a ray box so that it gives out a parallel beam that travels at least 50 cm along the table, and then install a single-slit mask to get a narrow ray.

Shine a ray of light obliquely on to a plane mirror. View the narrow strip of glass from above. Where does the reflection occur — at the front of the glass or at the back? Use this observation throughout the remainder of the investigation whenever you have to draw a line representing the reflecting surface.

Trace the reflecting line, the incident ray, and the reflected ray. Then construct the normal and measure the angle of incidence and the angle of reflection. What do you conclude?

Now, set a fresh piece of paper on a pinboard and shine the ray box at a pin about 10 cm in front of the mirror. Trace the reflecting line and the reflected ray. Look along the reflected ray towards the mirror. Does the reflected ray seem to be coming from the pin? Where does the pin seem to be? Move the ray box to a different position (such as B in the diagram shown), and again draw only the reflected ray. Look into the mirror to see where the pin seems to be. Remove the ray box and mirror and dot the two reflected rays straight backward until they intersect. That should be where the pin seemed to be. Measure the perpendicular distances from the real pin

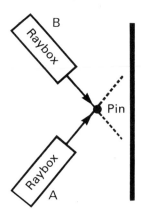

to the mirror (d_o) and from the image pin location to the mirror (d_i). How do they compare?

On a piece of paper, draw a mirror line and a half arrow. Use what you learned in the last paragraph to locate and draw the image of the half arrow. Then set a mirror on your paper and see if the image really is as you have drawn it. (You probably noticed something peculiar about the image when compared with the original object.) If the original was like this ↑ , use the following system to classify the image:

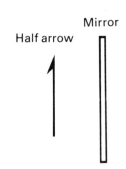

Mirror
Half arrow

↑	↾	↓	↓
no change	laterally inverted	inverted	inverted and laterally inverted

Finally, look at yourself in a corner mirror. You should be able to locate three images of yourself. Raise your right hand and observe and record what each image does.

CONCLUSIONS
1. Summarize what you have learned about the image in a plane mirror under the headings **Size of Image**, **Location of Image**, **Attitude of Image**, and **Type of Image**.
2. How *does* the image in a plane mirror differ from the original object?

QUESTIONS
1. Explain the peculiar properties of the centre image in a set of corner mirrors.
2. You have seen that the image in a plane mirror is the same size as the object. Why, then, when you are having your hair cut in a shop with mirrors both in front of and behind you, do you see images that seem to get smaller and smaller as they recede into the distance?

INVESTIGATION 3-11

Curved Mirrors

Reflectors in automobile headlights, aisle mirrors in corner stores, mirrors in fun houses at exhibitions, and wide-angle rearview mirrors in vehicles are all examples of curved mirrors. In this long investigation you will learn some of the terminology and qualitative properties of curved mirrors.

PROCEDURE
Allow three parallel rays to be reflected from the concave (that is, like a cave) side of a curved mirror so that the reflected rays converge to a point on the central incident ray. Trace the rays and mirror location. Mark the point of convergence as F, the *focal point*. The central ray hits the mirror at V, the *vertex* of the mirror. The vertex will be midway between the ends of the mirror. Label the line containing F and V as the *principal axis*. The mirror forms an arc of a circle. To find the centre of the circle, which will be along the principal axis somewhere, use a compass and open it along the principal axis until you can draw an arc that coincides with the mirror line. You should find that the centre of curvature is about twice the focal length from the vertex, where the *focal length* is the F to V distance. Label the centre of the circle as C, the *centre of curvature*.

Attitude: upright or inverted?
Types of Image:
(a) **Real**—a piece of paper can be put where the image seemed to be, and the image will appear on the paper. That is, the light actually passes through that point.
(b) **Virtual**—the image does not appear on a piece of paper placed at the image point. Light only *seems* to pass through that point.

An alternative method for studying concave mirrors is possible if the equipment is available. Follow the procedure of Investigation 3-17, using a concave mirror in place of a lens.

APPARATUS
ray box with mask
cylindrical mirrors, concave and convex

per class, 1 each of: a large diameter concave mirror and stand, a large diameter convex mirror and stand (each with their F and C points marked clearly in front of them)

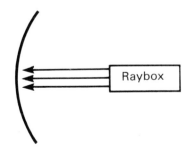

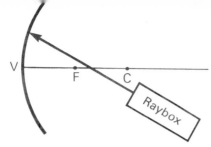

V · F · C

Raybox

Incident ray not parallel to the principal axis, and not incident on the vertex.

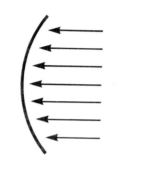

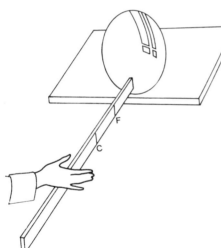

F
C

Magnification = $\dfrac{\text{height of image}}{\text{height of object}}$

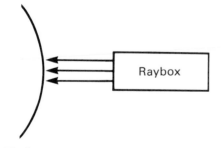

Raybox

Finding the focal point of a *convex* mirror

Now that you are familiar with curved mirror terminology, replace the mirror on the paper and relocate F, V, and C as before, but do not trace any rays on the page. Send in a *single* ray, *not* parallel to the principal axis and *not* incident on the vertex. Trace the ray and its reflection. The normal to a circle is a radius, so draw a line from the centre of curvature to the point of incidence. Does the law of reflection you found for plane mirrors hold for curved mirrors?

Now send five or more parallel rays in to a concave mirror. You will probably observe that not all the rays are reflected through the exact focal point, especially the outermost rays. This is due to *spherical aberration*, which occurs when incoming rays far from the principal axis are reflected in such a way that they pass close to but not through the focal point. This is an inherent feature of spherical mirrors and can only be overcome by using a different shape, such as a parabolic mirror. Draw a diagram showing the difference between a spherical shape and a parabolic shape (see page 190).

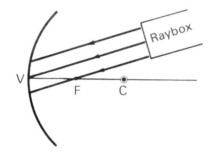

Raybox

V · F · C

Three parallel rays not parallel to the principal axis

Locate and draw the principal axis again for your concave mirror. Then send in three parallel rays *not* parallel to the principal axis. Do they converge to a point that is on the same side of the principal axis as the ray box or on the opposite side? Draw a diagram to illustrate this. This is called *inversion* (just ordinary inversion, not lateral inversion). You probably noticed it if you have ever looked in a large concave mirror at a distance from the mirror. If not, try it now with the large concave mirror in your classroom.

To observe a phenomenon that is not easily seen with ray boxes, have your partner bring his or her outstretched hand closer and closer to the mirror starting from across the room while you stay back. Classify the image when the object (partner's outstretched hand) is (a) far from the mirror relative to its indicated focal point and (b) closer to the mirror than the focal point.

You can also investigate the magnification of the mirror this way, where the magnification is the ratio of height of image over height of object. Have your partner stand with outstretched hand at various distances from the mirror while you look at him or her in the mirror from across the room. At what object distances relative to F and C does the magnification seem to be less than one? greater than one?

Now use a ray box and a small *convex* mirror. Find the focal point of the convex mirror—it will be behind the mirror. Draw a diagram to illustrate this. We say the focal point F is *virtual*. In your report, explain the difference between virtual and real focal points. Use the large convex mirror to investigate the inversion and magnification properties of this type of mirror, relative to the mirror's indicated F and C points.

CONCLUSIONS

In order for you to have something handy to study from and to help you to organize your observations, make a table with these headings: **Type of Mirror and Object**, **Attitude of Image (erect or inverted)**, **Size of Image Relative to Object**, and **Type of Image (real or virtual)**. Under the first heading, use these entries: Plane Mirrors with Any Object, Convex Mirrors with Any Object, Concave Mirrors with a Distant Object, Concave Mirrors with an Object between F and C, and Concave Mirrors with an Object closer than F. Use your observations to fill in the remainder of the table.

INVESTIGATION 3-12

Refraction of Light I (Rectangular Prism)

This investigation is designed to introduce you to the phenomenon of refraction of light. It is designed to be done before you study refraction of light in class.

PROCEDURE

Set up a ray box so that it sends a single ray of light towards a rectangular prism at an oblique angle. Notice that some of the light reflects and some enters the glass, bending as it does so. This bending as the light goes from one medium to another is called *refraction*. The fact that some of the light is reflected and some refracted is called *partial reflection and transmission*.

Trace the path of the incident ray coming from the ray box, the emergent ray coming out the other side of the prism, and the ray joining those two inside the prism. Also, trace the outline of the prism. Draw a normal at the front interface and measure the angle of incidence and the angle of refraction there. Repeat at the back interface. How does light bend when it *enters* a substance such as glass? How does light bend when it *leaves* glass for air? These two observations may be thought of as two elementary laws of refraction. They hold for substances other than glass, such as water, plastic, and diamond. The reason they are elementary is that they are not very precise—they do not tell us how *much* the light bends.

Try twisting the prism so that the incident ray hits the front interface at various angles, while you watch the ray reflected from the front interface. When is this reflected ray particularly strong and the refracted ray that goes into the prism particularly weak? Can you get the ray that refracts into the prism at the front interface to disappear? That is, can you get total reflection at the front interface?

Now for a trick that depends on the simple laws of refraction that you have just learned. Place a coin in the bottom of a beaker and hold your head so that the edge of the coin is just barely out of sight over the edge of the beaker. Have your partner slowly fill the beaker with water from a second beaker as you keep your head immobile. What do you notice as the beaker fills with water? In your report, use a ray diagram to explain why the coin becomes visible when the beaker is filled with water.

CONCLUSIONS

Summarize what you have learned about light by doing this investigation.

QUESTIONS

1. Partial reflection and transmission is fairly common—give an everyday example.
2. How would knowing the coin trick help you to spear fish from the edge of a lake?

APPARATUS

rectangular prism with bottom face ground or painted white so that you can see light rays as they pass through the prism

ray box and mask

2 beakers

coin

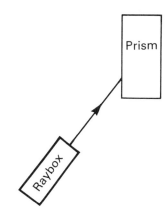

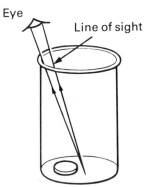

APPARATUS
rectangular prism with one face
    ground or painted white
ray box with mask
pinboard and pin

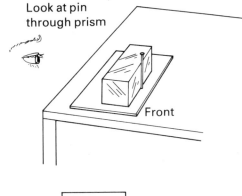

Look at pin
through prism

Front

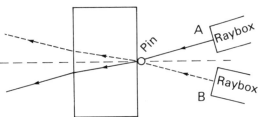

A

Raybox

Pin

Raybox

B

Back surface   Front surface

Angles in this diagram are exaggerated for
clarity. In practice A and B should be no
more than about 10° from the normal.

APPARATUS
ray box with mask
triangular prism with bottom face ground
    or painted white so that light passing
    through the prism can be seen
beaker and test tube

INVESTIGATION 3-13

Apparent Depth and Index of Refraction

In this investigation you will study the interesting phenomenon of apparent depth and be introduced to a number, called the index of refraction, that can be used to characterize a transparent substance.

PROCEDURE
Place a paper and prism on a pinboard, and stick a pin in the board so that it is against the front surface of the prism. Look through the other side of the prism at the pin and try to estimate where it appears to be. To locate the image pin, shine a ray of light at a small incident angle (say ten degrees—position A in the second diagram) at the pin and trace it as it goes through the prism. Shift the ray box and send a ray at the pin from the opposite side of the normal and again at a small angle (position B in the diagram). Trace it as it goes through the prism. Then remove the ray box and prism and draw the two emergent rays backward until they meet. Is this location approximately where the pin appeared to be?

 Measure the real depth of the pin, that is, how far it really is from the back surface of the prism. Then measure the apparent depth of the pin, that is, the distance between the back surface of the prism and the apparent location of the pin as found above. Calculate the ratio of real depth to apparent depth. This number is constant for any particular type of material and should match with that of other groups in the class using the same type of prism. This characteristic of the medium is called the *index of refraction* of the substance. Each transparent substance has its own characteristic index of refraction, and an investigation measuring index of refraction can be used to distinguish one transparent substance from another.

CONCLUSIONS
Summarize what you have learned about light by doing this investigation.

QUESTIONS
1. Why might it be unsafe to judge whether water will be over your head just by looking over the side of a boat?
2. Suppose you had a block of substance of index of refraction 2.0. If you repeated the procedure with this substance, how would the results differ?

INVESTIGATION 3-14

Refraction of Light II (Triangular Prism)

How is a rainbow formed? Why does an empty bottle held in water sometimes look as if it has a mirror in it? Why do binoculars have prisms in them? How does a periscope work? In this investigation you will take a look at two basic refraction phenomena, dispersion and total internal reflection. They are involved in the answers to these and many other questions.

PROCEDURE
1. *Dispersion.* Shine a ray of light on the side of a triangular prism as indicated in the diagram. Examine the following: ray BC in the glass, ray CD in the air, and the boundary RT between the glass and the air. Slowly rotate the prism in the counterclockwise direction and watch what happens to the ray CD. Try to keep C well away from R and T. When you see CD broken up into the colours of the rainbow, you are observing *dispersion*. You can probably

see the colours much more clearly if you hold the prism up to your eye and rotate it as you look through it at a straight-filament light bulb or at a crack in the curtains. Try this.

Replace the prism on the paper and use the ray box to draw a sketch of dispersion—be sure to include and label six colours: blue, green, orange, red, violet, and yellow. Which colour is refracted the most? That is, which colour is bent the most from the original path of the ray BC? Which colour is refracted the least? What is the order of the colours?

2. *Total Internal Reflection.* When you have completed part 1, continue to rotate the prism until the ray CD disappears, that is, until none of the light in the ray BC emerges from the glass to the air via CD. Where is the light? This phenomenon is called *total internal reflection.* Draw a sketch to illustrate total internal reflection. Label the totally internally reflected ray.

Now hold the prism up to your eye in normal room light (that is, with the lights on) and look through it as you rotate it. At some angles there appears to be a mirror inside it, even though you know there isn't. Why?

The same effect can be seen if you hold a test tube full of air at about 45° in a beaker of water and look down from above in normal room light.

3. *Critical Angle.* With the prism back on the paper, rotate the prism so that the angle of refraction of the ray CD is 90°, that is, so that ray CD falls along RT. The angle of incidence for which the angle of refraction is 90° is called the *critical angle* for the refracting medium. Figure out a way of measuring the angle of incidence (critical angle) of the ray BC where it meets RT. What is the critical angle of the substance of which your prism is made?

4. *Total Internal Reflection in Air?* Adjust the prism until the rays in the diagram can all be seen again. Consider the ray AB in air, the ray BC in glass, and the boundary RS. Slowly rotate the prism in one direction and then the other to try to get total internal reflection in air, that is, to cause ray BC to disappear. (Having the ray AB hit one of the corners R, S, or T is not allowed.) Is it possible? Explain clearly when total internal reflection *is* possible.

CONCLUSIONS
Summarize what you have learned about light by doing this investigation.

QUESTIONS
1. (a) What is dispersion? (b) What causes dispersion?
2. (a) Define critical angle. (b) What happens when the critical angle is exceeded?
3. Raindrops are not triangular, but rainbows are caused by dispersion and total internal reflection. Find out how and draw a diagram to illustrate it.

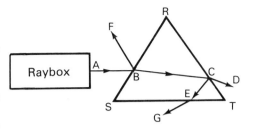

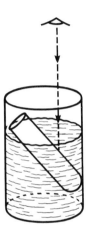

Is total internal reflection possible for water waves? How could you demonstrate it? If it is available, see the filmloop *Refraction of Water Waves.*

INVESTIGATION 3-15
Developing a Law of Refraction
For reflection, the angle of incidence equals the angle of reflection. For refraction, however, the situation is definitely not that simple. The angle of incidence does *not* equal the angle of refraction *except* when both are zero.

In this investigation you will collect a great deal of data about angles of incidence and angles of refraction. You will then use it to develop a law of refraction.

PRE-LAB
Before doing this investigation you should be familiar with the techniques of graphic analysis, that is, how to develop an equation from a graph of data. (See Investigations 1-1 and 1-2.)

APPARATUS
ray box with mask
semi-circular dish (PSSC-type)
polar graph paper
pinboard and pins

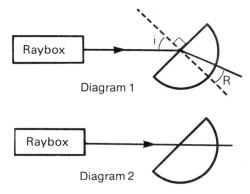

Diagram 1

Diagram 2

PROCEDURE
To measure the angles of incidence (*i*) and refraction (*R*), you will be using a semi-circular dish and ray box, as shown in the first diagram.

Get a ray box and dish. Later the dish will be filled with water. The water will be causing the refracting. In order to reassure yourself that the dish itself has little or no effect, place the empty dish in the path of the light ray with the flat side towards the slit, as shown in the second diagram. Vary the orientation of the dish with respect to the light ray. Is the direction of the light ray changed as it passes through the dish? (If there *is* some orientation in which the dish has an effect, you will have to avoid that particular direction later when there is water in the dish.)

Now half fill the dish with water. In order to measure angles rapidly and easily, and for another reason that will become apparent later, you will use polar graph paper. In order to get copies of the data for everyone in the group, you will use pinholes to mark the path of the light rays. If two or three sheets of polar graph paper are put together on a pinboard under the dish, the pinholes will make several identical copies simultaneously. Find and trace lightly with pencil the largest *complete* circle on your polar graph paper.

Align your dish on the polar graph paper so that the flat side of the dish is on the 90° line and so that the bottom of the vertical line on the dish falls exactly on the centre of the graph paper. Send a well-focused light ray in to the vertical scratch on the dish at an angle of 0° and use pins at the circumference of the largest complete circle on the graph paper to mark the path of the incident and refracted light rays. Increase the angle of incidence to 5° and repeat. (If you make any erroneous pinholes, circle them so that you will not become confused later.) Repeat this procedure in 5° intervals right up to as high an angle of incidence as you can get (80° if possible).

Make a data table showing your values of angles of incidence and corresponding angles of refraction. Look at the table. Does angle *i* equal angle *R*? Is angle *i* + angle *R* constant? Is angle *i* − angle *R* constant? To see if there is a direct or inverse variation, draw a graph of angle *i* versus angle *R*. You should find that the graph is almost a straight line, but deviates significantly at the larger angles. This exhausts the range of *simple* mathematical relationships we know about.

In 1621 a man called Snel made himself famous by discovering that if one concentrates on semi-chords rather than on angles, there *is* a simple relationship that describes refraction. You probably know what a chord of a circle is (a line crossing the circle, but not through the centre). A semi-chord is just half that (see the third diagram).

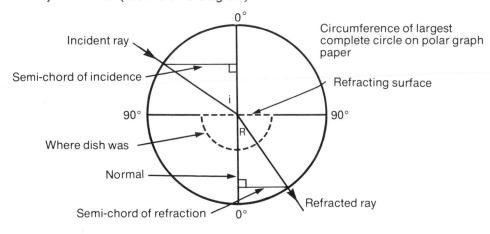

Diagram 3

Use a sharp pencil to draw all the semi-chords of incidence and semi-chords of refraction on your polar graph paper. *Make sure they are at 90° to the normal.* Measure their lengths and make up a table of semi-chords of incidence and their corresponding semi-chords of refraction. Use your knowledge of graphic analysis to find the relationship between semi-chord of incidence (for short, *SC* of *i*) and semi-chord of refraction (*SC* of *R*). The constant in your relation is called the *index of refraction* and is usually given the symbol *n*. Look up the index of refraction of water in the Appendix. By what percentage does your value differ from the accepted value?

In order to put Snel's law in a slightly more useful (and modern) form than *SC* of *i* = *n SC* of *R*, imagine that the outer circle had a radius of 1 cm. In that case, the *SC* of *i* and *SC* of *R* are called the *sine* of *i* and the *sine* of *R* respectively (for short, *sin i* and *sin R*). Sines of angles have been extensively tabulated (see Appendix). Thus, all one has to do is measure the angles and look up the sine values. In this form Snel's law becomes:

$$sin\ i = n\ sin\ R.$$

Often it is rearranged to look like this

$$\frac{sin\ i}{sin\ R} = n.$$

CONCLUSIONS
What did you learn about refraction of light by doing this investigation?

INVESTIGATION 3-16

Introduction to Lenses

Cameras, the eye, magnifying glasses, telescopes, microscopes, apartment door peepholes, glasses, and many other common devices have lenses in them. This investigation is designed as an introduction to some of the basic properties of lenses.

PROCEDURE
1. *Near Point.* First, you must learn about a property of the human eye called the *near point.* Hold a card with writing on it on a metre stick, and gradually bring the card towards your eye until you first have some difficulty seeing the card clearly. Then back it off until you do see it clearly without straining. The card is now at your near point, and the distance from the card to your eyes is your *near distance.* Measure your near distance and record it. (Measure it two or three times and take an average for accuracy. You will need it for the next part of the investigation.)

The *standard near distance* mentioned in books is taken as 25 cm for the average *adult* eye.
2. *Convex Lens.* Now get a convex lens (+10D), a lens holder, and a metre stick. The lens should be fingerprint free—you may have to clean it. Support the holder and lens with the metre stick and look through the lens at arm's length at a distant object out the window. Describe the size of the image relative to the object and the attitude of the image (upright or inverted).

Looking at the same distant object, move the lens closer and closer to your eye until the image is first seen with some difficulty, and then back the lens

APPARATUS
selection of lenses (−20D, +2.5D, +5D, +10D, +20D, etc., colour-coded with model paint around the rims so that you can tell one type from another)
lens holder for metre stick
two metre stick supports
card holder for metre stick
lens cleaning tissue

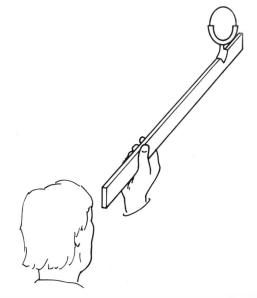

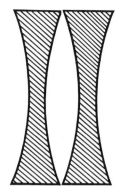

Concave lenses: a double power combination

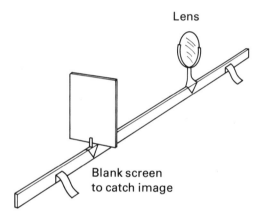

Lens

Blank screen to catch image

Distant object (sun) is off to the right. Move the screen back and forth until the image is in focus.

off a bit until you do see the image clearly. That is, the *image* will be at your near point. Measure the distance of the lens from your eye. Is the *lens* at your near point? Thus, since the *image* was at your near point, which side of the lens must the image be on, the side closer to you or the side farther from you? Figure out how far the image is from the lens. Draw a sketch showing your eye, the lens, the image location (that is, your near point), and the measured distances.

3. *Concave Lens.* Repeat all the steps of part 2, using a concave lens (-20D). If your near point in step 1 was exceptionally close (6 cm or less), you may have to use a -40D combination made by taping two -20D lenses together.

4. *Real Images.* Some lenses produce real images, that is, images that can be caught on paper. Use the setup shown in the diagram to find which of the two lenses you have used so far produces real images of a distant object. (You will have to do this in a semi-darkened room so that the image on the paper is not washed out.) Use the convex lens first and the concave lens second.

5. *Focal Length.* Use a screen as in part 4 to locate the image formed by a convex lens of the most distant object visible, such as the sun or distant buildings. Measure the distance between this image and the centre of the lens. This is called the *focal length* and is a very important property of a lens, as you will see soon in your study of lenses.

Measure the focal lengths of the various convex lenses available to you.

What is it about a lens, other than the type of substance of which it is made, that determines its focal length?

CONCLUSIONS
1. What have you learned about convex lenses by doing this investigation?
2. What have you learned about concave lenses by doing this investigation?

QUESTIONS
1. Define focal point.
2. Define near point.
3. Which is more restful to the eye, viewing something far away, in effect at infinity, or viewing something at the near point?

INVESTIGATION 3-17

Images in a Convex Lens

If you have ever held a convex lens out in front of you and approached an object, you know that what you see through the lens changes enormously as your distance from the object changes from far to very close. In this investigation you will make a systematic study of the various images of a convex lens.

PRE-LAB
Before doing this investigation you should have had some practical experience with a convex lens, as mentioned in the introduction above. In addition, you should know how to measure the focal length of a lens.

PROCEDURE
First, measure the focal length of the lens as accurately as you possibly can. The remainder of the investigation depends on an accurate measurement of focal length.

Set up a data table with the column headings **Object Distance (from lens),**

Image Size (compared with object), Image Attitude (erect or inverted), Kind of Image (real or virtual), and Image Distance (from lens). Use the following object distances, where *f* stands for the focal length of the lens: Well Beyond 2*f*, At 2*f*, Between *f* and 2*f*, and Inside *f*. Record image distance in terms of *f* in the same manner.

Remember that if you can't immediately find an image with the card, you can always stand back and look through the lens to see if there is an image and to see approximately where it is. For virtual images, leave a blank in the image distance column or, if your teacher instructs you how, use the method of no parallax.

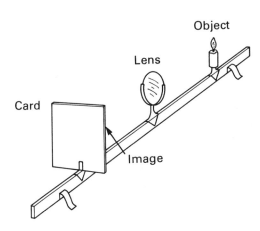

CONCLUSIONS
Can you see any systematic trend in the size and location of the image as the object gets closer and closer to the lens? In other words, try to discover some pattern that would help you remember all the things in your table.

QUESTIONS
1. What important change takes place at the 2*f* point?
2. What important changes must have taken place at the *f* position?
3. Draw accurate ray diagrams to illustrate your results for the four object locations.
4. For each of your four diagrams, name a simple device that uses a lens and object in that manner (see page 209).

INVESTIGATION 3-18

Pre-Telescope Investigation

A single lens cannot produce a magnified image of a distant object. (Try it with any lens available to you.) In this investigation you will learn some properties of single lenses that will be of use in the next investigation when you combine lenses to make a telescope.

PRE-LAB
Before doing this investigation, you should know how to draw accurate ray diagrams for lenses and how to find the focal length of a lens.

PROCEDURE
Obtain several lenses of various focal lengths. Use each to locate the image of a distant object, and measure the size of the object's image — record this size and the focal length of the lens in a data table. For such distant objects, how does the size of the image change with lens focal length?

Next, use each lens as a magnifying glass to obtain an upright virtual image of a very close object. Which type of focal length, long or short, gives the larger image of a close object?

APPARATUS
selection of 4 or 5 different lenses of various focal lengths
metre stick
lens holder
screen and screen holder
ruler

CONCLUSIONS
1. You can't use a single lens to magnify a distant object, but if you want the largest possible image of such an object, which focal length should you choose?
2. Which focal length gives the greatest magnification for close objects?

QUESTIONS
1. Draw an accurate set of diagrams (two are sufficient) to scale to show lenses imaging an extremely distant object (so distant that its rays incident at an angle to the principal axis of each lens are parallel to each other). Your pair of diagrams should support Conclusion 1.

2. Draw accurate ray diagrams of two lenses used to magnify two objects. (*Hint*: Start each diagram with the lens, its focal points, and a virtual image at 25 cm from the lens. Work the tracing rays backward to get the object.) Your diagrams should support Conclusion 2.

INVESTIGATION 3-19

Making a Telescope

In this investigation you will make a two-lens telescope and study its properties. It will have the disadvantage that everything you look at through it will be upside down. When one looks at the stars, however, that does not matter much. Thus the telescope you will make is often called an astronomical telescope.

PRE-LAB
Before doing this investigation you should have a thorough understanding of the various images of a convex lens and should be able to tell what focal length lens to choose to obtain the largest image of a distant object or of a close object.

APPARATUS
selection of convex lenses of various focal lengths
metre stick and supports
lens holder
screen and screen support

PROCEDURE
A telescope is used to magnify a distant object. This cannot be done with a single lens. The simplest type of telescope uses a converging lens to get a real image somewhere close to you, and then a magnifying glass to enlarge it once it is close. The first lens is called the *objective* lens, and the magnifying lens is called the *eyepiece*, as it ends up closer to the eye.

Use your knowledge of lens properties to choose a suitable objective lens from the lenses available to you. Mount it on a metre stick and locate the image of a distant object on a screen. Now choose a suitable lens to use as a magnifying glass, mount it on the side of the screen opposite the objective lens, and move it along the stick until you obtain a magnified image of the back side of the screen. Then remove the screen, and with minor fine adjustments, you will have a simple telescope.

To determine the magnification of your telescope, draw a series of close, equally spaced heavy vertical lines on the chalkboard on the far side of the room. View them from as far away as possible with your simple telescope. With your other eye, view them directly. Try to estimate how many spaces as seen with the unaided eye will fit into one space as seen with the telescope.

Measure and record the distance between the eyepiece and objective. How does it compare with the sum of the focal lengths of the two lenses you are using (slightly more? exactly the same? slightly less?)?

Compute the quotient of focal length of objective over focal length of eyepiece. How does it compare with the experimentally determined magnification?

CONCLUSIONS
Summarize what you have learned about the telescope by doing this investigation.

QUESTIONS
1. Draw an accurate ray diagram to scale to show how a telescope images a distant object. Label the diagram so that it becomes reasonably self-explanatory to someone else seeing it for the first time.
2. Can you suggest any improvements to the simple telescope you made? What are they?

INVESTIGATION 3-20

Telescopes and Microscopes

In this investigation you will make a Galilean telescope, a compound microscope, and a terrestrial telescope.

PRE-LAB
Before doing this investigation you should have a thorough knowledge of the properties of lenses and have made and understood a simple telescope.

PROCEDURE

1. *Galilean Telescope.* A Galilean telescope is a simple two-lens telescope that forms an *erect* final image and is conveniently short. Galilean telescopes are often sold as opera glasses because of these two facts and as telephoto lens systems for cameras because of their compactness. Galilean telescopes have the disadvantage that their magnification is quite limited.

Use a converging lens of long focal length and a diverging lens whose focal length is less than half that of the converging lens you have chosen. Mount the converging lens as an objective and use a card to locate the image of a distant object. Mount the diverging lens about halfway *between* the objective and the card, remove the card, put your eye right up to the diverging lens, and make fine adjustments until the distant object is in focus. You now have a Galilean telescope.

Estimate the power of your Galilean telescope using the method of Investigation 3-19. Measure and record the distance between lenses and the focal lengths of the lenses, and use these measurements to draw a ray diagram to scale to illustrate the working of this type of telescope. Label the diagram.

2. *Compound Microscope.* A microscope is used to magnify a close object. This can be done with a single lens, as you know, but with limited magnification. For larger magnification, two or more lenses must be used. In microscopes the quality of the lenses used becomes critical because a slight distortion in the first lens may be magnified many times by succeeding lenses to produce a greatly distorted final image.

As an object, use something with very fine print, such as the fine detail on a dollar bill. Mount a converging lens of short focal length (5 cm works well) in a clamp on a retort stand at a distance above the object that is slightly greater than the lens's focal length. Look down from above to locate the real (that is, inverted) magnified image. Then use a second converging lens of slightly longer focal length (10 cm works well) as a magnifying eyepiece and move it above the first lens until you obtain a final magnified image. The final magnified image should be larger than either lens alone can produce and will be inverted—this can serve as a check on whether you have succeeded. In your report, tell why the objective must be more than its focal length away from the object. Where must the real image have been located relative to the eyepiece lens?

Unless you are using expensive lenses called *achromatic doublets*, you will probably see coloured haloes around objects viewed through your compound microscope—this is called *chromatic aberration*. For your report, look up chromatic aberration on page 219: what causes it?

In your report, draw a ray diagram (not to scale) to illustrate the operation of this instrument. Label the diagram.

3. *Terrestrial Telescope.* The terrestrial telescope is an astronomical telescope with an extra lens added to get the final image upright instead of in-

APPARATUS
selection of convex and concave lenses of various focal lengths
metre stick
lens holders
screen and holder
retort stand with 2 test tube clamps

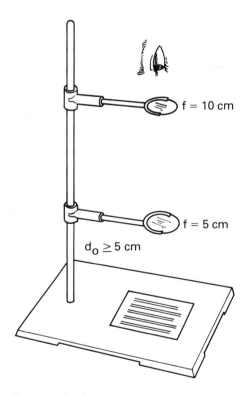

f = 10 cm

f = 5 cm

$d_o \geq 5$ cm

Compound microscope setup

verted. However, it can be tricky to set up unless you have a thorough understanding of lenses.

Set up a lens of about 20 cm focal length as an objective and use a card to locate its image. Use a 10 cm lens as the erector and place it so that it is 20 cm on the other side of the card. (In your report, explain why.) Finally, locate a 5 cm eyepiece lens slightly less than 25 cm from the erector lens (in your report, explain why). With the removal of the card and minor fine adjustments of the *erector lens*, you should have a terrestrial telescope.

Estimate the power of your terrestrial telescope using the method of Investigation 3-19. In your report, draw a ray diagram to scale to illustrate the working of this type of telescope. Label the diagram so that a stranger would have some idea of what it is all about and how it works.

CONCLUSIONS
Summarize what you have learned by doing this investigation.

PART FOUR
Atomic, Solid State, and Nuclear Physics

INVESTIGATION 4-1
Observing Spectra

In this investigation you will use a device called a diffraction grating to study the light given out when electricity is passed through a thin wire (a solid) and then when it is passed through a gas. Not only are the results beautiful, but they also lead to a deeper understanding of the behaviour of electrons in molecules of gases and solids.

PRE-LAB
Before doing this investigation, you should have done Investigation 3-9 and seen what happens to a multiple-slit interference pattern when the number of slits is increased. You should also be familiar with the Rutherford model of the atom and the objections to it.

APPARATUS
replica diffraction grating (5000 or more lines per centimetre)
straight filament lamp
variable transformer
gas tubes
5000 V power supply for gas tubes

PROCEDURE
Use a diffraction grating to analyze the light emitted by the hot filament of a lamp when full voltage is applied to the lamp. Describe the spectrum, naming at least six basic colours. (A sketch might help.)

Observe the various spectra emitted by the filament of the lamp as the voltage across it is slowly increased from zero to maximum. Which colours appear first? Which colours appear only at higher voltages? Thus, which colours of light must correspond to low energies? high energies?

Now use the diffraction grating to analyze the light given out by various gases when about 5000 V is applied across them. Describe the spectrum of one of the gases, making a sketch if possible. What do all gas emission spectra have in common? In what way or ways do they differ? How does the light emitted by excited gas atoms compare with the light emitted by excited atoms of a solid?

Note: With this simple apparatus, it is not possible to vary the energy supplied to the gases as was done to the filament. But if it is done, the results are the same as for solids: some colours correspond to higher energies and some to lower energies, and the correspondence is the same as it was for light given off by atoms of a solid.

CONCLUSIONS

1. Consult the text section dealing with the Bohr-Rutherford model of the atom (page 243). How did Bohr account for the observed properties of gas emission spectra? (A detailed answer is expected here.)

2. In a gas, the molecules are far enough apart that they are effectively isolated from one another. In a solid, on the other hand, the molecules are close enough together to affect one another. Consult the section of the text that deals with energy bands of solids (see page 257). What effect does crowding have on the unique and distinct energy levels as one compresses a gas into a solid?

3. Use the idea of energy bands in solids to account for the continuous nature of the spectrum of a solid.

4. Summarize what you have learned by doing this investigation.

INVESTIGATION 4-2

Light and a Pure Semiconductor

In this investigation you will use a cadmium sulphide photocell to study the effect of light on the resistance properties of a pure semiconductor.

PRE-LAB

Before doing this investigation you should be able to solve this problem: A certain electrical device will melt if it has to dissipate more than 0.5 W of power. Thus, what is the maximum safe current through it when it is connected to a 1.5 V dry cell?

You should also be able to name the precautions to take when using a multi-range electrical meter.

APPARATUS
large cadmium sulphide photocell (0.5 W or higher rating, e.g., Clairex CL5M5L or equivalent)
1.5 V dry cell
nichrome-wire rheostat (1 m of #20 gauge chromel wire wound on a pencil or test tube)
multi-range ammeter
multi-range voltmeter
short connecting leads
black masking tape

PROCEDURE

In a well-lit room, connect the CdS cell in series with the nichrome-wire rheostat, an ammeter, and a dry cell. The photocell is rated for 0.5 W power dissipation, and so you must use the rheostat to limit the current through the photocell to no more than 100 mA (see Pre-Lab).

Now, connect a voltmeter in parallel with the photocell. If the room is not well lit, shine a lamp on the photocell. Read the current through the photocell and the potential difference across it. Record both.

Cover the photocell with black masking tape and turn off any bright lights. Again record current and potential difference. If the current is too small to be detected, change the rheostat setting or eliminate the rheostat entirely.

Calculate the resistance of the semiconductor when it was well lit. Calculate the resistance of the semiconductor when it was in darkness.

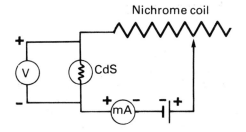

Nichrome coil

CONCLUSIONS

How does light affect a pure semiconductor such as cadmium sulphide? (Such a semiconductor is often called a *bulk-effect semiconductor* or a *photo-conductor* to distinguish it from other photocells which you will be studying.)

QUESTIONS

1. Consult the band theory of solids section of the text (pages 257-60). How can you explain the results of this investigation in terms of the band theory of solids?

APPARATUS

small bar of group-V-doped germanium (labelled n)

small bar of group-III-doped germanium (labelled p)

microammeter or galvanometer(100 μA or less full-scale deflection (FSD)

matches

2 leads, one with a probe that can be heated without damage

The doped germanium bars from the American Association of Physics Teachers (AAPT) Semiconductor Set work well in this investigation. They also have the advantage of being relatively inexpensive.

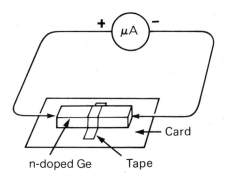

An effect involving the deflection of moving charge carriers by a magnetic field, called the *Hall effect*, also provides direct evidence for the existence of holes as the charge carriers in some semiconductors. The semiconductor is placed in a uniform magnetic field that is perpendicular to the charge flow. Charge carriers moving in the semiconductor then experience a transverse deflection toward one side or the other, depending on the sign of their charge. A sensitive galvanometer connected across the semiconductor will then register a small voltage, the sign of which depends on the type of charge carrier.

INVESTIGATION 4-3

Doped Semiconductors

In this investigation you will study the effect of heating one end of a doped semiconductor, an effect that gives direct evidence for the existence of holes as the charge-carriers in some semiconductors.

PRE-LAB

Before doing this investigation you should be able to tell how the resistance of conductors and semiconductors varies with temperature and be able to use a simple model to explain each. You should also know what is meant by doping.

PROCEDURE

Examine your microammeter or galvanometer to see which terminal is negative and which is positive. If the meter needle moves from left to right, electrons are flowing *into* the negative terminal and *out* of the positive.

Rather than heat the pieces of semiconductor directly, which might melt or destroy them, use a match to heat the end of one of the meter leads. (It is better to stick to matches than to use really hot flames such as Bunsen burners.) Touch one end of the n-type semiconductor bar firmly with the hot wire and the other end firmly with the cold wire. Observe the microammeter very closely for any small movement. Did the current, if any, remain constant?

On a diagram such as the one shown, indicate (a) which end of the germanium was hot, (b) what type of germanium you were using, (c) which way the needle deflected, and thus (d) which way the electrons in the connecting wires were moving. On the basis of your diagram of results, was the unheated end of the group-V-doped germanium positive or negative?

Now, repeat the procedure and diagram, this time using the p-type germanium. (The results should be different.) Was the unheated end of the group-III-doped germanium positive or negative?

CONCLUSIONS

1. What effect would heating one end have on the number of charge-carriers at that end of the semiconductor compared with the other end?
2. Since like charges repel, in which direction in the bar would there be a drift of charge-carriers? Thus, which end of the bar should accumulate a charge that is the same as that of the charge-carriers? Based on your observations and your answer to these questions, what was the sign of the charge-carriers in the group-V-doped germanium bar? the group-III-doped bar? In which bar was conduction apparently by holes and in which by electrons?
3. Summarize what you have learned by doing this investigation.

INVESTIGATION 4-4

The Photovoltaic Effect

In this investigation you will use a selenium photocell to observe the photovoltaic effect and a cadmium sulphide photocell as a comparison device that works by the photoconductive effect.

PRE-LAB

Before doing this investigation you should know what is meant by a p-n junction and what is meant by the depletion layer in such a junction.

PROCEDURE
Connect the selenium cell to the milliammeter. The p side of the junction usually has a red wire soldered to it and the n side a black wire. Expose the selenium cell to a bright light and observe the meter.

Next, connect the piece of undoped pure semiconductor (CdS) to the meter and repeat the observations.

Now, try the opposite of the photovoltaic effect. Connect a light-emitting diode to a 1.5 V dry cell. (The n side is often marked with a notch or dot.) Try reversing the connections to the diode. For the diode to function, what polarity must be connected to the n side? to the p side?

CONCLUSIONS
What is the photovoltaic effect? How does the photoconductive effect differ from it?

QUESTIONS
1. The light generates electron-hole pairs in the cadmium sulphide just as it does in the selenium junction. Why, then, is no voltage generated across the cadmium sulphide cell?

INVESTIGATION 4-5

The Semiconductor Diode and Rectification

In this investigation you will study the action of a semiconductor diode. You will also look at the use of such a diode as a half-wave rectifier and as a full-wave rectifier.

PRE-LAB
Before doing this investigation you should be able to state clearly how to avoid damaging a multi-range ammeter when using it to measure unknown currents. You should also know what depletion layer means in reference to a p-n junction.

APPARATUS
The second and third parts of this investigation, which deal with rectification, require the use of a cathode-ray oscilloscope. Since most schools are unlikely to have more than two or three of these, we recommend that the oscilloscope stations be set up in advance and student groups take turns while the rest of the class does the first part of this investigation or another investigation or both.

PROCEDURE
Draw a circuit diagram indicating how you will connect a 1.5 V dry cell, an ammeter, a voltmeter, and a diode in order to measure the resistance of the diode. *Do not proceed* until your diagram has been checked by your teacher.

Connect the apparatus and measure the resistance of the diode. Record whether the diode is forward biased or reverse biased, that is, whether the p side of the diode is connected to the positive of the dry cell or to the negative of the dry cell. (The n side of the diode is usually marked with a black or coloured band. If it isn't, ask your teacher which end is p and which is n.) Then reverse the connections to the diode and repeat.

Connect the circuit as shown in Figure 1 or examine the one at the pre-wired station. Use a cathode-ray oscilloscope (CRO) to display the voltage-time behaviour across the 6 V AC power supply. Record the pattern seen. Then use the CRO to display the voltage-time behaviour across the 1000 Ω

APPARATUS
photovoltaic cell (basically a p-type selenium n-type selenium junction, one side of which is very thin and transparent)
photoconductive cell (a piece of pure undoped cadmium sulphide semiconductor)
milliammeter (10mA FSD)
2 leads
light-emitting diode
1.5 V dry cell

Technically, a milli*volt*meter should be used to show the photo*voltaic* effect (rather than a milliammeter). Milliammeters, however, are more likely to be available in most schools than millivoltmeters, and so are specified for use in this investigation.

APPARATUS
semiconductor diode (25 or 40 A types, with any PRV rating, such as 1N1183A, work well; stud-type casings are easy to make connections to)
multi-range ammeter
voltmeter
1.5 V dry cell
connecting leads
cathode-ray oscilloscope (one per class)
10 Ω resistor (one per class)
6 V AC power supply (one per class)
1000 Ω resistor (one per class)
selection of capacitors, each with its capacitance clearly labelled (one per class)

An alternative, but not a very good one, to the cathode-ray oscilloscope is a pair of headphones. The small plug-in-ear type are inexpensive and readily available. You may have a pair at home that you could use for the second part of this investigation.

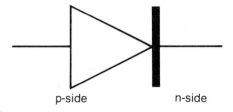

Circuit diagram for a diode

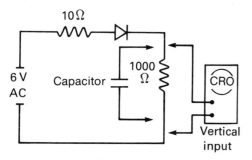

Figure 1. Half-wave rectifier

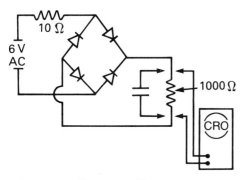

Figure 2. Full-wave rectifier

resistor. What happens to the pattern when you connect various capacitors in parallel with the 1000 Ω resistor? Which size of the capacitances available to you has the greatest effect?

Try reversing the diode in any of the procedures illustrated in Figure 1 and see what effect that has.

Connect the Figure 2 circuit (or examine the one at the pre-wired station). Repeat the procedures as outlined for Figure 1.

CONCLUSIONS
Summarize what you have learned by doing this investigation.

QUESTIONS
1. Explain in a paragraph or two why a p-n junction should have a very low resistance one way (tell which way) and a very high resistance to current passing through the other way.
2. Why is there any current at all when a diode is reverse biased?
3. What is meant by (a) half-wave rectification and (b) full-wave rectification?
4. What is the purpose of putting a storage device, such as a capacitor, in a rectifier circuit?

INVESTIGATION 4-6

Transistors and Amplification

In this investigation you will measure the amplification of a transistor. You will also study a simple one-transistor audio amplifier.

PRE-LAB
Before doing this investigation you should know what a transistor is and be able to explain why the base region is usually either very lightly doped or very thin or both.

APPARATUS
p-n-p power transistor (GE-16 or equivalent)
50 kΩ potentiometer (0.5 W or higher rating)
two 1.5 V dry cells
5 kΩ variable resistor (potentiometer)
100 Ω resistor
2 multi-range ammeters
9 connecting leads

6 V dry cell (one per class)
carbon microphone (one per class)
loudspeaker and output transformer (one per class)

PROCEDURE
Connect the circuit shown (Figure 1). Set the potentiometer to give a reading

Figure 1

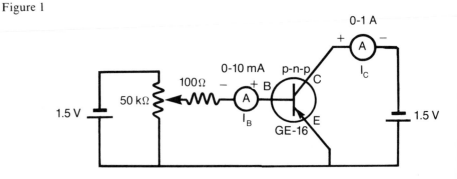

on both ammeters and record both readings. Then change the potentiometer setting and record the new currents. Calculate the amplification of the transistor.

Figure 2. A simple one-transistor audio amplifier

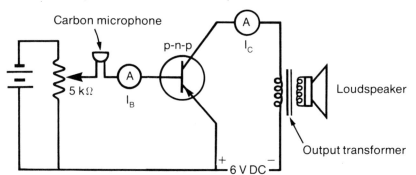

Carbon microphone
p-n-p
A
I_C
A
I_B
5 kΩ
Loudspeaker
Output transformer
+ 6 V DC −

$$\text{Amplification} = \frac{\text{large change}}{\text{causative small change}}$$

$$\beta = \frac{\triangle I_C}{\triangle I_B}$$

Headphones may be used in place of the transformer and speaker. Depending on the speaker, the circuit may also work without the output transformer.

Try the one-transistor audio amplifier shown (Figure 2). When you whistle or speak closely into the carbon microphone, what happens to the base current? to the collector current? Judging by these readings, is amplification taking place? Explain.

Are there settings of the potentiometer, either high or low, where the carbon microphone seems to have no effect? If so, note carefully the meter readings at these settings and in your report, explain your observations.

CONCLUSIONS
Summarize what you have learned by doing this investigation.

QUESTIONS
1. Draw a circuit diagram to show how you could use an n-p-n transistor (Figure 3) as an amplifier.
2. How might you use a second transistor to obtain even more amplification?

B
C
E

Figure 3

INVESTIGATION 4-7

The Cathode-Ray Tube as a Picture Tube

In this demonstration investigation you will study the use of a cathode-ray tube as a television picture tube to produce simple patterns.

PRE-LAB
Before doing this investigation you should know what function each of the following parts serves in a cathode-ray tube: filament and cathode, anode, grid, deflecting plates, phosphor screen.

PROCEDURE
Set the horizontal frequency generator of a cathode-ray oscilloscope to sweep the electron beam across the tube at 60 Hz. What pattern do you predict if the beam is simultaneously swept vertically at the same frequency? Connect a 60 Hz signal to the vertical input, and record the result. What do you predict will happen to the pattern if the grid (that is, the z-axis) is made strongly negative at a rate of about 300 Hz? Use a signal generator to produce a 300 Hz square wave and connect this to the z-axis input. Record the result. Try other multiples of 60 Hz fed to the z-axis input. Try changing the amplitude of the z-axis input and record the results. What difference does using a sine-wave input to the z-axis make?

APPARATUS
cathode-ray oscilloscope with connections for intensity modulation (z-axis input)
2 audio-frequency generators with 0 to 100 kHz vernier-controlled continuously variable frequency output at 0 to 20 V, each capable of generating sine and square waves

Once you have satisfied yourself about the function of the z-axis input, disconnect all signal leads from the oscilloscope. Try for a blank TV pattern (a *raster*) as follows. Connect a 60 Hz signal to the vertical input so that the electron beam sweeps up and down the tube at 60 Hz. If the beam were to sweep across 525 times for each time it went down once, predict (calculate) the horizontal deflection frequency necessary. Use the internal sweep generator set to that frequency, or as close as the controls will allow, and record the pattern seen. In your report, explain what is meant by "blanking the retrace" and in what ways a true TV raster differs from what you observed in this investigation.

Now predict what frequency would have to be applied to the z-axis input to blank the trace several times each time the beam swept down once. Connect that frequency and record the results. Then predict what frequency would have to be applied to the z-axis input to blank the trace several times each time the beam swept *across* the tube. Try that and record the results. Finally, predict what you would see if both frequencies you used in this section were input to the z-axis simultaneously. Try it.

CONCLUSIONS
Summarize what you learned by doing this investigation.

QUESTIONS
1. Consult your text to explain how interlaced scanning differs from the type of scanning used in this investigation.
2. How does a colour tube differ from the monochrome tube you used in this investigation?

INVESTIGATION 4-8

NUCLEAR RADIATION

In this long demonstration investigation you will study some of the properties of radioactive emissions.

APPARATUS

Geiger tube or silicon barrier detector

counter-scaler or ratemeter, preferably with provision for audio output

beta source, such as strontium 90

gamma source, such as cesium 137

detector and source holder

pieces of paper or card of uniform thickness

pieces of aluminum foil of uniform thickness (kitchen type is satisfactory)

pieces of lead foil of uniform thickness (0.08 cm usually works well)

strong magnet

pieces of thick lead foil for shielding

magnetic compass

PROCEDURE
1. Consult the operating manual for the detector and counter in order to set them up. With no radioactive source in the vicinity, let the detector operate for several minutes. Determine the background count rate. In your report explain the sources of this so-called background radiation.
2. Set the beta source at a distance from the detector that gives a high count. Determine the rate. Then put paper between the source and the detector, adding one thickness of paper at a time. Determine the rate of each time. Also, determine the thickness of paper that reduces the count rate to half.

Repeat for the same beta source, using aluminum and then lead absorbers. Then repeat for the gamma source for each of the three types of absorbers.

In your report comment on what your results show about the relative penetrating power of these beta and gamma rays. Also, comment on why alpha rays were not included in this investigation. As well, comment on the relative absorbing powers of identical thicknesses of different materials.
3. To study the effect of a magnetic field on beta particles, put your beta source in a 50 mL beaker and wrap the beaker with lead foil. Cut a narrow slit (0.5 cm by 2.5 cm) in the lead at the top of the beaker. Make an identical slit in another lead sheet and place this sheet over your detector. Mount the detector above the beaker at a distance that gives a good count rate. Make

sure that the detector is firmly clamped. Then insert or turn on the magnet so that the magnetic field is perpendicular to the line of the detector and the source and aligned with the long dimension of the slit. What happens to the count rate?

Keeping a firm grip on the detector, slowly move it in a 90° arc in various directions until you relocate the beam of radiation. Use a magnetic compass to determine the polarity of the magnet. Draw a diagram to show your results and use them to determine the charge, if any, on the beta particles. Then repeat for gamma radiation.

4. Set a thick lead absorber between your detector and the beta source as shown. Take a count with no scattering screen, that is, with air. Then, take counts, one at a time, with identical thicknesses (say, 1 mm) of aluminum, copper, lead, tin, and iron as scatterers. Look up the atomic number of each scattering material. How does the scattering of beta particles appear to depend on atomic number?

In your report try to explain why this scattering takes place. Do gamma rays scatter?

CONCLUSIONS

Summarize what you have learned about nuclear radiations by doing this investigation.

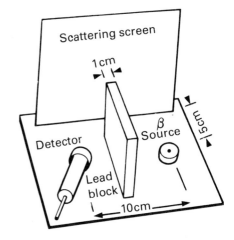

Appendices

Table 1

The International System of Units
Le système international d'unités

These tables contain definitions for all seven of the SI base units,
and for those derived units that are used in this book.

SI BASE UNITS

Quantity	Name	Symbol	Definition of Unit*
length	metre	m	Length of 1 650 763.73 wavelengths in vacuum of the radiation corresponding to the transition between the levels $2p_{10}$ and $5d_5$ of the krypton-86 atom.
mass	kilogram	kg	The mass of the international prototype of the kilogram.
time	second	s	Duration of 9 192 631 770 periods of the radiation corresponding to the transition between two hyperfine levels of the ground state of the caesium-133 atom.
electric current	ampere	A	Current in two straight parallel conductors of infinite length and negligible cross-section placed 1 m apart in a vacuum which would produce between those conductors a force equal to 2×10^{-7} newton per metre of length.
thermodynamic temperature	kelvin	K	1/273.16 of the thermodynamic temperature of the triple point of water – the equilibrium temperature between pure ice, airfree water, and water vapour ($0.01°C = 273.16$ K).
amount of substance	mole	mol	Amount of substance of a system containing as many elementary entities as there are atoms in 0.012 kg of carbon 12.
luminous intensity	candela	cd	Luminous intensity perpendicular from a surface of 1/600 000 m^2 of a black body at the temperature of solidifying platinum at a pressure of 101.325 kPa.

*All numerical values are exact.

SI DERIVED UNITS

Quantity	Name	Symbol	Description	
(a) Units with special names				
frequency	hertz	Hz	cycle per second	s^{-1}
force	newton	N	kilogram metre per second squared	$kg \cdot m/s^2$
pressure	pascal	Pa	newton per square metre	N/m^2
energy, work	joule	J	newton metre	$N \cdot m$
power	watt	W	joule per second	J/s
electric charge	coulomb	C	ampere second	$A \cdot s$
electric potential difference	volt	V	joule per coulomb	J/C
electric resistance	ohm	Ω	volt per ampere	V/A
activity of radionuclides	becquerel	Bq	emission per second	s^{-1}
absorbed dose of radiation	gray	Gy	joule per kilogram	J/kg
(b) Without special names				
area			square metre	m^2
volume			cubic metre	m^3
speed			metre per second	m/s
acceleration			metre per second squared	m/s^2
density			kilogram per cubic metre	kg/m^3
torque, moment of force			newton metre	$N \cdot m$

The following two non-SI units are permitted for specialized use:

energy	electronvolt	eV	1 eV = 0.160 218 aJ approximately
mass of an atom	unified atomic mass unit	u	1 u = 1.660 55 x 10^{-27} kg approximately.

Table 2

To work successfully with SI units, you should be able quickly to relate unit names, symbols, and definitions with one another and with the names of the quantities they measure. The following four lists are intended to help you to learn these relations. Put the four titles at the head of columns in your notebook. Put any *one* of the lists under the appropriate heading. Then, without aids, try to supply the information for the other three columns.

The lists are given in a particular order.
(a) Names of quantities are in their alphabetical order.
(b) Unit names are in alphabetical order.
(c) Unit symbols are in the order in which they are introduced in this text.
(d) The definitions are in order of dependence.

These lists have omitted:
(1) the base units kelvin, mole and candela, which are rarely used in this text, and the litre;
(2) derived units without special names, such as m/s for speed and m/s² for acceleration.
For the **Definition** column in your answers, four of the units will have to be designated simply as BASE units.

(a) Names of Quantities	(b) Names of Units	(c) Unit Symbols	(d) Definitions of Units*
activity of radionuclides	ampere	s	BASE (4 units)
charge	becquerel	kg	s^{-1} (2 units)
current	coulomb	m	$kg \cdot m/s^2$
energy	gray	Hz	N/m^2
force	hertz	N	$N \cdot m$
frequency	joule	Pa	J/s
length	kilogram	J	J/kg
mass	metre	W	A s
potential difference	newton	C	J/C
power	ohm	V	V/A
pressure	pascal	A	W/A
radiation dose	second	Ω	
resistance	volt	Bq	
time	watt	Gy	

*Two of these definitions give the same unit. Which unit is it?

APPENDIX II: PHYSICAL TABLES

Table 3

FUNDAMENTAL PHYSICAL CONSTANTS

Speed of light in vacuum	$c = 2.997\ 924\ 6 \times 10^8$ m/s
Planck constant	$h = 6.626\ 1 \times 10^{-34}$ J/Hz
Elementary charge	$e = 1.602\ 18 \times 10^{-19}$ C
Avogadro constant	$N_A = 6.022\ 1 \times 10^{23}$ mol^{-1}
Atomic mass unit	$1\ u = 1.660\ 55 \times 10^{-27}$ kg
Proton rest mass	$m_p = 1.007\ 276\ 5$ u
	$= 1.672\ 6 \times 10^{-27}$ kg
Neutron rest mass	$m_n = 1.008\ 665$ u
	$= 1.674\ 94 \times 10^{-27}$ kg
Electron rest mass	$m_e = 5.485\ 80 \times 10^{-4}$ u
	$= 9.109\ 5 \times 10^{-31}$ kg
Gravitational constant	$G = 6.67 \times 10^{-11}$ N m^2/kg^2

Table 4

MAGNETIC PERMEABILITIES

Copper	0.999 99	Cobalt	170
Water	0.999 999	Nickel	1000
Vacuum	1.000 000	Steel	1500
Oxygen	1.000 002	Iron	7000
Aluminum	1.000 02	Permalloy	100 000

Table 5

SPEED OF SOUND IN METRES PER SECOND

(gases at 0°C, others at 20°C)

Air	332
Carbon dioxide	260
Hydrogen	1270
Oxygen	317
Water	1410
Aluminum	5100
Brass	3500
Copper	3600
Iron	5000
Lead	1300
Mercury	1450

Table 6

INDICES OF REFRACTION
(for the orange-yellow light of sodium)

Diamond	2.42	Quartz	1.54
Fluorite	1.43	Ruby	1.76
Garnet	1.86	Silver chloride	2.07
Glass (crown)	1.52	Vermilion	2.85
Glass (flint)	1.65	Water	1.33
Niobite	2.26	Zircon	1.92

Table 7

DEPENDENCE OF REFRACTIVE INDICES ON COLOUR

Colour of light, with wavelength (10^{-7} m)

Material	Red (6.5)	Orange (6.0)	Yellow (5.8)	Green (5.2)	Blue (4.7)	Violet (4.1)
Crown glass	1.515	1.516	1.517	1.519	1.523	1.531
Flint glass	1.650	1.652	1.655	1.660	1.669	1.689
Diamond	2.410	2.415	2.417	2.426	2.444	2.458

Table 8

A FEW SPECTRAL EMISSION LINES

Element	Colour	Wavelength (nm)	Energy (eV)
Hydrogen	red	656.3	1.889
	blue-green	486.1	2.551
	blue	434.0	2.857
	violet	410.2	3.022
Mercury	yellow$_1$	579.1	2.076
	yellow$_2$	577.0	2.149
	green	546.1	2.270
	blue	435.8	2.845
Sodium	yellow$_1$	589.6	2.103
	yellow$_2$	589.0	2.105
Krypton 86	orange	605.8	2.047

Table 9

A LIST OF ELEMENTS WITH ATOMIC NUMBERS AND MASSES

Element	Symbol	Atomic number	Atomic mass of commonest isotope*	Element	Symbol	Atomic number	Atomic mass of commonest isotope*
Actinium	Ac	89	227	Mercury	Hg	80	200
Aluminum	Al	13	27	Molybdenum	Mo	42	98
Americium	Am	95	243*	Neodymium	Nd	60	142
Antimony	Sb	51	121	Neon	Ne	10	20
Argon	Ar	18	40	Neptunium	Np	93	237*
Arsenic	As	33	75	Nickel	Ni	28	58
Astatine	At	85	210*	Niobium	Nb	41	93
Barium	Ba	56	138	Nitrogen	N	7	14
Berkelium	Bk	97	247*	Nobelium	No	102	253*
Beryllium	Be	4	9	Osmium	Os	76	192
Bismuth	Bi	83	209	Oxygen	O	8	16
Boron	B	5	11	Palladium	Pd	46	106
Bromine	Br	35	79	Phosphorus	P	15	31
Cadmium	Cd	48	114	Platinum	Pt	78	195
Calcium	Ca	20	40	Plutonium	Pu	94	242*
Californium	Cf	98	249*	Polonium	Po	84	210
Carbon	C	6	12	Potassium	K	19	39
Cerium	Ce	58	140	Praseodymium	Pr	59	141
Cesium	Cs	55	133	Promethium	Pm	61	147*
Chlorine	Cl	17	35	Protactinium	Pa	91	231
Chromium	Cr	24	52	Radium	Ra	88	226
Cobalt	Co	27	59	Radon	Rn	86	222
Copper	Cu	29	63	Rhenium	Re	75	187
Curium	Cm	96	248*	Rhodium	Rh	45	103
Dysprosium	Dy	66	164	Rubidium	Rb	37	85
Einsteinium	Es	99	254*	Ruthenium	Ru	44	102
Erbium	Er	68	166	Samarium	Sm	62	152
Europium	Eu	63	153	Scandium	Sc	21	45
Fermium	Fm	100	253*	Selenium	Se	34	80
Fluorine	F	9	19	Silicon	Si	14	28
Francium	Fr	87	223	Silver	Ag	47	107
Gadolinium	Gd	64	158	Sodium	Na	11	23
Gallium	Ga	31	69	Strontium	Sr	38	88
Germanium	Ge	32	74	Sulfur	S	16	32
Gold	Au	79	197	Tantalum	Ta	73	181
Hafnium	Hf	72	180	Technetium	Tc	43	99*
Helium	He	2	4	Tellurium	Te	52	130
Holmium	Ho	67	165	Terbium	Tb	65	159
Hydrogen	H	1	1	Thallium	Tl	81	205
Indium	In	49	115	Thorium	Th	90	232
Iodine	I	53	127	Thulium	Tm	69	169
Iridium	Ir	77	193	Tin	Sn	50	120
Iron	Fe	26	56	Titanium	Ti	22	48
Krypton	Kr	36	84	Tungsten	W	74	184
Lanthanum	La	57	139	Uranium	U	92	238
Lawrencium	Lw	103	257*	Vanadium	V	23	51
Lead	Pb	82	208	Xenon	Xe	54	132
Lithium	Li	3	7	Ytterbium	Yb	70	174
Lutetium	Lu	71	175	Yttrium	Y	39	89
Magnesium	Mg	12	24	Zinc	Zn	30	64
Manganese	Mn	25	55	Zirconium	Zr	40	90
Mendelevium	Md	101	256*				

* Where an element has no naturally occurring isotope, the atomic mass of its artificially-created isotope with the longest half-life is given.

Table 10

PERIODIC TABLE OF THE ELEMENTS

(Arranged according to the energy levels of the shells and subshells of electrons)

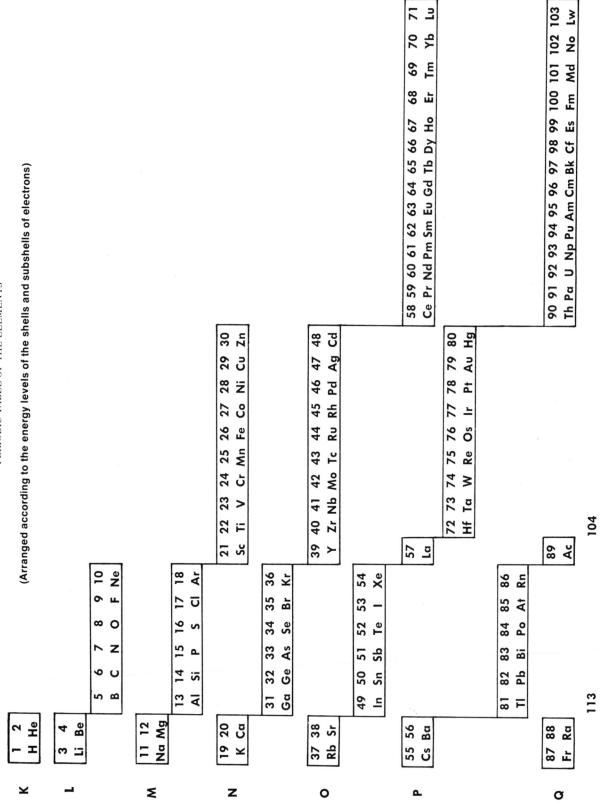

Table 11

PROPERTIES OF SOME ATOMS

Atomic number	Element	Atomic radius (10^{-10} m)	Ionization energy to remove first electron (eV)	Ionization energy to remove second electron (eV)	Mass numbers of natural isotopes (in order of abundance)	Average atomic mass ($^{12}C = 12$ u)
1	Hydrogen	0.3	13.6		1 2	1.007 97
2	Helium	0.93	24.6	54.4	4 3	4.0026
3	Lithium	1.52	5.4	75.6	7 6	6.939
4	Beryllium	1.10	9.3	18.2	9	9.0122
5	Boron	0.88	8.3	25.1	11 10	10.811
6	Carbon	0.77	11.3	24.4	12 13	12.011 15
7	Nitrogen	0.70	14.5	29.6	14 15	14.0067
8	Oxygen	0.66	13.6	35.1	16 18 17	15.9994
9	Fluorine	0.64	17.4	35.0	19	18.9984
10	Neon	1.12	21.6	41.1	20 22 21	20.183
11	Sodium	1.86	5.1	47.3	23	22.9898
12	Magnesium	1.60	7.6	15.0	24 25 26	24.312
13	Aluminum	1.43	6.0	18.8	27	26.9815
14	Silicon	1.17	8.2	16.3	28 29 30	28.086
15	Phosphorus	1.10	10.6	19.7	31	30.9738
16	Sulfur	1.04	10.4	23.4	32 34 33 36	32.064
17	Chlorine	0.99	13.0	23.8	35 37	35.453
18	Argon	1.54	15.8	27.6	40 36 38	39.948
19	Potassium	2.31	4.3	31.8	39 41 40*	39.102
20	Calcium	1.97	6.1	11.9	40 44 42 48 43 46	40.08
26	Iron	1.26	7.9	16.2	56 54 57 58	55.847
28	Nickel	1.24	7.6	18.2	58 60 62 61 64	58.71
29	Copper	1.28	7.7	20.3	63 65	63.54
30	Zinc	1.33	9.4	18.0	64 66 68 67 70	65.37
35	Bromine	1.14	11.8	21.6	79 81	79.909
36	Krypton	1.69	14.0	24.6	84 86 82 83 80 78	83.80
47	Silver	1.44	7.6	21.5	107 109	107.870
53	Iodine	1.33	10.4	19.0	127	126.9044
54	Xenon	1.90	12.1	21.2	132 129 131 134 136 130 128 124 126	131.30
74	Tungsten	1.37	8.0	17.7	184 186 182 180	183.85
78	Platinum	1.38	9.0	18.6	195 194 196 198 192 190 197	195.09
79	Gold	1.44	9.2	20.5	197	196.967
80	Mercury	1.55	10.4	18.8	202 200 199 201 198 204 196	200.59
82	Lead	1.75	7.4	15.0	208 206 207 204 210* 211* 212* 214*	207.19
92	Uranium	1.50	4.0		238* 235* 234*	238.03

* Radioactive isotope

Table 12

SINES OF ANGLES

	.0	.1	.2	.3	.4	.5	.6	.7	.8	.9
0°	·0000	0017	0035	0052	0070	0087	0105	0122	0140	0157
1	·0175	0192	0209	0227	0244	0262	0279	0297	0314	0332
2	·0349	0366	0384	0401	0419	0436	0454	0471	0488	0506
3	·0523	0541	0558	0576	0593	0610	0628	0645	0663	0680
4	·0698	0715	0732	0750	0767	0785	0802	0819	0837	0854
5	·0872	0889	0906	0924	0941	0958	0976	0993	1011	1028
6	·1045	1063	1080	1097	1115	1132	1149	1167	1184	1201
7	·1219	1236	1253	1271	1288	1305	1323	1340	1357	1374
8	·1392	1409	1426	1444	1461	1478	1495	1513	1530	1547
9	·1564	1582	1599	1616	1633	1650	1668	1685	1702	1719
10°	·1736	1754	1771	1788	1805	1822	1840	1857	1874	1891
11	·1908	1925	1942	1959	1977	1994	2011	2028	2045	2062
12	·2079	2096	2113	2130	2147	2164	2181	2198	2215	2233
13	·2250	2267	2284	2300	2317	2334	2351	2368	2385	2402
14	·2419	2436	2453	2470	2487	2504	2521	2538	2554	2571
15	·2588	2605	2622	2639	2656	2672	2689	2706	2723	2740
16	·2756	2773	2790	2807	2823	2840	2857	2874	2890	2907
17	·2924	2940	2957	2974	2990	3007	3024	3040	3057	3074
18	·3090	3107	3123	3140	3156	3173	3190	3206	3223	3239
19	·3256	3272	3289	3305	3322	3338	3355	3371	3387	3404
20°	·3420	3437	3453	3469	3486	3502	3518	3535	3551	3567
21	·3584	3600	3616	3633	3649	3665	3681	3697	3714	3730
22	·3746	3762	3778	3795	3811	3827	3843	3859	3875	3891
23	·3907	3923	3939	3955	3971	3987	4003	4019	4035	4051
24	·4067	4083	4099	4115	4131	4147	4163	4179	4195	4210
25	·4226	4242	4258	4274	4289	4305	4321	4337	4352	4368
26	·4384	4399	4415	4431	4446	4462	4478	4493	4509	4524
27	·4540	4555	4571	4586	4602	4617	4633	4648	4664	4679
28	·4695	4710	4726	4741	4756	4772	4787	4802	4818	4833
29	·4848	4863	4879	4894	4909	4924	4939	4955	4970	4985
30°	·5000	5015	5030	5045	5060	5075	5090	5105	5120	5135
31	·5150	5165	5180	5195	5210	5225	5240	5255	5270	5284
32	·5299	5314	5329	5344	5358	5373	5388	5402	5417	5432
33	·5446	5461	5476	5490	5505	5519	5534	5548	5563	5577
34	·5592	5606	5621	5635	5650	5664	5678	5693	5707	5721
35	·5736	5750	5764	5779	5793	5807	5821	5835	5850	5864
36	·5878	5892	5906	5920	5934	5948	5962	5976	5990	6004
37	·6018	6032	6046	6060	6074	6088	6101	6115	6129	6143
38	·6157	6170	6184	6198	6211	6225	6239	6252	6266	6280
39	·6293	6307	6320	6334	6347	6361	6374	6388	6401	6414
40°	·6428	6441	6455	6468	6481	6494	6508	6521	6534	6547
41	·6561	6574	6587	6600	6613	6626	6639	6652	6665	6678
42	·6691	6704	6717	6730	6743	6756	6769	6782	6794	6807
43	·6820	6833	6845	6858	6871	6884	6896	6909	6921	6934
44	·6947	6959	6972	6984	6997	7009	7022	7034	7046	7059

	.0	.1	.2	.3	.4	.5	.6	.7	.8	.9
45°	·7071	7083	7096	7108	7120	7133	7145	7157	7169	7181
46	·7193	7206	7218	7230	7242	7254	7266	7278	7290	7302
47	·7314	7325	7337	7349	7361	7373	7385	7396	7408	7420
48	·7431	7443	7455	7466	7478	7490	7501	7513	7524	7536
49	·7547	7559	7570	7581	7593	7604	7615	7627	7638	7649
50°	·7660	7672	7683	7694	7705	7716	7727	7738	7749	7760
51	·7771	7782	7793	7804	7815	7826	7837	7848	7859	7869
52	·7880	7891	7902	7912	7923	7934	7944	7955	7965	7976
53	·7986	7997	8007	8018	8028	8039	8049	8059	8070	8080
54	·8090	8100	8111	8121	8131	8141	8151	8161	8171	8181
55	·8192	8202	8211	8221	8231	8241	8251	8261	8271	8281
56	·8290	8300	8310	8320	8329	8339	8348	8358	8368	8377
57	·8387	8396	8406	8415	8425	8434	8443	8453	8462	8471
58	·8480	8490	8499	8508	8517	8526	8536	8545	8554	8563
59	·8572	8581	8590	8599	8607	8616	8625	8634	8643	8652
60°	·8660	8669	8678	8686	8695	8704	8712	8721	8729	8738
61	·8746	8755	8763	8771	8780	8788	8796	8805	8813	8821
62	·8829	8838	8846	8854	8862	8870	8878	8886	8894	8902
63	·8910	8918	8926	8934	8942	8949	8957	8965	8973	8980
64	·8988	8996	9003	9011	9018	9026	9033	9041	9048	9056
65	·9063	9070	9078	9085	9092	9100	9107	9114	9121	9128
66	·9135	9143	9150	9157	9164	9171	9178	9184	9191	9198
67	·9205	9212	9219	9225	9232	9239	9245	9252	9259	9265
68	·9272	9278	9285	9291	9298	9304	9311	9317	9323	9330
69	·9336	9342	9348	9354	9361	9367	9373	9379	9385	9391
70°	·9397	9403	9409	9415	9421	9426	9432	9438	9444	9449
71	·9455	9461	9466	9472	9478	9483	9489	9494	9500	9505
72	·9511	9516	9521	9527	9532	9537	9542	9548	9553	9558
73	·9563	9568	9573	9578	9583	9588	9593	9598	9603	9608
74	·9613	9617	9622	9627	9632	9636	9641	9646	9650	9655
75	·9659	9664	9668	9673	9677	9681	9686	9690	9694	9699
76	·9703	9707	9711	9715	9720	9724	9728	9732	9736	9740
77	·9744	9748	9751	9755	9759	9763	9767	9770	9774	9778
78	·9781	9785	9789	9792	9796	9799	9803	9806	9810	9813
79	·9816	9820	9823	9826	9829	9833	9836	9839	9842	9845
80°	·9848	9851	9854	9857	9860	9863	9866	9869	9871	9874
81	·9877	9880	9882	9885	9888	9890	9893	9895	9898	9900
82	·9903	9905	9907	9910	9912	9914	9917	9919	9921	9923
83	·9925	9928	9930	9932	9934	9936	9938	9940	9942	9943
84	·9945	9947	9949	9951	9952	9954	9956	9957	9959	9960
85	·9962	9963	9965	9966	9968	9969	9971	9972	9973	9974
86	·9976	9977	9978	9979	9980	9981	9982	9983	9984	9985
87	·9986	9987	9988	9989	9990	9990	9991	9992	9993	9993
88	·9994	9995	9 995	9996	9996	9997	9997	9997	9998	9998
89	·9998	9999	9999	9999	9999	1·000	1·000	1·000	1·000	1·000

Answers

CHAPTER 1 (page 17)

1. $10\,000 = 10^4$, $1\,000 = 10^3$, ..., $1 = 10^0$,
   $0.1 = 10^{-1}$, ... $0.0001 = 10^{-4}$, $0.000\,01 = 10^{-5}$
2. (a) 10^6 (b) 10^9 (c) 10^{12} (d) 10^{18} (e) 10^{-6} (f) 10^{-9}
   (g) 10^{-12}
3. (a) 10^{12} (b) 10^{-7} (c) 10^2 (d) 10^{-5} (e) 10^3 (f) 10^{-4}
   (g) 10^{-3} (h) 10^2 (i) 10^{23} (j) 10^{17} (k) 10^{-8}
4. (a) 10^2 (b) 10^4
5. 10^5
6. (a) 30 km (b) 70 μs (c) 4.6 mg (d) 300 Mm/s (e) 31 Pm
   (f) 620 ps (g) 8.9 Mg/m^3 (h) 400 nm
7. (a) 1.7500×10^4 (b) 3.5×10^{-4} (c) $4.37\,000 \times 10^5$
   (d) 8.945×10^{-5} (e) 6.9×10^{-6} (f) 8.4×10^{-2}
   (g) 2.57×10^5 (h) 4.3×10^{-9} (i) 6.03×10^{23}
   (j) 1.602×10^{-19}
8. (a) 5×10^3 m (b) 1.6×10^{-2} m (c) 3.50×10^8 Hz
   (d) 7.3×10^{-7} s (e) 5.83×10^{-7} m (f) 1.496×10^{11} m (g) 1.8×10^{-18} s (h) 5.13×10^{14} Hz
9. (a) 5.45 to 5.55×10^3 kg/m^3 (b) 1.735×10^6
   to 1.745×10^6 m (c) 8.75 to 8.85 light years
   (d) 1.2925 to 1.2935 kg/m^3 (e) $2.997\,925 \times 10^8$ to
   $2.997\,935 \times 10^8$ m/s
10. 1×10^3 m/s
11. (a) 38 m (b) 46 s (c) 31 cm^2 (d) 7.8×10^3 kg/m^3
    (e) 1.4×10^2 cm^3
12. (a) inverse (b) direct (c) direct (d) direct (e) inverse
    (f) direct (g) inverse (h) direct (i) inverse (j) inverse
    (k) inverse
13. (a) 0.36 (b) 0.80 (c) −0.50 (d) 0.38
14. $p = 0.33\ F$, 33, 136
15. $pv = 100$, 5, 3
16. $y = 2\ x$
17. $pA = 36$
20. (14) direct (15) inverse (16) direct (17) inverse
    (18) direct (19) inverse
21. (a) km (b) m^{-3} (c) 100 km (d) m^3 (e) s (f) kg·m/s^2
22. (a) 23% (b) 1940 (c) 1960 (d) smooth extrapolation
    gives about 40%, but can't be sure
23. (b) 8.8 L/100 km (d) $c = (0.088\ \text{L/km})d$
24. (b) $At = 0.143$ m^2·min
25. 1×10^{13} km
26. 0.4 kg
27. 44 m
28. 10^{78} atoms

CHAPTER 2 (page 28)

1. 80 km/h
2. 10.0 m/s
3. 7.729 m/s
4. 1.9 m/s
5. 4.0×10^2 km
6. 6.3×10^2 m
7. 1.4 m
8. (a) 300 Mm (b) 18.0 Gm (c) 1.08 Tm (d) 25.9 Tm
   (e) 9.47 Pm
9. 0.38 s
10. 4.9 h
11. 0.77 h = 46 min
12. 2.0×10^3 s = 33 min
13. (a) 3.6 m/s^2 (b) 2.9 m/s^2 (c) 2.3 m/s^2
14. 1.2 m/s^2
15. 0.90 m/s^2
16. 1.6×10^3 m/s^2
17. 32 m/s
18. 31 m/s
19. (a) 19 m/s (b) 11 m/s
20. 4.4 s
21. (a) 15 m (b) 35 m (c) 25 m
22. 39 m
23. 11 m/s
24. −20 m/s^2
25. (a) 2.9 s (b) 37 m
26. (a) 8.8 s (b) −0.34 m/s^2
27. (a) distance unchanging, $v = 0$ (b) $v = $ const.
    (c) $v = $ const. (d) v increasing from zero (e) v decreasing to zero from a positive value (f) v starts positive,
    increases, then decreases to zero. The d–intercept
    shows the starting location of the moving object
28. (a) $v = $ const., $a = 0$ (b) $v = $ const. (greater than in
    a if same scale), $a = 0$ (c) v increasing from zero,
    $a = $ const. (d) v increasing from a positive value,
    $a = $ const. (e) v decreasing to zero, $a = $ const. (negative) (f) v increasing from zero, levels off, then
    declines to zero; $a = $ pos. const., declines to zero,
    then becomes $|$neg. const.$| > $ first value of a
29. (a) no match if scales start at zero (b) matched by **a**
    and **b** (c) matched by **a** and **b** (d) matched by **c**
    (e) matched by **e** (f) almost matched by **f**
31. (a) $v = 12$ m/s, $a = 0$ (b) 5 m/s^2 (c) close to
    −8.0 m/s^2
32. (a) 25.0 m/s (b) 3.6 km/h
33. (a) 2.5 m/s^2 (b) 40 m/s^2 (c) −1 $\times$ 10^2 m/s^2
34. (a) 80 m (b) 7.50×10^5 m = 750 km (c) 2×10^1 m

35. 9.2 m/s
36. 80 s, 1.2 km from bicycle's start
37. The amateur's speeds are less than the pro's
38. Max. a = 190 m/s² (approx.)
39. 1.2 km, 60 s
40. At least 0.11 m and 5.5 ms

CHAPTER 3 (page 37) (The accuracy of your answers will likely depend more on the accuracy of your graphical analysis than on that of the given quantities.)

1. $\overrightarrow{BA}$ = 12 m [N], $\overrightarrow{CJ}$ = 26 m [E], $\overrightarrow{GC}$ = 26 m [E], $\overrightarrow{DF}$ = 12 m [S], $\overrightarrow{AG}$ = 8.5 m [S45°W], $\overrightarrow{FA}$ = 42 m [N73°W], $\overrightarrow{JD}$ = 8.5 m [N45°W]
3. 310 km [N56°E]
4. (a) 1.6 × 10² km [N63°E] (b) 1.6 × 10² km [S63°W]
  (c) 1.6 × 10² km [N63°E]
6. (a) 127 m [N] (b) 89.8 m [N45.0°W] (c) 199 m
  (d) 299 m
7. 894 km [S63.4°W] (assume 3-digit data)
8. 5.0 × 10² m [N]
9. (a) 250 km [S45°W] (b) 80 km [N45°E]
  (c) 130 km [S68°W] (d) 200 km [S8.1°E]
10. (a) 7.5 m/s [N] (b) 1.5 m/s [N] (c) 2.0 m/s [S]
  (d) 5.0 m/s [N37°W] (e) 5.2 m/s [N12°E]
  (f) 3.5 m/s [N30°E]
11. 31 cm [direction of hand at 11:30]
12. (a) 31 m [N82°E] (b) 7.8 m/s
13. 1.9 × 10² m/s [S18°W]
14. 55 m/s [W]
15. 52 m/s [N66°W]
16. (a) 8.0 × 10² m [E] (b)(i) 1.40 km [E]
  (ii) 2.0 × 10² m [E] (iii) 1.00 km [N53°E]
17. (a) 208 m (b) 30 s (c) 120 m
18. (a) 15 m/s [E] (b) 0 (c) 13 m/s [S63°E]
19. 30 m/s [45° from horizontal]
20. 25.0 m/s²
21. $\Delta\vec{v}$ = 17 m/s [S45°E], $\vec{a}$ = 42 m/s² [S45°E]
22. 1.2 × 10⁴ m/s² [N8.4°W]
23. (a) 50 m/s [W] (b) 10 m/s [E] (c) 36 m/s [N34°W]
  (d) 21 m/s [S3.3°W]
24. (a) 2.2 m (b) 18 m/s [34° from straight ahead]
25. (a) 10 m/s [N] (b) 38 m/s [E] (c) 0 (d) 9 m/s [W]
  (e) 23 m/s [E] (f) 26 m/s [S30°E]
26. (a) 7.5 × 10² s (b) 1.2 km, 2.9 m/s [N37°E]
  (c) N42°W, 1.8 m/s [N], 1.0 × 10³ s
27. Aim at N49.3°E to give $\vec{v}$ = 39.9 m/s [N71.6°E]
28. 25 m/s [N13°E], 24 m/s [N2°E]

CHAPTER 4 (page 45)

1. (a) constant (b) constant (c) not constant, force of road on tires (d) not constant, force of gravity (e) not constant, force of ice on puck (f) not constant, force of road on tires (g) not constant, force of gravity
2. (a) 0 (b) 1.5 kN [S] (c) 0.02 kN [N60°W] (d) 30 N [N] (e) 50 N [N53°W] (f) 2 N [E] The vertical part of the girl's pull merely reduces the force of the road upon the wheels by 35 N
3. (a) force of engine on wheels is balanced by resistance of air on car and road on tires (b) force of water at rear reacting to force of propeller is greater than force of water at front resisting the boat's motion (c) horizontal forces are essentially zero (d) force of road on tires is not balanced by any other horizontal force acting on the car (e) force of ice on stone is not balanced by any other force acting on the stone
4. (a) 40 N (b) 3.0 × 10³ N (c) 63 N
5. (a) 1.5 × 10² m/s² (b) 5.0 × 10³ m/s² (c) 0.33 m/s²
6. 9 × 10⁻³¹ kg
7. 3 kN
8. 3.3 × 10⁻⁴ m/s² [W]
9. (a) force of A on B = force of B on A (b) force of girl on boat = force of boat on girl (c) force of balloon on air within = force of air on balloon (d) force of helicopter on roof = force of roof on helicopter (e) force of sun on Venus = force of Venus on sun (f) your force on waterbed = force of waterbed on you
11. 3.6 N [E]
12. 80 N [S]
13. 100 m/s² [W], 13 m/s [W]
14. 5.2 × 10² N [S]
15. 5.3 kN [W]
16. (a) 1.9 m/s [W] (b) 4.9 m
17. (a) 9.28 × 10³ m/s (b) 619 s = 10.3 min
18. (a) 11 m/s [S45°E] (b) 0.99 kN [S45°E]
19. (a) 0.30 kN [W] (b) 0.30 kN [E]
20. (a) 8.0 × 10²/b m/s² [N] (b) 8/b kN [N]
  (c) 8/b kN [S] (d) 1.6/b m/s² [S] (e) 1.6 m/s [S]
21. (a) 7.2 N [W] (b) cart B (c) 7.2 N [E] (d) 1.2 m/s [E]
22. (a) 12/d m/s² [W] (b) 18/d N [W] (c) 18/d N [E]
  (d) 3/d m/s² [E] (e) 4.5 m/s [W]
23. $\vec{a}$ = 3.0 m/s² [E]; each block pushes the other with a force of 9.0 N; no
24. 0.10 kg; yes
25. 3.30 kg; no
26. 9.0 m/s²

CHAPTER 5 (page 58)

3. (to one digit) 10, 20, 30, 40, 50, 100 m/s
4. 10.2 m/s, 0.4 m/s, −9.4 m/s
6. 6 s, − 30 m/s
7. 0.43 kN
8. 1.76 kN
9. 0.150 kg
10. 62.1 kg
11. At sea level (a) poles (b) equator
12. Mexico City
13. (a) 9×10^4 N (b) 1×10^4 N (c) 1×10^2 N
14. (a) $30r$ (b) $6r$ (c) $600r$
15. 2.0×10^{20} N
16. (a) mass (b) mass (c) neither (d) force resulting from gravity (e) force of gravity (f) mass
17. (a) 2.2×10^2 N (b) 0.35 m
18. (a) 27 cm (b) 0.90 kN
19. 0.33 kN
20. 36 cm
21. (a) 10 mN (b) 1.0 g
22. 0.16 GPa
23. (a) 14 kN (b) 16 kN (c) 11 kN (d) 14 kN
24. (a) 3.98 s (b) 1.03 km (c) 263 m/s [81.5° from vertical]
25. (F or $g = 10$ m/s^2) 20, 80, 180, 320, 500 m
26. About 150 m
27. Between 40 s and 50 s
28. (a) 0.30 t (b) 325 m/s^2 (c) 488 m/s (d) 11.0 s (e) 35.3 g
29. (a) 34 m/s^2 (assuming m constant) (b) 3.4×10^2 m/s
30. 44 s, 7.5 km
31. (a) 49 N (b) 0.43 m/s^2 (c) 4.3 m/s (d) 22 m (e) 13 s; 5.5 m/s
32. 1.8 m/s^2
33. (a) 0.58 kN (b) 30 m/s (c) 6.1 s (d) 0.24 km [E]
34. 9.7 m/s^2
35. 1.7 mN
36. 8.3×10^2 kPa, about 8 atmospheres
37. (i) velocity (ii) acceleration
38. (a) $d = \frac{1}{2} gt^2$ (b) 9.8049 m/s^2
39. 0.14 s
40. (a) 4.00 s (b) 19.6 m/s (c) 3.74°
41. (a) 7.80, 8.20, 8.48, 8.80, 9.20 s (b) 356, 359, 360, 359, 354 m
42. (a) 33.6 m/s (b) 30.4 m/s (c) 1.40×10^2 m/s

CHAPTER 6 (page 80)

2. (a) kinetic to heat (b) chemical to kinetic (c) kinetic to gravitational potential (d) electric to heat

(e) gravitational potential to heat
4. 70 J
5. 4.3 TJ
6. (a) 0.12 kJ (b) 1.2 kN
7. 0.38 kN
8. 3.0×10^2 km
9. (a) 0.14 kJ (b) 0.15 kJ (c) 0.22 kJ (d) 0.45 kJ (e) 0.68 kJ (f) 2.8 kJ (g) 3.0 kJ
10. 1.5×10^2 t
11. 0.16 t
12. 1.7×10^{-27} kg
13. 30 m/s
14. (a) 0.24 kJ (b) 0.63 kJ
15. (a) 0.9 kJ (b) 9×10^1 MJ
16. 38 MJ
17. 68 m
18. 0.16 kg
19. (a) 0.12 kW (b) 0.40 kW (c) 3.3 kW
20. 2.0 kW
21. 40 kW
22. 120 kJ
23. 80 min
24. 60 kJ
25. The sum of potential and kinetic energies is the same in every row.
26. 18 m/s
27. 10 m, no
28. (a) 12 kJ (b) 15.0 m, 8.8 kJ (c) 2.9 kJ, 9.9 m/s (d) 12 kJ, 20 m/s
29. 5.9 m/s
30. 19 L
31. 9.0 kN
32. (a) 9.1 J (b) 3.0 m/s (c) 1.9 m/s (d) 1.6 – close to $\pi/2$
33. (a) 1.7 GJ (b) 30 GJ (c) 32 GJ
34. 40%
35. (a) 1.0 km/s, 1.8 GJ (b) 0.90 MN, 2.0 km (c) 8.0 s
36. (a) 2.0 km, 0.40 km/s [up] (b) 40 s, 10 km
37.
38. 0.57 m
39. 70 km/s
40. (a) 2.2×10^8 m/s (b) 27 fJ (c) about 2.6×10^8 m/s (d) 0.1 EJ
41. (a) 1 mW (b) 2×10^5 s = 50 to 60 h
42. 10^{19} J = 10 EJ (Answer would be 22 EJ except that data are only given to order of magnitude accuracy.)

CHAPTER 7 (page 95)

3. (a) neg. (b) pos. (c) neg. (d) neg. (e) pos.
5. (a) acetate to paper (b) negative

7. (a) repelled (b) attracted
10. (a) same (b) opposite
11. (a) $+e$ (b) $-e$
12. (a) -1.6×10^{-14} C (b) $+8.0$ nC
13. (a) deficit of 2.0×10^{11} (b) surplus of 5.0×10^6
14. (a) 12 V (b) 0.50 kV
15. 0.1 mJ
19. (a) 1×10^{-18} m² (b) 1×10^{-3} m² (c) 1×10^{15}
    (d) 1×10^{11} (e) 1×10^4 molecules per surplus electron
20. (a) 1.8 mN (b) 0.26 mJ (c) 26 kV
21. (a) 1 kV (b) 10 pC (c) 5 pF (d) 5 μC (e) 1 μF
23. 50 mJ

CHAPTER 8 (page 107)

2. (a) 0.12 kJ (b) 1.4 kJ
3. (a) 12 J (b) 1.9 aJ
4. (a) 0.30 A (b) 54 J
5. 0.16 kC
6. 14 kC
7. (a) 9.4 Ω (b) 0.64 A
8. 22 Ω
9. 0.90 W
10. 1.5 kW
12. 1.5 kΩ
13. 7.5 A
14. 0.14 kV
16. (a) 2 kA (b) 2 GJ
17. 2.4 kJ
18. (a) 0.36 MC (b) 4.3 MJ
19. (a) 11 kC (b) 1.3 MJ
20. 5.0 A
21. no, R increases as I increases
22. yes, within 1%
25. (a) 20.0 V (b) 10 Ω (c) 4.0 Ω, 6.0 Ω
26. (a) 0.24 kΩ (b) 0.50 A (c) 15 V
27. (a) 2.0 A (b) 1.0 Ω
28. 1.0 A
29. (a) 5.0 A (b) 2.4 Ω (c) 4.0 Ω, 6.0 Ω
30. (a) 1.2 Ω (b) 2.5 A
31. (a) 9.1 Ω (b) 133 Ω
32. 18 A
33. (a) 0.50 A (b) 0.25 A (c) 1.0 A
34. (a) 20.0 Ω (b) 6.0 A (c) 0.50 A
36. (a) 20 (b) 10 km/h
37. 6×10^{-3} cm/s
39. (b) 220 Ω, 110 Ω (c) 80 Ω (d) 1.4 V
40. (a) 0.30 A, 2.9 V (b) 3.0 A, 2.1 V
41. 0.10 Ω
42. (a) 0.28 Ω (b) 0.19 Ω

CHAPTER 9 (page 118)

2. (a) attraction (b) attraction (c) repulsion
4. Magnetic S pole near geographic north
5. greater
6. no
8. (a) high retentivity and high permeability (b) low retentivity and high permeability
9. (a) repulsive (b) attractive (c) repulsion (d) attraction
14. (a) force about 2 N (b) force very much less than 2 N (c) force about 0.3 N
15. west to east
16. (a) 1.5 N (b) 3.0 N
18. (a) bow

CHAPTER 10 (page 130)

5. 4.95 kΩ
6. (a) 0.990 Ω (b)(i) 10.0 A (ii) 100 mA
7. 0.010 Ω
11. 2×10^3 cars per hour
12. (a) 0.10 MΩ (b) 2.0 mΩ
13. 10 mA
17. (a) 0.3 N (b) 36 μN

CHAPTER 11 (page 150)

3. (a)(i) 4.0 A/s (ii) 2.0 A/s (iii) 8.0 A/s (b)(i) 2.0 A/s (ii) 1.0 A/s (iii) 4.0 A/s (c) 0.20 V, 0.10 V, 0.40 V; 0.10 V, 50 mV, 0.20 V
4. 0.25 V
11. (a) 1.6×10^3 W·h (b) 1.6 kW·h (c) 5.9 MJ
12. (a) 3.5×10^2 kW·h (b) 1.3×10^3 MJ
13. (a) 1.4 kW·h (b) 5.2 MJ
14. 1.8 W
15. 0.833 A
16. 1.00 kW
17. (a) 50 A (b) 5.0 A
18. (a) 0.36 kW (b) 3.6 W
19. 10.4 kW
20. (a) 34 units (b) 22 V
21. (a) 240 V (b) 60.0 V (c) 1.20 V (d) 2.40 kV
22. (a) 1.50×10^3 (b) 1.00×10^3 (c) 12.5 (d) 15.8
24. (a) 3.0 cents (b) 75 cents (c) 52 cents
25. (a) 20 mA (b) 10 mA
26. to the left
28. (a)(i) 2.0 mA (ii) 4.0 mA (b) 0.10 V, 0.20 V, 0.40 V (c) keeping resistance constant eliminates it as a factor in the comparison (d) 4.4 mA
30. (a) perpendicular (b) parallel

35. (a) $E = V^2t/R$ (b) $P = V^2/R$
36. (a) 15 Ω (b) 8.0 A (c) 64 W
37. (a) 0.50 MW (b) 1.8 kW
38. (a) 0.24 kW (b) 0.24 kW (c) 0.40 A, 0.60 A, 48 A, 38 A
39. 0.13 kV, 21 A
40. (a) 4.1 kW (b) 7.5 A
41. (c)
42. (b)
47. (a) 0.50 Ω (b) 50 Ω

CHAPTER 12 (page 168)

1. (a) longitudinal (b) longitudinal (c) torsional (d) transverse (e) torsional (f) transverse
2. (a) 1.5 s (b) 5.0 s (c) 0.60 s (d) 0.50 s (e) 2.360 Ms (f) 17 ms
3. (a) 2.0 Hz (b) 0.5 Hz (c) 80 Hz (d) 8 Hz
4. (a) 40 ms (b) 2.0 s (c) 3.3 ms (d) 9.569 ns
5. (a) 10 Hz (b) 0.25 Hz (c) 80 Hz (d) 0.20 kHz
6. (a) 1.6 m (b) 6.1 m (c) 270°
8. (a) 2 (b) 2
11. 0.85 m
12. 2.5 ms
13. (a) 1.3×10^2 m/s (b) 1.30 m (c) 1.5 kHz
14. (a) 335 m/s (b) 3.4×10^2 m/s
15. (a) 7×10^2 Hz (b) 0.47 kHz
16. (a) 2 m (b) 0.2 μm
18. (a) 24 cm (b) 12 cm (c) 8.0 cm (d) 6.0 cm
19. no
21. (a) 2.4 cm (b) 10 Hz (c) 24 cm/s
22. 1.7 s
23. 36 cm, 43 m/s
24. 0.35 km/s
26. (a) increase (b) decrease (c) negligible decrease (d) no effects if length stays at 100 cm
27. (a) 1.24 m (b)(i) 368 m/s (ii) 328 m/s (c)(i) 297 Hz (ii) 264 Hz

CHAPTER 13 (page 182)

2. (a) 347 m/s (b) 326 m/s
3. 8.8 km
4. aluminum, 51 m; air, 3.3 m
5. (a) pitch, loudness, timbre or quality (b)(i) pitch (ii) loudness (iii) timbre
6. (a) 1.57 kHz (b) 49 Hz
7. (a) quartered (b) quadrupled (c) cut to a sixteenth
8. (a) 10^9 pW/m^2 (b) 10^{16} pW/m^2 = 10 kW/m^2
9. 120 dB
10. 10^4 pW/m^2 = 40 dB

11. (b) 240 Hz, second harmonic; 360 Hz, third; 480 Hz, fourth
12. (a) 800 Hz (b) fifth
13. (a) one (b) two
15. 2 Hz
16. 253 Hz, 259 Hz
17. (a) 255 Hz (b) 253 Hz
18. decrease
19. (a) 253 Hz (b) 255 Hz
20. 57 Hz
24. (a) 1.0 m (b) 2.0 m
25. (a) 80 cm (b) 0.42 kHz
26. 0.35 km/s
27. 0.12 kHz
28. 24 cm, 48 cm
29. 0.874 m, 1.75 m
30. 315 m
31. 1.19 km
33. (a) 350 m/s (b) 2.5 m (c) 0.50 m (d) 30 cm
34. 0.86 m
35. 0.37 km/s
36. 0.10, 0.30, 0.50 kHz
37. 0.35 km/s
38. (a) 2.1 kHz (b) 1.0 kHz
39. (a) steel
40. (a) 0.32 kHz (b) 0.29 kHz
41. (a) 0.62 kHz (b) 0.31 kHz
42. 0.31 kHz

CHAPTER 14 (page 194)

1. (a) 1.5 m (b) horizontally
2. (a) frequency (b) amplitude
3. Goes to bright bands
6. 4 m/s
10. at infinity
11. (a) at the focus (b) in the focal plane, above the focus
12. d_i = 7.5 cm, real, inverted, h_i = 2.5 cm
13. (a) d_i = 2.0 m, h_i = 0.67 m (b) d_i = 3.0 m, h_i = 2.0 m
14. (a) 18 m from mirror (b) 0.17 m
18. 1.0 m
20. d_i = −75 cm, h_i = 50 cm, M = 2.5
21. (a) d_i = 3.5 cm (b) d_i = −2.6 cm
22. h_i = h_0, d_i = d_0, real, inverted
23. (a) d_i = 1.2 m, real, inverted, larger (b) the image is behind the student (c) d_i = −20 cm, virtual, upright, smaller
24. (a) 0.053 (b) 0.43 (c) 1.0 (d) 3.0 (e) infinite (f) 1.5

27. (a) brightness (b) hue (c) saturation
28. (a) receding (b) expanding

CHAPTER 15 (page 210)

1. (a) decreases (b) decreases (c) unchanged
3. 1.34
4. (a) 171 Mm/s (b) 444 nm
5. 0.235
6. 1.60
7. (a) 90° (b) 90°
10. d_1 = 4.0, 4.5, 6.0, 9.0 cm
11. (c) $s_o s_i = f^2$
12. (c) $h_i/h_o = f/s_o = s_i/f$
13. d_i = 20 cm, real, inverted, h_i = 6.7 cm
14. d_i = 1.12 m, real, inverted, h_i = 75 cm
15. 29°
16. 1.7
17. 70°
18. total internal reflection
19. (a) 24.4° (b) 48.8°
20. (a) 1.4 (b) 1.91
21. (a) 1.8 (b) 30° (c) 67° (d) 27° (e) 1.43 (f) 34.6°
22. 35.4°, 34.2°, 1.2°, dispersion
23. 12 m
24. s_i = 0.25 mm
25. d_i = −60 cm
26. (a) 12 cm (b)(i) 10 cm (ii) 7.5 cm
27. 4.0 cm
28. 50 μm
29. d_i = 2.4 cm
30. (a) s_i = 2.5 mm (b) 1.4 m by 1.4 m
32. (a) 56.1°, 56.1° (b) r_1 = 29.2°, i_2 = 30.8°, r_2 = 60.4° (c) 4.3°
34. $1/d_0 + 1/d_i = 1/f$

CHAPTER 16 (page 225)

9. twice the focal length of L_2
10. (a) 7 mm; larger than pupil of eye in daylight, wasting light (b) needs rigid support; e.g., tripod
11. (a) 25 cm (b) 8.1 (c) f greater than 25 cm
12. (a) 10 (b) 4 × 10^2
13. f_o/f_e = 20
14. (a) $f/16$ (b) $f/8$ (c) (1/400) s (d) reduce aperture to $f/22$

CHAPTER 17 (page 237)

10. (a) 2 (b) 6 (c) 1
11. (a) 25 cents or some more inflated price (b) one cent

16. (a) about 120 kV (b) about 15 cm
17. 2 × 10^3, same charge
18. 9.1 × 10^{-31} kg
19. 1.66 × 10^{-27} kg
21. (a) 4.1 × 10^{-9} eV (b) 4.1 × 10^{-5} eV (c) 1.2 eV (d) 4.1 eV (e) 1.2 × 10^3 eV
22. (a) 0.60 PHz (b) 2.5 eV
23. 2.9 eV
24. 0.24 PHz, 1.2 μm, infrared
25. (a) 12 EHz (b) 52 kV
27. (a) 6.6 × 10^{-13} J (b) 4.1 × 10^6 eV (c) 4.1 MeV
28. (a) 0.24 fJ (b) 0.36 EHz (c) 0.84 nm
29. 20 EHz (one digit), 10 pm (one digit)
31. cesium: red, green, violet; sodium: green, violet; calcium: violet; zinc: none
32. (a) 1.0 eV (b) 0.16 aJ (c) 0.6 Mm/s
33. 1.2 Mm/s

CHAPTER 18 (page 246)

3. (b)(i) 2, 4 (ii) 6, 12 (iii) 20, 40 (iv) 82, 208 (v) 92, 238 (vi) 103, 257
4. 12.00 u, 1.99 × 10^{-26} kg
8. (a) 2 × 10^{10} (b) 7 × 10^8 (c) 2 × 10^4
14. 0.053, 0.21, 0.48, 0.85 nm
15. (a) −0.38 eV (b) −0.28 eV
16. (a) 1.89 eV (b) 2.55 eV
17. (a) 0.46 PHz (b) 0.62 PHz
18. 2.9 PHz
19. 12.8 eV
20. −13.6 eV, −6.04 eV
21. (a) 3.6 fm (b) 6.0 fm (c) 7.2 fm
22. (a)(b)(c) 1.4 × 10^{44} u/m^3 = 2.3 × 10^{17} kg/m^3
23. 1 × 10^1 km
24. (a) 0.11 nm (b) 0.11 mm

CHAPTER 19 (page 256)

4. (a) 2 (b) 8 (c) 18
11. 2
12. 2
15. estimate between 3 and 4 eV (in fact, 4.2 eV)
16. estimate between 13 and 14 eV (in fact, 14 eV)
17. 3.9 eV, 12 eV
19. aluminum
21. 18 pm, 1.0 pm, 0.58 pm
22. 24 pm, 4.0 pm, 2.4 pm
27. about 40 eV

CHAPTER 20 (page 267)

3. conductors
4. (a) 5 eV (b) 0.02 eV
5. (a) decreases (b) increases
8. (a) electrons (b) holes
9. more negative; becomes more positive
14. 1 PHz, 0.2 μm, no
15. 8.8 mA
19. cool end
20. negative
21. 26 mA

CHAPTER 21 (page 279)

3. 300 Mm/s
4. (a) 1 MHz (b) 1 kHz
14. 1.50 MHz
15. 148.5
16. 2.5 Mm
17. 25 cm
18. 1.3 s
19. 8.3 min, no
20. 15.8 kHz
21. 60 Hz
23. vertical line
24. line at 45°
26. 25
27. 7

CHAPTER 22 (page 289)

4. (b)(i) decrease by 2 (ii) no change (iii) no change
(c)(i) decrease by 2 (ii) increase by 1 (iii) no change
5. alpha, beta, beta
6. beta
7. (b)(i) $A - Z$ (ii) Z
8. (a) 1, 0 (b) 2, 2 (c) 6, 6 (d) 8, 8 (e) 19, 21 (f) 82, 126
(g) 92, 146 (h) 98, 151
10. its charge (number of protons)
17. (a) ½ (b) ¼ (c) ⅛
19. (a) thorium (b) radon (c) neodymium (d) radium
20. (a) calcium (b) bismuth (c) yttrium (d) nitrogen
21. 1.1×10^3 kg/m^3
22. 1.2×10^3 kg/m^3
23. (a) electron (b) positron
24. 108
25. 63.6 (assuming abundances correct to 0.1%)
26. 7.4×10^9 s^{-1}, 7.4 GBq

27. (a) 7 weeks (b) 4 weeks (c) 2 weeks (d) 1 week
28. (a) 14 weeks (b) 6 weeks (c) 4 weeks (d) 2 weeks
29. (a) 10 mBq/L (b) 6×10^2 disintegrations per minute
per cubic metre
30. (a) 3.7 GBq (b) 1.8 GBq (c) 0.46 GBq (d) 12 mg
31. 1.5 ka
32. (a) 97 mBq = 5.8 dis./min (b) 52 mBq = 3.1
dis./min
33. 7.2 ka
37. 10
38. 203
39. (a) 50% (b) 30% (c) 16%

CHAPTER 23 (page 305)

2. (a) ^{4}He (b) ^{13}C (c) ^{10}B (d) ^{10}Be
3. (a) ^{110}Ag (b) ^{96}Rb (c) ^{1}H (d) ^{2}H (or ^{2}D)
4. (a) (c) (f)
6. (b)(i) 0.2 pJ (ii) 0.2 fJ
8. 5×10^{15} d, 10 Ta
14. (a) 1 mGy
16. (a) 0.6 m (b) 0.9 m
18. (a) 3.5 mu = 5.8×10^{-30} kg
(b) 4.4 mu = 7.3×10^{30} kg
19. (a) 0.52 pJ (b) 0.66 pJ
20. 0.36 pJ
21. Other fission nuclei are ^{138}Te, ^{143}Xe, ^{102}Y
23. 1.6 PJ
24. 12 PJ
25. 4×10^{31} J, 0.5 GJ
26. 0.3 Gg, 6×10^{-18} %
27. 0.8 keV
28. 9 cm
29. 0.03 kg

CHAPTER 24 (page 314)

10. (a) ^{1}n + ^{23}Na→^{24}Na (b) ^{1}n + ^{59}Co→^{60}Co
11. ^{102}Y ($Z = 39$)
12. (a) 300 s^{-1} (b) 4800 s^{-1}
13. (a) 30 nJ (b) 0.2 pJ (c) 2×10^5
14. (a) 200 (b) 0.15 km
15. 31 am; about 400 x-ray wavelengths in the diameter
of a nucleus of $A = 125$
16. 1.0 MeV
17. (a) 0.1 kW (b) 130 Mm/s, 260 Mm/s^2, 0.44 aN
(neglecting relativistic effects)
18. 32 MHz

Index